N	0	1	2	3	4	5	6	7	8	9	N	0	1	2	3	4	5	6	7	8	9
0		000	301	477	602	699	778	845	903	954	50	699	700	701	702	702	703	704	705	706	707
1	000	041	079	114	146	176	204	230	255	279	51	708	708	709	710	711	712	713	713	714	715
2	301	322	342	362	380	398	415	431	447	462	52	716	717	718	718	719	720	721	722	723	723
3	477	491	505	519	531	544	556	568	580	591	53	724	725	726	727	728	728	729	730	731	732
4	602	613	623	633	643	653	663	672	681	690	54	732	733	734	735	736	736	737	738	739	740
5	699	708	716	724	732	740	748	756	763	771	55	740	741	742	743	744	744	745	746	747	747
6	778	785	792	799	806	813	820	826	833	839	56	748	749	750	751	751	752	753	754	754	755
7	845	851	857	863	869	875	881	886	892	898	57	756	757	757	758	759	760	760	761	762	763
8	903	908	914	919	924	929	934	940	944	949	58	763	764	765	766	766	767	768	769	769	770
9	954	959	964	968	973	978	982	987	991	996	59	771	772	772	773	774	775	775	776	777	777
10	000	004	009	013	017	021	025	029	033	037	60	778	779	780	780	781	782	782	783	784	785
11	041	045	049	053	057	061	064	068	072	076	61	785	786	787	787	788	789	790	790	791	792
12	079	083	086	090	093	097	100	104	107	111	62	792	793	794	794	795	796	797	797	798	799
13	114	117	121	124	127	130	134	137	140	143	63	799	800	801	801	802	803	803	804	805	806
14	146	149	152	155	158	161	164	167	170	173	64	806	807	808	808	809	810	810	811	812	812
15	176	179	182	185	188	190	193	196	199	201	65	813	814	814	815	816	816	817	818	818	819
16	204	207	210	212	215	217	220	223	225	228	66	820	820	821	822	822	823	823	824	825	825
17	230	233	236	238	241	243	246	248	250	253	67	826	827	827	828	829	829	830	831	831	832
18	255	258	260	262	265	267	270	272	274	276	68	833	833	834	834	835	836	836	837	838	838
19	279	281	283	286	288	290	292	294	297	299	69	839	839	840	841	841	842	843	843	844	844
20	301	303	305	308	310	312	314	316	318	320	70	845	846	846	847	848	848	849	849	850	851
21	322	324	326	328	330	332	334	336	338	340	71	851	852	852	853	854	854	855	856	856	857
22	342	344	346	348	350	352	354	356	358	360	72	857	858	859	859	860	860	861	862	862	863
23	362	364	365	367	369	371	373	375	377	378	73	863	864	865	865	866	866	867	867	868	869
24	380	382	384	386	387	389	391	393	394	396	74	869	870	870	871	872	872	873	873	874	874
25	398	400	401	403	405	407	408	410	412	413	75	875	876	876	877	877	878	879	879	880	880
26	415	417	418	420	422	423	425	427	428	430	76	881	881	882	883	883	884	884	885	885	886
27	431	433	435	436	438	439	441	442	444	446	77	886	887	888	888	889	889	890	890	891	892
28	447	449	450	452	453	455	456	458	459	461	78	892	893	893	894	894	895	895	896	897	897
29	462	464	465	467	468	470	471	473	474	476	79	898	898	899	899	900	900	901	901	902	903
30	477	479	480	481	483	484	486	487	489	490	80	903	904	904	905	905	906	906	907	907	908
31	491	493	494	496	497	498	500	501	502	504	81	908	909	910	910	911	911	912	912	913	913
32	505	507	508	509	511	512	513	515	516	517	82	914	914	915	915	916	916	917	918	918	919
33	519	520	521	522	524	525	526	528	529	530	83	919	920	920	921	921	922	922	923	923	924
34	531	533	534	535	537	538	539	540	542	543	84	924	925	925	926	926	927	927	928	928	929
35	544	545	547	548	549	550	551	553	554	555	85	929	930	930	931	931	932	932	933	933	934
36	556	558	559	560	561	562	563	565	566	567	86	934	935	936	936	937	937	938	938	939	939
37	568	569	571	572	573	574	575	576	577	579	87	940	940	941	941	942	942	942	943	943	944
38	580	581	582	583	584	585	587	588	589	590	88	944	945	945	946	946	947	947	948	948	949
39	591	592	593	594	596	597	598	599	600	601	89	949	950	950	951	951	952	952	953	953	954
40	602	603	604	605	606	607	609	610	611	612	90	954	955	955	956	956	957	957	958	958	959
41	613	614	615	616	617	618	619	620	621	622	91	959	960	960	960	961	961	962	962	963	963
42	623	624	625	626	627	628	629	630	631	632	92	964	964	965	965	966	966	967	967	968	968
43	633	634	635	636	637	638	639	640	641	642	93	968	969	969	970	970	971	971	972	972	973
44	643	644	645	646	647	648	649	650	651	652	94	973	974	974	975	975	975	976	976	977	977
45	653	654	655	656	657	658	659	660	661	662	95	978	978	979	979	980	980	981	981	981	982
46	663	664	665	666	667	668	669	669	670	671	96	982	983	983	984	984	985	985	985	986	986
47	672	673	674	675	676	677	678	679	679	680	97	987	987	988	988	989	989	989	990	990	991
48	681	682	683	684	685	686	687	688	688	689	98	991	992	992	993	993	993	994	994	995	995
49	690	691	692	693	694	695	695	696	697	698	99	996	996	997	997	997	998	998	999	999	000
N	0	1	2	3	4	5	6	7	8	9	N	0	1	2	3	4	5	6	7	8	9

Basic Mathematics for Electronics

Nelson M. Cooke,

Lieutenant Commander, United States

Navy Retired, Senior Member, Institute of Radio Engineers,

is President of Cooke Engineering Company, an electronics

research and development organization. This book is a

revision of "Mathematics for Electricians and Radiomen,"

published in 1942 and so well received that it was re-

printed 32 times. "Basic Mathematics for Electronics"

faithfully follows the successful plan of the

earlier book, with the addition of up-to-date

examples, refinement in presentation,

and an improved format.

Second Edition

BASIC MATHEMATICS
FOR ELECTRONICS
NELSON M. COOKE

McGraw-Hill Book Company, Inc.

New York, Toronto, London 1960

IV

PREFACE

This is the second edition of the textbook originally entitled "Mathematics for Electricians and Radiomen."

Compared with today's vast effort, the scope of the electronics field was very limited when the first edition was published in 1942. To mention only a few developments, radar was still in the secret category, electronic computers as we know them today did not exist, television was in the experimental stage, and very few visualized the guided missile. If one can generalize, the field was devoted mainly to communications, and the technician who operated and maintained the equipment was called a radioman.

Since then, due mainly to the necessity for specialization in an ever-widening field, the radioman has been forced to narrow his endeavor, and the title has taken on a new meaning. Today the radioman is engaged largely in operations; he is a communications specialist. He and the formerly electronics-oriented electrician have been replaced in the technical portion of the field by the highly specialized electronics technician, whose skill and knowledge may approach those at the engineering level. Hence, the new and more meaningful title, "Basic Mathematics for Electronics," for this revision.

The purpose of this new edition is unchanged. It was written to provide students of electronics and electrical subjects with a sound background in basic mathematics. Wherever possible, mathematical concepts and processes are related directly to electrical and electronics applications, and some chapters deal solely with applications.

The format of the second edition has been carefully redesigned to make functional use of two colors. The second color is used for emphasis and to call attention to important equations or to a particular portion of a figure. As such, the second color serves as an added teaching tool for instructors and an aid to comprehension and understanding for students.

As the result of extensive correspondence with teachers and students using the first edition and a national survey conducted by the publisher, a review of the basic operations in arithmetic has been included in Chaps. 2 through 6. This review was included for the large number of students whose abilities in "figuring" had lessened mainly because time had elapsed since they had needed to employ these skills.

The original chapter dealing with electrical units, now Chap. 11, has been expanded to include computations with elementary dimensions so that the result of an applicable computation will be expressed in a correct unit or dimension.

Meter Circuits, Chap. 19, is new. It contains Ohm's law applications to ammeter, voltmeter, and ohmmeter circuitry.

Voltage-divider and Distribution Circuits, Chap. 20, has been enlarged so as to contain material on voltage-divider circuits.

The material on logarithms and their applications, Chaps. 36 and 37, has been placed at the end of the book to afford better mathematical continuity.

The great majority of the problems are new, and wherever possible those dealing with applications have been updated to reflect recent developments in the field. Answers are given for even-numbered problems.

I want to thank E. H. Rietzke, founder and President of Capitol Radio Engineering Institute, Washington, D.C., for the opportunity to class-test the manuscript of this new edition in the Institute. The staff and students worked all of the problems and were most cooperative. In particular, L. M. Upchurch and J. P. Evans devoted considerable time to this project, and their criticism and suggestions have been most valuable.

Appreciation is due Samuel L. Oppenheimer, President of the Ohio Technical Institute, Columbus, Ohio, and the Institute staff for reviewing the manuscript. Mr. Oppenheimer contributed several new problems and suggestions.

Miss Mary D. Hopkins spent considerable time in reviewing the early chapters and in checking and working the problems therein.

Many other people have contributed their suggestions toward the betterment of this book: teachers, resident and home-study students, and practicing engineers and technicians. Space does not permit a complete listing. All of them have my gratitude and the knowledge that they have assisted in this revision.

Last, but by no means least, I am again much indebted to my wife for her untiring assistance in typing and proofreading, and for her constant encouragement.

As usual, comments and criticism are always welcome. It is requested that they be addressed to me in care of the publisher.

Nelson M. Cooke

ACKNOWLEDGMENTS

FIRST EDITION

In common with many textbooks, this book is based upon lecture notes which were compiled over a period of years. During this time, with no thought of eventual publication, material was drawn from many excellent sources which, with the passage of time, have become obscure or of unknown origin. It is impossible, therefore, to list these sources or to give credit where it is so justly due.

The author is indebted to the instructors of the Radio Matériel School, Naval Research Laboratory, and former students for much helpful criticism and suggestions. In particular, Classes Thirty-two, Thirty-three, and Thirty-four of the Radio Matériel School deserve credit for their efforts in mimeographing the final material and offering valuable suggestions while using it as a text.

Special credit is due Lt. Comdr. Wallace J. Miller, U.S. Navy, officer in charge of the Radio Matériel School, for his sympathetic attitude, encouragement, and many helpful suggestions.

The students of Class Fourteen of the Warrant Officers Radio Engineering Course, Radio Matériel School, offered invaluable criticism and suggestions for the improvement of the text. Three of these are deserving of special mention: Radio Electrician I. L. McNally, U.S. Navy, for submitting many original problems; Radio Electrician J. R. True, U.S. Navy, and Radio Electrician A. J. Beaudoin, U.S. Navy, for proofreading the manuscript and offering much valuable comment.

The author is indebted to M. E. Beard, radioman first class, U.S. Navy, for his aid in compiling the answers.

Last, but by no means least, the author is much indebted to his wife for her untiring assistance in preparing the manuscript and for her constant encouragement.

The author welcomes any corrections or suggestions for improvement.

Nelson M. Cooke

CONTENTS

Appendix

TABLES

CHAPTER 1
INTRODUCTION

In the legions of textbooks on the subject of mathematics, all the basic principles contained here have been expounded in admirable fashion. However, students of electricity, radio, and electronics have need for a course in mathematics that is directly concerned with application to electric and electronic circuits. This book is intended to provide those students with a sound mathematical background and to further their understanding of basic circuits.

1 – 1   Mathematics—a language

The study of mathematics may be likened to the study of a language. In fact, mathematics is a language, the language of number and size. Just as the rules of grammar must be studied in order to master English, so must certain concepts, definitions, rules, terms, and words be learned in the pursuit of mathematical knowledge. These form the vocabulary or structure of the language. The more a language is studied and used, the greater becomes the vocabulary; the more mathematics is studied and applied, the greater becomes its usefulness.

There is one marked difference, however, between the study of a language and the study of mathematics. A language is based on words, phrases, expressions, and usages that have been brought together through the ages in more or less haphazard fashion according to the customs of the times. Mathematics is built upon the firm foundation of sound logic and orderly reasoning and progresses smoothly, step by step, from the simplest numerical processes to the most complicated and advanced applications, each step along the way resting squarely upon those which have gone before. This makes mathematics the fascinating subject that it is.

1 – 2   Mathematics—a tool

As the builder works with his square and compasses, so does the engineer employ mathematics. A thorough grounding in this subject is essential to proficiency in any of the numerous branches of engineering. In no other branch is this more apparent than in the study of electrical and electronic subjects, for most of our basic ideas of electric phenomena are based upon mathematical reasoning and stated in mathematical terms. This is a fortunate circumstance, for it enables us to build a structure of electrical knowledge with precision, assembling and expressing the components in clear and concise mathematical terms and arranging the whole in logical order. Without mathematical assistance, the technician must content himself with the long and painful process of accumulating bits of information, details of experience, etc., and he may never achieve a thorough understanding of the field in which he lives and works.

1 – 3   Mathematics—a teacher

In addition to laying a foundation for technical knowledge and assisting in the practical application of knowledge already possessed, mathematics offers unlimited advantages in respect to mental training. The solution of a problem, no matter how simple, demands logical thinking for it to be possible to state the facts of the problem in mathematical terms and then proceed with the solution. Continued study in this orderly manner will increase the mental capacity of the student, enabling him to solve more difficult problems, to understand more complicated engineering principles, and to cope more successfully with the everyday problems of life.

1 – 4   Methods of study

Before beginning detailed study of this text the student should carefully analyze it, in its entirety, in order to form a mental outline of its
contents, scope, and arrangement. Another preliminary survey of
individual chapters should be made before attempting detailed study
of their subject matter. After such detailed study, problems should
be worked until all principles are fixed firmly in mind before proceeding to new material.

In working problems, the same general procedure is recommended.
First, a problem should be analyzed in order to determine the best
method of solution. The problem should then be stated in mathematical terms, the principles that are applicable being utilized. If but
little progress is made, it is probable the student has not completely
mastered the principles explained in the text, and a review is in order.

The author is a firm believer in the use of a workbook, preferably
in the form of a loose-leaf notebook, which contains all the problems
the student has worked, together with the numerous notes made
while studying the text. Such a book is an invaluable aid for purposes
of review. The habit of jotting down notes during reading or studying should be cultivated. Such notes in the student's own words will
provide a better understanding of a concept.

1 – 5   Rate of progress

Home-study students should guard against too rapid progress. There
is a tendency, especially in studying a chapter whose contents are
familiar or easy of comprehension, to hurry to the next chapter. Hasty
reading may cause the loss of a particular meaning that a section or a
paragraph is intended to convey. Proficiency in mathematics depends upon thorough understanding of each step as it is encountered
so that it can be used to master that which follows.

1 – 6   Importance of problems

Full advantage should be taken of the many problems distributed
throughout the text. There is no approach to a full and complete
understanding of any branch of mathematics other than the solution
of numerous problems. Application of what has been learned from
the text to practical problems in which the student is primarily interested not only will help with the subject matter of the problem but

will serve the purpose of fixing in mind the mathematical principles involved.

In general, the arrangement of problems is such that the most difficult appear at the end of each group. It is apparent that the working of the simpler problems first will tend to make the more difficult ones easier of solution. The home-study student is therefore urged to work all problems in the order given. At times, this may appear to be useless, and the student may have the desire to proceed to more interesting things, but time spent in working problems will amply repay the student in giving him a depth of understanding to be obtained in no other manner. This does not mean that progress should cease if a problem appears impossible of solution. Return to such problems when the mind is fresh, or mark them for solution during a review period.

1 – 7   Illustrative examples

Each of the illustrative examples in this book is intended to make clear some important principle or method of solution. The subject matter of these examples will be more thoroughly assimilated if, after careful analysis of the problem set forth, an independent solution is made and the method and results are compared with the illustrative example.

1 – 8   Review

Too much stress cannot be placed upon the necessity for frequent and thorough review. Often points that have been missed in the original study of the text will stand out clearly upon careful review. A review of each chapter before proceeding with the next is recommended.

1 – 9   Section references

Throughout this book you will be referred to earlier sections for review or to bring to attention similar material pertaining to the subject under discussion. For the purpose of ready reference and convenience, the headings of right-hand pages contain two section numbers. The first number denotes the *first* section beginning on the facing page, and the second number denotes the *last* section beginning on that page. Thus, wherever the reader opens the book, these section numbers show the section coverage of the pages in view. For example, Sec. 8–10 is easily found on page 72 by leafing through the book while noting the inclusive section numbers.

CHAPTER 2
REVIEW OF ARITHMETIC
ADDITION AND SUBTRACTION

Chapters 2 through 6 are devoted to a short *review* of some of the basic operations in arithmetic. These chapters have been written with the assumption that you have studied arithmetic but that your abilities in "figuring" (calculating) have lessened, mainly because considerable time may have elapsed since you needed to do much calculation.

The solution of nearly every practical problem eventually reduces to an arithmetical computation; that is, the desired answer, or the information we are seeking, must be expressed as a *number*. It is essential, therefore, that one be able to perform the necessary arithmetical operations with accuracy as the first goal and with speed attained through repeated practice and drill. In this connection, at the end of Chap. 6 is a group of review problems. At this time, if you can solve them correctly in the specified times, you are probably safe in going on to Chap. 7.

2 – 1   Numbers

Our system of *numbers* is composed of the 10 digits 1, 2, 3, 4, 5, 6, 7, 8, 9, and 0. All numbers consist of combinations of these digits. Arithmetic consists of the relations of numbers and the methods of computing with numbers.

In every number each digit has a certain *place value*, and the position of a digit in a number gives the digit its value. From right to left these values are units, tens, hundreds, thousands, ten thousands, and so on. For example, in the four-digit number 9,547, the digit 7 has a value of 7 units, the 4 is in the tens place and has a value of 4 tens (40 units), the 5 is in the hundreds place with a value of 5 hundreds (500 units), and the 9 in the thousands place has a value of 9 thousands (9,000 units).

An *abstract number* is one that has no reference to any quantity or object. For example, the number 16, when used by itself, is an abstract number. In general, you will be concerned with abstract numbers only when dealing with basic mathematical principles and procedures.

Technicians and engineers are more concerned with concrete numbers. A *concrete number* is one that is connected with a particular quantity or object and therefore consists of two parts. The first part is a number which tells us *how much;* the second part specifies the unit of measurement or object and tells us *what.* For example, 60 cycles, 25 ohms, 10 microfarads, and 30 henrys are concrete numbers. In Chap. 11 you will study some interesting methods of dealing with concrete numbers as applied to units and dimensions relating to electricity and electronics.

2 – 2   Addition

In general, concrete numbers should be added only when they are related to the *same kind* of *units* or *things.* For example, it would not make sense to add 47 ohms and 2 horsepower. However, this rule cannot be followed blindly because it *would* be sensible to add 40 resistors and 35 capacitors to obtain 75 parts, or objects. Here, we would be adding parts, or *things.*

The word "plus" indicates addition and is denoted by +. The equality sign = means "is equal to." Thus, in the language of mathematics $6 + 8 = 14$. In English this says that 6 plus 8 is equal to 14. The quantity, or number, obtained by adding two or more numbers is known as the *sum* of those numbers. Therefore, as indicated above, the sum of 6 and 8 is 14.

EXAMPLE 1   Find the sum of 6,473, 1,092, and 968.

SOLUTION   Write the numbers to be added in a column so that each unit digit of a number is under the unit digit of the number above it. This will place the tens, hundreds, and thousands digits of all numbers in their respective columns. Draw a line under the numbers so that the sum, which is to be written below the line, will be separated from the numbers to be added. Thus:

$$
\begin{array}{r}
6,473 \\
1,092 \\
968 \\
\hline
\text{Sum} = 8,533
\end{array}
$$

Units column:

$$
\begin{array}{r}
{}^{1} \\
6,473 \\
1,092 \\
968 \\
\hline
3
\end{array}
$$

Begin by adding downward in the units column: 3 plus 2 is equal to 5, and this 5 plus 8 is equal to 13. Since 13 contains one tens value plus three units, we write the 3 in the units column of the sum and carry over the 1 to the tens column to be added there.

Tens column:

$$
\begin{array}{r}
{}^{21} \\
6,473 \\
1,092 \\
968 \\
\hline
33
\end{array}
$$

Starting with the 1 carried into the tens column: 1 plus 7 is equal to 8, this 8 plus 9 is equal to 17, and this 17 plus 6 gives 23. Now this 23 is in the hundreds and tens values, so we write the 3 in the tens column of the sum and carry the 2 over to the hundreds column to be added there.

Hundreds column:

$$
\begin{array}{r}
{}^{1\ 2} \\
6,473 \\
1,092 \\
968 \\
\hline
533
\end{array}
$$

Starting with the 2 carried over to the hundreds column: 2 plus 4 is equal to 6, this 6 plus 0 is equal to 6, and this same 6 plus 9 gives 15. This 15 is in the thousands and hundreds values, therefore the 5 is written in the hundreds column of the sum and the 1 is carried over to the thousands column to be added there.

Thousands column:

$$
\begin{array}{r}
{}^{1} \\
6,473 \\
1,092 \\
968 \\
\hline
8,533
\end{array}
$$

Starting with the 1 carried over to the thousands column: 1 plus 6 is equal to 7, and this 7 plus 1 gives 8. Since there is nothing to be added in the thousands column of 968, the addition has been completed and we write the 8 in the thousands column of the sum which now amounts to 8,533.

The reason for "carrying" values from one column to the next one to the left is better illustrated by performing the foregoing addition by another method. This is accomplished by adding the digit col-

umns separately, placing their sums in their proper columns of value,
and then adding these individual sums as shown below.

$$
\begin{array}{r}
6473 \\
1092 \\
968 \\
\hline
13 \\
22 \\
13 \\
7 \\
\hline
8533
\end{array}
$$

This is a good way of checking your addition, although if you get
the same sum by adding *upward*, after adding the columns *downward*,
your answer is probably correct.

When adding, you should not form the habit of adding in the manner of the solution of Example 1, which was written for explanatory
purposes. For example, instead of thinking in terms of "3 plus 2 is 5,
5 plus 8 is 13," you should think right down the column and omit the
in-between steps. For example, when adding the units column, you
should automatically add and think "3, 5, 13"; write down the 3 and
proceed to the tens column and think "1, 8, 17, 23"; and so on for the
other columns as illustrated below. This will increase your speed.

Adding units column

```
  1
6,473   three
1,092   five
  968   thirteen
───
    3
```

Adding tens column

```
 21     one
6,473   eight
1,092   seventeen
  968   twenty-three
───
   33
```

Adding hundreds column

```
1 2     two
6,473   six
1,092
  968   fifteen
───
  533
```

Adding thousands column

```
1       one
6,473   seven
1,092   eight
  968
─────
8,533
```

PROBLEMS 2 – 1

Add:

1 $208 + 43 + 6,955$ 2 $71 + 979 + 856$ 3 $3,594 + 2,216 + 634$
4 $8,015 + 32 + 500 + 47,183$ 5 $29 + 87,645 + 913 + 9,769$

6	6,493	7	10,532	8	6,742
	9,781		49		8,967
	7,634		617		14
	5,028		8,052		5,032
			98,135		

9	4,379	10	67,841	11	60,215
	261		80,936		430
	5,083		245		1,942
	9,752		10,987		76,853
					109,732

12	264	13	457,981	14	807
	58,198		34		465,190
	70		17,052		8,143,276
	4,589		897,523		99
	63,266		3,160,932		2,380,572

15	4,512,607
	9,087,124
	3,465,563
	1,907,835
	2,361,009

16 The air-line distance from the Azores to London is 1,562 miles, and it is 2,604 miles from New York to the Azores. How far is it from London to New York via the Azores?

17 A distributor, after selling 1,027 tubes to one dealer and 975 to another, had 2,573 tubes on hand. How many tubes had he at first?

18 The Pacific Ocean has an area of approximately 63,801,000 square miles; Atlantic Ocean, 31,830,000 square miles; Caribbean Sea, 750,000 square miles. What is their total area?

19 Arkansas has an area of 53,102 square miles; Michigan, 58,216 square miles; Virginia, 40,815 square miles; Iowa, 56,280 square miles. What is the total area of these four states?

20 A television technician's jobs and sales for one day were:
Mr. Wheeler: Labor $3.50, parts $8.65.
Mr. Atwell: Labor $5.40.
Mr. Haskins: Parts $10.57.
Mr. Barline: Labor $2.85, parts $9.78.
Mr. Hart: Labor $10.95, parts $25.06.
(a) What were his receipts for the day? (b) How much of the receipts was for labor?

2 – 3   Some fundamentals of circuitry

In circuit diagrams, symbols are used to represent various components that make up a circuit. Three of the most common symbols are shown in Fig. 2–1.

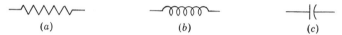

(a)   (b)   (c)

Fig. 2–1 Symbols used in schematic diagrams: (a) resistor, (b) inductor, (c) capacitor.

When two or more resistors are connected end to end, as illustrated in Fig. 2–2, they are said to be connected in *series*, thereby forming a

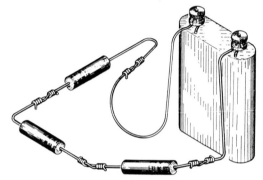

Fig. 2–2 Battery and three resistors connected in series.

series circuit. Figure 2–3 is a *schematic diagram* of the circuit of Fig. 2–2. A circuit schematic diagram is a diagram made up of circuit symbols with connecting lines representing the wires, or conductors, that connect the components together.

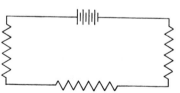

Fig. 2–3 Schematic diagram of the circuit arrangement of Fig. 2–2.

When resistors are connected in series, the total resistance of the circuit thus formed is equal to the sum of the individual resistances. You will study series circuits in more detail in Chap. 13.

When resistors are connected as shown in Figs. 2–4 and 2–5, they are said to be connected in *parallel*, thereby forming a *parallel circuit*.

Capacitors (condensers) connected in parallel are illustrated in Figs. 2–6 and 2–7.

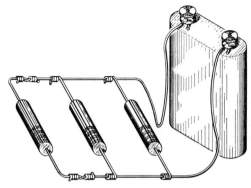

FIG. 2–4 Battery and three resistors connected in parallel.

When capacitors are connected in parallel, the total capacitance (capacity) of the circuit is equal to the sum of the individual capacitances.

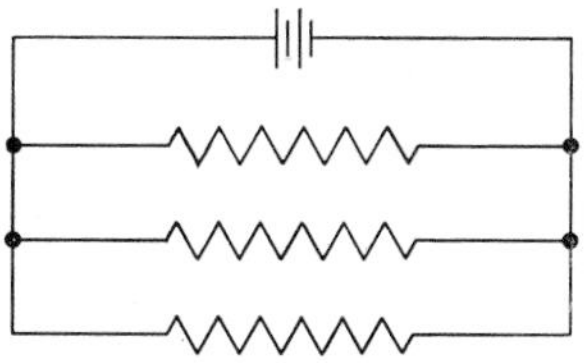

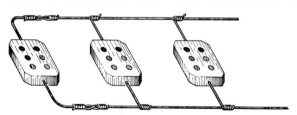

FIG. 2–5 Schematic diagram of the circuit arrangement of Fig. 2–4.

PROBLEMS 2 – 2

1 From left to right the resistors of Fig. 2–2 are 10 ohms, 22 ohms, and 47 ohms. What is their total resistance?

2 Two resistors of 5,600 ohms and 4,700 ohms are connected in series. What is their combined resistance?

3 Four resistors are connected in series. Their values are 100 ohms, 1,000

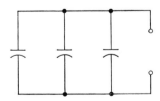

FIG. 2–6 Three capacitors connected in parallel.

ohms, 39 ohms, and 470 ohms. What is their total resistance?

4 The capacitors of Fig. 2–7 have the following values: 25 microfarads, 10 microfarads, and 8 microfarads. What is the total capacitance of the circuit?

5 Four capacitors of 250 micromicrofarads, 500 micromicrofarads, 5 micromicrofar-

FIG. 2–7 Schematic diagram of the circuit of Fig. 2–6.

ads, and 1,000 micromicrofarads are connected in parallel. What is their total capacitance?

2 – 4   Subtraction

Subtraction consists of finding the difference between two numbers. Fortunately, when one has learned to add, he is well on the way to having mastered subtraction as well. For example, knowing that you get 9 when you add 4 and 5, you know that 5 taken away from 9 leaves 4. In arithmetic the minus sign − indicates subtraction. Thus, $9 − 5 = 4$.

The number to be subtracted is called the *subtrahend*. The number from which the subtrahend is to be subtracted is called the *minuend*. The result is called the *remainder* or *difference*.

In subtraction, the subtrahend is written directly under the minuend, with the digits of the units, tens, hundreds, etc., aligned in their proper columns as is done in addition. The remainder is written with the digits placed in *their* proper places; also as in addition.

EXAMPLE 2   Subtract 4,365 from 9,687.
SOLUTION
$$\begin{aligned}
\text{Minuend} &= 9{,}687 \\
\text{Subtrahend} &= 4{,}365 \\
\hline
\text{Remainder} &= 5{,}322
\end{aligned}$$

When digits are to be subtracted from smaller digits, we proceed with methods similar to those used in addition.

EXAMPLE 3   Subtract 7,648 from 9,452.
SOLUTION
$$\begin{aligned}
\text{Minuend} &= 9{,}452 \\
\text{Subtrahend} &= 7{,}648 \\
\hline
\text{Remainder} &= 1{,}804
\end{aligned}$$

Units column:

944 *(12)*
764   *8*
─────
       4

Since *8* cannot be subtracted from 2, we take one tens value from the tens column in the minuend and add it to the 2 in the units column. This results in $10 + 2 = 12$ units from which we now subtract *8* and get *4* for the units value of the remainder.

Tens column:

94*4* (12)
76*4*   8
─────
  0   4

Taking the one tens value from the 5 in the minuend left *4* in the tens column, from which we now subtract the *4* in the tens column of the subtrahend. This results in *0* for the tens value in the remainder.

Hundreds column:

8 *(14)* 4 *(12)*
   6   4   8
───────────
   8   *0*   *4*

Since *6* cannot be subtracted from 4, we take one thousands value from the 9 in the thousands column of the minuend and add it to the 4 in the hundreds column. This results in *14* from which we subtract the

6 in the hundreds column of the subtrahend. This leaves *8* for the hundreds value of the remainder.

Thousands column:

8 (14) 4 (12)

7	6	4	8
1	8	0	4

Taking the one thousands value from the 9 in the minuend left *8* in the thousands column. From this *8* is subtracted the *7* in the thousands column of the subtrahend. This leaves *1* which is for the thousands value of the remainder.

This completes the subtraction, which results in a remainder of 1,804 when 7,648 is subtracted from 9,452.

The accuracy of subtraction can be checked by adding the subtrahend and the remainder, which should result in a sum equal to the minuend. This is illustrated below for Example 3:

$$\begin{array}{rr} \textbf{Minuend} & \textbf{\textit{9,452}} \\ -\text{Subtrahend} & \underline{7,648} \\ \text{Remainder} = & 1,804 \\ +\text{Subtrahend} & \underline{7,648} \\ \textbf{Minuend} = & \textbf{\textit{9,452}} \end{array}$$

PROBLEMS 2-3

Subtract:

1	46	2	94	3	62
	25		32		49

4	783	5	561	6	724
	572		138		687

7	950	8	4,259	9	8,432
	63		1,399		853

10	7,001	11	58,761	12	70,605
	2,134		14,398		61,926

13	82,570	14	63,711	15	93,010
	52,491		28,008		83,914

16	70,109
	69,099

17 How much greater is 10,000 than 2,949?

18 How much less than 87,004 is 76,975?

19 From the sum of 56,783 and 26,895, subtract 14,769.

20 Subtract 38,096 from the sum of 24,097 and 75,093.

21 Subtract the sum of 14,296 and 11,683 from the sum of 34,758 and 19,010.

22 A tank contained 18,700 gallons of water. After 210 gallons was lost by evaporation and 100 gallons by leakage, 795 gallons was pumped into the tank. How much is now in the tank?

23 The owner of an appliance store started the day with $250.00 cash on hand. During the day he sold a television set for $199.95, another for $249.75, and a radio for $47.45. He paid $36.02 for parts from the wholesaler and donated $25.00 to a charitable organization. In addition, Mr. Martin paid a repair bill amounting to $19.75. How much money should the store owner have on hand?

24 What must be done to a minuend so that the remainder is increased by 87 if the subtrahend is increased by 64?

25 A subtrahend is increased by 73. What must be done with the minuend so that the remainder is unchanged?

CHAPTER 3
REVIEW OF ARITHMETIC
MULTIPLICATION AND DIVISION

This chapter is devoted to a short review of multiplication and division of whole numbers.

3 – 1 Multiplication

The sign $\times$ indicates *multiplication*, which is often defined as the *process of continued addition*. Thus, $2 \times 3 = 6$ may be thought of as adding 2 three times: $2 + 2 + 2 = 6$.

The *product* is the result obtained in multiplying two or more numbers. For example, 12 is the product of 6×2; that is, $6 \times 2 = 12$. The 6 and 2 are called the *factors*.

The *multiplicand* is the number to be multiplied by another number, which is called the *multiplier;* that is,

$$\text{Multiplicand} \times \text{multiplier} = \text{product}$$

EXAMPLE 1   Multiply 846 by 63.

SOLUTION

Multiplicand	=	846
Multiplier	=	63
Multiplicand $\times$ 3 =		2538
Multiplicand $\times$ 6 =		5076
Adding: Product	=	53298

As shown above, the multiplier 63 is written under the multiplicand 846, with the unit digits in the units column, tens digits in the tens column, and so on, as was done in addition and subtraction.

Units multiplier:

$$\begin{array}{r} {\scriptstyle 1} \\ 846 \\ 63 \\ \hline 8 \end{array}$$

Multiply 846 by the *3* of the multiplier, starting with the units digit 6 of 846. Thus, 6 multiplied by *3* is 18, or $3 \times 6 = 18$. Since 18 is one tens value plus eight units, we write the *8* in the units column of this first product. The *1* of the 18 is carried over to the tens column of the multiplicand to be added to the next multiplication.

$$\begin{array}{r} {\scriptstyle 11} \\ 846 \\ 63 \\ \hline 38 \end{array}$$

Next multiply the 4 in the tens column of 846 by *3*. $3 \times 4 = 12$ plus the *1* carried over is 13, which is one hundreds and three tens in value. Therefore, the *3* is written in the tens column and the *1* is carried over to the hundreds column of the multiplicand to be added to the next multiplication.

$$\begin{array}{r} {\scriptstyle 1} \\ 846 \\ 63 \\ \hline 2538 \end{array}$$

Similarly, the 8 in the hundreds column of 846 is multiplied by *3*. $3 \times 8 = 24$ plus the *1* carried over is 25. Since this finishes multiplication by *3*, the *25* is written with the *5* in the hundreds column and the *2* in the thousands column.

Tens multiplier:

$$\begin{array}{r} {\scriptstyle 3} \\ 846 \\ 63 \\ \hline 2538 \\ 6 \end{array}$$

846 is multiplied in a similar manner, except now the multiplier *6* is in the tens column; therefore, there will be no digit in the units column for the product of the multiplier *6*. Thus, $6 \times 6 = 36$ with the *6* being written in the tens column and the *3* carried over to be added to the next multiplication.

$$\begin{array}{r} {\scriptstyle 23} \\ 846 \\ 63 \\ \hline 2538 \\ 76 \end{array}$$

Next $6 \times 4 = 24$ plus the *3* carried over gives 27. The *7* is written in the hundreds column and the *2* is carried over to be added to the next multiplication.

$$\begin{array}{r} {\scriptstyle 2} \\ 846 \\ 63 \\ \hline 2538 \\ 5076 \end{array}$$

Finally, $6 \times 8 = 48$ plus the *2* carried over results in 50. Since this finishes the multiplication by *6*, the *50* is written with the *0* in the thousands column, and the *5* in the ten-thousands column.

$$\begin{array}{r} 846 \\ 63 \\ \hline 2538 \\ 5076 \\ \hline 53298 \end{array}$$

The results of the multiplications are then added to obtain *53298*, which is the product of 846 and 63.

You can prove to yourself that when you multiply two or more numbers, it makes no difference which factors are chosen as the multiplicand or the multiplier. In fact, a good way to check your multiplication is to interchange multiplicand and multiplier as shown below in the multiplication of 5,826 and 1,973:

```
      5826                    1973
      1973                    5826
     17478                   11838
     40782                    3946
     52434                   15784
      5826                    9865
   11494698                11494698
```

PROBLEMS 3-1

Multiply:

1	96	2	493	3	6,705		
	6		7		3		
4	8,210	5	78	6	154		
	9		54		82		
7	209	8	853	9	7,613		
	17		63		54		
10	2,409	11	8,674	12	2,153		
	28		19		709		
13	6,924	14	8,137	15	4,072		
	462		308		5,816		
16	5,389	17	6,019	18	4,387		
	3,504		7,002		9,876		
19	61,051	20	97,826				
	3,007		8,967				

21 Seven resistors of 4,700 ohms each are connected in series. What is their total resistance?

22 Nine 250-micromicrofarad capacitors are connected in parallel. What is their total capacitance?

23 The owner of an appliance store pays $3 per square foot per year rent. The store has an area of 1,400 square feet. What is his yearly rent?

24   Aircraft *A* departed from an airport at 8:00 A.M. flying at a speed of 280 miles per hour. Aircraft *B* departed from the same airport at 11:00 A.M., flying at 425 miles per hour, on the same course (direction) as *A*. How far apart were they at 5:00 P.M.?

25   Plane *C* left New York for San Francisco at 7:00 A.M. flying at 350 miles per hour. Plane *D* left San Francisco for New York at 8:00 A.M. flying at 575 miles per hour. The air-line distance from New York to San Francisco is 2,606 miles. How far apart were they at noon?

3 – 2   Division

The signs $\div$, ——, and / all indicate *division*, which is the process of finding how many times one number, the *dividend*, contains another number, the *divisor*. Thus, $6 \div 3$, $\dfrac{6}{3}$, and 6/3 all indicate that 6 is to be divided by 3. The result obtained by division is called the *quotient;* that is,

$$\frac{\text{Dividend}}{\text{Divisor}} = \text{quotient}$$

3 – 3   Short division

In *short division* the divisor is such that the process of division can be carried out mentally without writing down the intermediate steps.

EXAMPLE 2   Divide 864 by 4.

SOLUTION   Divisor   4)864   dividend
                            216   quotient

4)864
 2

The divisor *4* is contained in the first digit of the dividend 8 exactly *2* times. The *2* is written as the first digit of the quotient.

4)864
 21

Next, *4* is contained in *6* one time with 2 left over. The *1* is written as the next digit of the quotient.

    2
4)864
 216

The *2* left over, which has a value of two tens units, is carried over to the units place and added to the *4* units. This results in *24* which, when divided by *4*, gives *6* as the last digit of the quotient. This completes the division.

EXAMPLE 3   Divide 2,893 by 6.

SOLUTION   Divisor   6)2,893   dividend
                            482⅙   quotient

6)2,893
 4

It is seen that 2, the first digit of the dividend, cannot be divided by *6;* therefore *28* is divided by 6. This results in *4* for the first digit of the quotient, with 4 left over.

$$\begin{array}{r}4\\6\overline{)2,893}\\48\end{array}$$

The *4* which was left over is carried and combined with the next digit *9* in the dividend to make *49*. The divisor *6* is contained in *49* eight times with 1 left over. The *8* is written as the next digit of the quotient.

$$\begin{array}{r}1\\6\overline{)2,893}\\482\end{array}$$

The *1* left over is combined with the next digit *3* of the dividend to make *13*. This *13* when divided by *6* results in *2* with 1 left over. The *2* is written as the final digit of the dividend.

$$\begin{array}{r}6\overline{)2,893}\\482\frac{1}{6}\end{array}$$

Since this is as far as the division can be carried out, the remaining division is indicated by writing ⅙ as part of the quotient. This completes the division.

3 – 4   Long division

In *long division* the divisor is such that the successive steps of the division cannot readily be carried out mentally and therefore must be written down. In general, long division is classified as any division wherein the divisor consists of more than one digit.

EXAMPLE 4   Divide 4128 by 16.

SOLUTION

$$\begin{array}{r}258 \quad \text{quotient}\\ \text{Divisor} \quad 16\overline{)4128} \quad \text{dividend}\\ 32\\ \overline{92}\\ 80\\ \overline{128}\\ 128\end{array}$$

$$\begin{array}{r}2\\16\overline{)4128}\\32\\9\end{array}$$

The divisor *16* cannot be divided into *4;* therefore, *41* is divided by *16*. You know that *16* is contained in *41* more than one time, because that would give a remainder greater than *16*. Also, you know that *16* is not contained in *41* more than two times, because that would result in a product greater than *41*. Since *41* divided by *16* gives *2* with *9* left over, the *2* is written as the first digit of the quotient directly above the last digit *1* of the *41* into which *16* was divided. The *2*, now in the quotient, is used as a multiplier of *16*, which results in a product of 32. The *32* is written under the *41* in the dividend and subtracted therefrom, leaving a remainder of *9*.

$$\begin{array}{r}25\\16\overline{)4128}\\32\\ \overline{92}\\80\\ \overline{12}\end{array}$$

2, the next digit in the dividend, is brought down beside the remainder *9* to make a new dividend of *92*. *16* is contained in *92* five times with *12* left over. The *5* is written as the second digit of the quotient and used as a multiplier of *16*, which results in a product of 80. This *80* is written under the *92* and subtracted, leaving a remainder of *12*.

$$\begin{array}{r} 258 \\ 16\overline{)4128} \\ 32 \\ \hline 92 \\ 80 \\ \hline 128 \\ 128 \\ \hline \end{array}$$

8, the next digit in the dividend, is brought down beside the remainder *12* to make a new dividend of *128*. *16* is contained in *128* exactly eight times. The *8* is written as the third and last digit of the quotient and used as a multiplier of *16*, which results in a product of *128*. There is no remainder, and the division is complete.

EXAMPLE 5

Divide 15421 by 74.

SOLUTION

$$\text{Divisor}\quad 74\overline{)15421}\quad \begin{array}{l} 208\,^{29}\!/_{74}\quad \text{quotient} \\ \text{dividend} \end{array}$$

$$\begin{array}{r} 148 \\ \hline 621 \\ 592 \\ \hline 29 \quad \text{remainder} \end{array}$$

$$\begin{array}{r} 2 \\ 74\overline{)15421} \\ 148 \\ \hline 6 \end{array}$$

The divisor *74* cannot be divided into *1* or *15*; therefore, *154* is divided by *74*, giving 2 as a partial quotient. This *2* is written as the first digit of the quotient and used as a multiplier of *74*, which results in a product of 148. The *148* is written under *154* and subtracted, leaving a remainder of *6*.

$$\begin{array}{r} 20 \\ 74\overline{)15421} \\ 148 \\ \hline 62 \end{array}$$

2, the next digit of the dividend, is brought down beside the remainder *6* to make an intermediate dividend of *62*. Now, *62* cannot be divided by *74*; therefore, *0* (zero) is written as the next digit of the quotient.

$$\begin{array}{r} 208 \\ 74\overline{)15421} \\ 148 \\ \hline 621 \\ 592 \\ \hline 29 \end{array}$$

Since *62* cannot be divided by *74*, the next digit *1* of the dividend is brought down to make an intermediate dividend of *621*. This, when divided by *74*, results in a partial quotient of 8. The *8* is written as the third digit of the quotient and used as a multiplier of *74*, which results in a product of 592. The *592* is written under *621* and subtracted, leaving a remainder of *29*.

$$\begin{array}{r} 208\,^{29}\!/_{74} \\ 74\overline{)15421} \\ 148 \\ \hline 621 \\ 592 \\ \hline 29 \end{array}$$

Since this is as far as the division can be carried out, the remaining division is indicated by writing $^{29}\!/_{74}$ as part of the quotient. This completes the division.

The result of a division can be checked by multiplying the quotient by the divisor and adding the remainder, if any. The product thus obtained should equal the dividend. In Example 2, 864 divided by 4 resulted in a quotient of 216. To check, we multiply 216 by 4, which results in a product of 864, proving the division to be correct. Similarly, in Example 5, the dividend 15,421 was divided by 74, which resulted in a quotient of 208 with a remainder of 29. To check, we multiply 208 by 74 and obtain 15,392 which, when added to the remainder 29, gives a sum of 15,421. Since this is equal to the dividend, the division is correct.

PROBLEMS 3 – 2

Divide:

1 7)322   2 4)388   3 8)1,576

4 3)2,919   5 9)44,156   6 17)717

7 23)20,529   8 67)7,035   9 19)5,585

10 93)651,625   11 124)9,052   12 637)56,893

13 309)33,063   14 713)34,937   15 1,793)130,000

16 A tank has a capacity of 5,130 gallons. In how many hours will it be filled if water is pumped in at the rate of 270 gallons per hour?

17 An airplane is flying from New York to Paris, an air-line distance of 3,600 miles, at the rate of 450 miles per hour. How much time will be required for the trip?

18 One hundred and twenty-seven tons of coal was purchased for $2,032. What was the price per ton?

19 The salary of a technician is $5,408 per year. With 52 weeks to the year, what is his weekly salary?

20 A farmer sold his 165-acre farm for $42,240. How much did he receive per acre?

21 Into how many parts must 17,813 be divided so that each part is equal to 379?

22 What number must be divided by 239 to obtain a quotient of 57?

23 What number, multiplied by 397, gives 80,591 as a product?

24 What number, divided by 83, gives a quotient of 37 with a remainder of 23?

25 What number, multiplied by 73, results in a product of 53,947?

3 – 5   Averages

To find the *average* of several numbers, or items, the numbers are added and the sum is divided by the number of items in the group.

The results of measurements such as voltages, currents, and resistances or other data taken by experimental observations are always liable to error.   For example, two technicians reading an ammeter might not agree on the exact amount of current flowing in a circuit because of a difference in interpreting the position of the ammeter pointer.   Furthermore, two seemingly identical voltmeters connected in the same circuit might not indicate exactly the same voltages. Therefore, in many instances, in order to arrive at a result which can be relied upon, several measurements or observations are taken and the average result is calculated.

EXAMPLE 6   Find the average of 126, 154, 143, and 133.
SOLUTION   There are four numbers and the average is their sum divided by 4:

$$
\begin{array}{r}
126 \\
154 \\
143 \\
133 \\
\hline
4\overline{)556} = \text{sum} \\
\hline
139 = \text{average}
\end{array}
$$

EXAMPLE 7   Five voltmeters were connected to a power line, and the readings were as follows: 234 volts, 232 volts, 235 volts, 234 volts, and 235 volts.   What is your estimate of the true line voltage?
SOLUTION   The best estimate of the correct line voltage would be the average of the voltmeter readings:

$$
\begin{array}{r}
234 \\
232 \\
235 \\
234 \\
235 \\
\hline
\text{Number of readings} = 5\overline{)1{,}170} = \text{sum of all readings} \\
\hline
234 = \text{average of all readings}
\end{array}
$$

3 – 6   Some fundamentals of circuitry

When *equal* resistances are connected in *parallel*, as shown in Figs. 2–4 and 2–5, the resistance of the circuit thus formed is equal to the value of one resistance divided by the number of resistances connected in parallel.

EXAMPLE 8   If each of the three resistances in the circuit of Fig. 2–5 has a resistance of 3,900 ohms, what is their combined resistance?
SOLUTION $\dfrac{3{,}900}{3} = 1{,}300$ ohms

When capacitors (condensers) of *equal* capacitance (capacity) are connected in *series*, as shown in Figs. 3–1 and 3–2, the capacitance of the combination is equal to the value of one capacitance divided by the number of capacitors connected in series.

FIG. 3–1   Three fixed capacitors connected in series.

EXAMPLE 9   Each of the capacitors in Fig. 3–2 has a capacitance of 510 micromicrofarads. What is their combined capacitance?

SOLUTION $\dfrac{510}{3} = 170$ micromicrofarads

PROBLEMS 3 – 3

1 Find the average of 57, 45, 63, and 71.

2 What is the average of 1,356, 2,165, 1,042, 2,307, and 3,390?

3 In a certain factory department the following weekly salaries are paid: Mr. White, $104; Mr. Jones, $89; Mr. Hawkins, $73; Mr. Smith, $110; Mr. Black, $65; Mr. Henderson, $93. Based on a 52-week year, what is the average annual salary in this department?

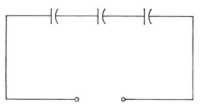

FIG. 3–2   Schematic diagram of the circuit of Fig. 3–1.

4 A technician purchased eight 4,700-ohm, 10 per cent tolerance resistors. When he measured them, he obtained resistance measurements as follows: 4,710 ohms, 5,000 ohms, 4,900 ohms, 4,520 ohms, 4,600 ohms, 4,200 ohms, 5,100 ohms, and 4,850 ohms. What is the average value of his resistors?

5 An appliance-store owner had daily receipts as follows: Monday, $480; Tuesday, $975; Wednesday, $809; Thursday, $727; Friday, $1,043; Saturday, $2,980. What were the average daily receipts?

6 A technician measured five fixed capacitors as follows: 255 micromicrofarads, 273 micromicrofarads, 290 micromicrofarads, 246 micromicrofarads, and 251 micromicrofarads. What is the average capacitance?

7 Four resistors of 5,600 ohms each are connected in parallel. What is their combined resistance?

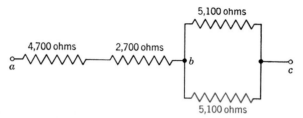

FIG. 3–3 Combination of resistors connected in series and parallel.

8   Five capacitors of 250 micromicrofarads each are connected in series. What is their combined capacitance?

9   In Fig. 3–3, what is the resistance (*a*) between points *a* and *b*, (*b*) between points *b* and *c*, (*c*) between points *a* and *c*?

10 In Fig. 3–3, if the resistor shown in red became open circuited, or was removed from the circuit, what would be the resistance between points *a* and *c*?

CHAPTER 4
REVIEW OF ARITHMETIC
COMMON FRACTIONS

This chapter continues with a *review* of arithmetic and deals with common fractions. It contains somewhat more detail than preceding chapters because it is essential for one to have a good grounding in fractions in order to carry out computations. Furthermore, as stated in Chap. 16, the student who really knows arithmetical fractions rarely has much trouble with algebraic fractions.

4 – 1   Definitions

A *common fraction*, as distinguished from a decimal fraction (Chap. 5), is an indicated division of two whole numbers and expresses one or more of the equal parts into which a thing is divided. For example, the common fraction $\frac{5}{6}$ has two meanings, either that 5 is to be divided by 6 or that something has been divided into 5 of 6 equal parts.

The number *above* the line of a fraction, the dividend, is called the *numerator* of the fraction. The number *below* the line, the divisor, is called the *denominator* of the fraction. Note that the numerator states *how many* of the *equal parts* that are contained in the denominator. Thus,

$$\text{A fraction} = \frac{\text{numerator}}{\text{denominator}} = \frac{\text{how many parts}}{\text{number of equal parts}}$$

A fraction in which the numerator is less than the denominator is called a *proper fraction*. $\frac{1}{3}$, $\frac{5}{8}$, and $\frac{12}{13}$ are proper fractions.

An *improper fraction* is one containing a numerator equal to or greater than the denominator. $\frac{4}{4}$, $\frac{9}{9}$, $\frac{3}{2}$, and $\frac{9}{4}$ are improper fractions.

4 – 2   Fundamental properties of fractions

When working with fractions, it is necessary to make frequent use of the following important principles.

1   The numerator and the denominator of a fraction can be multiplied by the same number, except zero, without changing the value of the fraction.

2   The numerator and the denominator of a fraction can be divided by the same number, except zero, without changing the value of the fraction.

EXAMPLE 1 $\dfrac{4}{5} = \dfrac{4 \times 3}{5 \times 3} = \dfrac{12}{15} = \dfrac{4}{5}$

EXAMPLE 2 $\dfrac{12}{15} = \dfrac{12 \div 3}{15 \div 3} = \dfrac{4}{5} = \dfrac{12}{15}$

It will be noted that no new principles are involved in performing these operations, because multiplying or dividing both numerator and denominator by the same number, except zero, is the same as multiplying or dividing the fraction by 1. Multiplication and division by zero is discussed in Chap. 16.

4 – 3   Reduction of whole or mixed numbers to improper fractions

You will recall that a *whole number* contains no fraction and that a *mixed number* consists of a whole number plus a fraction. Thus, the mixed number $2\frac{3}{5}$ means $2 + \frac{3}{5}$.

When working with whole or mixed numbers, it is often necessary to convert them into fractions in order to accomplish one or more of the operations of addition, subtraction, multiplication, or division.

Naturally, any whole or mixed number so converted will result in an improper fraction. Why is this true?

EXAMPLE 3   Reduce 6 to sevenths.

SOLUTION   Since $\frac{7}{7} = 1$

$$6 \times \frac{7}{7} = \frac{42}{7}$$

EXAMPLE 4   Change $5\frac{3}{4}$ to fourths.

SOLUTION   Since $5\frac{3}{4} = 5 + \frac{3}{4}$

$$5\frac{3}{4} = 5 \times \frac{4}{4} + \frac{3}{4} = \frac{20}{4} + \frac{3}{4} = \frac{23}{4}$$

The foregoing may be stated by the following:

RULE   To reduce to improper fractions,
1   If a whole number is to be reduced, convert 1 to a fraction of the desired denominator and multiply the numerator by the whole number.
2   If a mixed number is to be reduced, reduce the whole-number part to an improper fraction, then add to this numerator the numerator of the fractional part of the mixed number.

PROBLEMS 4 – 1

1   Reduce the following to fifths: (a) 1, (b) 3, (c) 8, (d) 13, (e) 23.
2   Reduce the following to ninths: (a) 9, (b) 7, (c) 17, (d) 43, (e) 68.
3   Convert to improper fractions: (a) $2\frac{1}{2}$, (b) $5\frac{2}{3}$, (c) $7\frac{4}{9}$, (d) $8\frac{3}{8}$, (e) $6\frac{4}{7}$.
4   Reduce to improper fractions: (a) $9\frac{3}{11}$, (b) $7\frac{8}{13}$, (c) $41\frac{5}{23}$, (d) $51\frac{8}{19}$, (e) $73\frac{4}{43}$.
5   Reduce to improper fractions: (a) $15\frac{9}{17}$, (b) $47\frac{17}{57}$, (c) $891\frac{9}{79}$, (d) $123\frac{36}{101}$, (e) $793\frac{198}{423}$.

4 – 4   **Reduction of improper fractions to whole or mixed numbers**

RULE   To reduce to whole or mixed numbers,
1   Perform the indicated division, and if there is no remainder, the fraction reduces to a whole number of units.
2   If there is a remainder, the quotient becomes a mixed number of which the quotient is the whole-number part and the remainder is the numerator of the fractional part.

EXAMPLE 5   Reduce $\dfrac{40}{8}$ to a whole number.

SOLUTION $\dfrac{40}{8} = 40 \div 8 = 5$

EXAMPLE 6   Reduce $\dfrac{37}{5}$ to a mixed number.

SOLUTION $\dfrac{37}{5} = 37 \div 5 = 7\frac{2}{5}$

PROBLEMS 4 – 2

1 Reduce to whole or mixed numbers: (a) $^{64}\!/_{8}$, (b) $^{72}\!/_{8}$, (c) $^{84}\!/_{7}$, (d) $^{889}\!/_{7}$, (e) $^{113}\!/_{15}$.

2 Reduce to whole or mixed numbers: (a) $^{85}\!/_{3}$, (b) $^{176}\!/_{9}$, (c) $^{528}\!/_{23}$, (d) $^{1,005}\!/_{87}$, (e) $^{996}\!/_{473}$.

4 – 5   Reduction to lowest terms

A fraction is in its *lowest terms* when there is no number that can be divided evenly into both numerator and denominator.

RULE   To reduce a fraction to its lowest terms, divide both numerator and denominator by their common factors or divide them by their greatest common divisor.

EXAMPLE 7   Reduce $\dfrac{6}{9}$ to its lowest terms.

SOLUTION $\dfrac{6}{9} = \dfrac{6}{9} \div \dfrac{3}{3} = \dfrac{2}{3}$

EXAMPLE 8   Reduce $\dfrac{156}{195}$ to its lowest terms.

SOLUTION $\dfrac{156}{195} = \dfrac{156}{195} \div \dfrac{3}{3} = \dfrac{52}{65}$

$\dfrac{52}{65} = \dfrac{52}{65} \div \dfrac{13}{13} = \dfrac{4}{5}$

If it had been recognized that both 156 and 195 could have been divided by 39, the greatest common divisor, the reduction could have been made in one operation.

PROBLEMS 4 – 3

Reduce the following fractions to their lowest terms:

1 $^{9}\!/_{15}$	2 $^{10}\!/_{20}$	3 $^{8}\!/_{12}$
4 $^{21}\!/_{28}$	5 $^{24}\!/_{32}$	6 $^{45}\!/_{120}$
7 $^{48}\!/_{60}$	8 $^{80}\!/_{96}$	9 $^{126}\!/_{144}$

10 $28/126$ 11 $120/192$ 12 $140/252$

13 $96/224$ 14 $96/144$ 15 $512/576$

16 $1,430/1,320$ 17 $1,344/1,472$ 18 $3,525/3,600$

19 $3,172/2,196$ 20 $2,208/3,072$

4 - 6 Prime factors

The following definitions have been included in order to refresh your memory and assist you in understanding the processes used in handling fractions.

You will recall that a *factor* of a whole number is any whole number that will exactly divide it. Thus, 2, 3, 4, and 6 are factors of 12. Generally, the factors 1 and the number itself are omitted (1 and 12 in this instance).

A *prime number* is one which has no whole-number factors except 1 and itself. 2, 3, 5, 7, 11, and 13 are examples of prime numbers.

By combining the foregoing definitions, it follows that the *prime factors* of a whole number are all the prime numbers that exactly divide the whole number. For example, 2, 3, and 5 are the prime factors of 30.

To find the prime factors of a number, we begin by dividing it by the smallest prime number, 2, and continue dividing all consecutive quotients by it until an odd quotient is obtained. We then try to divide this quotient, now a dividend, by successively higher prime numbers and continue the divisions until 1 is obtained as a final quotient.

EXAMPLE 9   Find the prime factors of 3,696.

SOLUTION   This is usually performed by arranging the work as follows:

$$2)\overline{3,696}$$
$$2)\overline{1,848}$$
$$2)\overline{924}$$
$$2)\overline{462}$$
$$3)\overline{231}$$
$$7)\overline{77}$$
$$11)\overline{11}$$
$$1$$

Therefore 3,696 can be expressed as a product of its prime factors as follows:

$$3,696 = 2 \cdot 2 \cdot 2 \cdot 2 \cdot 3 \cdot 7 \cdot 11$$

EXAMPLE 10   Find the prime factors of 5,460.
SOLUTION   2)5,460

              2)2,730

              3)1,365

              5)455

              7)91

              13)13

              1

That is, $5,460 = 2 \cdot 2 \cdot 3 \cdot 5 \cdot 7 \cdot 13$

PROBLEMS 4 – 4

Find the prime factors of the following:

1 24	2 60	3 210
4 525	5 2,695	6 1,001
7 805	8 1,131	9 34,255

10 201,960

4 – 7   Lowest common multiple

A *multiple* of a whole number is a whole number that is divisible by the given number. Thus, 15 is a multiple of 5, and 28 is a multiple of 7.

If a number can be divided by two or more numbers, it is a *common multiple* of them. The lowest such number is called the *lowest common multiple* and is abbreviated LCM. 48 and 24 are common multiples of 4, 8, and 12, but 24 is the LCM.

RULE   To find the LCM of two or more numbers,

1   Factor each number into its prime factors.

2   Multiply all the different prime factors, using each one the greatest number of times it appears in any one number.

EXAMPLE 11   Find the LCM of 6, 8, and 12.
SOLUTION   Expressing in prime factors:

$$6 = 2 \times 3$$
$$8 = 2 \times 2 \times 2$$
$$12 = 2 \times 2 \times 3$$

2 appears once as a prime factor of 6, three times as a prime factor of 8, and twice as a factor of 12. 3 appears once each as a prime factor of 6 and 12.

Therefore, 2 must be used as a product three times, and 3 used as a product one time.

Therefore, $\qquad$ LCM $= 2 \times 2 \times 2 \times 3 = 24$

EXAMPLE 12 Find the LCM of 24, 36, and 45.

SOLUTION Expressing in prime factors:

$$24 = 2 \times 2 \times 2 \times 3$$
$$36 = 2 \times 2 \times 3 \times 3$$
$$45 = 3 \times 3 \times 5$$

Therefore, $\qquad$ LCM $= 2 \times 2 \times 2 \times 3 \times 3 \times 5 = 360$

PROBLEMS 4-5

Find the LCM of:

1	12, 16, 24	2	12, 18, 30	3	10, 15, 20
4	11, 55, 33	5	7, 11, 13	6	45, 75, 81
7	5, 9, 16	8	27, 18, 60, 90	9	48, 80, 108

10 24, 108, 135, 216

4-8 Lowest common denominator

The *lowest common denominator* of two or more fractions is the lowest common multiple of their denominators and is abbreviated LCD.

RULE To reduce fractions to their LCD,
1 Find the LCM of their denominators. This is the LCD.
2 For each fraction, divide the LCD by the denominator, and multiply both numerator and denominator by the quotient thus obtained.

EXAMPLE 13 Reduce $\frac{2}{3}$ and $\frac{3}{8}$ to their LCD.

SOLUTION The LCM of the denominators 3 and 8 is 24. To change the denominator 3 of the fraction $\frac{2}{3}$ to the LCD, which is 24, we multiply the 3 by 8 ($24 \div 3$). In order not to change the value of the fraction, the numerator 2 must also be multiplied by 8.

Hence, $\qquad$ $\dfrac{2}{3} = \dfrac{2 \times 8}{3 \times 8} = \dfrac{16}{24}$

For $\frac{3}{8}$, the second fraction, we must multiply the denominator by 3 in order to obtain a new denominator of 24 ($24 \div 8$). The numerator must also be multiplied by 3 to maintain the value of the fraction.

Hence, $\qquad$ $\dfrac{3}{8} = \dfrac{3 \times 3}{8 \times 3} = \dfrac{9}{24}$

EXAMPLE 14   Reduce $\frac{1}{2}$, $\frac{2}{3}$, and $\frac{4}{5}$ to their LCD.

SOLUTION   The LCD is 30.

Therefore,

$$\frac{1}{2} = \frac{1 \times 15}{2 \times 15} = \frac{15}{30}$$

$$\frac{2}{3} = \frac{2 \times 10}{3 \times 10} = \frac{20}{30}$$

$$\frac{4}{5} = \frac{4 \times 6}{5 \times 6} = \frac{24}{30}$$

Examples 13 and 14 show that when a numerator and a denominator are multiplied or divided by the same number, except zero, the form of the fraction is changed, but not its *value*. Therefore, two fractions having the same value but not the same form are called *equivalent fractions*.

PROBLEMS 4 – 6

Reduce to equivalent fractions having their LCD:

1   $\frac{1}{8}$, $\frac{5}{6}$, $\frac{1}{12}$
2   $\frac{1}{16}$, $\frac{5}{12}$, $\frac{1}{24}$
3   $\frac{3}{11}$, $\frac{4}{7}$, $\frac{6}{7}$

4   $\frac{7}{10}$, $\frac{1}{4}$, $\frac{2}{5}$
5   $\frac{4}{5}$, $\frac{2}{3}$, $\frac{3}{11}$
6   $\frac{3}{20}$, $\frac{4}{5}$, $\frac{7}{25}$

7   $\frac{3}{5}$, $\frac{8}{9}$, $\frac{7}{16}$
8   $\frac{13}{18}$, $\frac{7}{30}$, $\frac{13}{55}$, $\frac{5}{6}$
9   Which is larger: $\frac{13}{24}$ or $\frac{11}{20}$?

10   Which is the smaller: $\frac{41}{125}$ or $\frac{16}{50}$?

4 – 9   Addition and subtraction

When two or more fractions having the *same* denominator are added, we have the following:

RULE   Add the numerators and write the result over the common denominator.

EXAMPLE 15 $$\frac{2}{11} + \frac{1}{11} + \frac{6}{11} = \frac{2 + 1 + 6}{11} = \frac{9}{11}$$

When you subtract two fractions having the *same* denominator, the method is similar.

RULE   Subtract the numerator of the subtrahend from the numerator of the minuend and write the result over the common denominator.

EXAMPLE 16 $$\frac{5}{7} - \frac{2}{7} = \frac{5 - 2}{7} = \frac{3}{7}$$

For fractions with *unlike* denominators, we observe the following:

RULE   To add or subtract fractions with unlike denominators,
1   Reduce them to equivalent fractions having their LCD.
2   Add or subtract the numerators of the equivalent fractions.

EXAMPLE 17 $\quad \dfrac{1}{9} + \dfrac{2}{3} + \dfrac{5}{12} = \dfrac{4}{36} + \dfrac{24}{36} + \dfrac{15}{36} = \dfrac{4 + 24 + 15}{36} = \dfrac{43}{36} = 1\frac{7}{36}$

EXAMPLE 18 $\quad \dfrac{4}{5} - \dfrac{7}{15} = \dfrac{12}{15} - \dfrac{7}{15} = \dfrac{12 - 7}{15} = \dfrac{5}{15} = \dfrac{1}{3}$

EXAMPLE 19 $\quad 2\frac{3}{4} + 5\frac{1}{3} = \dfrac{11}{4} + \dfrac{16}{3} = \dfrac{33}{12} + \dfrac{64}{12} = \dfrac{97}{12} = 8\frac{1}{12}$

When the result of an addition or subtraction is a proper fraction,
reduce to lowest terms; if an improper fraction, reduce to a whole or
mixed number.

PROBLEMS 4 – 7

Perform the following indicated additions and subtractions:

1   $\frac{1}{6} + \frac{1}{6}$ 2 $\frac{3}{14} + \frac{3}{14}$
3   $\frac{5}{12} - \frac{1}{12}$ 4 $\frac{5}{6} + \frac{1}{6}$
5   $\frac{2}{3} + \frac{1}{2}$ 6 $\frac{3}{5} + \frac{1}{10} + \frac{6}{20}$
7   $\frac{5}{8} - \frac{1}{3}$ 8 $\frac{7}{11} - \frac{1}{2}$
9   $\frac{3}{4} + \frac{5}{8} - \frac{1}{10}$ 10 $\frac{5}{6} + \frac{5}{12} - \frac{1}{3}$
11 $2\frac{1}{2} + 3\frac{1}{2}$ 12 $1\frac{1}{8} + \frac{3}{5}$
13 $3\frac{3}{4} + 4\frac{1}{3} - 2\frac{1}{6}$ 14 $3\frac{5}{7} + \frac{1}{2} + 5\frac{2}{3}$
15 $\frac{3}{16} + \frac{1}{8} + 4\frac{7}{10}$ 16 $\frac{4}{9} + 17\frac{3}{5} - 8\frac{5}{6}$
17 $\frac{3}{5} + 2\frac{5}{11} + \frac{3}{8}$ 18 $6\frac{7}{10} + 13\frac{1}{2} - 5\frac{4}{15}$
19 $1\frac{5}{32} + \frac{3}{4} - \frac{1}{5}$ 20 $3\frac{7}{40} + \frac{1}{8} + \frac{4}{5} - 1\frac{9}{20}$

4 – 10   Multiplication

RULE   To multiply a fraction by a whole number, multiply the
numerator of the fraction by the whole number and write the result
over the denominator.

EXAMPLE 20 $\quad \dfrac{3}{5} \times 4 = \dfrac{12}{5} = 2\frac{2}{5}$

EXAMPLE 21 $\quad \dfrac{7}{16} \times 8 = \dfrac{56}{16} = 3\frac{1}{2}$

RULE   To multiply one fraction by another fraction, multiply the
numerators together to obtain a new numerator and the denominators together to obtain a new denominator.

EXAMPLE 22 $\dfrac{3}{5} \times \dfrac{5}{8} = \dfrac{15}{40} = \dfrac{3}{8}$

EXAMPLE 23 $\dfrac{3}{4} \times \dfrac{2}{3} \times \dfrac{5}{6} = \dfrac{30}{72} = \dfrac{5}{12}$

EXAMPLE 24 $1\frac{3}{4} \times 5\frac{3}{10} = \dfrac{7}{4} \times \dfrac{53}{10} = \dfrac{371}{40} = 9\frac{11}{40}$

Note that when you multiply a number by a fraction, the resulting product is always *less* than the multiplicand.

4 – 11   Division

RULE   To divide by a fraction, invert the divisor and multiply.

EXAMPLE 25 $8 \div \dfrac{2}{3} = 8 \times \dfrac{3}{2} = \dfrac{24}{2} = 12$

EXAMPLE 26 $\dfrac{3}{7} \div \dfrac{5}{6} = \dfrac{3}{7} \times \dfrac{6}{5} = \dfrac{18}{35}$

EXAMPLE 27 $5\frac{3}{5} \div 2\frac{1}{2} = \dfrac{28}{5} \div \dfrac{5}{2} = \dfrac{28}{5} \times \dfrac{2}{5} = \dfrac{56}{25} = 2\frac{6}{25}$

Note that when you divide a number by a fraction, the resulting quotient is always *greater* than the dividend.

PROBLEMS 4 – 8

Perform the following indicated multiplications and divisions:

1 $\frac{1}{4} \times \frac{1}{3}$	2 $\frac{1}{2} \times \frac{1}{8}$	3 $\frac{7}{8} \times \frac{3}{4}$
4 $\frac{3}{4} \times \frac{7}{9}$	5 $\frac{5}{9} \times \frac{18}{25}$	6 $6 \times \frac{3}{4}$
7 $\frac{2}{5} \times 16$	8 $15 \times \frac{2}{3}$	9 $16 \times 3\frac{1}{8}$
10 $13\frac{2}{3} \times 4\frac{5}{8}$	11 $4 \div \frac{1}{2}$	12 $3 \div \frac{1}{4}$
13 $\frac{8}{9} \div \frac{5}{7}$	14 $\frac{3}{5} \div \frac{6}{25}$	15 $\frac{8}{9} \div \frac{4}{27}$
16 $2\frac{1}{2} \div 1\frac{1}{3}$	17 $12\frac{1}{8} \div 10\frac{1}{4}$	18 $6\frac{3}{13} \div 8\frac{2}{5}$
19 $18\frac{14}{25} \div 6\frac{3}{7}$	20 $25\frac{19}{30} \div 25\frac{3}{5}$	

CHAPTER 5
REVIEW OF ARITHMETIC
DECIMAL FRACTIONS

This chapter contains a brief review of decimal fractions, commonly called decimals. The material purposely has been made brief because in Chap. 10 you will have available more powerful and easier methods for computing with decimals. However, you will be handicapped in using these methods without an understanding of the decimal system.

5 – 1   Decimal values

Decimals are fractions that have 10, 100, 1,000, etc., for denominators. Thus, $\frac{3}{10}$, $\frac{27}{100}$, $\frac{3,185}{1,000}$, and $\frac{816}{1,000}$ are decimal fractions. In writing decimals and computing with decimals, it is convenient to omit the denominator and write a "point" (.), called the *decimal point*, in the numerator so that there are as many digits to the right of the decimal point as there are zeros in the denominator.

EXAMPLE 1   Write $\frac{25}{100}$ as a decimal.

SOLUTION   There are two zeros in the denominator; therefore, there must be two digits to the right of the decimal point.

Hence, $$\frac{25}{100} = 0.25$$

EXAMPLE 2 $$\frac{253}{1,000} = 0.253$$

EXAMPLE 3 $$\frac{3,185}{1,000} = 3.185$$

It will be noted that when there is no number to the left of the decimal point, as in Examples 1 and 2, zero is written to the left of the decimal point. This is done for clarity.

RULE When there are fewer digits in the numerator than there are zeros in the denominator, add zeros to the left of the number so that there will be as many decimal places as there are zeros in the denominator.

EXAMPLE 4 $$\frac{814}{10,000} = 0.0814$$

EXAMPLE 5 $$\frac{25}{100,000} = 0.00025$$

Each digit of a whole number has a certain place value (Sec. 2–1), and the same is true for decimals. The value of a digit depends upon its position with respect to the decimal point as shown below:

Millions	Hundred Thousands	Ten Thousands	Thousands	Hundreds	Tens	Units	Decimal point	Tenths	Hundredths	Thousandths	Ten-thousandths	Hundred-thousandths	Millionths
0	0	0	0	0	0	0	.	0	0	0	0	0	0

You will recall that the correct way of reading a whole number, such as 1,693, is "one thousand six hundred ninety-three." The word *and* is not used.

We read a decimal like a whole number except the name of the last decimal to the right is added. For example, the 0.253 in Example 2 would be read "two hundred fifty-three thousandths." The 0.0814 in Example 4 is read "eight hundred fourteen ten-thousandths."

When reading a mixed number, the word *and* is used between the whole-number part and the decimal part. Thus, the 3.185 in Example 3 is read "three *and* one hundred eighty-five thousandths." It is common practice, particularly when reading numbers to another person for writing or checking figures, to read the digits singly and substitute the word *point* for *and*. For example, 3.185 would be read "three *point* one eight five."

5 – 2 Addition with decimals

In the addition of decimals we proceed as with whole numbers, observing the following:

RULE Write the numbers so that the decimal points will be under each other. Add the digits and place the decimal point in the sum under the other decimal points.

EXAMPLE 6 Add 67.35, 0.0032, and 193.684.

SOLUTION
$$\begin{array}{r} 67.35 \\ 0.0032 \\ 193.684 \\ \hline 261.0372 \end{array}$$

5 – 3 Subtraction with decimals

When subtracting with decimals, the methods are similar to addition.

RULE Write the numbers so that the decimal points will be under each other. Subtract the digits and place the decimal point of the remainder under the other decimal points.

EXAMPLE 7 Subtract 84.253 from 168.105.

SOLUTION
$$\begin{array}{r} 168.105 \\ 84.253 \\ \hline 83.852 \end{array}$$

EXAMPLE 8 Subtract 23.452 from 80.

SOLUTION
$$\begin{array}{r} 80. \\ 23.452 \\ \hline 56.548 \end{array}$$

PROBLEMS 5 – 1

Add:

1	24.6	2	168.5	3	0.002
	32.85		0.123		0.1368

4 38.72, 9.683, 0.002   5 0.002, 7.46, 123

  6 674.26, 105.03, 0.01, 17.635
  7 0.000893, 0.00347, 6.7, 0.187, 16.0003
  8 174.95, 90.462, 3.004, 67.34, 952
  9 0.00462, 0.00047, 0.08627, 0.43, 19
10 186.3, 523.6, 7.63, 10.05, 0.0487, 69.2

Subtract:

11	12.6	**12**	93.25	**13**	108.436
	9.8		6.42		99.587

14	0.00068	**15**	19.005	**16**	1.875
	0.00032		17.846		0.9755

17 Subtract 0.000672 from 0.2.
18 Subtract 0.00324 from 1.
19 Subtract 8.275 from the sum of 4.872 and 5.0004.
20 From the sum of 0.0003 and 1.75 subtract 0.03.

5 – 4 Multiplication with decimals

When multiplying with decimals, the methods are similar to those used with whole numbers except care must be used in placing the decimal point in the product.

RULE To multiply with decimals,
1 Multiply as with whole numbers.
2 Point off as many decimal places in the product as there are decimal places in both factors.

EXAMPLE 9   Multiply 13.6 by 2.43.
SOLUTION

$$
\begin{array}{r}
1\,3.6 \\
2.4\,3 \\
\hline
4\,0\,8 \\
5\,4\,4 \\
2\,7\,2 \\
\hline
3\,3\,0\,4\,8
\end{array}
$$

Multiplication without regard to the decimals results in 33048 as shown above. Since there is one decimal place in the multiplicand and two in the multiplier, there must be three decimal places in the product; counting from right to left. Thus,

$$13.6 \times 2.43 = 33.048$$

If there are fewer digits in the product than required for the proper number of decimal places, zeros are added before the product digits in order to make up the proper number of decimal places.

EXAMPLE 10   Multiply 0.00025 by 0.003.
SOLUTION   0.*00025*
                      0.*003*
                 _____
                 0.*00000075*

5 – 5 Division with decimals

When dividing a decimal by a whole number, or when dividing any number by a larger one, care must be taken in placing the decimal point in the quotient.

In short division the decimal point in the quotient is placed under the decimal point of the dividend.

EXAMPLE 11   Divide 0.045 by 3.
SOLUTION   3)0.*045*
                  _____
                   0.*015*

EXAMPLE 12   Divide 32.675 by 5.
SOLUTION   5)32.*675*
                  _____
                  6.*535*

In long division the method is the same, except the decimal point in the quotient is placed over the decimal point of the dividend.

EXAMPLE 13   Divide 5,418.984 by 23.
                     235.*608*
SOLUTION   23)5,418.*984*
                 46
                 ___
                  81
                  69
                 ___
                 128
                 115
                 ___
                 139
                 138
                 ___
                  184
                  184

When the divisor is a decimal or a mixed number, it is often more convenient to make the divisor a whole number. This avoids confusion in placing the decimal point in the quotient. In Sec. 4–2 it was shown that the numerator and denominator of a fraction can be multiplied by the same number, except zero, without changing the value of the fraction. This principle can be used to convert the divisor to a whole number.

EXAMPLE 14   Divide 48 by 0.02.

SOLUTION   Multiplying both dividend and divisor by 100:

$$\frac{48}{0.02} = \frac{48 \times 100}{0.02 \times 100} = \frac{4,800}{2} = 2,400$$

EXAMPLE 15   Divide 38.0052 by 2.346.

SOLUTION $\dfrac{38.0052}{2.346} = \dfrac{38.0052 \times 1,000}{2.346 \times 1,000} = \dfrac{38,005.2}{2,346} = 16.2$

When divisions do not come out even, add zeros to the dividend until a remainder is exactly divisible by the divisor or until the quotient contains the desired number of figures.

EXAMPLE 16   Divide 747.4 by 4.8 to three decimal places.

SOLUTION   Convert the dividend and divisor so the latter will be a whole number, then divide. Thus,

```
          155.708
     48)7474.000
        48
        ──
        267
        240
        ───
        274
        240
        ───
        340
        336
        ───
        400
        384
        ───
         16
```

For the time being, when divisions do not come out even, the last figure of the quotient is written one larger if the next figure of the quotient is 5 or more. Thus, 8.2667 would become 8.267 if it was desired to drop the last digit. If the next figure of the quotient is less than 5, it is dropped. Thus, 74.2463 would become 74.246.

In Chap. 10 you will study significant figures and their relation to practical computations.

PROBLEMS 5 – 2

Multiply:

1	163	2	176	3	0.678
	0.2		0.25		41

4   3.87×9.42 5 67.3×0.0045

6   93.42×6.14 7 400×6.28

8   60 × 3.1416   9   0.00250 × 377
10   0.000505 × 8.936

Divide:
11   0.00275 by 5   12   0.9912 by 0.4
13   218.88 by 3.2   14   321.574 by 68.42
15   0.00036 by 0.375   16   29.145 by 0.000067

Divide to three decimal places:
17   0.33762 by 0.753   18   2.494 by 3.14
19   0.002543 by 0.00628   20   1.025 by 3.77
21   One kilogram is equal to 2.2046 pounds. How many pounds are there in 350 kilograms?
22   One inch is equal to 2.54 centimeters. How many centimeters are there in 1 yard?
23   An automobile averages 17.7 miles per gallon of gasoline. How many gallons would be required for a trip of 600 miles?
24   At 32.4 cents per gallon of gasoline, what would be the cost of gasoline for the automobile trip of Prob. 23?
25   Holes that measure $\frac{7}{16}$ in. are to be reamed twenty-five ten-thousandths of an inch oversize. What will be the diameter of the reamed holes?

5 – 6   Ratio

Two quantities measured in terms of the *same unit* can be compared by dividing one by the other. The quotient is called their *ratio*. A ratio may be expressed as an integer, a fraction, a decimal, or a per cent. Percentage is explained in the following section.

EXAMPLE 17   The ratio of 10 feet to 2 feet is $\dfrac{10 \text{ feet}}{2 \text{ feet}} = 5$.

Note that in the above division the units (feet) cancel, leaving an abstract number for a ratio.

EXAMPLE 18   The ratio of 10 ohms to 20 ohms is $\dfrac{10 \text{ ohms}}{20 \text{ ohms}} = \frac{1}{2}$ or 0.5.

5 – 7   Percentage

Per centum, commonly called *per cent*, means "by the hundred." Thus, 1 per cent means one-hundredth part of a quantity or number. The % sign denotes per cent; hence, 10 per cent is often written 10%. The important thing to remember is that the per cent sign does the duty of two decimal places.

EXAMPLE 19   15 per cent of 60 = 0.15 × 60 = 9.

EXAMPLE 20   25 per cent of 120 = 0.25 × 120 = 30.

In electric, electronic, and related circuits you will deal with percentages quite often. For example, many resistors and capacitors are color coded to express their percentage of *tolerance*, or allowable variation from their actual rated values. If you purchased a 10 per cent, 4,700-ohm resistor, the actual value of resistance could be between 4,700 − (0.10 × 4,700) = 4,230 ohms and 4,700 + (0.10 × 4,700) = 5,170 ohms.

When it is desired to express a given number as a percentage of another number, we divide the given number by the number with which it is being compared.

EXAMPLE 21   What per cent of 2,500 is 1,600?

SOLUTION $\dfrac{1,600}{2,500} = 0.64 = 64$ per cent

PROBLEMS 5 – 3

1   What is the ratio of 30 feet to 60 feet?
2   What is the ratio of 230 volts to 115 volts?
3   What is 15 per cent of 80?
4   What is 26 per cent of 82?
5   What is 17½ per cent of 350?
6   What per cent of 1,600 is 40?
7   What per cent of 4,000 is 560?
8   What per cent of 576 is 720?
9   What are the allowable limits for a 10 per cent, 2,200-ohm resistor?
10 A technician purchased a 5 per cent, 560-ohm resistor. Its actual value was measured and found to be 530 ohms. Was the resistor within tolerance?

CHAPTER 6
REVIEW OF ARITHMETIC
SQUARE ROOTS

This chapter contains a review of the methods used in finding the square roots of numbers. In the application of mathematics to electric circuits you will often find it necessary to deal with computations involving square roots.

6 – 1   Definitions

The *root* of a number is one of its *equal factors*. For example, the two equal factors of 25 are 5 and 5 (25 = 5 × 5). Therefore, 5 is a root of 25. Likewise the three equal factors of 27 are 3, 3, and 3. Therefore, 3 is a root of 27.

When there are *two* equal factors or roots, either one is called the *square root*. Thus, 5 is the square root of 25.

When there are *three* equal factors or roots, any of the factors is called the *cube root*. Thus, 3 is the cube root of 27. If there are *four* equal factors, they are known as *fourth roots*, and so on. However, in this chapter we are concerned with finding the square roots of numbers.

The process of computing one of the two equal factors of a number is called *extracting the square root* of that number.

The symbol used for indicating the root of a number is $\sqrt{}$ and is called the *radical sign*. Thus, when we want to express mathematically that the square root of 25 is 5, we write $\sqrt{25} = 5$.

Instead of writing $5 \times 5 = 25$, we can write $5^2 = 25$. Similarly, for $3 \times 3 \times 3 = 27$, we can write $3^3 = 27$. The small number placed to the right and above a number indicates how many times that number, called the *base*, is to be taken as a factor. The small number is called an *exponent*. The statement $5^2 = 25$ is read "five squared is equal to twenty-five." Thus, since $5^2 = 25$ and $\sqrt{25} = 5$, we see that squaring a number is the inverse operation of extracting a square root.

6 – 2   Square root of a perfect square

A number which is the exact square of another number is called a *perfect square*. The numbers 1, 4, 9, 16, 25, 36, 49, 64, and 81 are the perfect squares of 1, 2, 3, 4, 5, 6, 7, 8, and 9, respectively. These should be remembered.

Although square roots can be taken from tables or computed with the aid of logarithms (Chap. 36), the following illustrative examples show the arithmetical processes.

EXAMPLE 1   Find the square root of 1,521.

SOLUTION

15 21)‾‾‾‾

1   Divide the number into two-digit groups, starting at the right, and draw lines as shown.

|15 21)3‾
| 9
| 621

2   Beginning with the first two-digit group *15*, decide what number multiplied by itself will equal or be a little less than *15*. $4 \times 4 = 16$ is too much. The next smaller number is 3. $3 \times 3 = 9$. Therefore, *3* is the *first* figure of the root. Write it to the right of 1,521 as shown. Square this number, and write the square *9* under the *15* and subtract. Bring down the next two-digit group 21, and write it beside the remainder *6*.

|15 21)3‾
| 9
6| 621

3   Multiply *3*, the first figure of the root, by 2, and write the product *6* to the left of 621 as shown. The *6* is called the *trial divisor*.

$\lfloor$15 21$\overline{)39}$ = root
  9
69$\lfloor\overline{621}$
   621

4 Find how many times 6, the trial divisor, can be divided into the first two figures 62 of 621. The quotient is 9, which is the *second* figure of the root. Write 9 in the root as shown. Also, write the 9 to the right of the trial divisor 6. This now becomes 69, which is the *complete divisor*. Multiply this divisor by the 9 written in the root, and write the product 621 under the 621 as shown. There is no remainder; therefore $\sqrt{1,521}$ = 39.

You can check the result by squaring the root: $39 \times 39 = 1,521$.

EXAMPLE 2   Find the square root of 223,729.
SOLUTION

22 37 29$\overline{)}$

1 Divide the number into two-digit groups, starting at the right, and arrange the work as before. Since there are three groups, there will be three figures in the root.

$\lfloor$22 37 29$\overline{)4}$
  16
$\lfloor\overline{637}$

2 Find what number, when squared, will equal or be a little less than the first group 22. 5 is too large because $5^2 = 25$. The next smaller number is 4. $4^2 = 16$. Therefore, 4 is the *first* figure of the root. Write it in its proper place as shown. Square the 4, and write its square 16 under the 22 and subtract. Bring down the next two-digit group 37, and write it beside the remainder 6.

$\lfloor$22 37 29$\overline{)4}$
  16
8$\lfloor\overline{637}$

3 Multiply 4, the first figure of the root, by 2, and write the product 8 to the left of 637 as shown. This 8 now becomes the trial divisor.

$\lfloor$22 37 29$\overline{)47}$
  16
87$\lfloor\overline{637}$
    609
    $\overline{28}$29

4 Find how many times the trial divisor 8 can be divided into the first two figures 63 of 637. The quotient is 7, which is the *second* figure of the root and is written in the root as shown. Also, write 7 to the right of the trial divisor 8, which results in a *complete divisor* of 87. Multiply this divisor by the 7 in the root, write the product 609 under the 637 as shown, and subtract. The remainder is 28. Bring down the next two-digit group 29, and write it beside the remainder 28.

22 37 29)47
16
87 | 637
609
94 | 2829

5   Multiply 47, the first two figures of the root, by 2, and write the product 94 to the left of 2,829. The 94 is the trial divisor.

22 37 29)473
16
87 | 637
609
943 | 2829
2829

6   Find how many times the trial divisor 94 can be divided into 282, the first three figures of 2,829. The quotient is 3, which is the *third* figure of the root and is written in the root as shown. Also write the 3 to the right of the trial divisor 94. This now becomes 943, which is the complete divisor. Multiply this divisor by the 3 written in the root, and write the product 2,829 under the 2,829 as shown. There is no remainder, therefore $\sqrt{223,729} = 473$.

How can you check?

Examples 3, 4, and 5 show the work of extracting square roots but with no explanation. Work them and compare your work with the examples.

EXAMPLE 3   Find the square root of 857,476.
SOLUTION   85 74 76) 926 = square root
81
182 | 474
364
1846 | 11076
11076

EXAMPLE 4   Find the square root of 43,681.
SOLUTION   4 36 81) 209 = square root
4
40 | 36
00
409 | 3681
3681

EXAMPLE 5   Find the square root of 13,749,264.
SOLUTION   13 74 92 64) 3708 = square root
9
67 | 474
469
740 | 592
000
7408 | 59264
59264

Very few numbers are perfect squares, but the square root of any number can be found to any desired number of decimal places. When you are extracting the square root of a number not a perfect square, determine how many decimal places you want in the root, then add zeros to the right of the number until there are as many two-zero groups as there are decimal places desired in the root.

EXAMPLE 6   Find the square root of 179 to three decimal places.

SOLUTION

$$\begin{array}{r|l}
 & 1\ 79.00\ 00\ 00)13.379 = \text{square root} \\
 & \underline{1} \\
23 & 79 \\
 & \underline{69} \\
263 & 1000 \\
 & \underline{789} \\
2667 & 21100 \\
 & \underline{18669} \\
26749 & 243100 \\
 & \underline{240741} \\
 & 2359
\end{array}$$

6-3 Square root of a mixed number

When you extract the square root of a number containing a decimal, divide the mixed number into two-digit groups, beginning at the decimal point. The whole-number part is divided to the left, and the decimal part is divided to the right.

EXAMPLE 7   Find the square root of 276.1063 to two decimal places.

SOLUTION

$$\begin{array}{r|l}
 & 2\ 76.10\ 63)16.61 = \text{square root} \\
 & \underline{1} \\
26 & 176 \\
 & \underline{156} \\
326 & 2010 \\
 & \underline{1956} \\
3321 & 5463 \\
 & \underline{3321} \\
 & 2142
\end{array}$$

6-4 Square root of a decimal

When extracting the square root of a decimal, divide the decimal into two-digit groups beginning at the decimal point and dividing to the right. If the decimal consists of an odd number of digits, add a zero to the right in order to make a two-digit group.

EXAMPLE 8   Find the square root of 0.018225.

SOLUTION

$$\underline{0.01\ 82\ 25}\ )\overline{0.135} = \text{square root}$$

$$
\begin{array}{r|l}
 & 1 \\
23 & \overline{82} \\
 & 69 \\
265 & \overline{1325} \\
 & 1325 \\
\end{array}
$$

6 – 5   Square root of a fraction

If both numerator and denominator of a fraction are perfect squares, the square root of the fraction is obtained by extracting the square roots of numerator and denominator separately.

EXAMPLE 9 $\sqrt{\dfrac{25}{64}} = \dfrac{5}{8}$

EXAMPLE 10 $\sqrt{\dfrac{49}{81}} = \dfrac{7}{9}$

EXAMPLE 11 $\sqrt{\dfrac{144}{169}} = \dfrac{12}{13}$

If numerator and denominator are not each a perfect square, reduce the fraction to decimal form and extract the square root.

EXAMPLE 12 $\sqrt{\dfrac{3}{8}} = \sqrt{0.3750} = 0.613$

EXAMPLE 13 $\sqrt{\dfrac{3}{7}} = \sqrt{0.42857} = 0.654$

PROBLEMS 6 – 1

Extract the square root of:

1	625	2	256	3	1,296
4	3,969	5	7,921	6	16,641
7	495,616	8	11,881	9	49,014,001
10	5,821.69	11	2.6569	12	0.020164
13	0.01	14	904.2049	15	0.0000017424

Extract the square root to three decimal places:

16	41.422	17	69.2224	18	0.53
19	0.03725	20	0.0000001714	21	$\frac{9}{64}$
22	$1\frac{6}{49}$	23	$1\frac{9}{50}$	24	$1\frac{1}{50}$
25	$\frac{1}{1,000}$				

6 – 6   **Square root from tables**

When you know the accuracy of your measurements or circuit values with which you are working, a good estimate or "educated guess" will often serve as a satisfactory practical answer to many problems. For example, one way of finding the voltage across a resistor is to extract the square root of the product obtained by multiplying the power expended in the resistor by its resistance. That is,

Voltage in volts $= \sqrt{\text{power in watts} \times \text{resistance in ohms}}$

Suppose you have bought a 10 per cent tolerance, 10-ohm, 2-watt resistor and want to know how much voltage must be across the resistor for it to expend 2 watts of power. For a resistance of *exactly* 10 ohms, the voltage would be

$$\sqrt{2 \times 10} = \sqrt{20} \text{ volts}$$

You know that $\sqrt{16} = 4$ and $\sqrt{25} = 5$, so $\sqrt{20}$ is between 4 and 5. Also, since 20 is roughly halfway between 16 and 25, you estimate that $\sqrt{20}$ is 4.5. Actually, $\sqrt{20} = 4.472$, so your estimate was high by $4.5 - 4.472 = 0.028$ volt. As an exercise, find your *percentage* of error.

Actually, your chances of having obtained a 10-ohm resistor are remote because it may be from 9 to 11 ohms and still be within tolerance. As an additional exercise prove that even if your resistance was within 1 per cent of tolerance, your estimate of voltage is reasonable.

The foregoing does not mean that one can be careless with his mathematics. Mathematics is an exact science. You will encounter measurements and circuit values that have been held to a high degree of accuracy, and they will require precise computations. The important thing to know is what accuracy is required. This will come mainly from study and experience.

The use of a table for finding square roots will save you time and labor. Table 8, in the appendix, gives the squares, square roots, and reciprocals of numbers from 1 to 1,000. (The reciprocal of a number is 1 divided by that number.)

EXAMPLE 14   Find the square root of 392.

SOLUTION   Look in the number column of Table 8 and find 392. Opposite 392 in the square root column find 19.7990. Thus,

$$\sqrt{392} = 19.7990$$

EXAMPLE 15   Find the square root of 392.7.
SOLUTION   From Table 8,
$$\sqrt{393} = 19.8242$$
$$\sqrt{392} = 19.7990$$
$$\text{Difference} = \ \ 0.0252$$

Since the difference between 392 and 393 is 1 and the difference in the square roots is 0.0252, we see that an increase of 1 results in a square-root difference of 0.0252. Therefore, we are justified in estimating that an increase of 0.7 (392.7 = 392 + 0.7) will cause the square root to increase 0.7 × 0.0252 = 0.01764. This amount added to the square root of 392 results in

$$\sqrt{392} = 19.7990$$
$$0.7 \times \text{difference} = \ \ 0.01764$$
$$\sqrt{392.7} = 19.81664$$

Dropping the last decimal place, $\sqrt{392.7} = 19.8166$. Actually, $(19.8166)^2 = 392.697$, which is very nearly equal to 392.7.

Square roots of other numbers can be found by remembering that moving the decimal point two places in the number moves the decimal point one place in the square root.

EXAMPLE 16   Find the square root of 1.56.

SOLUTION $1.56 = \dfrac{156}{100}$

Therefore, $\sqrt{1.56} = \dfrac{\sqrt{156}}{\sqrt{100}} = \dfrac{12.49}{10} = 1.249$

EXAMPLE 17 $\sqrt{28,900} = \sqrt{289} \times \sqrt{100} = 17 \times 10 = 170$

In actual practice you mentally move the decimal place of the number right or left an even number of places and place the decimal point in the square root one place, right or left, for each two places moved in the number.

PROBLEMS 6 – 2
Using Table 8, find the square roots of:

1	4.5	2	1.68	3	20.5
4	19,000	5	32,400	6	593.5
7	108.8	8	27,620	9	1.465
10	0.0842				

REVIEW PROBLEMS

When you work Probs. 6–3, 6–4, and 6–5, do not write the problems on your work sheet. Instead, place your work sheet over this page with an edge of the work sheet under the problem you are working. This will allow you to do the computations on your work sheet without writing the problem.

PROBLEMS 6 – 3

Time allowed: 2 minutes, 30 seconds.
Add:

1	346	2	38.07	3	9.7564
	782		15.91		1.2436

4	478.9	5	12	6	0.5109
	1.02		908		0.3873
	8,509.		6,742		6.453
			650		

7	201.2	8	18,273	9	0.3405
	39.47		64,509		9.8643
	5,760.9		8,172.6		0.0721
					5.107

10   8,670.03
     2,549.69
        30.97
         8.54
       516.78

PROBLEMS 6 – 4

Time allowed: 2 minutes, 10 seconds.
Subtract:

1	492	2	7,350	3	83.46
	181		6,296		57.38

4	0.0253	5	164	6	5.621
	0.0094		39.07		0.5478

7	9,000.87	8	7.9132	9	0.000253
	8,909.78		6.9823		0.0000256

10   10.6451
      9.6542

PROBLEMS 6 – 5

Time allowed: 6 minutes, 50 seconds.
Multiply:

1	237 6	2	508 49	3	14.69 1.7
4	6,327 0.058	5	418.9 302	6	0.00532 0.76
7	9,476 0.02398	8	8,501 5,146	9	80,063 0.00735
10	74,290 0.8942				

PROBLEMS 6 – 6

Time allowed: 7 minutes, 20 seconds.   (Includes writing problems.)
Divide:

1   2,019 by 3   2   28,032 by 73
3   859,792 by 98.6   4   655.806 by 435
5   7.312 by 0.014624   6   1.697605 by 0.00845

PROBLEMS 6 – 7

Time allowed: 7 minutes, 40 seconds.   (Includes writing problems.)
Add:

1   $\frac{1}{4} + \frac{1}{2}$ 2 $\frac{1}{3} + \frac{2}{9}$ 3 $\frac{3}{5} + \frac{5}{20}$
4   $1\frac{2}{3} + 6\frac{5}{9}$ 5 $8\frac{7}{8} + 24\frac{9}{12}$ 6 $67\frac{3}{15} + 89\frac{1}{3}$
7   $\frac{3}{8} + 1\frac{3}{32} + \frac{5}{64}$ 8 $\frac{3}{20} + \frac{2}{3} + 7\frac{11}{12}$ 9 $8\frac{1}{2} + 9\frac{3}{13} + \frac{1}{52}$
10   $16\frac{1}{8} + \frac{9}{10} + 8\frac{3}{20} + 0.001$

PROBLEMS 6 – 8

Time allowed: 5 minutes, 50 seconds.   (Includes writing problems.)
Multiply:

1   $4\frac{5}{9} \times \frac{3}{82}$ 2 $16\frac{4}{5} \times 2\frac{1}{12}$ 3 $27\frac{1}{9} \times 1\frac{1}{18}$
4   $87\frac{1}{2} \times 0.002$ 5 $0.126 \times 24\frac{1}{42}$
Divide:

6   $4\frac{5}{6}$ by $2\frac{5}{12}$ 7 $17\frac{3}{5}$ by $2\frac{14}{15}$ 8 $20\frac{4}{7}$ by 0.016

PROBLEMS 6 – 9

Time allowed: 8 minutes, 20 seconds.   (Includes writing problems.)
Extract the square root of:

1   1,089   2   14.1376   3 $\frac{625}{1,225}$

4   $\frac{729}{6,561}$ 5   0.00002401

CHAPTER 7
ALGEBRA
GENERAL NUMBERS

In general, arithmetic consists of the operations of addition, subtraction, multiplication, and division of a type of numbers represented by the digits 1, 2, 3, . . . , 9, 0. By using the above operations or combinations of them, we are able to solve many problems. However, a knowledge of mathematics limited to arithmetic is inadequate and a severe handicap to one interested in acquiring an understanding of electric circuits. Proficiency in performing even the most simple operations of algebra enables you to solve problems and determine relations that would be impossible with arithmetic alone.

7 – 1   The general number

Algebra may be thought of as a continuation of arithmetic in which letters and symbols are used to represent definite quantities whose actual values may or may not be known. For example, in electrical and radio texts, it is customary to represent currents by the letters I or i; voltages by E, e, V, or v; resistances by R or r; etc. The base of a triangle is often represented by b, and the altitude may be specified as *a*. Such letters or symbols used for representing quantities in a general way are known as *general numbers* or *literal numbers*.

The importance of the general-number idea cannot be overemphasized. Although it is possible to express in English the various laws and facts concerning electricity, they are more concisely and compactly expressed in mathematical form in terms of general numbers. As an example, Ohm's law states, in part, that the current in a certain part of a circuit is proportional to the potential difference (voltage) across that part of the circuit and inversely proportional to the resistance of that part. This same statement, in mathematical terms, says

$$I = \frac{E}{R}$$

where *I* represents the current, *E* is the potential difference, and *R* is the resistance. Such an expression is known as a *formula*.

Although the expression (as formulas) of various laws and relationships of science, in the language of mathematics, gives a more compact form of notation, therein is not the real value of the formula. As you attain proficiency in algebra, the value of general formulas will become more apparent. Our studies of algebra will consist mainly in learning how to add, subtract, multiply, divide, and solve such general algebraic expressions, or formulas, in order to attain a better understanding of the fundamentals of electricity and related fields.

7 – 2   Signs of operation

In algebra the signs of operation $+$, $-$, $\times$, and $\div$ have the same meanings as in arithmetic. The sign $\times$ is generally omitted between literal numbers. For example, $I \times R$ is written IR and means that I is to be multiplied by R. Similarly, $2\pi fL$ means 2 times π times f times L. Sometimes the symbol $[\cdot]$ is used to denote multiplication. Thus $I \times R$, $I \cdot R$, and IR all mean I times R.

7 – 3   The order of signs of operation

In performing a series of different operations, it has been agreed that the multiplications must be performed first, next the divisions, and then the additions and subtractions. Thus,

$$16 \div 4 + 8 + 4 \times 5 - 3 = 4 + 8 + 20 - 3 = 29$$

7 – 4   Algebraic expressions

An *algebraic expression* is one that expresses or represents a number by the signs and symbols of algebra. A *numerical algebraic expression* is one consisting entirely of signs and numerals. A *literal algebraic expression* is one containing general numbers or letters. An example of a numerical algebraic expression is $8 - (6 + 2)$; I^2R is a literal algebraic expression.

7 – 5 The product

As in arithmetic, a *product* is the result obtained in multiplying two or more numbers. Thus, 12 is the product of 6×2.

7 – 6 The factor

If two or more numbers are multiplied together, each of them or the product of any combination of them is called a *factor* of the product. For example, in the product $2xy$, 2, x, y, $2x$, $2y$, and xy are all factors of $2xy$.

7 – 7 Coefficients

Any factor of a product is known as the *coefficient* of the product of the remaining factors. In the foregoing example, 2 is the coefficient of xy, x is the coefficient of $2y$, y is the coefficient of $2x$, etc. It is common practice to speak of the numerical part of an expression as the *coefficient* or as the *numerical coefficient*. If an expression contains no numerical coefficient, 1 is understood to be the numerical coefficient. Thus, $1abc$ is the same as abc.

7 – 8 Primes and subscripts

In a formula in which, for example, two resistances are being compared or where it is desirable to make a distinction between them, the resistances may be represented by R_1 and R_2 or R_a and R_b. The small numbers or letters written at the right of and below the Rs are called *subscripts*. They are generally used to denote different values of the same units.

R_1 and R_2 are read "R sub one" and "R sub two" or simply "R one" and "R two."

Care must be used in distinguishing between subscripts and exponents. Thus E^2 is an indicated operation that means $E \cdot E$, whereas E_2 is used to distinguish one quantity from another of the same kind.

Primes and *seconds*, instead of subscripts, are often used to denote quantities. Thus one current might be denoted by I' and another by I''. The first is read "I prime" and the latter is read "I second."

I' resembles I^1 (I to the first power), but in general this causes little confusion.

7 – 9   Evaluation

To *evaluate* an algebraic expression is to find its numerical value. In Sec. 7–1, it was stated that in algebra certain signs and symbols are used to represent definite quantities. Also, in Sec. 7–4, an algebraic expression was defined as one that represents a number by the signs and symbols of algebra. We can find the numerical, or definite, value of an algebraic expression only when we know the values of the letters in the expression.

EXAMPLE 1   Find the value of $2ir$ if $i = 5$ and $r = 11$.

SOLUTION $2ir = 2 \times 5 \times 11 = 110$

EXAMPLE 2   Evaluate the expression $23E - 3ir$ if $E = 10$, $i = 3$, and $r = 22$.

SOLUTION $23E - 3ir = 23 \times 10 - 3 \times 3 \times 22 = 230 - 198 = 32$

EXAMPLE 3   Find the value of $\dfrac{E}{R} - 3I$ if $E = 230$, $R = 5$, and $I = 8$.

SOLUTION $\dfrac{E}{R} - 3I = \dfrac{230}{5} - 3 \times 8 = 46 - 24 = 22$

PROBLEMS 7 – 1

1   (a) What is meant by the expression $16Z$?
    (b) What is the meaning of $6r$?
    (c) What does $9I$ mean?

2   What is the value of (a) $7i$ when $i = 5$ amperes, (b) $4W$ when $W = 60$ watts, (c) $32Z$ when $Z = 0.3$ ohm?

3   One capacitor costs \$1.50.
    (a) What will one dozen capacitors cost?
    (b) What will n capacitors cost?

4   Eighteen resistors cost a total of \$6.30.
    (a) What is the cost of each resistor?
    (b) What is the cost of x resistors?

5   The current in a certain circuit is $60I$ amperes. What is the value of the current if it is reduced to one-half this value?

6   There are three resistances of which the second is three times the first and the third is six times the second. Let R represent the first resistance, in ohms, and then express the others in terms of R.

7   There are four voltages of which the second is one-third the first, the third is four times the second, and the fourth is fifteen times the third.

Let E represent the first voltage, in volts, and then express the others in terms of E.

If $R = 4$, $r = 2$, and $x = 6$, find the value of each of the following:

8   $R + r$ 9 $x + r - R$ 10 $\dfrac{x}{r}$

11   $\dfrac{R + x}{r}$ 12 $\dfrac{x - r}{R}$

13   Write the expression that will represent each of the following: (a) a resistance of 25 ohms more than R ohms, (b) a current of i amperes less than $8I$ amperes, (c) a voltage of e volts less than $32E$ volts.

14   A circuit has a resistance of 25 ohms. Express a resistance four times this value diminished by R ohms.

15   A capacitance C exceeds another capacitance C_1 by 250 micromicro-farads. Express the capacitance C_1 in terms of C.

16   When two capacitors C_1 and C_2 are connected in series the resultant capacitance C_t of the combination is

$$C_t = \frac{C_1 C_2}{C_1 + C_2}$$

What is the resultant capacitance if capacitors are connected in series as follows: (a) 4 and 6 microfarads, (b) 250 and 350 micromicrofarads?

17   The current in any part of an electric circuit is given by $I = \dfrac{E}{R}$, in which I is the current in amperes through that part, E is the voltage in volts across that part, and R is the resistance in ohms of that part. What is the current through a circuit with (a) a voltage of 230 volts and a resistance of 46 ohms, (b) a voltage of 110 volts and a resistance of 44 ohms?

18   The delay between the transmission of a radar pulse and the reception of its echo from a target is $t = \dfrac{2R}{c}$ seconds, where t is the delay time in seconds, R is the range in miles, and c is the speed at which light and radio waves travel. (c = 186,000 miles per second.) What is the time between the transmission of a pulse and the reception of its echo from a target at a distance of 100 miles?

19   The relation $t = \dfrac{2R}{c}$ in the foregoing problem is applicable to the trans-mission of sound in air and in water. Owing to slower speeds of propagation R is usually expressed in feet and c is expressed in feet per second. (In air $c \cong 1,100$ feet per second, and in salt water $c \cong 4,800$ feet per second.) (a) What is the time between the transmission of a short pulse of sound through air and the reception of its echo at a

distance of 3,000 feet? (*b*) What time will elapse if the sound pulse is transmitted under sea water at the same distance?

20 The relation between the wavelength λ of a wave, the frequency *f* in cycles per second, and the speed *c* at which the wave is propagated is $\lambda = \dfrac{c}{f}$. If λ is expressed in meters, then *c* must be expressed in meters per second; that is, λ and *c* must be expressed in the same units of length such as feet and feet per second, respectively. (*a*) What is the wavelength in miles of a radio wave having a frequency of 15 kilocycles? (15 kilocycles = 15,000 cycles per second.) (*b*) What is the wavelength in feet of a sound wave of the same frequency but transmitted through sea water? (*c*) What is the wavelength in feet of a sound wave of the same frequency but transmitted through air?

21 It is desired to construct an underwater transducer diaphragm having a diameter of 8 wavelengths and operating at a frequency of 24,000 cycles per second. What is the diaphragm diameter in feet?

7 – 10 Exponents

If we want to express "*x* is to be taken as a factor four times," instead of writing *xxxx*, it has been generally agreed to express this as x^4.

An *exponent*, or *power*, is a number written at the right of and above another number to indicate how many times the latter is to be taken as a factor. The number to be multiplied by itself is called the *base*.

Thus, I^2 is read "*I* square" or "*I* second power" and means that *I* is to be taken twice as a factor; e^3 is read "*e* cube" or "*e* third power" and means that *e* is to be taken as a factor three times. Likewise, 5^4 is read "5 fourth power" and means that 5 is to be taken as a factor four times; thus,

$$5^4 = 5 \times 5 \times 5 \times 5 = 625$$

When no exponent, or power, is indicated, the exponent is understood to be 1. Thus, *x* is the same as x^1.

7 – 11 The radical sign

The radical sign $\sqrt{}$ has the same meaning in algebra as in arithmetic. $\sqrt{e}$ means the square root of *e*, $\sqrt[3]{x}$ means the cube root of *x*, $\sqrt[4]{i}$ means the fourth root of *i*, etc. The small number in the angle of a radical sign, like the 4 in $\sqrt[4]{i}$, is known as the *index* of the root.

7 – 12 Terms

A *term* is an expression or portion of an expression whose parts are not separated by a plus or a minus sign. $3E^2$, *IR*, and $-2e$ are terms of the expression $3E^2 + IR - 2e$.

Although the value of a term depends upon the values of its literal factors, it is customary to refer to a term whose sign is plus as a *positive term*. Likewise, we refer to a term whose sign is minus as a *negative term*.

Terms having the same literal parts are called *like terms* or *similar terms*. $2a^2bx$, $-a^2bx$, $18a^2bx$, and $-4a^2bx$ are like terms.

Terms that are not alike in their literal parts are called *unlike terms* or *dissimilar terms*. $5xy$, $6ac$, $9I^2R$, and EI are *unlike terms*.

An algebraic expression consisting of but one term is known as a *monomial*.

A *polynomial*, or *multinomial*, is an algebraic expression consisting of two or more terms.

A *binomial* is a polynomial of two terms. $e + ir$, $a - 2b$, and $2x^2y + xyz^2$ are binomials.

A *trinomial* is a polynomial of three terms. $2a + 3b - c$, $IR + 3e - E^2$, and $8ab^3c + 3d + 2xy$ are trinomials.

PROBLEMS 7 – 2

If $a = 4$, $b = 6$, and $c = 5$, evaluate the following:

1 $3a^2bc$ 2 $4a^2b^2c^2 + a^2bc^2$ 3 $10ac^2 - 3a^2b$

4 $\sqrt{4a^2c^2}$ 5 $16\sqrt{36b^2c^2} - 3a^2$

If $E = 5$, $I = 12$, and $R = 10$, evaluate the following:

6 $7I^2R$ 7 $I^2R - \dfrac{120E^2}{R}$ 8 $\dfrac{9I^3R^2}{3IR} - \sqrt{\dfrac{10E^2}{R}}$

9 $\dfrac{48E^2IR}{I^2R} - R^2$ 10 $\sqrt{E^4I^2R^2} - \dfrac{E^3IR^2}{\sqrt{100R^2}}$

State which of the following are monomials, binomials, and trinomials:

11 IR 12 $\dfrac{\rho l}{d^2} + r$ 13 $I + \sqrt{\dfrac{P}{R}} + \dfrac{E}{R}$

14 $2\pi fL$ 15 $\dfrac{R}{pf} + Z + r$ 16 $R + jx$

17 $\dfrac{L}{RC} + ei - IR$ 18 $E_g + \dfrac{E_p}{\mu}$ 19 $\dfrac{\Delta E_p}{\Delta E_g} - \mu e_g + \mu e_g Z$

20 $\dfrac{2(\mu E_g)^2}{9r_p}$

21 In Probs. 1 to 20, state which expressions are polynomials.

Write the statements of Probs. 22 to 30 in algebraic symbols.

22 E is equal to I times R.

23 I is equal to E divided by R.

24 P is equal to I square times R.

25 C_t is equal to the sum of C_1 and C_2.

26 Z^2 is equal to $R^2 + X^2$.

27 R is equal to the product ρ and l divided by d square.

28 M is equal to k times the square root of the product of L_1 and L_2.

29 R_t is equal to the product of R_1 and R_2 divided by the sum of R_1 and R_2.

30 η is equal to P divided by the product of E_p and I_p.

31 The approximate inductance of a single-layer air-core coil, such as used in the tuning circuits of radio receivers, can be calculated by the formula

$$L = \frac{r^2 n^2}{9r + 10l}$$

where L = inductance in microhenrys

r = radius of winding in inches

n = number of turns of wire in winding

l = length of winding in inches

What is the inductance of a coil 1 inch in diameter, 3 inches long, and having 150 turns of wire?

32 The winding is removed from the coil form in Prob. 31 and smaller wire substituted for rewinding so that the number of turns are doubled but the length of winding remains the same. Calculate the new inductance.

33 The power in any part of an electric circuit is given by the formula $P = I^2 R$, in which P is the power in watts, I is the current in amperes through that part, and R is the resistance in ohms of that part. Find the power expended when (*a*) current = 20 amperes, resistance = 5 ohms; (*b*) current = 0.150 ampere, resistance = 10,000 ohms.

34 The power in any part of an electric circuit is also given by the formula $P = \dfrac{E^2}{R}$, in which P is the power in watts, E is the voltage across that part, and R is the resistance of that part. Find the power expended when (*a*) voltage = 230 volts, resistance = 100 ohms; (*b*) voltage = 24 volts, resistance = 2 ohms.

35 In Prob. 33, everything else remaining constant, what happens to the power in an electric circuit when the current is (*a*) halved, (*b*) doubled, (*c*) tripled?

36 In Prob. 34, everything else remaining constant, what happens to the power when the voltage is (*a*) halved, (*b*) doubled, (*c*) tripled, (*d*) quadrupled?

37 In Prob. 34, everything else remaining constant, what happens to the power when the resistance is doubled?

CHAPTER 8
ALGEBRA
ADDITION AND SUBTRACTION

The problems of arithmetic deal with positive numbers only. A *positive number* may be defined as any number greater than zero. Accepting this definition, we know that when such numbers are added, multiplied, and divided, the results are always positive. Such is the case in subtraction if a number is subtracted from a larger one. However, if we attempt to subtract a number from a smaller one, arithmetic furnishes no rule for carrying out this operation nor a meaning for the result.

8 – 1   Negative numbers

Limiting our knowledge of mathematics to positive numbers would place us under a severe handicap, for there are many instances when it becomes necessary to deal with numbers that are called negative. For the time being, we shall define a *negative number* as a number less than zero.   Negative numbers are prefixed with the minus sign. Thus, negative 2 is written -2, negative $3ac$ is written $-3ac$, etc. If no sign precedes a number, it is assumed to be positive.

6 1

Numerous examples of the uses of negative numbers could be cited. For example, zero degrees on the centigrade thermometer has been chosen as the temperature of melting ice—commonly referred to as freezing temperature. Now everyone knows that in some climates it gets much colder than "freezing." Such temperatures are referred to as so many "degrees below zero." How shall we state, in the language of mathematics, a temperature of "10 degrees below zero"? Ten degrees *above* zero would be written 10°. Because 0° is the reference point, it is logical to assume that 10° *below* zero would be written as −10°, which, for our purposes, makes it a negative number.

8 – 2   Practical need for negative numbers

The need for negative numbers often arises in the consideration of voltages or currents in electrical and radio circuits. It is common practice to select the ground, or earth, as a point of zero potential. This does not mean, however, that there can be no potentials below ground, or zero, potential. Consider the case of the three-wire feeders connected as shown in Fig. 8–1.

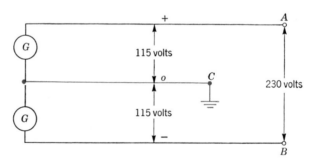

Fig. 8–1   Two 115-volt generators connected in series with neutral wire grounded.

The generators G, which maintain a voltage of 115 volts each, are connected in series so that their voltages add to give a voltage of 230 volts across points A and B, and the neutral wire is grounded at C. Since C is at ground, or zero, potential, point A is 115 volts positive with respect to C and point B is 115 volts negative with respect to C. Therefore the voltage at A with respect to ground, or zero, potential could be denoted as 115 volts and the voltage at B with respect to ground could be −115 volts.

Similar conditions exist in vacuum-tube circuits as illustrated by the schematic circuit diagram of a type 6C5 vacuum tube in Fig. 8–2. The plate current indicated by the arrow flows through the cathode resistor R and creates a difference of potential of 8 volts across R so that point A is +8 volts with respect to ground. Since the grid G is connected directly to ground, the grid is −8 volts with respect to the cathode K.

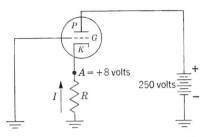

FIG. 8–2 The grid G is negative with respect to cathode K.

8 – 3 The mathematical need for negative numbers

From a purely mathematical viewpoint the need for negative numbers can be seen from a succession of subtractions where we subtract successively larger numbers from 5 as shown below.

5	5	5	5	5	5	5	5	5
0	1	2	3	4	5	6	7	8
5	4	3	2	1	0	−1	−2	−3

The above subtractions result in the remainders becoming less until zero is reached. When the remainder becomes less than zero, this is indicated by placing the negative sign before it. This is one reason for defining a negative number as a number less than zero. Mathematically, the definition is correct if we consider only the signs that precede the numbers.

You must not lose sight of the fact, however, that as far as magnitude, or size, is concerned, a negative number may represent a larger absolute value than some positive number. *The positive and negative signs simply denote reference from zero.* For example, if some point in an electric circuit is 1,000 volts negative with respect to ground, you can denote it by writing −1,000 volts. If you make good contact with your body between that point and ground, your chances of being electrocuted are just as good as if that point was positive 1,000 volts with respect to ground—and you wrote it +1,000 volts! In this case, *how much* is far more important than a matter of sign preceding the number.

8 – 4 The absolute value of a number

The numerical, or *absolute*, value of a number is its value without regard to sign. Thus, the absolute values of −1, +4, −6, and +3 are 1, 4, 6, and 3, respectively. Note that different numbers such as −9 and +9 may have the same absolute value. To specify the absolute value of a number, such as Z, we write $|Z|$.

8 – 5   Addition of positive and negative numbers

Positive and negative numbers can be represented graphically as in Fig. 8–3. Positive numbers are shown as being directed toward the right of zero, which is the reference point, whereas negative numbers are directed toward the left.

Fɪɢ. 8–3   Graphical representation of numbers from −10 to +10.

Such a scale of numbers can be used to illustrate both addition and subtraction as performed in arithmetic. Thus, in adding 3 to 4, we can begin at 3 and count 4 units to the right, obtaining the sum 7. Or, because these are positive numbers directed toward the right, we could draw them to scale, place them end to end, and measure their total length to obtain a length of 7 units in the positive direction. This is illustrated in Fig. 8–4.

Fɪɢ. 8–4   Graphical addition of 3 and 4 to obtain 7.

In like manner, −2 and −3 can be added to obtain −5 as shown in Fig. 8–5.

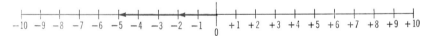

Fɪɢ. 8–5   Illustrating the addition of −2 and −3. The result is −5.

Note that adding −3 and −2 is the same as adding −2 and −3 as in the foregoing example. The sum −5 is obtained, as shown in Fig. 8–6.

Fɪɢ. 8–6   Adding −3 and −2 is the same as adding −2 and −3; both result in −5.

Suppose we add +6 and −10. This could be accomplished on the scale by first counting 6 units to the right and from *that* point counting 10 units to the left. In so doing, we end up at −4, which is the sum of +6 and −10. Similarly, we could have started by first counting 10 units to the left, from zero, and from that point could have counted 6 units to the right for the +6. Again we should have arrived at −4.

Adding +6 and −10 can be accomplished graphically as in Fig. 8-7. The +6 is drawn to scale, and then the tail of the −10 is joined

Fɪɢ. 8–7 Graphical addition of +6 and −10.

with the head of +6. The head of the −10 is then on −4. As would be expected, the same result is obtained by first drawing in the −10 and then the +6.

The following examples can be checked graphically in order to verify their correctness:

$$
\begin{array}{rrrrrr}
+8 & +9 & +6 & -5 & -7 & -17 \\
+4 & -3 & -9 & +2 & +9 & -14 \\
\hline
+12 & +6 & -3 & -3 & +2 & -31 \\
\end{array}
$$

Consideration of the above examples enables us to establish the following rule:

RULE
1 To add two or more numbers with like signs, find the sum of their absolute values and prefix this sum with the common sign.
2 To add a positive number to a negative number, find the difference of their absolute values and prefix to the result the sign of the one that has the greater absolute value.

When three or more algebraic numbers are to be added, differing in signs, find the sum of the positive numbers and then the sum of the negative numbers. Add these sums algebraically, using Rule 2 above to obtain the total algebraic sum.

The *algebraic sum* of two or more numbers is the result obtained by adding them according to the preceding rules. Hereafter, the word "add" will mean "find the algebraic sum."

PROBLEMS 8 – 1

Add:

1	48	2	37	3	−76
	63		−23		41

4	−14	5	108	6	−348
	−57		−763		−897

7	67.43	8	−0.0005	9	−93.04
	−78.27		0.00034		0.03
					− 3.25

10	47.63	11	$5\frac{1}{2}$	12	$-3\frac{1}{4}$
	−10.04		$-8\frac{1}{2}$		$-8\frac{5}{9}$
	23.87				

13	$-\frac{1}{5}$	14	$-\frac{1}{4}$	15	$-\frac{2}{15}$
	$\frac{1}{3}$		$-\frac{1}{7}$		$\frac{1}{16}$

8 – 6   The subtraction of positive and negative numbers

We may think of subtraction as the process of determining what number must be added to a given number in order to produce another given number. Thus, when we subtract 5 from 9 and get 4, we have found that 4 must be added to 5 in order to obtain 9. From this it is seen that subtraction is the inverse of addition.

EXAMPLE 1 $(+5) - (+2) = ?$

SOLUTION   In the above the question is asked, "What number added to +2 will give +5?" Using the scale of Fig. 8–8, start at +2 and count to the right (positive direction), until +5 is reached. This requires three units. Therefore, the difference is +3, or $(+5) - (+2) = +3$.

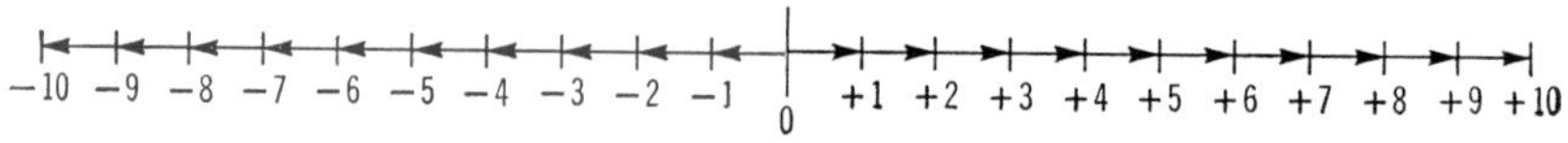

Fig. 8–8   Scale for graphical subtraction of positive and negative numbers.

EXAMPLE 2 $(+5) - (-2) = ?$

SOLUTION   In the above the question is asked, "What number added to −2 will give +5?" Using the scale, start at −2 and count the number of units to +5. This requires seven units, and because it was necessary to count in the positive direction, the difference is +7, or $(+5) - (-2) = +7$.

EXAMPLE 3 $(-5) - (+2) = ?$

SOLUTION In this example the question is, "What number added to $+2$ will give -5?" Again using the scale, we start at $+2$ and count the number of units to -5. This requires seven units, but because it was necessary to count in the negative direction, the difference is -7, or $(-5) - (+2) = -7$.

EXAMPLE 4 $(-5) - (-2) = ?$

SOLUTION Here the question is, "What number added to -2 will give -5?" Using the scale, we start at -2 and count the number of units to -5. This requires three units in the negative direction. Hence, $(-5) - (-2) = -3$.

Summing up the foregoing examples, we have the following subtractions:

$$\begin{array}{cccc} +5 & +5 & -5 & -5 \\ +2 & -2 & +2 & -2 \\ \hline +3 & +7 & -7 & -3 \end{array}$$

A study of the foregoing examples illustrates the following principles:

1 Subtracting a positive number is equivalent to adding a negative number of the same absolute value.

2 Subtracting a negative number is equivalent to adding a positive number of the same absolute value.

These principles can be used for the purpose of establishing the following rule:

RULE To subtract one number from another, change the sign of the subtrahend and add algebraically.

As in arithmetic, the number to be subtracted is called the *subtrahend*. The number from which the subtrahend is subtracted is called the *minuend*. The result is called the *remainder* or *difference*.

$$\begin{array}{lcr} \text{Minuend} & = & -642 \\ \text{Subtrahend} & = & 403 \\ \hline \text{Remainder} & = & -1,045 \end{array}$$

PROBLEMS 8-2*

Subtract:

1	26	2	45	3	-283
	87		-93		-638

*Refer to Table 3 in the Appendix, which contains a list of abbreviations used henceforth.

4	-36	5	436	6	43.14
	$\underline{68}$		$\underline{-209}$		$\underline{-19.96}$

7	-0.0509	8	0.0075	9	75.27
	$\underline{-0.73}$		$\underline{0.084}$		$\underline{87.62}$

10	-1.063	11	$6\frac{2}{3}$	12	$-13\frac{7}{8}$
	$\underline{0.749}$		$\underline{14\frac{3}{5}}$		$\underline{-\ 6\frac{3}{5}}$

13	$-16\frac{1}{2}$	14	$-\frac{1}{3}$	15	$\frac{1}{12}$
	$\underline{8\frac{3}{10}}$		$\underline{-\frac{1}{10}}$		$\underline{-\frac{1}{13}}$

How many degrees must the temperature rise to change from:

16 $+2$ to $+20°$?   **17** -11 to $70°$?   **18** -20 to $-3°$?

How many degrees must the temperature fall to change from:

19 -5 to $-23°$?   **20** $+8$ to $-15°$?   **21** $+86$ to $+35°$?

22 A certain point in a circuit is 230 volts negative with respect to ground. Another point in the same circuit is 115 volts positive with respect to ground. What is the potential difference between the two points?

23 In Fig. 8–2 what is the potential difference between the plate P and the cathode K?

8 – 7 Addition and subtraction of like terms

In arithmetic, it is never possible to add unlike quantities. For example, we should not add inches and gallons and expect to obtain a sensible answer. Neither should we attempt to add volts and amperes, kilocycles and microfarads, ohms and watts, etc. So it goes on through algebra—we can never add quantities unless they are expressed in the same units.

The addition of two like terms such as $6EI + 12EI = 18EI$ can be checked by substituting numbers for the literal factors. Thus, if $E = 1$ and $I = 2$,

$$
\begin{aligned}
6EI &= 6 \times 1 \times 2 = 6 \times 2 = 12 \\
\underline{12EI} &= \underline{12 \times 1 \times 2 = 12 \times 2 = 24} \\
18EI &= 18 \times 1 \times 2 = 18 \times 2 = 36
\end{aligned}
$$

From the foregoing, it is apparent that like terms may be added or subtracted by adding or subtracting their coefficients.

The addition or subtraction of unlike terms cannot be carried out but can only be indicated, because the unlike literal factors may stand for entirely different quantities.

EXAMPLE 5   Addition of like terms:

$$
\begin{array}{ccc}
-3i^2r & -16IR & 13jIX \\
\underline{8i^2r} & \underline{14IR} & \underline{-20jIX} \\
5i^2r & -3IR & -32jIX \\
& \underline{-5IR} & \underline{-39jIX} \\
\end{array}
$$

EXAMPLE 6   Subtraction of like terms:

$$
\begin{array}{ccc}
-8e_1 & 6iZ & -28L^2R \\
\underline{3e_1} & \underline{-13iZ} & \underline{-29L^2R} \\
-11e_1 & 19iZ & L^2R \\
\end{array}
$$

EXAMPLE 7   Addition of unlike terms:

$$
\begin{array}{ccc}
3e & -3r & 3EI \\
-3IX & 4R & 10I^2R \\
\underline{4E} & \underline{-16R_t} & \underline{-46W} \\
3e - 3IX + 4E & 4R - 3r - 16R_t & 3EI + 10I^2R - 46W \\
\end{array}
$$

8-8   Addition and subtraction of polynomials

Polynomials are added or subtracted by arranging like terms in the same column and then combining terms in each column, as with monomials.

EXAMPLE 8   Addition of polynomials:

$$
\begin{array}{ll}
-3ab + 6cd + x^2y & 6E + 3RI - 8IZ \\
14ab - 5x^2y & RI - 2IZ \\
\underline{ab - 3cd} & \underline{-7E + 3IZ} \\
12ab + 3cd - 4x^2y & -E + 4RI - 7IZ \\
\end{array}
$$

EXAMPLE 9   Subtraction of polynomials:

$$
\begin{array}{ll}
3mn + 16pq - xy^2 & 11R + 4x \\
\underline{-9mn + 7xy^2} & \underline{15R - 18Z} \\
12mn + 16pq - 8xy^2 & -4R + 4x + 18Z \\
\end{array}
$$

PROBLEMS 8-3

Add:

1 $3i,\ 8i,\ -16i,\ 9i$
2 $6i^2r,\ 9i^2r,\ -20i^2r,\ -37i^2r$
3 $-16IZ,\ -23IZ,\ 38IZ,\ -72IZ,\ IZ$
4 $28ei,\ -73ei,\ ei,\ 11ei,\ -9ei$
5 $-3jX,\ 14jX,\ -25jX,\ 19R,\ 16jX$
6 $3i + 8I,\ -6i -17I$
7 $-25IX + 41EI,\ 36IX - 82EI,\ -5IX + 53EI$
8 $16\theta - 63\phi,\ -20\theta + 18\phi,\ 49\theta - 73\phi$

9 $-23\omega L + 13R, -16R + 46\omega L - 26Z$

10 $19IZ - 3EI + 28\omega L_1, 37IZ - 16\omega L_1 + 9EI$

11 $i^2r + 14W - 7ei + 72w, -9i^2r - 18w + 10ei, 19ei - 8W + 2i^2r - w$

12 $3IX - 8IZ + 10IR, 13IZ - 21IR, 7IR - IZ - 4IX$

13 $0.25ei - 3.02eZ + 0.0036eX, 2.85eZ - 0.0035eX + ei$

14 $3.06I^2R - 0.062eI + 32W, 0.72eI - 3I^2R$

15 $\frac{1}{5}\omega L - \frac{1}{2}R + \frac{2}{3}Z, \frac{1}{3}\omega L + \frac{3}{5}R - \frac{5}{6}Z$

16 From $16IR - 13iZ$ subtract $20iZ - 19IR$.

17 From $46\theta + 3\phi$ subtract $-22\theta - 6\phi$.

18 From $3.62\omega L - 0.03X + 25Z$ subtract $6X - 6.2\omega L + 21$.

19 From the sum of $38irZ - 3.02E + IR$ and $16iZ + 3.1E - 18IR$, subtract $11IR - 0.2E + 0.7irZ$.

20 Subtract $\frac{2}{3}i^2r + ei - \frac{2}{5}I^2x$ from the sum of $\frac{1}{2}i^2r - \frac{2}{3}ei + \frac{3}{8}I^2x$ and $i^2r + \frac{3}{4}ei - \frac{5}{6}I^2x$.

21 Take $6.03iR - 0.73Iz + 3.07Ix$ from $2.06Iz + 0.02Ix - 0.23iR$.

22 How much more than $2\mu E_g + 36E_s$ is $3\mu E_g - 15E_s$?

23 What must be added to $23E - 14IR$ to obtain $18E + 3IR$?

24 What must be subtracted from $6.7\omega L + 10.3Z$ to obtain $8\omega L - 16Z$?

25 Subtract $13eI - 3i^2r$ from $8ei + 9I^2r$.

8–9 Signs of grouping

Often it is necessary to express or group together quantities that are to be affected by the same operation. Also, it is desirable to be able to represent that two or more terms are to be considered as one quantity.

In order to meet the above requirements, signs of grouping have been adopted. These signs are the *parentheses* ( ), the *brackets* [ ], the *braces* { }, and the *vinculum* ———. The first three are placed around the terms to be grouped, as $(E - IR)$, $[a + 3b]$, and $\{x^2 + 4y\}$. All have the same meaning, that the enclosed terms are to be considered as one quantity.

Thus, $16 - (12 - 5)$ means that the quantity $(12 - 5)$ is to be subtracted from 16. That is, 5 is to be subtracted from 12, and then the remainder 7 is to be subtracted from 16 to give a final remainder of 9. In like manner, $E - (IR + e)$ means that the sum of $IR + e$ is to be subtracted from E.

Carefully note that the sign preceding a sign of grouping, as the minus sign between E and $(IR + e)$ above, is a sign of *operation* and does not denote that $(IR + e)$ is a negative quantity.

The vinculum is used mainly with radical signs and fractions, as

$$\sqrt{7{,}245} \quad \text{and} \quad \frac{a + b}{x - y}$$

In the latter case the vinculum denotes the division of $a + b$ by $x - y$, in addition to grouping the terms in the numerator and denominator. When studying later chapters, you will avoid many mistakes by remembering that *the vinculum is a sign of grouping.*

In working problems involving signs of grouping, the operations within the signs of grouping should be performed first.

EXAMPLE 10 $a + (b + c) = ?$
SOLUTION   This means, "What result will be obtained when the sum of $b + c$ is added to a?" Because both b and c are denoted as positive, it follows that we can write

$$a + (b + c) = a + b + c$$

because it makes no difference in which order we add.

EXAMPLE 11 $a + (b - c) = ?$
SOLUTION   This means, "What result will be obtained when the difference of $b - c$ is added to a?" Again, because it makes no difference in which order we add, we can write

$$a + (b - c) = a + b - c$$

EXAMPLE 12 $a - (b + c) = ?$
SOLUTION   Here the sum of $b + c$ is to be subtracted from a. This is the same as if we first subtract b from a and from this remainder subtract c. Therefore,

$$a - (b + c) = a - b - c$$

or, because this is subtraction, we could change the signs and add algebraically, remembering that b and c are denoted as positive, as shown below.

$$
\begin{array}{r}
a \\
b + c \\
\hline
a - b - c
\end{array}
$$

EXAMPLE 13 $a - (-b - c) = ?$
SOLUTION   This means that the quantity $-b - c$ is to be subtracted from a. Performing this subtraction, we obtain

$$
\begin{array}{r}
a \\
-b - c \\
\hline
a + b + c
\end{array}
$$

Therefore, $a - (-b - c) = a + b + c$

A study of the foregoing examples enables us to state the following:

RULES

1 Parentheses or other signs of grouping preceded by a plus sign can be removed without any other change.

2 To remove parentheses or other signs of grouping preceded by a minus sign, change the sign of every term within the sign of grouping.

Although not apparent in the examples, another rule can be added as follows:

3 If parentheses or other signs of grouping occur one within another, remove the inner grouping first.

EXAMPLES $(x + y) + (2x - 3y) = x + y + 2x - 3y = 3x - 2y$

$$3a - \overline{2b + c} - a = 3a - 2b - c - a = 2a - 2b - c$$

$$10x - (-3x - 4y) + 2y = 10x + 3x + 4y + 2y = 13x + 6y$$

$$x - [2x + 3y - (3x - y) - 4x] = x - [2x + 3y - 3x + y - 4x]$$
$$= x - 2x - 3y + 3x - y + 4x$$
$$= 6x - 4y$$

PROBLEMS 8 – 4

Simplify by removing signs of grouping and combining similar terms:

1   $(E - 3I + 2) - (E + 5I - 8)$

2   $(6\theta - 9\phi) - (-3\phi + 2\theta - 2)$

3   $(2R + 6Z - 10X) - (8X + 3Z - 6R + 4)$

4   $7i^2r + [-3ei + (-i^2r - 4ei) - 5ei] + 8$

5   $-6I^2R - [-4EI + (11I^2R - \overline{4EI + 3I^2R + 2W})]$

6   $R - \{2\omega L - [3R - (\omega L + 6R)]\}$

7   $3\theta - \{\theta + \phi - [\theta + \phi + \omega - (\theta + \phi + \omega) - 2\omega] - 3\phi\}$

8   $- \{-ei - [ei + w - ei - (w - ei) - ei] - 2w - 3\}$

9   $3IX - [-4IX - (-3IR + IZ) - (5IR - \overline{8IX + 6IZ})]$

10   $24R - 3Z - \overline{14X - 8R} - [-16Z - (-2R - 5X) - 6Z + 18]$

8 – 10   Inserting signs of grouping

To enclose terms within signs of grouping preceded by a plus sign, rewrite the terms without changing their signs.

EXAMPLE 14 $a + b - c + d = a + (b - c + d)$

To enclose terms within signs of grouping preceded by a minus sign, rewrite the terms changing the signs of the terms enclosed.

EXAMPLE 15 $a + b - c + d = a + b - (c - d)$

No difficulty need be encountered when inserting signs of grouping because, by removing the signs of grouping from the result, the original expression should be obtained.

EXAMPLE 16 $x - 3y + z = x - (3y - z) = x - 3y + z$

PROBLEMS 8 - 5

Enclose the last three terms of the following expressions in parentheses preceded by a plus sign:

1 $2R + r - X + Z$

2 $\theta + 2\phi - 6\omega - \lambda$

3 $8ei - 6I^2R + \dfrac{3E^2}{R} - 6W$

4 $\dfrac{E}{Z} - \dfrac{3E}{R} - \dfrac{e}{z} + \dfrac{6e}{r}$

5 $6\omega M + 3\omega L - \dfrac{1}{\omega C} - Z + 3X$

Enclose the last three terms of the following expressions in parentheses preceded by a minus sign:

6 $6i^2r + 2ei - iz + 9I^2R$

7 $X + Z - 2r + 9R$

8 $3\phi - 13\theta + 2\omega - 16°$

9 $0.2Z - 3R - \dfrac{1}{\omega C} - 4\omega L$

10 $\dfrac{e}{r} + \dfrac{E}{X} + \dfrac{E}{Z} - 9i - 0.5I$

11 Write the amount by which P is greater than $(ei - i^2r)$.

12 The sum of two currents is 80 amp; the larger current is I amp. Express the smaller current.

13 The difference between two voltages is 25 volts; the smaller voltage is E volts. Express the greater voltage.

14 Write the amount by which Z exceeds $\sqrt{r^2 + x^2}$.

15 Write the larger part of Z if $(r + j\omega L)$ is the smaller part.

CHAPTER 9
ALGEBRA
MULTIPLICATION AND DIVISION

Multiplication is often defined as the *process of continued addition*. Thus, 2×3 may be thought of as adding 2 three times, or $2 + 2 + 2 = 6$.

Considering multiplication as a shortened form of addition is not satisfactory, however, when the multiplier is a fraction. For example, it would not be sensible to say that $5 \times \frac{2}{7}$ was adding 5 two-sevenths of a time. This problem could be rewritten as $\frac{2}{7} \times 5$, which would be the same as adding $\frac{2}{7}$ five times. But this is only a temporary help, for if two fractions are to be multiplied together, as $\frac{3}{4} \times \frac{5}{6}$, the original definition of multiplication will not apply. However, the definition has been extended to include such cases, and the product of $5 \times \frac{2}{7}$ is taken to mean 5 multiplied by 2 and this product divided by 7; that is, by $5 \times \frac{2}{7}$ is meant $\dfrac{5 \times 2}{7}$.

Also, $$\frac{3}{4} \times \frac{5}{6} = \frac{3 \times 5}{4 \times 6} = \frac{15}{24}$$

9 – 1   **Multiplication of positive and negative numbers**

Because we are now dealing with both positive and negative numbers, it becomes necessary to determine what sign the product will have when combinations of these numbers are multiplied.

When two numbers only are to be multiplied, there can be but four possible combinations of signs, as follows:

[1] $(+2) \times (+3) = ?$
[2] $(-2) \times (+3) = ?$
[3] $(+2) \times (-3) = ?$
[4] $(-2) \times (-3) = ?$

Combination [1] means that $+2$ is to be added three times:

$$(+2) + (+2) + (+2) = +6$$
or $$(+2) \times (+3) = +6$$

In the same manner, combination [2] means that -2 is to be added three times:

$$(-2) + (-2) + (-2) = -6$$
or $$(-2) \times (+3) = -6$$

Combination [3] means that $+2$ is to be subtracted three times:

$$-(+2) - (+2) - (+2) = -6$$
or $$(+2) \times (-3) = -6$$

Note that this is the same as subtracting 6 once, -6 being thus obtained. Combination [4] means that -2 is to be subtracted three times:

$$-(-2) - (-2) - (-2) = +6$$
or $$(-2) \times (-3) = +6$$

This may be considered to be the same as subtracting -6 once, and because subtracting -6 once is the same as adding $+6$, we obtain $+6$ as above.

From the foregoing we have these rules:

RULES
1   The product of two numbers having like signs is positive.
2   The product of two numbers having unlike signs is negative.
3   If more than two factors are multiplied, the foregoing rules are to be used successively.

4   The product of an even number of negative factors is positive.
The product of an odd number of negative factors is negative.

These rules can be summarized in general terms as follows:

Rule 1	$(+a)(+b) = +ab$
Rule 1	$(-a)(-b) = +ab$
Rule 2	$(+a)(-b) = -ab$
Rule 2	$(-a)(+b) = -ab$
Rule 3	$(-a)(+b)(-c) = +abc$
Rule 4	$(-a)(-b)(-c)(-d) = +abcd$
Rule 4	$(-a)(-b)(-c) = -abc$

PROBLEMS 9 – 1

Find the products of the following:

1   $8, -6$ 2 $-5, 3$

3   $-7.3, -4.2$ 4 $-2.5, 3.2, -8.6$

5   $-\frac{3}{4}, \frac{4}{5}, -1$ 6 $\frac{3}{8}, -\frac{1}{3}, \frac{5}{6}, -\frac{2}{5}$

7   $-0.005, -10, -0.03, 200$ 8 $3,000, -0.04, 180, -0.0035$

9   $\alpha, -\beta, \theta$ 10 $-m, -n, o, -p$

11   $-2, \pi, -f, L$ 12 $\frac{1}{\theta}, -\frac{1}{\phi}, -\frac{\lambda}{\beta}$

13   $\frac{1}{2}, -\frac{1}{\pi}, -\frac{1}{f}, \frac{1}{C}$ 14 $I^2, -R, \frac{1}{r}, -\frac{1}{i}$

15   $E^2, \frac{1}{R}, -i^2, r, -eI$

9 – 2   Graphical representation

Our system of representing numbers is a graphical one, as illustrated
in Fig. 8–3.   It might be well at this time to consider certain facts regarding multiplication.

When a number is multiplied by any other number except 1, we can
think of the operation as having changed the absolute value of the
multiplicand.   Thus, 3 inches × 4 becomes 12 inches, 6 amp × 3 becomes 18 amp, etc.   Such multiplications could be represented graphically by simply extending the multiplicand the proper amount, as
shown in Fig. 9–1.

The case of multiplying a negative number by a positive number is
shown in Fig. 9–2.

From these examples, it is evident that a positive multiplier simply
changes the absolute value, or magnitude, of the number being

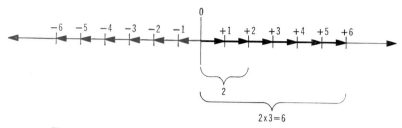

FIG. 9-1 Representation of the multiplication 2 × 3 = 6.

multiplied. What happens if the multiplier is negative? As an example, consider the case of 2 × (−3) = −6. How shall this be represented graphically?

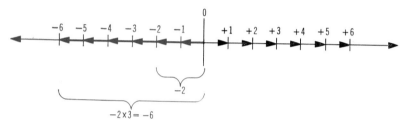

FIG. 9-2 Representation of the multiplication −2 × 3 = −6.

Now, 2 × (−3) = −6 is the same as

$$2 \times (+3) \times (-1) = -6$$

Therefore, let us first multiply 2 × 3 to obtain +6 and represent it as shown in Fig. 9-1. We must multiply by −1 to complete the problem and in so doing should obtain −6, but −6 must be represented as a number six units in length and directed toward the left, as illustrated in Fig. 9-2. We therefore agree that multiplication by −1 rotates a number in a counterclockwise direction so that it will be directed oppositely from its original direction. This is illustrated in Fig. 9-3.

If both multiplicand and multiplier are negative, as

$$(-2) \times (-3) = +6$$

the representation is as illustrated in Fig. 9-4. Again,

$$(-2) \times (-3) = +6$$

is the same as

$$(-2) \times (+3) \times (-1) = +6$$

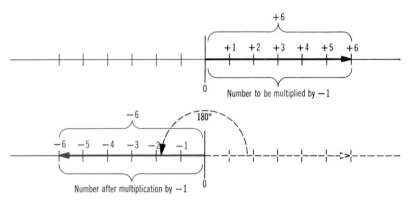

FIG. 9–3   Multiplication by −1 rotates multiplicand counterclockwise through 180°.

The product has an absolute value of 6, and at the same time there has been rotation to +6 because of multiplication by −1.

The foregoing representations are also applicable for division, since the law of signs is the same as in multiplication.

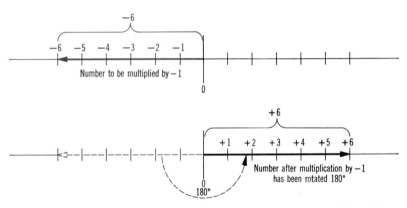

FIG. 9–4   Illustration of −6 rotated counterclockwise through 180° becoming +6 due to multiplication by −1.

The important thing to bear in mind is that multiplication or division by −1 causes rotation of a number in a counterclockwise direction to an exactly opposite direction from the original direction. The number −1, when used as a multiplier or divisor, should be considered as an *operator* for the purpose of rotation. It is important that you clearly understand this concept, for you will encounter it later on.

9 – 3 Law of exponents in multiplication

As explained in Sec. 7–10, an exponent indicates how many times a number is to be taken as a factor. Thus $x^4 = x \cdot x \cdot x \cdot x$, $a^3 = a \cdot a \cdot a$, etc.

Because $\quad\quad\quad x^4 = x \cdot x \cdot x \cdot x$

and $\quad\quad\quad\quad x^3 = x \cdot x \cdot x$

then $\quad\quad x^4 \cdot x^3 = x \cdot x \cdot x \cdot x \cdot x \cdot x \cdot x = x^7$

or $\quad\quad\quad x^4 \cdot x^3 = x^{4+3} = x^7$

Thus, we have the rule:

RULE To find the product of two or more powers having the same base, add the exponents.

EXAMPLES
$$a^3 \cdot a^2 = a^{3+2} = a^5$$
$$x^4 \cdot x^4 = x^{4+4} = x^8$$
$$6^2 \cdot 6^3 \cdot 6^5 = 6^{2+3+5} = 6^{10}$$
$$a^2 \cdot b^3 \cdot b^3 \cdot a^5 = a^{2+5} \cdot b^{3+3} = a^7 b^6$$
$$e \cdot e^3 = e^{1+3} = e^4$$
$$3^2 \cdot 3^4 = 3^{2+4} = 3^6$$
$$e^a \cdot e^b = e^{a+b}$$

From the foregoing examples, it is seen that the law of exponents can be expressed in the well-known general form

$$a^m \cdot a^n = a^{m+n}$$

where $a \neq 0$ and m and n are literal numbers and may represent any number of factors.

9 – 4 Multiplication of monomials

RULES

1 Find the product of the numerical coefficients, giving it the proper sign, plus or minus, according to the rules for multiplication (Sec. 9–1).

2 Multiply this numerical product by the product of the literal factors, using the law of exponents as applicable.

EXAMPLE 1 Multiply $3a^2b$ by $4ab^3$.

SOLUTION
$$(3a^2b)(4ab^3) = +(3 \cdot 4) \cdot a^{2+1} \cdot b^{1+3}$$
$$= 12a^3b^4$$

EXAMPLE 2 Multiply $-6x^3y^2$ by $3xy^2$.

SOLUTION
$$(-6x^3y^2)(3xy^2) = -(6 \cdot 3) \cdot x^{3+1} \cdot y^{2+2}$$
$$= -18x^4y^4$$

EXAMPLE 3   Multiply $-5e^2x^4y$ by $-3e^2x^2p$.

SOLUTION $(-5e^2x^4y)(-3e^2x^2p) = +(5 \cdot 3)e^{2+2} \cdot p \cdot x^{4+2} \cdot y$
$= 15e^4px^6y$

PROBLEMS 9 – 2

Multiply:

1	$b^3 \cdot b^4$	2	$-n^2 \cdot n$
3	$i^2 \cdot i^3 \cdot -i^4$	4	$\theta \cdot -\theta^3 \cdot -\phi^2$
5	$(3a^2)(4b)$	6	$(12\alpha)(-4\beta^2)$
7	$(-4\lambda^2)(-3.05\Delta)$	8	$(-0.03R)(4.06I^2)$
9	$(-6r)^2$	10	$(3a^n)(-5a^n)$
11	$(0.4\theta^\alpha)(0.1\theta^\beta)$	12	$(5i^2R)^3$
13	$(-6a^2bc^2d^3)(-0.3ab^2cd^2)$	14	$(-\frac{1}{2}i^2z)(-\frac{4}{5}irz)$
15	$(-\frac{1}{8}\theta^2\phi)(\frac{2}{3}\theta\beta)(-\frac{3}{5}\theta\phi^2)$	16	$(0.0025E^2eI^2)(100eI)(-0.1I^2eR)$
17	$(-\frac{1}{3}\omega L)^2(\frac{3}{8}\omega M^2)(-\frac{4}{7}j\omega C^2)$	18	$(10^3)^2$
19	$(10^2)^3$		
20	$(6IZ)(-0.2I^2R)(-0.03eZR^2)(-4.2i^2rZ^2)$		

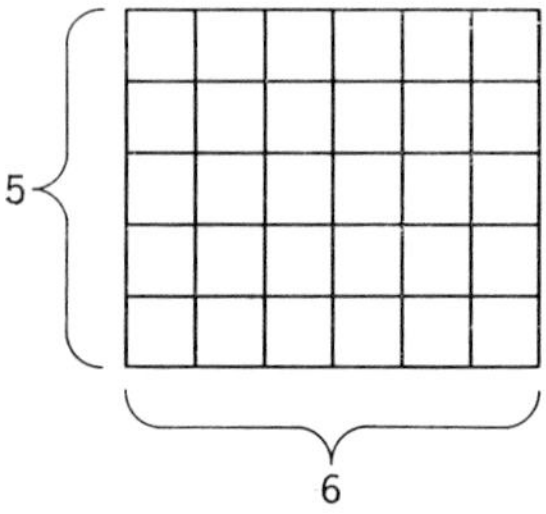

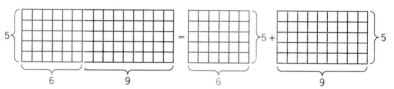

FIG. 9–5   Graphical representation of the multiplication $5 \times 6 = 30$.

9 – 5   Multiplication of polynomials by monomials

Another method of graphically representing the product of two numbers is as shown in Fig. 9–5.   The product $5 \times 6 = 30$ is shown as a rectangle whose sides are 5 and 6 units in length; therefore, the rectangle contains 30 square units.

Similarly, the product of $5(6 + 9)$ can be represented as illustrated in Fig. 9–6.

FIG. 9–6   Graphical representation of the multiplication $5(6 + 9) = 75$.

Thus, $5(6 + 9)$
$= 5 \times 15$
$= 75$

Also, $5(6 + 9)$
$= (5 \times 6) + (5 \times 9)$
$= 30 + 45$
$= 75$

In like manner the product $a(c + d) = ac + ad$ can be illustrated as in Fig. 9–7.

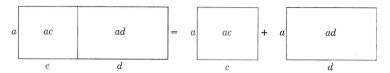

FIG. 9–7   Illustration of the product $a(c + d) = ac + ad$.

From the foregoing, you can show that

$$3(4 + 2) = 3 \times 4 + 3 \times 2 = 12 + 6 = 18$$
$$4(5 + 3 + 4) = 4 \times 5 + 4 \times 3 + 4 \times 4$$
$$= 20 + 12 + 16 = 48$$
$$x(y + z) = xy + xz$$
$$p(q + r + s) = pq + pr + ps$$

Note that, in all cases, each term of the polynomial (the terms enclosed in parentheses) is multiplied by the monomial. From these examples, we develop the following rule:

RULE   To multiply a polynomial by a monomial, multiply each term of the polynomial by the monomial and write in succession the resulting terms with their proper signs.

EXAMPLE 4 $3x(3x^2y - 4xy^2 + 6y^3) = ?$
SOLUTION   Multiplicand $= 3x^2y - 4xy^2 + 6y^3$
              Multiplier $= 3x$
              Product $= 9x^3y - 12x^2y^2 + 18xy^3$

EXAMPLE 5 $-2ac(-10a^3 + 4a^2b - 5ab^2c + 7bc^2) = ?$
SOLUTION   Multiplicand $= -10a^3 + 4a^2b - 5ab^2c + 7bc^2$
              Multiplier $= -2ac$
              Product $= 20a^4c - 8a^3bc + 10a^2b^2c^2 - 14abc^3$

EXAMPLE 6   Simplify $5(2e - 3) - 3(e + 4)$.
SOLUTION   First multiply $5(2e - 3)$ and $3(e + 4)$, and then subtract the second result from the first, thus:

$$5(2e - 3) - 3(e + 4) = (10e - 15) - (3e + 12)$$
$$= 10e - 15 - 3e - 12$$
$$= 7e - 27$$

PROBLEMS 9 – 3

Multiply:

1   $4i + 7I$ by $6R$ 2 $2R - 9r$ by $3i$
3   $5I^2 - 7i^2$ by $-3R_1$ 4 $6.3 - jX$ by $5x$

5 $\theta^2 - 4\phi + 3\omega$ by -4ϕ 6 $\alpha^3 - 8\alpha^2 - 5\alpha$ by -3α

7 $7\alpha\beta^2 - 21\alpha\beta^4 - 4\beta^5$ by $7\alpha\beta$ 8 $4\omega^2L^2 - 7\omega^2M - 14\omega f$ by $-3\omega L^2M$

9 $e^4 - e^2i^2 - i^4$ by $-e^3i^3$ 10 $2\theta^3\phi + 4\theta^2\phi^2 - 9\theta\phi^3 - 4$ by $3\theta\phi^2$

11 $\dfrac{i^2r}{2} - \dfrac{i^2R^2}{3} + \dfrac{iZ}{5}$ by $10iZ$

12 $0.02\alpha^2 - 0.001\alpha\beta + 0.0003\beta^2$ by $\dfrac{\alpha^2\beta}{2}$

13 $\dfrac{I^2R_1}{4} + \dfrac{I^2R_2}{3} - \dfrac{IR_3^2}{6} - IR_4$ by $\dfrac{3iI^2R_5}{2}$

14 $\dfrac{-e^3i^2}{2} + \dfrac{e^2i}{8} - \dfrac{e}{5} + \dfrac{1}{4}$ by $-\dfrac{2ei^2r}{3}$

15 $1.06E^2Z - 0.004E^3Z^2 - 4.13E^4Z^3$ by $0.01eEZ$

Simplify:

16 $5(4C + 2c) + 2(2C + 3c)$ 17 $8(4E - 3e) - 3(E - 9e)$

18 $I(3R + R_1) - 2I(R + 6R_1)$ 19 $2R(i^2 - 3I^2) - R(6I^2 - 8i^2)$

20 $2\omega(M + 3L) + \omega(6L - 5M)$

21 $2I^2(R_1 + 3R_2 - 7r) - 6I^2(r - 3R_1 + 0.1R_2)$

22 $\phi(\alpha^2 - 9\beta + 4\theta) + 2\phi(\theta - 0.2\beta - 6\alpha^2)$

23 $0.3L^2(0.02\omega^2 - 6\omega M) - 0.01L^2(\omega^2 + 0.1\omega M)$

24 $6\left(\dfrac{E}{2} - \dfrac{e}{3} + \dfrac{E_1}{6}\right)$ 25 $8\left(\dfrac{I^2R}{4} + \dfrac{i^2r}{2} - \dfrac{P}{6}\right)$

26 $15\left(\dfrac{IR}{3} - \dfrac{ir}{5} + \dfrac{e}{6}\right)$ 27 $\frac{1}{3}\theta\phi(6\theta^2\phi + 3\theta\phi^2 - 12\phi^3 - 4\alpha)$

28 $36I\left(\dfrac{R}{6} - \dfrac{R_1}{9} + \dfrac{r}{3}\right) - 12I\left(\dfrac{r}{12} - \dfrac{R}{3} + \dfrac{R_1}{6}\right)$

29 $0.1i^2(r + 3R - 7R_1) - 0.02i^2(6R_1 - 10r + 0.2R)$

30 $-2\lambda^2\left(\dfrac{\alpha^2}{3} - \dfrac{\beta^2\theta}{4} + \dfrac{\theta^2\phi}{5}\right) + 3\lambda^2\left(\dfrac{\theta^2\phi}{6} - \dfrac{\alpha^2}{2} - \dfrac{\beta^2\theta}{5}\right)$

9 – 6 Multiplication of a polynomial by a polynomial

It is apparent that

$$(3 + 4)(6 - 3) = 7 \times 3 = 21$$

The above multiplication can also be accomplished in the following manner:

$$
\begin{aligned}
(3 + 4)(6 - 3) &= 3(6 - 3) + 4(6 - 3) \\
&= (18 - 9) + (24 - 12) \\
&= 9 + 12 \\
&= 21
\end{aligned}
$$

Similarly,

$$(2a - 3b)(a + 5b) = 2a(a + 5b) - 3b(a + 5b)$$
$$= (2a^2 + 10ab) - (3ab + 15b^2)$$
$$= 2a^2 + 10ab - 3ab - 15b^2$$
$$= 2a^2 + 7ab - 15b^2$$

From the foregoing, we have the following:

RULE   To multiply polynomials, multiply every term of the multiplicand by each term of the multiplier, and add the partial products.

EXAMPLE 7   Multiply $2i - 3$ by $i + 2$.

SOLUTION

Multiplicand	$= 2i - 3$	
Multiplier	$= i + 2$	
i times $(2i - 3)$	$= 2i^2 - 3i$	
2 times $(2i - 3)$	$= 4i - 6$	
Adding, Product	$= 2i^2 + i - 6$	

EXAMPLE 8   Multiply $a^2 - 3ab + 2b^2$ by $2a^2 - 3b^2$.

SOLUTION

Multiplicand $\qquad = a^2 - 3ab + 2b^2$

Multiplier $\qquad = 2a^2 - 3b^2$

$2a^2$ times $(a^2 - 3ab + 2b^2) = 2a^4 - 6a^3b + 4a^2b^2$

$-3b^2$ times $(a^2 - 3ab + 2b^2) = -3a^2b^2 + 9ab^3 - 6b^4$

Adding,   Product $\qquad = 2a^4 - 6a^3b + a^2b^2 + 9ab^3 - 6b^4$

Products obtained by multiplication can be tested by substituting any convenient numerical values for the literal numbers.   It is not good practice to substitute the number 1; if there are exponents, the test will not be a proof of correct work, for 1 to any power is still 1.

EXAMPLE 9   Multiply $a^2 - 4ab - b^2$ by $a + b$, and test by letting $a = 2$ and $b = 2$.

SOLUTION

$a^2 - 4ab - b^2 \qquad = 4 - 16 - 4 = -16$

$a + b \qquad\qquad = 2 + 2 \qquad = 4$

$\overline{a^3 - 4a^2b - ab^2} \qquad\qquad\qquad = -64$

$ a^2b - 4ab^2 - b^3$

$\overline{a^3 - 3a^2b - 5ab^2 - b^3} = 8 - 24 - 40 - 8 = -64$

PROBLEMS 9–4

Multiply:

1 $i + 1$ by $i + 1$ $\qquad\qquad$ 2 $i - 1$ by $i - 1$

3 $i + 1$ by $i - 1$ $\qquad\qquad$ 4 $R + 3$ by $R + 3$

5 $R - 3$ by $R - 3$ $\qquad\qquad$ 6 $R + 3$ by $R - 3$

7 $e + 6$ by $e + 7$ 8 $Z - 10$ by $Z - 3$

9 $P + 4$ by $P + 9$ 10 $\omega L - 11$ by $\omega L + 13$

NOTE Parentheses or other signs of grouping are often used to indicate a product. Thus, $(ir + e)(2ir - 3e)$ means $(ir + e)$ times $(2ir - 3e)$. Perform the indicated multiplications:

11 $(r + 3)(r - 12)$ 12 $(3P + W)(P - 6W)$

13 $(7\alpha - 4\beta)(3\alpha + 7\beta)$ 14 $(3\theta + 6\phi)(8\theta - \phi)$

15 $(14ei - 2P)(2ei - 8P)$ 16 $(E - 6IR)(5E + 4IR)$

17 $(2\pi r + 3c)(2\pi r - 9c)$ 18 $(12R_1 - 3R_2)(6R_1 + R_2)$

19 $(E + 6e)(8E - 7e)$ 20 $(0.02Z - 0.15z)(0.4Z + 1.2z)$

21 $(2I^2R + 3P)(8I^2R - 0.03P)$ 22 $(13E^2 - 4i^2z^2)(0.3E^2 - 0.005i^2z^2)$

23 $(E + e)(E^2 + 2Ee + e^2)$ 24 $(E + e)(E + e)(E + e)$

25 $(i^2 - ir + r^2)(i + r)$ 26 $(6I^2 - 3I + 7)(I + 4)$

27 $(R - r)^2$ 28 $(R - r)(R^2 - 2Rr + r^2)$

29 $(R - r)^3$ 30 $(2Z^2 - 3Z + 4)^2$

31 $7(eI - 4P + 3W)(eI + 4P)$ 32 $(\frac{3}{5}R_1 - \frac{5}{6}R_2)(\frac{2}{3}R_1 - \frac{6}{5}R_2)$

33 $(i + I)(i^2 + I^2) - (i - I)(i^2 - I^2)$

34 $(6e^2 - 2e - 1)(e^2 - 18e + 3)$

35 $6(\theta - 3\phi)(7\theta + 5\phi) - 2(4\theta - 9\phi)(\theta - 10\phi)$

36 $9(I + 3)(I + 2)(I - 6) - 4(3I - 1)(2I + 2)(I - 7)$

37 $2Z^2[Z^2 - 3Z(2Z - 1)] + 3Z^2[6Z^2 - 8Z(6Z + 3)]$

38 $2R^2[R^2 - 3R(R - X)] - (R^2 + 3RX - 2X^2)(R^2 - 2RX - X^2)$

39 $6\theta(3\theta - 5\phi + 3\lambda)^2 + 2\theta(\theta + 7\phi - 4\lambda)^2$

40 $3\omega^2(5\alpha - \beta + \omega)^2 - \omega^2(\alpha + 7\beta - 2\omega)^2$

9 – 7 Division

The division of algebraic expressions requires the development of certain rules and new methods in connection with operations involving exponents. However, if you have mastered the processes of the preceding sections, algebraic division will be an easy subject.

For the purpose of review the following definitions are given:

1. The *dividend* is a number, or quantity, that is to be divided.

2. The *divisor* is a number by which a number, or quantity, is to be divided.

3. The *quotient* is the result obtained by division.

That is, $\dfrac{\text{Dividend}}{\text{Divisor}} = \text{quotient}$

9 – 8 Division of positive and negative numbers

Because division is the inverse of multiplication, the methods of the latter will serve as an aid in developing methods for division. For example, because $\qquad$ $6 \times 4 = 24$

then $\qquad$ $24 \div 6 = 4$

and $\qquad$ $24 \div 4 = 6$

These relations can be used in applying the rules for multiplication to division.

All the possible cases can be represented as follows:

$$(+24) \div (+6) = ?$$
$$(-24) \div (+6) = ?$$
$$(+24) \div (-6) = ?$$
$$(-24) \div (-6) = ?$$

Because division is the inverse of multiplication, we apply the rules for multiplication of positive and negative numbers and obtain the following:

$(+24) \div (+6) = +4$	because	$(+4) \times (+6) = +24$
$(-24) \div (+6) = -4$	because	$(-4) \times (+6) = -24$
$(+24) \div (-6) = -4$	because	$(-4) \times (-6) = +24$
$(-24) \div (-6) = +4$	because	$(+4) \times (-6) = -24$

Therefore, we have the following:

RULE   To divide positive and negative numbers,

1   If dividend and divisor have like signs, the quotient is positive.

2   If dividend and divisor have unlike signs, the quotient is negative.

PROBLEMS 9 – 5

Divide the first number by the second in Probs. 1 to 10:

1	$15, -5$	2	$-24, 8$	3	$-14, -7$
4	$-72, -0.009$	5	$0.00025, -50$	6	$-\frac{3}{5}, \frac{1}{3}$
7	$-\frac{1}{2}, -\frac{3}{4}$	8	$E^2, -R$	9	$-\theta, -\phi^2$
10	$42e, -6r$				

Supply the missing divisors:

11   $\dfrac{-20}{?} = 5$ $\qquad$ 12 $\dfrac{18}{?} = -3$ $\qquad$ 13 $\dfrac{-30}{?} = \dfrac{1}{3}$

14   $\dfrac{6}{?} = -\dfrac{1}{2}$ $\qquad$ 15 $\dfrac{-0.0009}{?} = 0.00002$

9 – 9   **The law of exponents in division**

By previous definition of an exponent (Sec. 7–10),

$$x^6 = x \cdot x \cdot x \cdot x \cdot x \cdot x$$

and

$$x^3 = x \cdot x \cdot x$$

Then, $x^6 \div x^3 = \dfrac{x^6}{x^3} = \dfrac{\cancel{x} \cdot \cancel{x} \cdot \cancel{x} \cdot x \cdot x \cdot x}{\cancel{x} \cdot \cancel{x} \cdot \cancel{x}} = x^3$

This result is obtained by canceling common factors in numerator and denominator. The above could be expressed as

$$x^6 \div x^3 = \frac{x^6}{x^3} = x^{6-3} = x^3$$

In like manner, $\dfrac{a^7}{a^3} = a^{7-3} = a^4$

From the foregoing, it is seen that the law of exponents can be expressed in the general form

$$a^m \div a^n = \frac{a^m}{a^n} = a^{m-n}$$

where $a \neq 0$ and m and n are general numbers.

9 – 10   **The zero exponent**

Any number, except zero, divided by itself results in a quotient of 1. Thus,

$$\frac{6}{6} = 1$$

Also, $\dfrac{a^3}{a^3} = 1$

Therefore, $\dfrac{a^3}{a^3} = a^{3-3} = a^0 = 1$

Then, in the general form, $\dfrac{a^m}{a^n} = a^{m-n}$

If $m = n$

then $m - n = 0$

and $\dfrac{a^m}{a^n} = a^{m-n} = a^0 = 1$

The foregoing leads to the definition that

Any base, except zero, affected by zero exponent is equal to 1.

Thus, a^0, x^0, y^0, 3^0, 4^0, etc., all equal 1.

— 11 The negative exponent

If the law of exponents in division is to apply to all cases, it must apply when n is greater than m. Thus,

$$\frac{a^2}{a^5} = \frac{\not{a} \cdot \not{a}}{\not{a} \cdot \not{a} \cdot a \cdot a \cdot a} = \frac{1}{a^3}$$

or

$$\frac{a^2}{a^5} = a^{2-5} = a^{-3}$$

Therefore,

$$a^{-3} = \frac{1}{a^3}$$

Also,

$$a^{-n} = \frac{1}{a^n}$$

This leads to the definition that

Any base affected by a negative exponent is the same as 1 divided by that same base but affected by a positive exponent of the same absolute value as the negative exponent.

EXAMPLES

$$x^{-4} = \frac{1}{x^4}$$

$$2^{-2} = \frac{1}{2^2} = \frac{1}{4}$$

$$3^{-3} = \frac{1}{3^3} = \frac{1}{27}$$

$$\frac{4^3}{4^5} = \frac{\not{4} \times \not{4} \times \not{4}}{\not{4} \times \not{4} \times \not{4} \times 4 \times 4} = \frac{1}{4 \times 4} = \frac{1}{4^2} = 4^{-2}$$

or

$$\frac{4^3}{4^5} = 4^{3-5} = 4^{-2}$$

It follows, from the consideration of negative exponents, that

Any *factor* of an algebraic term may be transferred from numerator to denominator, or vice versa, by changing the sign of the exponent of the *factor*.

EXAMPLE 10

$$3a^2x^3 = \frac{3a^2}{x^{-3}} = \frac{3}{a^{-2}x^{-3}} = \frac{3x^3}{a^{-2}}$$

— 12 Division of one monomial by another

RULE   To divide one monomial by another,

1   Find the quotient of the absolute values of the numerical coefficients, affixing the proper sign according to the rules for division of positive and negative numbers (Sec. 9–8).

2   Determine the literal coefficients with their proper exponents, and write them after the numerical coefficient found in 1 above.

EXAMPLE 11   Divide $-12a^3x^4y$ by $4a^2x^2y$.

SOLUTION $$\frac{-12a^3x^4y}{4a^2x^2y} = -3ax^2$$

EXAMPLE 12   Divide $-7a^2b^4c$ by $-14ab^2c^3$.   Express the quotient with positive exponents.

SOLUTION $$\frac{-7a^2b^4c}{-14ab^2c^3} = \frac{ab^2}{2c^2}$$

EXAMPLE 13   Divide $15a^{-2}b^2c^3d^{-4}$ by $-5a^2bc^{-1}d^{-2}$.   Express the quotient with positive exponents.

SOLUTION $$\frac{15a^{-2}b^2c^3d^{-4}}{-5a^2bc^{-1}d^{-2}} = -\frac{3bc^4}{a^4d^2}$$

Division can be checked by substituting convenient numerical values for the literal factors or by multiplying the divisor by the quotient, the product of which should result in the dividend.

PROBLEMS 9 – 6

Divide:

1   $16a^3b^4$ by $-4ab^2$

2   $-27x^6y^4z^2$ by $9x^2y^4z$

3   $-12\theta^3\phi^2\beta^4$ by $-\theta\phi\beta^3$

4   $108\omega^5L^6M^2$ by $-27\omega^2L^2M^2$

5   $-105i^6r^2z^8$ by $-15i^6rz^7$

6   $-42I^3R^4Z^7$ by $14I^2R^3Z^7$

7   $35i^3r^2P^3W^4$ by $-0.007irP^3W^3$

8   $-0.056\alpha^7\beta^3\theta^2$ by $14\alpha^3\beta^2\theta$

9   $\frac{2}{3}s^3t^2u^5$ by $-\frac{4}{9}st^2u^3$

10   $-\frac{4}{5}p^5q^6r^2s^3$ by $-\frac{8}{15}p^5qr^2s^2$

11   $\dfrac{22a^2b^3c}{11a^3b^2c^2}$

12   $\dfrac{-65x^4y^2z}{13xy^3z^2}$

13   $\dfrac{70EI^2RZ^3}{-14E^2IR^3Z}$

14   $\dfrac{-0.08\alpha^4\beta\theta^5\lambda^2}{-16\alpha^5\beta\theta^3\lambda^3}$

15   $\dfrac{i^2re^5R^2Z}{-0.00025i^3e^3R^3Z}$

16   $\dfrac{-3\theta^{-2}\phi^2\omega^{-4}}{8\theta^3\phi^{-1}\omega^2}$

17   $\dfrac{17s^3t^2u^{-8}v^3}{-85s^4tu^{-5}v^2}$

18   $\dfrac{-0.000189m^3n^2p^{-8}}{270m^7n^{-2}p}$

19   $\dfrac{-0.493E^{-1}I^2R^4Z^{-6}}{-0.00029E^{-2}I^2R^{-4}Z^{-5}}$

20   $\dfrac{\frac{5}{7}x^{-2}y^4z^2\beta^{-3}}{-\frac{3}{4}x^{-3}y^{-3}z\beta^{-3}}$

9 – 13   Division of a polynomial by a monomial

Because $2 \times 8 = 16$

then $\dfrac{16}{2} = 8$

This result is written

$$x^2 + 5 + \frac{14}{x^2 - 2}$$

which is as it would be written in an arithmetical division that did not divide
out evenly.

PROBLEMS 9 – 8

Divide:

1 $a^2 + 5a + 6$ by $a + 3$ 2 $x^2 + 8x + 15$ by $x + 3$

3 $E^2 - E - 72$ by $E + 8$ 4 $R^2 - 11R + 30$ by $R - 5$

5 $3\theta^2 - \theta - 14$ by $2 + \theta$ 6 $12 - 14\omega + 3\omega^2 + 3\omega^3$ by $\omega + 3$

7 $27\lambda^3 + 9\lambda^2 - 3\lambda - 10$ by $3\lambda - 2$ 8 $96r^2 - 15Z^2 - 4rZ$ by $12r - 5Z$

9 $21\alpha^2 + 24\beta^2 - 65\alpha\beta$ by $8\beta - 3\alpha$ 10 $I^3 + 6I^2 + 7I - 8$ by $I - 1$

11 $R^2 - Z^2$ by $R - Z$ 12 $R^3 - Z^3$ by $R - Z$

13 $R^4 - Z^4$ by $R - Z$ 14 $R^3 + Z^3$ by $R + Z$

15 $R^4 - 1$ by $R^2 - 1$ 16 $R^5 + Z^5$ by $R + Z$

17 $R^7 + Z^7$ by $R + Z$ 18 $R^4 - Z^4$ by $R + Z$

19 $\alpha^3 - \alpha^2 - 9\alpha - 12$ by $\alpha^2 + 3\alpha + 3$

20 $\theta^3 - 7\theta^2 + 13\theta - 3$ by $\theta^2 - 4\theta + 1$

21 $4\phi^3 - \phi^4 + 6\phi^5 - 15 - \phi - 5\phi^2$ by $3 - \phi + 2\phi^2$

22 $1 - 2\lambda - 3\lambda^2 - 4\lambda^3 - \lambda^4$ by $\lambda^2 + \lambda + 1$

23 $\frac{1}{4}\theta^3 + \frac{1}{72}\theta\phi^2 + \frac{1}{12}\phi^3$ by $\frac{1}{2}\theta + \frac{1}{3}\phi$

24 $\frac{1}{3}i - 6r + 36r^2 + \frac{1}{4} + \frac{1}{9}i^2 - 4ir$ by $6r - \frac{1}{3}i - \frac{1}{2}$

25 $\frac{9}{16}I^4 - \frac{3}{4}I^3 - \frac{7}{4}I^2 + \frac{4}{3}I + 1\frac{5}{9}$ by $\frac{3}{2}I^2 - I - \frac{8}{3}$

CHAPTER 10
THE SLIDE RULE
POWERS OF TEN

The slide rule is an instrument, or tool, designed for the purpose of saving time and labor in calculating.

A complete description of various slide rules or of a particular type of rule is not within the scope of this book. Briefly, the slide rule is a mechanical equivalent of a table of logarithms. Each rule consists of a number of scales so graduated and arranged that the operations of multiplication, division, squaring, cubing, extracting roots, and many others can be performed with facility. Furthermore, problems involving trigonometry, logarithms, etc., can be worked on the slide rule. Addition and subtraction are not feasible except on specially constructed rules.

Every technician should be proficient in the operation of some type of slide rule. The solution of every practical problem, where a concrete answer is desired, eventually reduces to an arithmetical computation. Valuable time is wasted performing a series of multiplications, divisions, square roots, etc., with a pencil and paper when there is an instrument available that will do the work satisfactorily in a fraction of the time and with a fairly high degree of accuracy. Very few people enjoy performing numerical computations simply for the joy of "figuring." The practical man wants concrete answers; therefore, he should use whatever tools or devices are available to assist him in arriving at those answers with a minimum expenditure of time and effort.

0 – 1   Types of slide rule

Types of slide rule range from inexpensive beginner's slide rules to those comparable to calculating machines. Most of them are designed for use in general mathematical operations; some are designed especially for use in specific professions or trades.

No attempt is made here to advise you as to just what type of rule is best suited to your use. If you are attending a technical school, your instructors are qualified to advise as to the type of rule they believe best. If you are professionally employed, your technical associates will be able to assist in your selection of a rule.

Among the many types developed, the Cooke Radio Slide Rule has met with moderate sucess. This rule employs a minimum number

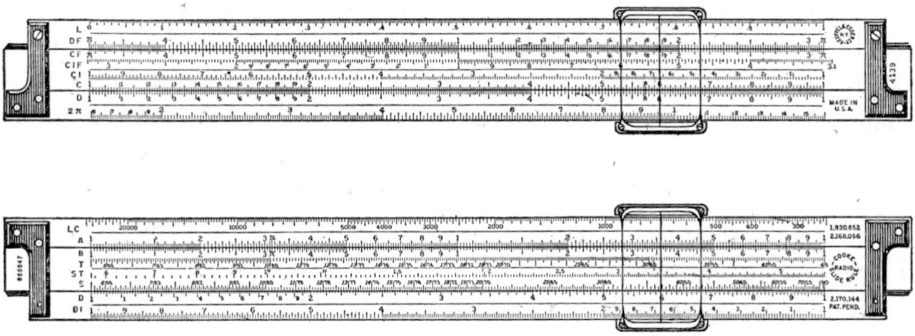

FIG. 10–1   Front and back views of Cooke Radio Slide Rule. (*Courtesy Keuffel and Esser Company.*)

of scales but at the same time allows almost as wide a mathematical scope as may be desired. The scales have been designed and arranged for the express purpose of completing the more common electronics and electrical problems in a simple and straightforward manner. The instruction book furnished with this rule has been written so that the examples and exercises follow these subjects as closely as is consistent with clarity.

Instruction books are furnished with all slide rules; thus, the beginner needs no instructor but merely a reasonable amount of practice in order to become proficient in using them.

It is therefore strongly recommended that the student acquire a rule and learn to use it while studying this text. Many hours devoted to figuring with a pencil will be saved that can be well spent in the study of mathematics or other essential subjects, to say nothing of lightening otherwise tedious computations.

10 – 2   Accuracy of slide rules

From an electronics or electrical viewpoint, except possibly where extremely accurate measurements are needed, the accuracy of a slide rule leaves nothing to be desired. Its accuracy is nearly proportional to the length of scales used. The 10-in. scales give results accurately to within 1 part in 1,000, or one-tenth of 1 per cent.

When practical electronic or electric circuits are taken into consideration, slide-rule computations are more accurate than the circuit components involved. For example, the tolerances of resistors, inductors, and capacitors used in the usual radio and television receivers do well to average ± 10 per cent. Also, the average switchboard meter is seldom correct to within 3 per cent throughout its calibration. Suppose we go into a store to buy a 10 per cent tolerance, 10,000-Ω resistor and ask the salesman to check the resistance on his ohmmeter. If the resistance measures anywhere between 9,000 and 11,000 Ω, which is within the ± 10 per cent tolerance, we should be satisfied. However, if his ohmmeter has an accuracy within ± 2 per cent, he is to be congratulated on having a good meter. Because, in all probability, he does not know just how accurate the meter is, we leave the store *hoping* we have a resistor somewhere near the correct value. Actually, such a resistor would be entirely satisfactory for ordinary requirements, as we shall see later.

Other circuit components, except those used in the laboratory, vary in much the same manner, and when temperature, humidity, and other variations are taken into consideration, the slide-rule results more than meet all practical needs.

From the foregoing, it might appear that mathematical accuracy in the calculation of electric circuits is unnecessary. Far from it—the laws of electricity follow concise mathematical concepts and we *can* construct circuit components and measuring equipment that are very precise. However, mainly for economical reasons, it is neither practical nor necessary to maintain such a high degree of accuracy in average circuits.

The important point is that we must first know how accurate our available circuit components and measuring equipment are and then depend upon this accuracy to a reasonable extent. Some students thoughtlessly make computations of quantities that have been found by measurements, instrument readings, etc., and carry the operations to several unnecessary decimal places. Not only does this computation consume a considerable amount of time; worse still, the results often give a false impression of accuracy. In this connection, it is safe to assume that the constants of any electronic- or electric-circuit components or the calibration of meters, excluding precision measuring equipments, are generally not correct beyond three significant figures.

10 - 3   Significant figures

In mathematics, a number is generally considered as being exact. For example, 220 would mean 220.0000, etc., for as many added zeros as desired. However, a meter reading, for example, is always an *approximation*. We might read 220 volts on a certain switchboard type of voltmeter, but a precision instrument might show the voltage to be 220.3 volts, and a series of precise measurements might show the voltage to be 220.36 volts. It should be noted that the position of the decimal point does not determine the accuracy of a number. For example, 115 volts, 0.115 kv, and 115,000 mv are of identical value and equally accurate.

Any number representing a measurement, or the amount of some quantity, expresses the accuracy of the measurement. The figures required are known as *significant figures*.

The *significant figures* of any number are the figures 1, 2, 3, 4, . . . , 9, in addition to such ciphers, or zeros, as may occur between them or as may have been retained in properly rounding them off.

EXAMPLES   0.00236   is correct to *three* significant figures.
                 3.14159   is correct to *six* significant figures.
                 980,000.0 is correct to *seven* significant figures.
                 24.   is correct to *two* significant figures.
                 24.0   is correct to *three* significant figures.
                 0.02500   is correct to *four* significant figures.

After studying the powers of 10, we shall return to a more detailed discussion of significant figures and how to express them.

10 – 4   Rounded numbers

A number is *rounded off* by dropping one or more figures at its right. If the last figure dropped is 6 or more, we increase the last figure retained by 1. Thus 3,867 would be rounded off to 3,870, 3,900, or 4,000. If the last figure dropped is 4 or less, we leave the last figure retained as it is. Thus 5,134 would be rounded off to 5,130, 5,100, or 5,000. If the last figure dropped is 5, add 1 if it will make the last figure retained *even;* otherwise do not. Thus, 55.7$\not{5}$ = 55.8, but 67.6$\not{5}$ = 67.6.

10 – 5   Decimals

Two important considerations arise in making computations involving decimals:

1. A slide rule gives only the significant figures of the result of a mathematical operation. For example, suppose that we have performed some operation on the slide rule and read as the result the significant figures 432. Now the slide rule does not indicate whether this answer is 0.0432, 0.432, 4.32, 4,320, 43,200, etc. Therefore, it becomes necessary for the slide-rule operator to fix the decimal point; that is, the operator must first determine the *approximate* answer in order that he may use the more accurate figures taken from the slide-rule scales.

2. Unfortunately, electrical engineers and particularly electronics engineers are required to handle cumbersome numbers, the numbers ranging from extremely small fractions of electrical units to very large numbers, as represented by radio frequencies. The fact that these wide limits of numbers are encountered in the same problem does not simplify matters. This situation is becoming more complicated owing to the trend to the higher radio frequencies with attendant smaller fractions of units represented by circuit components.

For these reasons, in using a slide rule, the decimal point *cannot* be fixed "by inspection" except in the simpler problems. Accordingly, many beginners interested in using the slide rule for solving electronics and electrical problems have become discouraged by the difficulty of placing the decimal points due to the above-mentioned wide range of numbers encountered in the average problem.

The problem of properly placing the decimal point and thus reducing unnecessary work presents little difficulty to the man who has a working knowledge of the powers of 10.

10 – 6 Powers of 10

The powers of 10 are sometimes termed the "engineer's shorthand." A thorough knowledge of the powers of 10 and the ability to apply the theory of exponents will greatly assist in determining an approximation. If a slide rule is used with the powers of 10, the average problem reduces to the usual slide-rule operations plus simple mental arithmetic. If a slide rule is not used for computation, the powers of 10 enable one to work all problems by using convenient whole numbers. Either offers a convenient method for obtaining a final answer with the decimal point in its proper place.

Some of the multiples of 10 may be represented as follows:

Number		Power of 10		Expressed in English
0.000001	=	10^{-6}	=	ten to the negative *sixth* power
0.00001	=	10^{-5}	=	ten to the negative *fifth* power
0.0001	=	10^{-4}	=	ten to the negative *fourth* power
0.001	=	10^{-3}	=	ten to the negative *third* power
0.01	=	10^{-2}	=	ten to the negative *second* power
0.1	=	10^{-1}	=	ten to the negative *first* power
1	=	10^{0}	=	ten to the *zero* power
10	=	10^{1}	=	ten to the *first* power
100	=	10^{2}	=	ten to the *second* power
1,000	=	10^{3}	=	ten to the *third* power
10,000	=	10^{4}	=	ten to the *fourth* power
100,000	=	10^{5}	=	ten to the *fifth* power
1,000,000	=	10^{6}	=	ten to the *sixth* power

From the above, it is seen that any decimal may be expressed as a whole number times some negative power of 10. This may be expressed by the following:

RULE   To express a decimal as a whole number times a power of 10, move the decimal point to the right and count the number of places to the original point. The number of places counted is the proper negative power of 10.

EXAMPLES $0.00687 = 6.87 \times 10^{-3}$
$0.0000482 = 4.82 \times 10^{-5}$

$$0.346 \quad = 34.6 \times 10^{-2}$$
$$0.08643 \quad = 86.43 \times 10^{-3}$$

Also, it is seen that any large number can be expressed as some smaller number times the proper power of 10. This can be expressed by the following rule:

RULE To express a large number as a smaller number times a power of 10, move the decimal point to the left and count the number of places to the original decimal point. The number of places counted will give the proper positive power of 10.

EXAMPLES
$$435 = 4.35 \times 10^2$$
$$964,000 = 96.4 \times 10^4$$
$$6,835.2 = 6.8352 \times 10^3$$
$$5,723 \quad = 5.723 \times 10^3$$

PROBLEMS 10 – 1

Round off the following numbers to three significant figures and express them as numbers between 1 and 10 times the proper power of 10:

1 896,100	2 7,856	3 4,755,000
4 6,845	5 0.0002538	6 0.000000009435
7 0.163542	8 0.0276	9 276×10^{-6}
10 $57,255 \times 10^{-3}$	11 $57,250 \times 10^{-3}$	12 $0.00002678 \times 10^{-4}$
13 $8,734,000 \times 10^6$	14 0.0002045×10^5	15 5,006,000,000
16 $0.0000030027 \times 10^{-6}$	17 2,000,640,000	18 $1,425,320 \times 10^{-12}$
19 $0.0000010352 \times 10^{-3}$	20 0.010375×10^{-8}	

10 – 7   Multiplication with powers of 10

In Sec. 9–3 the law of exponents in multiplication was expressed in the general form

$$a^m \cdot a^n = a^{m+n} \quad \text{(where } a \neq 0\text{)}$$

This law is directly applicable to the powers of 10.

EXAMPLE 1   Multiply 1,000 by 100,000.
SOLUTION $1,000 = 10^3$ and $100,000 = 10^5$
Then $1,000 \times 100,000 = 10^3 \times 10^5 = 10^{3+5} = 10^8$

EXAMPLE 2   Multiply 0.000001 by 0.001.
SOLUTION $0.000001 = 10^{-6}$ and $0.001 = 10^{-3}$
Then

$$0.000001 \times 0.001 = 10^{-6} \times 10^{-3} = 10^{-6+(-3)} = 10^{-6-3} = 10^{-9}$$

EXAMPLE 3   Multiply 23,000 by 7,000.

SOLUTION $23,000 = 2.3 \times 10^4$ and $7,000 = 7 \times 10^3$

Then $23,000 \times 7,000 = 2.3 \times 10^4 \times 7 \times 10^3$

$$= 2.3 \times 7 \times 10^7$$

$$= 16.1 \times 10^7, \text{ or } 161,000,000$$

EXAMPLE 4   Multiply 0.000037 by 600.

SOLUTION $0.000037 \times 600 = 3.7 \times 10^{-5} \times 6 \times 10^2$

$$= 3.7 \times 6 \times 10^{-3}$$

$$= 22.2 \times 10^{-3}, \text{ or } 0.0222$$

EXAMPLE 5   Multiply $72,000 \times 0.000025 \times 4,600$.

SOLUTION $72,000 \times 0.000025 \times 4,600$

$$= 7.2 \times 10^4 \times 2.5 \times 10^{-5} \times 4.6 \times 10^3$$

$$= 7.2 \times 2.5 \times 4.6 \times 10^2$$

$$= 82.8 \times 10^2, \text{ or } 8,280$$

You will find that by expressing all numbers between 1 and 10 times the proper power of 10, the determination of the proper place for the decimal point will become a matter of inspection.

PROBLEMS 10-2

Multiply the following. Although all factors are not expressed to three significant figures, express answers to three significant figures as numbers between 1 and 10 times the proper power of 10:

1   $0.001 \times 10,000 \times 0.01$ 2 $1,000 \times 0.000001 \times 10^6$

3   $0.0005 \times 96,000$ 4 $0.00025 \times 12 \times 10^{-6} \times 19 \times 10^2$

5   $452,000 \times 0.00035 \times 0.000013$

6   $0.432 \times 8,350,000 \times 10^{-3} \times 5.63 \times 10^3$

7   $0.0000387 \times 10^{-5} \times 0.076 \times 10^6 \times 81,000,000$

8   $934,000 \times 6.28 \times 10^{12} \times 0.00000053 \times 10^{-5}$

9   $377 \times 10^8 \times 159,000 \times 10^6 \times 0.00075 \times 10^{-9}$

10   $0.00462 \times 0.000055 \times 10^{-3} \times 103 \times 10^{-6} \times 0.00000814 \times 10^{12}$

The alternating-current inductive reactance of a circuit or an inductor is given by $X_L = 2\pi f L$ Ω, in which X_L is the inductive reactance in ohms, f is the frequency of the alternating current in cycles per second, and L is the inductance of the circuit, or inductor, in henrys. Compute the inductive reactances when:

11   $f = 60$ cycles, $L = 10$ henrys

12   $f = 400$ cycles, $L = 0.5$ henry

13   $f = 800$ cycles, $L = 0.25$ henry

14   $f = 100,000$ cycles, $L = 0.0015$ henry

15   $f = 14,000,000$ cycles, $L = 0.0000035$ henry

10 – 8   Division with powers of 10

The law of exponents in division (Secs. 9–9 to 9–11) can be summed
up in the following general form:

$$\frac{a^m}{a^n} = a^{m-n} \qquad (\text{where } a \neq 0)$$

EXAMPLE 6 $\dfrac{10^5}{10^3} = 10^{5-3} = 10^2$

or $\dfrac{10^5}{10^3} = 10^5 \times 10^{-3} = 10^2$

EXAMPLE 7 $\dfrac{72{,}000}{0.0008} = \dfrac{72 \times 10^3}{8 \times 10^{-4}} = \dfrac{72}{8} \times 10^{3+4} = 9 \times 10^7$

or $\dfrac{72{,}000}{0.0008} = \dfrac{72 \times 10^3}{8 \times 10^{-4}} = \dfrac{72}{8} \times 10^3 \times 10^4 = 9 \times 10^7$

EXAMPLE 8 $\dfrac{169 \times 10^5}{13 \times 10^5} = \dfrac{169}{13} \times 10^{5-5} = 13 \times 10^0 = 13 \times 1 = 13$

or $\dfrac{169 \times \cancel{10^5}}{13 \times \cancel{10^5}} = 13$

It is apparent that powers of 10 which are factors and have the
same exponents in numerator and denominator can be canceled.
Also, you will note that powers of 10 which are factors can be transferred at will from denominator to numerator, or vice versa, if the
sign of the exponent is changed when the transfer is made (Sec. 9–11).

10 – 9   Combined multiplication and division

This is most conveniently accomplished by alternately multiplying
and dividing until the problem is completed.

EXAMPLE 9   Simplify

$$\frac{0.000644 \times 96{,}000 \times 3{,}300}{161{,}000 \times 0.00000120}$$

SOLUTION   First convert all numbers in the problem to numbers between
1 and 10 times their proper power of 10, thus:

$$\frac{6.44 \times 10^{-4} \times 9.6 \times 10^4 \times 3.3 \times 10^3}{1.61 \times 10^5 \times 1.2 \times 10^{-6}} = \frac{6.44 \times 9.6 \times 3.3 \times 10^4}{1.61 \times 1.2}$$

The problem as now written consists of multiplication and division of simple
numbers. If the remainder of the problem is solved by slide rule, rough
multiplication and division can be carried along mentally with no danger of
misplacing the decimal point. If the problem is solved without the aid of
a slide rule, there are no small decimals and no cumbersome large numbers
to handle.

Instead of first finding the product of the numerator and dividing it by the product of the denominator, it is best to divide and multiply alternately. Thus, we divide 6.44 by 1.61 to obtain 4. Then we multiply this 4 by 9.6 to obtain 38.4. The 38.4 is then divided by 1.2, which results in a quotient of 32. Finally, 32 is multiplied by 3.3, which results in a product of 105.6. Because we still have a factor of 10^4, the answer is 105.6×10^4. If we desire to express the answer in powers of 10, it would be written 1.056×10^6, but written out, without the power of 10, it would be 1,056,000.

The method of alternately dividing and multiplying offers the slide-rule operator the advantage of working the problem straight through without the necessity of jotting down the product of the factors of the numerator before proceeding to find the product of the denominator factors.

10 – 10 Reciprocals

In radio and electrical problems, many formulas are used that involve reciprocals, such as

$$\frac{1}{R_t} = \frac{1}{R_1} + \frac{1}{R_2}$$

$$X_C = \frac{1}{2\pi f C}$$

$$f = \frac{1}{2\pi \sqrt{LC}}$$

The *reciprocal* of a number is 1 divided by that number. Such problems present no difficulty if the powers of 10 are used properly.

EXAMPLE 10   Simplify $\dfrac{1}{40,000 \times 0.00025 \times 125 \times 10^{-6}}$

SOLUTION   First convert all numbers in the denominator to numbers between 1 and 10 times their proper power of 10, thus:

$$\frac{1}{4 \times 10^4 \times 2.5 \times 10^{-4} \times 1.25 \times 10^{-4}} = \frac{10^4}{4 \times 2.5 \times 1.25}$$

Multiplying the factors of the denominator results in

$$\frac{10^4}{12.5}$$

Instead of writing out the numerator as 10,000 and then dividing by 12.5, the numerator is written as two factors in order better to divide mentally. The problem can be written

$$\frac{10^2 \times 10^2}{12.5} \text{ or } \frac{100}{12.5} \times 10^2 = 8 \times 10^2$$

This method is of particular advantage to the slide-rule operator because of the ease of estimating the number of figures in the final result.

If the final result is a decimal, rewriting the numerator into two factors allows fixing the decimal point with the least effort.

EXAMPLE 11   Simplify $\dfrac{1}{625 \times 10^4 \times 2{,}000 \times 64{,}000}$

SOLUTION   First convert all numbers in the denominator to numbers between 1 and 10 times their proper power of 10, thus:

$$\frac{1}{6.25 \times 10^6 \times 2 \times 10^3 \times 6.4 \times 10^4} = \frac{10^{-13}}{6.25 \times 2 \times 6.4}$$

Multiplying the factors in the denominator results in

$$\frac{10^{-13}}{80}$$

Instead of writing out the numerator as 0.0000000000001 and dividing it by 80, the numerator is written as two factors in order better to divide mentally. The problem can be written as follows:

$$\frac{10^2 \times 10^{-15}}{80} \text{ or } \frac{100}{80} \times 10^{-15} = 1.25 \times 10^{-15}$$

If the value of the denominator product was over 100 and less than 1,000, we should break up the numerator so that one of the factors would be 10^3 or 1,000, and so on. This method will always result in a final quotient of a number between 1 and 10 times the proper power of 10.

PROBLEMS 10 – 3

Perform the indicated operations. Round off the figures in the results, if necessary, and express answers to three significant figures as a number between 1 and 10 times the proper power of 10.

1 $\dfrac{0.000600}{12{,}000}$

2 $\dfrac{102{,}000}{0.000034}$

3 $\dfrac{4{,}914{,}000}{0.0078 \times 63{,}000}$

4 $\dfrac{0.000256 \times 0.000000338}{865{,}000{,}000}$

5 $\dfrac{156{,}000 \times 10^4 \times 248 \times 10^6}{67 \times 10^{-3}}$

6 $\dfrac{704 \times 10^{-6} \times 485{,}000 \times 10^3}{573 \times 10^{-8} \times 6.28 \times 10^{12}}$

7 $\dfrac{159 \times 10^3}{90 \times 10^{-6} \times 375 \times 10^{-12}}$

8 $\dfrac{1}{6.28 \times 60 \times 25 \times 10^{-6}}$

9 $\dfrac{1}{6.28 \times 2{,}500 \times 10^3 \times 0.00025 \times 10^{-6}}$

10 $\dfrac{1}{6.28 \times 400 \times 10^{12} \times 50 \times 10^{-12}}$

The alternating-current capacitive reactance of a circuit, or capacitor, is given by $X_C = \dfrac{1}{2\pi fC}$ Ω, in which X_C is the capacitive reactance in ohms, f is the frequency of the alternating current in cycles per second, and C is the capacitance of the circuit, or capacitor, in farads. Compute the capacitive reactances when:

11 $f = 60$ cycles, $C = 0.000004$ farad

12 $f = 800$ cycles, $C = 0.0000015$ farad

13 $f = 1,000,000$ cycles, $C = 0.0000000005$ farad

14 $f = 28,000,000$ cycles, $C = 0.000000000025$ farad

15 $f = 144,000,000$ cycles, $C = 0.000000000002$ farad

–11 The power of a power

It becomes necessary, in order to work a variety of problems utilizing the powers of 10, to consider a few new definitions concerning the laws of exponents before we study them in algebra. This, however, should present no difficulty.

In finding the power of a power the exponents are multiplied. That is, in general,

$$(a^m)^n = a^{mn} \qquad \text{(where } a \neq 0)$$

EXAMPLE 12 $\qquad (100)^3 = 100 \times 100 \times 100 = 1,000,000 = 10^6$

or $\qquad\qquad\ (100)^3 = 10^2 \times 10^2 \times 10^2 = 10^6$

Then $\qquad\qquad (100)^3 = (10^2)^3 = 10^{2 \times 3} = 10^6$

Numbers can be factored when raised to a power in order to reduce the labor in obtaining the correct number of significant figures, or properly fixing the decimal point.

EXAMPLE 13 $\qquad (19,000)^3 = (1.9 \times 10^4)^3$

$\qquad\qquad\qquad\qquad\ = (1.9)^3 \times 10^{4 \times 3} = 6.859 \times 10^{12}$

EXAMPLE 14 $\qquad (0.0000075)^2 = (7.5 \times 10^{-6})^2 = (7.5)^2 \times 10^{(-6) \times 2}$

$\qquad\qquad\qquad\qquad\qquad = 56.25 \times 10^{-12} = 5.625 \times 10^{-11}$

In Example 13, 19,000 was factored into 1.9×10^4 in order to allow an easy mental check. Because 1.9 is nearly 2 and $2^3 = 8$, it is apparent that the result of cubing 1.9 must be 6.859, not 0.6859 or 68.59.

In Example 14, the 0.0000075 was factored for the same reason. We know that $7^2 = 49$; therefore the result of squaring 7.5 must be 56.25, not 0.5625 or 5.625.

10 – 12   The power of a product

The power of a product is the same as the product of the powers of the factors. That is, in general,

$$(abc)^m = a^m b^m c^m$$

EXAMPLE 15 $(10^5 \times 10^3)^3 = 10^{5 \times 3} \times 10^{3 \times 3}$
$$= 10^{15} \times 10^9 = 10^{24}$$

or $(10^5 \times 10^3)^3 = (10^8)^3 = 10^{8 \times 3} = 10^{24}$

10 – 13   The power of a fraction

The power of a fraction equals the power of the numerator divided by the power of the denominator. That is,

$$\left(\frac{a}{b}\right)^m = \frac{a^m}{b^m}$$

EXAMPLE 16 $\left(\dfrac{10^5}{10^3}\right)^2 = \dfrac{10^{5 \times 2}}{10^{3 \times 2}} = \dfrac{10^{10}}{10^6} = 10^4$

The above can be solved by first clearing the exponents inside the parentheses and then raising to the required power. Thus,

$$\left(\frac{10^5}{10^3}\right)^2 = (10^{5-3})^2 = (10^2)^2 = 10^4$$

10 – 14   The root of a power

The root of a power in exponents is given by

$$\sqrt[n]{a^m} = a^{m \div n} \quad \text{(where } a \neq 0\text{)}$$

EXAMPLE 17 $\sqrt{25 \times 10^8} = \sqrt{25} \times \sqrt{10^8} = 5 \times 10^{8 \div 2} = 5 \times 10^4$
EXAMPLE 18 $\sqrt[3]{125 \times 10^6} = \sqrt[3]{125} \times \sqrt[3]{10^6} = 5 \times 10^{6 \div 3} = 5 \times 10^2$

In the general case where m is evenly divisible by n, the process of extracting roots is comparatively simple. When m is not evenly divisible by n, the result obtained by extracting the root is a fractional power.

EXAMPLE 19 $\sqrt{10^5} = 10^{5 \div 2} = 10^{\frac{5}{2}}$, or $10^{2.5}$

Such fractional exponents are encountered in various phases of engineering mathematics and are conveniently solved by the use of logarithms. However, in using the powers of 10, the fractional exponent is cumbersome for obtaining a final answer. It becomes necessary, therefore, to devise some means of extracting a root whereby an integer can be obtained as an exponent in the final result.

This is accomplished by expressing the number, the root of which is desired, as some number times the proper power of 10, the power of 10 being evenly divisible by the index of the required root. As an example, suppose it is desired to extract the square root of 400,000. Though it is true that

$$\sqrt{400,000} = \sqrt{4 \times 10^5} = \sqrt{4} \times \sqrt{10^5} = 2 \times 10^{2.5}$$

we have a fractional exponent that is not readily reduced to actual figures. However, if we express the number differently, we obtain an integer as an exponent. Thus,

$$\sqrt{400,000} = \sqrt{40 \times 10^4} = \sqrt{40} \times \sqrt{10^4} = 6.32 \times 10^2$$

It will be noted that there are a number of ways of expressing the above square root, such as

$$\sqrt{400,000} = \sqrt{0.4 \times 10^6}$$
or
$$\sqrt{4,000 \times 10^2}$$
or
$$\sqrt{0.004 \times 10^8}$$

All are equally correct, but you should try to write the problem in a form that will allow a rough mental approximation in order that the decimal may be properly placed with respect to the significant figures.

PROBLEMS 10 – 4

Perform the indicated operations. Where answers do not come out in round numbers, express to three significant figures.

1 $(10^5)^2$

2 $(10^3 \times 10^4)^3$

3 $(10^{-4})^2$

4 $(6 \times 10^{-4})^2$

5 $(3 \times 10^3)^4$

6 $(8 \times 10^{-3})^3$

7 $(5 \times 10^3 \times 3 \times 10^{-2})^2$

8 $\left(\dfrac{6 \times 10^3}{2 \times 10^2}\right)^3$

9 $\sqrt{0.0009 \times 0.0036}$

10 $\sqrt{0.00064 \times 0.016}$

11 $\sqrt{49 \times 10^3 \times 25 \times 10^{-3}}$

12 $\sqrt[3]{27 \times 10^{-3} \times 64 \times 10^6}$

13 $\left(\dfrac{87 \times 10^4 \times 34 \times 10^{-3}}{0.0000013}\right)^2$

14 $\dfrac{1}{6.28\sqrt{25 \times 10^{-2} \times 10^{-9}}}$

15 $\dfrac{1}{6.28\sqrt{45 \times 10^{-6} \times 2.5 \times 10^{-10}}}$

The resonant frequency of a circuit is given by $f = \dfrac{1}{2\pi\sqrt{LC}}$ cps

where f = frequency in cycles per second

L = inductance of circuit in henrys

C = capacitance of circuit in farads

Compute the resonant frequencies when:

16 $L = 30$ henrys, $C = 0.0000001$ farad

17 $L = 4$ henrys, $C = 0.00000001$ farad

18 $L = 50 \times 10^{-5}$ henry, $C = 4 \times 10^{-10}$ farad

19 $L = 50 \times 10^{-6}$ henry, $C = 0.00025 \times 10^{-6}$ farad

20 $L = 0.245 \times 10^{-6}$ henry, $C = 5 \times 10^{-12}$ farad

CHAPTER 11
UNITS AND DIMENSIONS

As previously stated, the solution of every practical problem, where a concrete answer is desired, eventually reduces to an arithmetical computation; that is, the answer reduces to some *number*. In order for this answer, or number, to have a concrete meaning, it must be expressed in some *unit*. For example, if you were told that the resistance of a circuit is 16, the information would have no meaning unless you knew to what unit the 16 referred.

From the foregoing it is apparent that the expression for the magnitude of any physical quantity must consist of two parts. The first part, which is a number, specifies "how much"; the second part specifies the unit of measurement, or "what," for example, 16 Ω, 20 amp, 100 ft, etc.

It is necessary, therefore, before beginning the study of circuits, to define a few of the more common electrical and dimensional units used in electrical and electronics engineering.

1 – 1   The volt

The *volt* is the practical unit of electromotive force (emf), or electric potential. It is that potential which will cause a current of 1 ampere to flow through a resistance of 1 ohm.

11 – 2   The ampere

The *ampere* is the practical unit of electric current. It is that amount of current which will flow through a resistance of 1 ohm when a potential of 1 volt is applied across the resistance.

11 – 3   The ohm

The *ohm* is the practical unit of resistance. It is that amount of resistance which will permit 1 ampere to flow at a potential difference of 1 volt.

11 – 4   The mho

The *mho* is the unit of conductance. It is the reciprocal of resistance; that is, the relation between conductance G and resistance R is given by

$$G = \frac{1}{R} \quad \text{mhos}$$

If the resistance is thought of as representing the *difficulty* with which an electric current is forced through a circuit, the conductivity may be thought of as the *ease* with which an electric current may be forced through the same circuit. Note that the word "mho" is simply "ohm" spelled backward.

11 – 5   The watt

The *watt* is the unit of electrical power. In direct-current circuits the power in watts is the product of the voltage times the current, or

$$P = EI \quad \text{watts}$$

11 – 6   The henry

The *henry* is the unit of inductance. A circuit, or inductor, is said to have a self-inductance of 1 henry when a counter electromotive force of 1 volt is generated by a rate of change of current of 1 ampere per second.

11 – 7   The farad

The *farad* is the unit of capacitance. A circuit, or capacitor, is said to have a capacitance of 1 farad when a change of 1 volt per second across it produces a current of 1 ampere.

1 – 8   Frequency

A current that reverses itself at regular intervals is called an *alternating current*. When this current rises from zero to maximum, returns to zero, increases to maximum in the opposite direction, and finally falls to zero again, it is said to have completed one *cycle*. The number of times this cycle is repeated in 1 second is known as the *frequency* of the alternating current. Thus the average house current is 60 cycles per second. The frequency of radio waves may be as high as many millions of cycles per second.

1 – 9   Ranges of units

As stated in Sec. 10–5, the fields of communication and electrical engineering embrace extremely wide ranges in values of the foregoing units. For example, at the input of a radio receiver, we deal in millionths of a volt, whereas the output circuit of a transmitter may develop hundreds of thousands of volts. An electric clock might consume a fraction of a watt, whereas the powerhouse furnishing this power probably has a capability of millions of watts.

Furthermore, two of these units, the henry and the farad, are very large units, especially the latter. The average radio receiver employs inductances ranging from a few millionths of a henry, as represented by tuning inductance, to several henrys for power filters. The farad is so large that even the largest capacitors are rated in millionths of a farad. Smaller capacitors used in radio circuits are often rated in terms of so many millionths of one-millionth of a farad.

The use of some power of 10 is very convenient in converting to larger multiples or smaller fractions of the basic so-called *practical* units.

– 10   Milliunits

The *milliunit* is one-thousandth of a unit. Thus, 1 volt is equal to 1,000 millivolts, 500 milliamperes is equal to 0.5 ampere, etc. This unit is commonly used in connection with volts, amperes, henrys, and watts. It is abbreviated m. Thus, 10 mh = 10 millihenrys.*

– 11   Microunits

The *microunit* is one-millionth of a unit. Thus, 1 ampere is equal to 1,000,000, or 10^6, microamperes; 2,000,000 microfarads is equal to 2

*See Table 3 in the Appendix for abbreviations.

farads, etc. This unit is commonly used in connection with volts, amperes, ohms, mhos, henrys, and farads. It is represented by μ. Thus, 5 μf means 5 microfarads.

In some electrical texts, it will be noted, the term *microfarad* is abbreviated Mfd; also some capacitors are marked in the same manner. This is simply an abbreviation for microfarad. The preferred abbreviation is μf.

11 – 12   Micromicrounits

The *micromicrounit* is one-millionth of one-millionth of a unit. Thus, 1 farad is equal to 1,000,000,000,000, or 10^{12}, micromicrofarads. This unit is seldom used for other than farads. It is represented by $\mu\mu$. Thus, 250 $\mu\mu$f means 250 micromicrofarads.

11 – 13   Kilounits

The *kilounit* is 1,000 basic units. Thus, 1 kilovolt is equal to 1,000 volts. This unit is commonly used with cycles, volts, amperes, ohms, watts, and volt-amperes. It is abbreviated k. Thus, 35 kw means 35 kilowatts; 2,000 cycles = 2 kc (2 kilocycles per second).

11 – 14   Megunits

The *megunit* is 1,000,000, or 10^6, basic units. Thus, 1 megohm is equal to 10^6 ohms. This unit is used mainly with ohms and cycles. It is represented by M. Thus, 3,000,000 cycles = 3,000 kc = 3 Mc.

11 – 15   Conversion factors

Although Table 4 of the Appendix consists of conversion factors, Table 11-1 is included here to enable you to see the whole picture of unit conversion in simplified form.

TABLE 11 – 1

Multiply	By	To obtain
Micromicrounits	10^{-6}	Microunits
Micromicrounits	10^{-9}	Milliunits
Micromicrounits	10^{-12}	Units
Microunits	10^6	Micromicrounits
Microunits	10^{-3}	Milliunits
Microunits	10^{-6}	Units
Milliunits	10^9	Micromicrounits
Milliunits	10^3	Microunits

Milliunits	10^{-3}	Units
Units	10^{12}	Micromicrounits
Units	10^6	Microunits
Units	10^3	Milliunits
Units	10^{-3}	Kilounits
Units	10^{-6}	Megunits
Kilounits	10^3	Units
Kilounits	10^{-3}	Megunits
Megunits	10^6	Units
Megunits	10^3	Kilounits

EXAMPLE 1 Convert 8 μf to farads.

SOLUTION $8 \, \mu f = 8 \times 10^{-6} \text{ farad}$

EXAMPLE 2 Convert 250 ma to amperes.

SOLUTION $250 \text{ ma} = 250 \times 10^{-3} \text{ amp} = 2.50 \times 10^{-1} \text{ amp}$

or $= 0.250 \text{ amp}$

EXAMPLE 3 Convert 1,500 watts to kilowatts.

SOLUTION $1,500 \text{ watts} = 1,500 \times 10^{-3} \text{ kw}$

or $= 1.5 \text{ kw}$

EXAMPLE 4 Convert 200,000 Ω to megohms.

SOLUTION $200,000 \, \Omega = 200,000 \times 10^{-6} \text{ M}\Omega = 0.2 \text{ M}\Omega$

EXAMPLE 5 Convert 2,500 kc to megacycles.

SOLUTION $2,500 \text{ kc} = 2,500 \times 10^{-3} \text{ Mc} = 2.500 \text{ Mc}$

EXAMPLE 6 Convert 0.000450 mho to micromhos.

SOLUTION $0.000450 \text{ mho} = 0.000450 \times 10^6 \text{ } \mu\text{mhos}$

or $= 450 \text{ } \mu\text{mhos}$

EXAMPLE 7 Convert 5 μsec to seconds.

SOLUTION $5 \, \mu\text{sec} = 5 \times 10^{-6} \text{ sec}$

PROBLEMS 11 – 1

Express answers as numbers between 1 and 10 times the proper power of 10:

1 65 volts =   (a)_____mv?   (b)_____μv?   (c)_____kv?

2 5.25 amp =   (a)_____ma?   (b)_____μa?

3 0.45 volt =   (a)_____kv?   (b)_____μv?   (c)_____mv?

4 75 ma =   (a)_____μa?   (b)_____amp?

5 2,500 Ω =   (a)_____kΩ?   (b)_____MΩ?   (c)_____mho?

6 5 μf =   (a)_____μμf?   (b)_____farad?

7	200 $\mu\mu$f =	(a)_____farad?	(b)_____μf?	
8	25 henrys =	(a)_____mh?	(b)_____μh?	
9	125 watts =	(a)_____kw?	(b)_____mw?	(c)_____μw?
10	3.5 sec =	(a)_____msec?	(b)_____μsec?	
11	1,500 kc =	(a)_____cps?	(b)_____Mc?	
12	50 kΩ =	(a)_____Ω?	(b)_____mho?	(c)_____MΩ?
13	600 mw =	(a)_____watts?	(b)_____kw?	
14	150 μh =	(a)_____mh?	(b)_____henrys?	
15	15,000 cps =	(a)_____Mc?	(b)_____kc?	
16	5 μsec =	(a)_____sec?	(b)_____msec?	
17	0.045 amp =	(a)_____μa?	(b)_____ma?	
18	6.6 kv =	(a)_____volts?	(b)_____Mv?	(c)_____mv?
19	3.2 MΩ =	(a)_____Ω?	(b)_____kΩ?	
20	0.25 kw =	(a)_____watts?	(b)_____mw?	(c)_____μw?
21	2,250 mh =	(a)_____μh?	(b)_____henry?	
22	440 Mc =	(a)_____kc?	(b)_____cps?	
23	0.00025 μf =	(a)_____$\mu\mu$f?	(b)_____farad?	
24	500 msec =	(a)_____μsec?	(b)_____sec?	
25	0.005 mho =	(a)_____μmho?	(b)_____Ω?	
26	2,500 μmhos =	(a)_____mho?	(b)_____Ω?	
27	6,750 μa =	(a)_____amp?	(b)_____ma?	
28	0.01 kv =	(a)_____volts?	(b)_____mv?	
29	10 Mw =	(a)_____watts?	(b)_____kw?	
30	28,100 kc =	(a)_____cps?	(b)_____Mc?	

11 – 16   Systems of measurement

The practical electrical units previously discussed are more or less
international in scope. However, other physical units, such as those
for the measurement of length, are expressed in two systems which
are known as the *metric system* and the *English system*. Although the
English system is widely used in the United States and other English-
speaking countries, it is essential that the technical man be familiar
with both systems and be able to convert from one to the other.

11 – 17   Metric system

In the metric system the standard unit of length is the *meter*, which
was originally intended to be one-millionth of the distance from the
Equator to the North Pole, measured along a meridian. The meter
is sometimes abbreviated m. Other units of length related to the
meter are

$$1 \text{ millimeter (mm)} = \frac{1}{1,000} \text{ meter} = 10^{-3} \text{ meter}$$

$$1 \text{ centimeter (cm)} = \frac{1}{100} \text{ meter} = 10^{-2} \text{ meter}$$

$$1 \text{ kilometer (km)} = 1,000 \text{ meters} = 10^{3} \text{ meters}$$

-18 English system

In the English system the standard unit of length is the *yard*, which is a length of 3 ft. Some of the relations between units are

$$12 \text{ inches (in.)} = 1 \text{ foot (ft)}$$
$$3 \text{ feet (ft)} = 1 \text{ yard (yd)}$$
$$5,280 \text{ feet (ft)} = 1 \text{ statute mile}$$

-19 Relations between systems

Since the metric system is based on a decimal plan and the English system is not, there is no one numerical factor or constant that can be used for conversion from one system of length units to the other. Although Table 4 in the Appendix contains a number of conversion factors, a few approximate length equivalents are given for convenience:

$$1 \text{ in.} = 2.540 \text{ cm}$$
$$1 \text{ ft} = 0.3048 \text{ meter}$$
$$1 \text{ mile} = 1.609 \text{ km}$$
$$1 \text{ meter} = 39.37 \text{ in.}$$
$$1 \text{ km} = 0.6214 \text{ mile}$$

-20 Computations with units

When computations are performed with units, they can be added, subtracted, multiplied, and divided like *literal algebraic factors* to obtain the units in which the final results are expressed.

EXAMPLE 8 $3 \Omega + 6 \Omega = 9 \Omega$

230 volts $-$ 115 volts $=$ 115 volts

EXAMPLE 9 $2 \text{ ft} \times 4 \text{ ft} = 2 \times 4 \times \text{ft} \times \text{ft} = 8 \text{ ft}^2 = 8 \text{ sq ft}$

$3 \text{ ft} \times 5 \text{ ft} \times 2 \text{ ft} = 3 \times 5 \times 2 \times \text{ft} \times \text{ft} \times \text{ft} = 30 \text{ ft}^3$
$$= 30 \text{ cu ft}$$

$6 \text{ meters} \times 10 \text{ meters} = 6 \times 10 \times \text{meters} \times \text{meters}$
$$= 60 \text{ meters}^2 = 60 \text{ sq meters}$$

$$\frac{18 \text{ sq ft}}{3 \text{ ft}} = \frac{18 \text{ ft}^2}{3 \text{ ft}} = 6 \text{ ft}$$

When a ratio between identical units is expressed, such as $\dfrac{60 \text{ ft}}{12 \text{ ft}}$, the units cancel and the result of the division becomes only a number with no dimension.

EXAMPLE 10 $\dfrac{60 \text{ ft}}{12 \text{ ft}} = \dfrac{60 \text{ ft}}{12 \text{ ft}} = 5$

When quantities having different units are multiplied or divided, the result must express the operation.

EXAMPLE 11 $4 \text{ ft} \times 5 \text{ lb} = 4 \times 5 \times \text{ft} \times \text{lb} = 20 \text{ ft-lb}$

EXAMPLE 12 $\dfrac{30 \text{ ft}}{10 \text{ sec}} = \dfrac{30 \text{ ft}}{10 \text{ sec}} = 3 \dfrac{\text{ft}}{\text{sec}} = 3 \text{ ft/sec} = 3 \text{ fps}$

EXAMPLE 13 $\dfrac{45 \ \Omega}{15 \text{ ft}} = \dfrac{45 \ \Omega}{15 \text{ ft}} = 3 \dfrac{\Omega}{\text{ft}} = 3 \ \Omega/\text{ft}$

In Example 12 above, note that ft/sec is read as "feet per second," and in Example 13, Ω/ft is read as "ohms per foot." "Per" means *divided by*.

Thus the equivalent lengths stated in Sec. 11–19 can be expressed respectively as follows:

> **There are 2.540 cm/in.**
> **There is 0.3048 meter/ft.**
> **There are 1.609 km/mile.**
> **There are 39.37 in./meter.**
> **There is 0.6214 mile/km.**

Utilizing relations in such form whereby units are treated mathematically as literal factors facilitates conversions and assures that results will be obtained with correct units.

EXAMPLE 14   Convert 3 in. to centimeters.

SOLUTION $3 \text{ in.} \times 2.54 \dfrac{\text{cm}}{\text{in.}} = 3 \times 2.54 \cdot \text{in.} \cdot \dfrac{\text{cm}}{\text{in.}} = 7.62 \text{ cm}$

EXAMPLE 15   How many meters are there in 236 ft?

SOLUTION $236 \text{ ft} \times 0.3048 \dfrac{\text{meter}}{\text{ft}} = 236 \times 0.3048 \cdot \text{ft} \cdot \dfrac{\text{meter}}{\text{ft}}$

$= 71.93 \text{ meters}$

EXAMPLE 16   A certain resistance wire has a resistance of 3 Ω/ft. What is the resistance of 6 ft of this wire?

SOLUTION $3 \dfrac{\Omega}{\text{ft}} \times 6 \text{ ft} = 3 \times 6 \cdot \dfrac{\Omega}{\text{ft}} \cdot \text{ft} = 18 \ \Omega$

EXAMPLE 17   Convert 1,500 kilocycles per second to cycles per second.

SOLUTION   There are 10^3 cycles per kilocycle; that is, $10^3 \dfrac{\text{cycles}}{\text{kc}}$. Then

$$1,500 \frac{\text{kc}}{\text{sec}} \times 10^3 \frac{\text{cycles}}{\text{sec}} = 1,500 \times 10^3 \frac{\cancel{\text{kc}}}{\text{sec}} \cdot \frac{\text{cycles}}{\cancel{\text{kc}}}$$

$$= 1.5 \times 10^6 \text{ cycles/sec}$$

EXAMPLE 18   The wavelength λ of a radio wave in meters, the frequency f of the wave in cycles per second, and the velocity of propagation c in meters per second are related to one another by the formula

$$\lambda = \frac{3 \times 10^8}{f} \quad \text{meters}$$

Derive a formula for wavelength expressed in feet.

SOLUTION   Since there are 3.28 ft/meter, this factor must be applied to express λ in feet. Thus,

$$\lambda = \frac{3 \times 10^8}{f} \text{ meters} \times 3.28 \frac{\text{ft}}{\text{meter}}$$

$$= \frac{3 \times 3.28 \times 10^8}{f} \cdot \text{meter} \cdot \frac{\text{ft}}{\text{meter}} = \frac{9.84 \times 10^8}{f} \text{ ft}$$

EXAMPLE 19   Using the formula $\lambda = \dfrac{3 \times 10^8}{f}$ meters, derive a formula for wavelength in meters when the frequency is expressed in megacycles.

SOLUTION   In the above formula f is expressed in cycles and it is desired to express the frequency in megacycles. Since Mc = cycles $\times 10^6$, this is substituted for f in the formula. Thus,

$$\lambda = \frac{3 \times 10^8}{f \times 10^6} \text{ meters} = \frac{3 \times 10^2}{\text{Mc}} \text{ meters} = \frac{300}{\text{Mc}} \text{ meters}$$

PROBLEMS 11-2

1   3 yd   = (a)_____in.?   (b)_____cm?   (c)_____mm?
2   3.5 meters = (a)_____ft?   (b)_____yd?   (c)_____km?
3   205 cm   = (a)_____in.?   (b)_____yd?   (c)_____meters?
4   3 miles   = (a)_____km?   (b)_____ft?   (c)_____cm?
5   4.63 km   = (a)_____miles?   (b)_____meters? (c)_____yd?
6   An automobile is traveling at a rate of 60 mph. What is its speed in feet per second?
7   The wavelength of radio waves at a frequency of 300 Mc is 10 cm. What is this wavelength in inches?
8   The diameter of No. 10 wire is 0.102 in. What is its radius in centimeters?
9   A power line 90 miles long was measured and found to have an inductance of 0.337 henry. What is the inductance per mile?
10   The capacitance of a certain power line is 8.02×10^{-3} μf/mile. What is the capacitance per kilometer?
11   A length of waveguide 125 ft long was found to have an attenuation loss of 1.5 db. What is the attenuation in decibels per 100 ft?

12   A certain grade of twisted-pair transmission line has a loss of 6.4 db per 100 ft. What is the loss in decibels per meter?

13   The high-frequency resistance of No. 10 copper wire at a frequency of 100 Mc is 0.00321 Ω/cm. What is the resistance of 3 ft of this wire at the same frequency?

14   The capacitive reactance of a circuit, or capacitor, is given by $X_C = \dfrac{1}{2\pi f C}$ Ω, in which X_C is the capacitive reactance in ohms, f is the frequency in cycles, and C is the capacitance of the circuit, or capacitor, in farads. Show that $X_C = \dfrac{159 \times 10^3}{fC}$ when f is in megacycles and C is in micro-microfarads.

15   Referring to Prob. 14, what is the capacitive reactance of a capacitor of 0.00025 μf at a frequency of 1,000 Mc?

16   The inductive reactance of a circuit, or inductor, can be computed by the formula $X_L = 2\pi f L$ Ω, where X_L is the inductive reactance in ohms, f is the frequency in cycles, and L is the inductance of the circuit, or inductor, in henrys. Derive a formula for X_L in ohms when f is in megacycles and L is in microhenrys.

17   Referring to Prob. 16, a video amplifier coil has an inductance of 30 μh. What is the inductive reactance of the coil at a frequency of 4 Mc?

18   The resonant frequency of any circuit is $f = \dfrac{1}{2\pi\sqrt{LC}}$ cps, in which f is the frequency in cycles, L is the inductance of the circuit in henrys, and C is the capacitance of the circuit in farads. Derive a formula for f expressed in megacycles when L is in microhenrys and C is in micromicrofarads.

19   Referring to Prob. 18, what is the resonant frequency of a circuit with an inductance of 0.5 μh and a capacitance of 8 $\mu\mu$f?

20   In ordinary copper conductors used for transmission lines the depth of penetration δ of high-frequency currents is stated by the formula $\delta = \dfrac{6.62}{\sqrt{f}}$ cm, where f is the frequency in cycles. Derive a formula for current penetration in inches when the frequency is in megacycles.

21   Referring to Prob. 20, to what depth in inches will a current of 3,000 Mc penetrate a copper conductor?

22   The high-frequency resistance R_{ac} in ohms per centimeter of round copper wire or tubing can be computed by the formula $R_{ac} = 83.2 \times 10^{-9}\dfrac{\sqrt{f}}{d}$ Ω/cm, where f is the frequency in cycles and d is the outside diameter of the conductor in centimeters. From this derive a formula expressing R_{ac} in ohms per foot when the frequency is in megacycles and the diameter is in inches.

23 Referring to Prob. 22, No. 10 wire has a diameter of 0.102 in.   What is
    the resistance per foot at a frequency of 85 Mc?

24 Using the formula in Example 18 show that $\lambda = \dfrac{3 \times 10^4}{f}$ cm when f is in
    megacycles.

25 Using the formula in Example 18 derive a formula for wavelength in
    inches when f is in megacycles.

26 The mid-frequency of television channel 6 is 85 Mc.   Using the formula
    derived in Prob. 25, what is the length of one wavelength in inches?

FIG. 11–1 Dipole antenna.

27 The great majority of television receiving antennas consists of various
    combinations of dipoles.   A dipole antenna is one that is approximately
    one-half wavelength long, such as the one illustrated in Fig. 11-1.   The
    actual length is slightly less than a half wave owing to "end effect"
    caused by the capacitance of the antenna, and it has been determined
    that dipoles used for television reception should be approximately 6 per
    cent shorter than one-half wavelength.   Using the formula in Prob. 25,
    derive a formula for the length of a dipole antenna in inches when the
    frequency is in megacycles.

28 The mid-frequency of television channel 4 is 69 Mc.   Using the formula
    derived in Prob. 27, what length would you make a receiving antenna for
    this channel?

29 If a wire approximately one-half wavelength long is placed behind a
dipole antenna, the wire acts as a reflector and increases the directivity of
the antenna. This results in the reception of stronger signals when the
dipole and reflector are pointed at the transmitting station as illustrated
in Fig. 11–2. For best results the reflector should be 5 per cent longer
than the dipole. Referring to the formula for the length of a dipole
derived in Prob. 27, derive a formula for the length of a reflector in
inches when f is in megacycles.

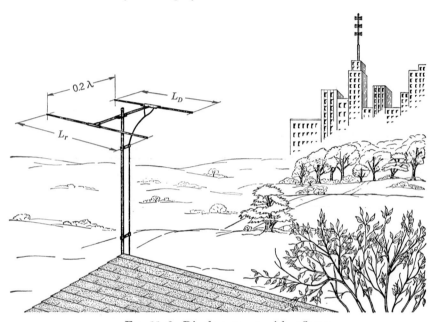

FIG. 11–2 Dipole antenna with reflector.

30 The distance between a dipole and its reflector should be approximately
two-tenths of one wavelength ($0.2\,\lambda$) as shown in Fig. 11–2. Referring to
previously derived formulas, compute the following for the mid-frequency
of television channel 10, which is 195 Mc: (a) length of dipole, (b) length
of reflector, (c) spacing between dipole and reflector.

31 The directivity of a dipole-reflector combination, as shown in Fig. 11–2,
can be increased by the installation of a conductor in *front* of the dipole
as illustrated in Fig. 11–3. This wire, which is known as a director, is
usually placed one-tenth wavelength ($0.1\,\lambda$) from the dipole and should
be about 5 per cent shorter than the dipole. Derive a formula for the
length of a director in feet when f is in megacycles.

32 Referring to Fig. 11–3, compute the following for the mid-frequency of
television channel 13, which is 213 Mc: (a) length of dipole, (b) length of

reflector, (c) length of director, (d) spacing between dipole and reflector, (e) spacing between dipole and director.

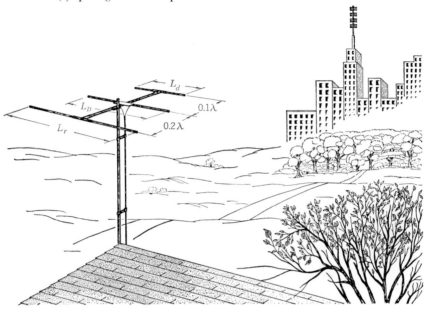

Fig. 11–3 Dipole antenna with reflector and director.

– 21 Ranges of units

In Secs. 10–5 and 11–9 and in several instances through the use of examples and problems, attempts have been made to emphasize the fact that extremely wide ranges in values of units are encountered in electrical and electronics computations. This has been done in order to impress you with the necessity of exercising care in making computations if accurate results are to be obtained. For example, in computing inductive reactances, the frequency may be in megacycles and the inductance in microhenrys. In radar and other applications we are concerned with the velocity of propagation of radio waves (186,000 miles per second) and with time intervals in microseconds. This is equally true in television reception, particularly as it relates to the production of duplicate images, usually called *ghosts*. As an example, Fig. 11–4 illustrates how a television receiver can receive a picture signal from a transmitting station by different paths. One path is the direct wave received from the transmitter, while the other signal arrives at the receiving antenna via a path 1 mile longer than

the direct path as a result of being reflected. Because the velocity of
radio waves is 186,000 miles per second, the reflected signal arrives at

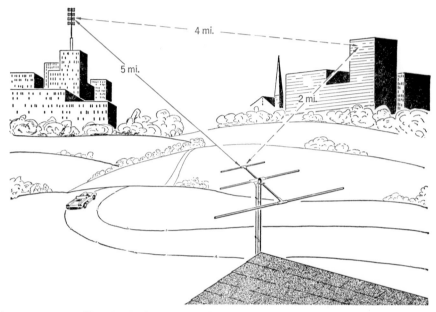

FIG. 11–4 Antenna receiving picture signal via two paths.

the receiver 1/186,000 sec, or about 5.4 μsec, later than the signal received via the direct path between transmitter and receiver. Since

FIG. 11–5 Television ghost. (Courtesy of Radio Corporation of America.)

the electron scanning beam scans one horizontal line in approximately
55 μsec, on a picture 10 in. wide the beam will scan about 1 in. in 5.5

μsec. Therefore the reflected signal arriving 5.4 μsec late will produce a second picture 1 in. to the right in the direction of scanning as shown in Fig. 11-5. This duplicate image produced by the reflected wave is called a ghost.

– 22 Significant figures

The subjects of accuracy and significant figures were discussed in Secs. 10–2 and 10–3. Now that we have some idea of the various units used in electrical and radio problems, two questions arise:

1. To how many significant figures should an answer be expressed?
2. How can we definitely show that an answer is correct to just so many significant figures?

The answer to the first question is comparatively easy. No answer can be more accurate than the figures, or data, used in the problem. As stated in Sec. 10–2, it is safe to assume that the values of the average circuit components and calibrations of meters that we use in our everyday work are not known beyond three significant figures. Therefore, in the future we shall round off long answers and express them to three significant figures. The exception will be when it is necessary to carry figures out in order carefully to demonstrate some fact or law.

The second question brings out some interesting points. As an example, suppose we have a resistance of 500,000 Ω and we want to write this value so that it will be apparent to anyone that the figure 500,000 is correct to three significant figures. This can be accomplished by writing

$$500 \times 10^3 \ \Omega$$
$$50.0 \times 10^4 \ \Omega$$
$$5.00 \times 10^5 \ \Omega, \text{ etc.}$$

Any of these expressions definitely shows that the resistance is correct to three significant figures. Similarly, suppose we had measured the capacitance of a capacitor to be 3,500 $\mu\mu$f. How shall we specify that the figure 3,500 is correct to three significant figures? Again, this is accomplished by writing

$$350 \times 10 \ \mu\mu f$$
$$35.0 \times 10^2 \ \mu\mu f$$
$$3.50 \times 10^3 \ \mu\mu f, \text{ etc.}$$

As in the previous example, there are definitely three figures in the first factor that show the degree of accuracy.

CHAPTER 12
EQUATIONS

In the preceding chapters, considerable time has been spent in the study of the fundamental operations of algebra. These fundamentals will be of little value unless they can be put to practical use in the solution of problems. This is accomplished by use of the equation, the most valuable tool in mathematics.

12 – 1   Definitions

An *equation* is a mathematical statement that two numbers, or quantities, are equal. The *equality sign* (=) is used to separate the two equal quantities. The terms to the left of the equality sign are known as the *left member* of the equation, and the terms to the right are the *right member* of the equation. For example, in the equation

$$3E + 4 = 2E + 6$$

$3E + 4$ is the left member and is equal to $2E + 6$, which is the right member.

An *identical equation, or identity*, is an equation whose members are equal for all values of the literal numbers contained in the equation. The equation

$$4I(r + R) = 4Ir + 4IR$$

is an identity because if

$$I = 2 \qquad r = 3 \qquad \text{and} \qquad R = 1$$

then
$$4I(r + R) = 4 \cdot 2(3 + 1) = 32$$

Also,
$$4Ir + 4IR = 4 \cdot 2 \cdot 3 + 4 \cdot 2 \cdot 1 = 24 + 8 = 32$$

Any other values of I, r, and R substituted in the equation will produce equal numerical results in the two members of the equation.

An equation is said to be *satisfied* if, when numerical values are substituted for the literal numbers, the equation becomes an identity. Thus, the equation

$$ir - iR = 3r - 3R$$

is satisfied by $i = 3$, because when this value is substituted in the equation we obtain

$$3r - 3R = 3r - 3R$$

which is an identity.

A *conditional equation* is one consisting of one or more literal numbers that is not satisfied by all values of the literal numbers. Thus, the equation

$$e + 3 = 7$$

is not satisfied by any value of e except $e = 4$.

To *solve* an equation is to find the value or values of the unknown number that will satisfy the equation. This value is called the *root* of the equation. Thus, if

$$i + 6 = 14$$

the equation becomes an identity only when i is 8, and therefore 8 is the root of the equation.

2–2 Axioms

An *axiom* is a truth, or fact, that is self-evident and needs no formal proof. The various methods of solving equations are derived from the following axioms:

1 If equal numbers are added to equal numbers, the sums are equal.

EXAMPLE 1   If $x = x$,

then
$$x + 2 = x + 2$$

because, if $x = 4$,
$$4 + 2 = 4 + 2$$

or
$$6 = 6$$

Therefore, *the same number can be added to both members of an equation without destroying the equality.*

2   If equal numbers are subtracted from equal numbers, the remainders are equal.

EXAMPLE 2   If $x = x$,
then $x - 2 = x - 2$
because, if $x = 4$, $4 - 2 = 4 - 2$
or $2 = 2$

Therefore, *the same number can be subtracted from both members of an equation without destroying the equality.*

3   If equal numbers are multiplied by equal numbers, their products are equal.

EXAMPLE 3   If $x = x$,
then $3x = 3x$
because, if $x = 4$, $3 \cdot 4 = 3 \cdot 4$
or $12 = 12$

Therefore, *both members of an equation can be multiplied by the same number without destroying the equality.*

4   If equal numbers are divided by equal numbers, their quotients are equal.

EXAMPLE 4   if $x = x$,

then $\dfrac{x}{2} = \dfrac{x}{2}$

because, if $x = 4$, $\dfrac{4}{2} = \dfrac{4}{2}$

or $2 = 2$

Therefore, *both members of an equation can be divided by the same number without destroying the equality.*

5   Numbers that are equal to the same number or equal numbers are equal to each other.

EXAMPLE 5   If $a = x$ and $b = x$,
then $a = b$
because, if $x = 4$, $a = 4$ and $b = 4$

Therefore, *an equal quantity can be substituted for any term of an equation without destroying the equality.*

6 Like powers of equal numbers are equal.

EXAMPLE 6   If $x = x$,
then $x^3 = x^3$
because, if $x = 4$, $4^3 = 4^3$
or $64 = 64$

Therefore, *both members of an equation can be raised to the same power without destroying the equality.*

7 Like roots of equal numbers are equal.

EXAMPLE 7   If $x = x$,
then $\sqrt{x} = \sqrt{x}$
because, if $x = 4$, $\sqrt{4} = \sqrt{4}$
or $2 = 2$

Therefore, *like roots can be extracted of both members of an equation without destroying the equality.*

2 – 3   Notation

In order to shorten the *explanations* of the solutions of various equations, we shall employ the letters **A, S, M,** and **D** for "add," "subtract," "multiply," and "divide," respectively.

Thus, **A:** 6 will mean "add 6 to both members of the equation."

S: $- 6x$ will mean "subtract $- 6x$ from both members of the equation."

M: $- 3a$ will mean "multiply both members of the equation by $- 3a$."

D: 2 will mean "divide both members of the equation by 2."

2 – 4   The solution of equations

A considerable amount of time and drill must be spent in order to become proficient in the solution of equations. It is in this branch of mathematics that you will find you must be familiar with the more elementary parts of algebra.

Some of the methods used in the solutions are very easy, so easy, in fact, that there is a tendency to employ them mechanically. This is all very well, but one should not let himself become so mechanical that he forgets the reason for performing certain operations.

We shall begin the solution of equations with very easy cases and attempt to build up general methods of procedure for all equations as we proceed to the more difficult problems.

If you are studying equations for the first time, you are urged to study the following examples carefully until you thoroughly understand the methods and the reasons behind them.

EXAMPLE 8   Find the value of x, if $x - 3 = 2$.
SOLUTION   In this equation, it is seen by inspection that x must be equal to 5. However, to make the solution by the methods of algebra, proceed as follows:

Given	$x - 3 = 2$	
A:3,	$x = 2 + 3$	(Axiom 1)
Collecting terms,	$x = 5$	

EXAMPLE 9   Solve for e, if $e + 4 = 12$.
SOLUTION

Given	$e + 4 = 12$	
S:4,	$e = 12 - 4$	(Axiom 2)
Collecting terms,	$e = 8$	

EXAMPLE 10   Solve for i, if $3i + 5 = 20$.
SOLUTION

Given	$3i + 5 = 20$	
S:5,	$3i = 20 - 5$	(Axiom 2)
Collecting terms,	$3i = 15$	
D:3,	$i = 5$	(Axiom 4)

EXAMPLE 11   Solve for r, if $40r - 10 = 15r + 90$.
SOLUTION

Given	$40r - 10 = 15r + 90$	
S:15r,	$40r - 10 - 15r = 90$	(Axiom 2)
A:10,	$40r - 15r = 90 + 10$	(Axiom 1)
Collecting terms,	$25r = 100$	
D:25,	$r = 4$	(Axiom 4)

From the foregoing examples, it will be noted that adding or subtracting a term from both members of an equation is equivalent to *transposing* that number from one member to the other and changing its sign. This fact leads to the following rule:

RULE   A *term* can be transposed from one member of an equation to the other provided that its sign is changed.

By transposing all terms containing the unknown to the left member and all others to the right member, by collecting terms and dividing both members by the numerical coefficient of the unknown, the equation has been solved for the value of the unknown.

2 – 5 **Canceling terms in an equation**

EXAMPLE 12   Solve for x, if $x + y = z + y$.

SOLUTION

Given $x + y = z + y$

S:y, $x = z$ (Axiom 2)

The term y in both members of the given equation does not appear in the next equation as the result of subtraction. The result is the same as if the term were dropped from both members. This fact leads to the following rule:

RULE   If the same *term* preceded by the same sign occurs in both members of an equation, it can be canceled.

2 – 6 **Changing signs in an equation**

EXAMPLE 13   Solve for x, if $8 - x = 3$.

SOLUTION

Given $8 - x = 3$

S:8, $-x = 3 - 8$ (Axiom 2)

M:−1, $x = -3 + 8$ (Axiom 3)

Collecting terms, $x = 5$

Note that multiplication by -1 has the effect of changing the signs of all terms. This gives the following rule:

RULE   The signs of all the *terms* of an equation can be changed without destroying the equality.

Although the foregoing rules involving mechanical methods are valuable, you should not lose sight of the fact that they are all derived from fundamentals, or axioms, as outlined in Sec. 12–2.

2 – 7 **Checking the solution**

If there is any doubt that the value of the unknown is correct, the solution can be checked by substituting the value of the unknown in the original equation. If the two members reduce to an identity, the value of the unknown is correct.

EXAMPLE 14   Solve and test $3i + 14 + 2i = i + 26$.

SOLUTION

Given $3i + 14 + 2i = i + 26$

Transposing, $3i + 2i - i = 26 - 14$

Collecting terms, $4i = 12$

D:4, $i = 3$

Test by substituting $i = 3$ in given equation.

Check: $(3 \cdot 3) + 14 + (2 \cdot 3) = 3 + 26$

$9 + 14 + 6 = 3 + 26$

$29 = 29$

PROBLEMS 12 – 1

Solve for the unknown in the following equations:

1 $3R - 4 = 8$

2 $4E - 3 = 2E + 7$

3 $3r + 4 = 7r - 8$

4 $5i - 10 - 3i = 4$

5 $2e - 3 = 3e - 7$

6 $19 - 16Z = 27 - 28Z$

7 $39 - 3\alpha = 2\alpha - 25 + 3\alpha$

8 $\phi + 26 - 2\phi = 14 + 3\phi$

9 $6I + 8 - 23I = 16I - 3$

10 $14\theta + 7 - 8\theta = \theta - 2 + 7\theta$

11 $16 - (2i - 3) = 2i + 3$

12 $2(r + 7) = 4(3 + r) + 15(r - 1)$

13 $10 - (E - 2) - E = -27 + (E + 3)$

14 $16Z - (-14Z + 47) = -64 - Z + 13 + 35Z$

15 $163 - 15(2R - 5) - 157 + 21(R + 3) = 0$

16 $5\alpha - (3\alpha - 7) - [4 - 2\alpha - (6\alpha - 3)] - 10 = 0$

17 $0 = 25I - 19 - [3 - (4I - 15)] - 3I + (6I + 21)$

18 $(i + 3)(2i + 3) - 14 = (i + 1)(2i + 1)$

19 $4(e + 2)(e + 1) - 24 = 6(e^2 - 3e + 2) - 2(e^2 - 1)$

20 $4I^2 - (5I + 3)(I - 4) - 64 - 2(I - 4) + (I^2 + I - 20) = 0$

12 – 8   Forming and solving equations

As previously stated, we are continually trying to express certain laws and relations in the language of mathematics.

EXAMPLES

Words	*Algebraic symbols*
The sum of the voltages E and e	$E + e$
The difference between resistances R and R_1	$R - R_1$
The excess of current I_1 over current I_2	$I_1 - I_2$
The number of inches in f ft	$12f$
The number of cents in d dollars	$100d$
The voltage E is equal to the product of the current I and the resistance R	$E = IR$

The solution of most problems consists in writing an equation that connects various observed data with known facts.   This, then, is nothing more than translating from ordinary English, or speech, into the language of mathematics. In relatively simple problems the translation can be made directly, almost word by word, into algebraic symbols.

EXAMPLE 15   Five times a certain voltage diminished by 3,

$$5 \quad \times \qquad\qquad E \qquad - \qquad 3$$

gives the same result as the voltage increased by 125.

$$= \qquad\qquad E \qquad + \qquad 125$$

That is, $5E - 3 = E + 125$
or $E = 32$ volts

EXAMPLE 16   What number increased by 42 is equal to 110?

$$x \qquad + \qquad 42 \qquad = \qquad 110?$$

That is, $x + 42 = 110$
or $x = 68$
    Check: $68 + 42 = 110$

It is almost impossible to lay down a set of rules for the solution of general problems, for they could not be made applicable to all cases. However, no rules will be needed if you thoroughly understand what is to be translated into the language of mathematics from the wording or facts of the problem at hand. The following outline will serve as a guide:

1   Read the problem carefully so that every fact in it is understood and the relations between the facts recognized.
2   Determine what is to be found (the unknown quantity), and denote it by some letter. If there are two or more unknowns, try to represent them in terms of one of them.
3   Find two expressions which, according to the facts of the problem, represent the same quantity, and set them equal to each other. The resulting equation can then be solved for the unknown.

PROBLEMS 12-2

1   Express algebraically (a) the distance d traveled in h hr at a rate of 20 mph, (b) the distance d traveled in h hr at a rate of v mph, (c) your age a in y years if your present age is x years, (d) the time t required to go d miles at the rate of v mph, (e) a fraction f whose denominator exceeds its numerator n by 5.
2   The difference between two currents is I amp. The smaller current is i amp. What is the larger current?

3   The sum of two voltages is E volts.   One voltage is 115 volts.   What is the other voltage?

4   If a certain resistance R is doubled and the result diminished by 30 Ω, the remainder is 80 Ω.   What is the resistance R?

5   If three times a certain number n is subtracted from five times that number, the remainder is 28.   What is the number n?

6   The sum of two consecutive numbers is 75.   What are the numbers?

7   Find three consecutive numbers whose sum is 165.

8   From what must 37 be subtracted so that the result will be 58?

9   To what number must 26 be added so that the result will be -15?

10   The volume of a box is v ft³.   Express the height h in feet if the width is w ft and the length is l ft.

11   Write in algebraic symbols that P is equal to the product of I squared times R minus P_1.

12   Write in algebraic symbols that E exceeds e as much as R is less than r.

13   A room is 5 ft longer than it is wide.   The perimeter (the sum of the lengths of its sides) is 58 ft.   Find its length and width.

14   Find the three sides of a triangle with a perimeter of 170 ft if the second side is four times the third side and the first side exceeds the third by 50 ft.

15   The sum of the three angles in any triangle is 180°.   The first angle of a certain triangle is 40° less than the second angle.   The first angle exceeds the third angle by 10°.   How many degrees does each angle contain?

12 – 9   Literal equations—formulas

A *formula* is a rule, or law, generally pertaining to some scientific relationship expressed as an equation by means of letters, symbols, and constant terms.

EXAMPLE 17   The area A of a rectangle is equal to the product of its base b by its altitude h.   This statement written as a formula is

$$A = bh$$

EXAMPLE 18   The power P expended in an electric circuit is equal to the product of its current I squared times the resistance R of the circuit.   Stated as a formula

$$P = I^2R$$

The ability to handle formulas is of the utmost importance.   The usual formula is expressed in terms of other quantities, and it is often desirable to solve for *any* quantity contained in a formula.   This is readily accomplished by using the knowledge gained in solving equations.

EXAMPLE 19   The voltage E across a part of a circuit is given by the product of the current I through that part of the circuit times the resistance R of that part. That is,

$$E = IR$$

Suppose E and I are given but it is desired to find R.

Given $E = IR$

D:I, $\dfrac{E}{I} = R$ (Axiom 4)

or $R = \dfrac{E}{I}$

Similarly, if we wanted to solve for I,

Given $E = IR$

D:R, $\dfrac{E}{R} = I$ (Axiom 4)

or $I = \dfrac{E}{R}$

EXAMPLE 20   Solve for I, if $e = E - IR$.

SOLUTION

Given $e = E - IR$

Transposing, $IR = E - e$

D:R, $I = \dfrac{E - e}{R}$ (Axiom 4)

EXAMPLE 21   Solve for C, if $X_C = \dfrac{1}{2\pi f C}$.

SOLUTION

Given $X_C = \dfrac{1}{2\pi f C}$

D:X_C, $1 = \dfrac{1}{2\pi f C X_C}$ (Axiom 4)

M:C, $C = \dfrac{1}{2\pi f X_C}$ (Axiom 3)

It will be noted from the foregoing examples that if the numerator of a member of an equation contains but one term, any *factor* of that term may be transferred to the denominator of the other member as a *factor*. In like manner if the denominator of a member of an equation contains but one term, any *factor* of that term may be transferred to the numerator of the other member as a *factor*. These mechanical transformations simply make use of Axioms 3 and 4, and you should not lose sight of the real reasons behind them.

PROBLEMS 12–3

Given	*Solve for*
1 $Q = CV$	C and V
2 $I = \dfrac{E}{Z}$	E and Z
3 $R^2 = Z^2 - X^2$	Z^2
4 $R = \dfrac{P}{I^2}$	P
5 $L = \dfrac{Rm}{K}$	R and K
6 $R_2 = R_t - R_1 - R_3$	R_t
7 $f = \dfrac{v}{\lambda}$	λ
8 $C = 2\pi r$	r
9 $R = \dfrac{\omega L}{Q}$	L
10 $L = \dfrac{X_L}{2\pi f}$	X_L
11 $C = \dfrac{1}{2\pi f X_C}$	X_C
12 $H = \dfrac{\phi}{A}$	ϕ
13 $H = \dfrac{N + 2}{P}$	P
14 $N_s = \dfrac{E_s N_p}{E_p}$	N_p
15 $B = \dfrac{E10^8}{Lv}$	E and L
16 $P = \dfrac{120f}{N}$	N and f
17 $E_s I_s = E_p I_p$	E_s
18 $L = \dfrac{F}{Hi}$	F
19 $R = \dfrac{E - e}{I}$	I
20 $\mu = G_m R_p$	G_m
21 $t = \dfrac{\theta}{\omega}$	ω
22 $h = \dfrac{V^2}{2g}$	g
23 $V_o = 2V - V_t$	V

24 $n = \dfrac{\omega}{2\pi}$ ω

25 $m = \dfrac{2KE}{V^2}$ KE

26 $\mu = \dfrac{B^2Al}{8\omega}$ l and ω

27 $C = \dfrac{F(R-r)}{Z_t}$ Z_t

28 $r = \dfrac{F}{4\pi^2n^2m}$ m and F

29 $R_L = \dfrac{E_b - e_b}{i}$ e_b

30 $K = \dfrac{C-D}{2}$ C

31 $R = \dfrac{\rho l}{d^2}$ l

32 $\mathrm{pf} = \dfrac{R}{X}$ R

33 $C = \dfrac{0.0884KA(n-1)}{d}$ A

34 $M = k\sqrt{L_1L_2}$ k

35 $Z_r = \dfrac{L}{RC}$ L and C

36 The power P in any part of an electric circuit is given by $P = \dfrac{E^2}{R}$ watts, in which E is the voltage across that part of the circuit and R is the resistance of that part. What is the resistance of a circuit in which 1,210 watts is expended at a voltage of 110 volts?

37 The voltage E across any part of a circuit can be computed by the formula $E = IZ$ volts, where I is the current in amperes through that part of the circuit and Z is the impedance in ohms of that part. What is the impedance of a circuit in which flows a current of 19 amp at a voltage of 230 volts?

38 To find the frequency f of an alternator in cycles per second, the number of pairs of poles P is multiplied by the speed of the armature S in revolutions per second; that is, $f = PS$. A tachometer connected to the armature of a 60-cycle alternator reads 1,800 rpm. How many poles has the alternator?

39 For radio waves the relationship between frequency f in megacycles and wavelength λ in feet is expressed by the formula $f = \dfrac{984}{\lambda}$. What is the wavelength of a radio wave at a frequency of 300 Mc?

40   The length of a broad-band dipole L_{fD} used for television reception can be

computed by the formula $L_{fD} = \dfrac{5562}{f}$ in., where f is the frequency in

Fig. 12–1   Folded dipole of Prob. 40.

megacycles.   The folded dipole illustrated in Fig. 12–1 is 80.6 in.   For
what frequency was it constructed?

CHAPTER 13
OHM'S LAW
SERIES CIRCUITS

Ohm's law for the electric circuit is the foundation of electric-circuit analysis and is, therefore, of fundamental importance. The various relations of Ohm's law are easily learned and readily applied to practical circuits. A thorough knowledge of these relations and their applications is essential to an understanding of the electric circuit.

This chapter concerns itself with the study of Ohm's law in d-c series circuits as applied to *parts* of a circuit. For this reason, the internal resistance of a source of voltage, such as a generator or a battery, and the resistance of the wires connecting the parts of a circuit will not be discussed in this chapter.

3 – 1   The electric circuit

An electric circuit consists of a source of voltage which is connected by means of conductors to the apparatus that is to use the electrical energy.

An electric current will flow between two points in a conductor when a difference of potential exists across these points. The most generally accepted concept of an electric current is that it consists of a motion, or flow, of electrons from the negative toward a more positive point in a circuit. The force that causes the motion of electrons is called an *electromotive force*, or a *potential difference*, and the opposition to their motion is called *resistance*.

The basic theories of electrical phenomena and the methods of producing currents are not within the scope of this book. You will find these adequately treated in the great majority of textbooks on the subject.

13 – 2   Ohm's law

Ohm's law for the electric circuit, reduced to plain terms, states the relation that exists among voltage, current, and resistance. One way of stating this relation is as follows: The voltage across any *part* of a circuit is proportional to the product of the current through that *part* of the circuit and the resistance of that *part* of the circuit. Stated as a formula the foregoing is expressed as

$$E = IR$$ [1]

where E = voltage, or potential difference, volts
   I = current, amp
   R = resistance, Ω

If any two factors are known the third can be found by solving Eq. [1]. Thus,

$$I = \frac{E}{R}$$ [2]

and $$R = \frac{E}{I}$$ [3]

13 – 3   Methods of solution

The general outline for working problems given in Sec. 12–8 is applicable to the solution of circuit problems. In addition, a neat, simplified diagram of the circuit should be drawn for each problem. The diagram should be labeled with all the known values of the circuit such as voltage, current, and resistances. In this manner the circuit and problem can be visualized and understood. Solving a problem by making purely mechanical substitutions in the proper formulas is not conducive to a complete understanding of any problem.

EXAMPLE 1   How much current will flow through a resistance of 150 Ω
if the applied voltage across the resistance is 117 volts?

SOLUTION   The circuit is represented in Figs. 13–1 and 13–2.

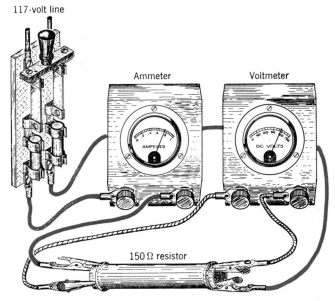

117-volt line

Ammeter

Voltmeter

150 Ω resistor

FIG. 13–1 Sketch of the circuit of Example 1, showing how the
parts are connected to form the circuit.

Given $E = 117$ volts
and $R = 150 \, \Omega$
                   $I = ?$

$$I = \frac{E}{R} = \frac{117}{150} = 0.780 \text{ amp}$$

EXAMPLE 2   A   voltmeter   connected across a resistance reads 220
volts, and an ammeter connected
in series with the resistance reads
2.60 amp. What is the value of the
resistance?

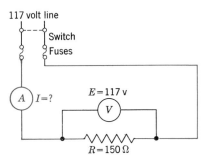

117 volt line

Switch
Fuses

A $I = ?$

$E = 117$ v

V

$R = 150 \, \Omega$

FIG. 13–2   Schematic circuit diagram of Example 1.

SOLUTION   The circuit is represented in Fig. 13–3.

Given $E = 220$ volts   and $I = 2.60$ amp
                      $R = ?$

$$R = \frac{E}{I} = \frac{220}{2.60} = 84.6 \, \Omega$$

EXAMPLE 3   A current of 1.40 amp flows through a resistance of 450 Ω. What should be the reading of a voltmeter when connected across the resistance?

SOLUTION   The diagram of the circuit is shown in Fig. 13–4.

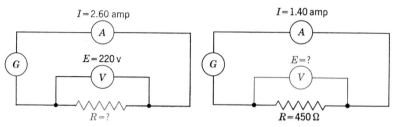

FIG. 13–3 Circuit of Example 2.   FIG. 13–4 Circuit of Example 3.

Given $I = 1.40$ amp   and $R = 450$ Ω
                         $E = ?$
                         $E = IR = 1.40 \times 450 = 630$ volts

EXAMPLE 4   A measurement shows a potential difference of 63.0 μv across a resistance of 300 Ω. How much current is flowing through the resistance?

SOLUTION   The circuit is represented in Fig. 13–5.

Given $E = 63.0$ μv $= 6.3 \times 10^{-5}$ volts   and $R = 300$ Ω
           $I = ?$

$$I = \frac{E}{R} = \frac{6.3 \times 10^{-5}}{300} = \frac{6.3 \times 10^{-7}}{3.00} = 2.1 \times 10^{-7} \text{ amp}$$

or $I = 0.21$ μa

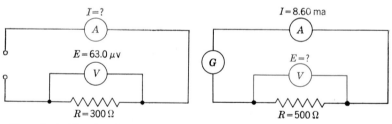

FIG. 13–5 Circuit of Example 4.   FIG. 13–6 Circuit of Example 5.

EXAMPLE 5   A current of 8.60 ma flows through a resistance of 500 Ω. What voltage exists across the resistance?

SOLUTION   The circuit is represented in Fig. 13–6.

Given $I = 8.60$ ma $= 8.60 \times 10^{-3}$ amp   and $R = 500$ Ω
           $E = ?$

$$E = IR = 8.60 \times 10^{-3} \times 500 = 8.60 \times 10^{-3} \times 5 \times 10^{2}$$
$$= 8.60 \times 5 \times 10^{-1} = 4.30 \text{ volts}$$

Carefully note, as illustrated in Examples 4 and 5, that the equations expressing Ohm's law are in units, that is, volts, amperes, and ohms.

PROBLEMS 13 – 1

1   How much current will flow through a resistance of 40.0 Ω if a potential of 230 volts is applied across it?

2   A certain soldering iron draws 1.30 amp from a 115-volt line. What is the resistance of the soldering-iron heating unit?

3   What voltage is required for a current flow of 6.20 amp through a resistance of 71.0 Ω?

4   A milliammeter connected in series with a 5-kΩ resistor reads 6.0 ma. What is the voltage across the resistor?

5   A microvoltmeter connected across a 100-Ω resistor reads 50 μv. What current is flowing through the resistor?

6   What voltage is required to cause a current flow of 12.5 ma through a resistance of 6 kΩ?

7   A certain milliammeter, with a scale of 0 to 1.0 ma, has a resistance of 27 Ω. If this milliammeter is connected directly across a 115-volt line, how much current will flow until the meter is destroyed?

8   The current flowing through a 3,650-Ω resistor is 7.7 ma. What should a voltmeter read when connected across the resistor?

9   The cold resistance of a carbon filament lamp is 210 Ω, and the hot resistance is 189 Ω. What is the current that flows at the instant it is connected across a 115-volt line and the current when the constant operating temperature is reached?

10   A type SN954 half-wave rectifier tube filament draws a current of 450 ma at its rated voltage of 6.3 volts. What is the resistance of the filament when the tube is in operation?

13 – 4   Power

In specifying the rating of electrical equipment, it is customary to state not only the voltage for which it was designed to operate but also the rate at which it produces or consumes electrical energy.

The rate of producing or consuming energy is called *power*, and electrical energy is measured in watts or kilowatts. Thus, your study lamp may be rated 100 watts at 117 volts; a generator may be rated 2,000 kw at 440 volts; etc.

Electric motors are generally rated in terms of the mechanical horsepower they will develop. The conversion from electrical energy to equivalent mechanical energy is given by the relation

$$746 \text{ watts} = 1 \text{ hp}$$

13 – 5   The watt

Energy is expended at a rate of 1 watt-sec every second when 1 volt causes a current of 1 amp to flow. In this case, we say that the power represented when 1 volt causes 1 amp to flow is 1 watt. This relation is expressed as

$$P = EI \qquad [4]$$

This is a useful equation when the voltage and current are known.

Because, by Ohm's law, $E = IR$, this value of E can be substituted in Eq. [4]. Thus,

$$P = (IR)I$$
or
$$P = I^2R \qquad [5]$$

This is a useful equation when the current and resistance are known.

By substituting the value of I of Eq. [2] in Eq. [4],

$$P = E\frac{E}{R}$$
or
$$P = \frac{E^2}{R} \qquad [6]$$

This is a useful equation when the voltage and resistance are known.

Watthours—Kilowatthours. The consumer of electric energy pays for the amount of energy used by his electrical equipment. This is measured by instruments known as *watthour* or *kilowatthour meters.* These meters record the amount of energy taken by the consumer.

Electrical energy is sold at so much per kilowatthour. One watt-hour of energy is consumed when 1 watt of power continues in action for 1 hr. Similarly, 1 kilowatthour is consumed when the power is 1,000 watts and the action continues for 1 hr or when a 100-watt rate persists for 10 hr, etc. Thus the amount of energy consumed is the product of the power and the time.

13 – 6   Losses

The study of the various forms in which energy may occur and the transformation of one kind of energy into another has led to the important principle known as the principle of the *conservation of energy.*

Briefly, this states that energy can never be created or destroyed. It can be transformed from one form to another, but the total amount remains unchanged. Thus, an electric motor converts electric energy into mechanical energy, the incandescent lamp changes electric energy into heat energy, the loud-speaker converts electric energy into sound energy, the generator converts mechanical energy into electric energy, etc. In each instance the transformation from one type of energy to another is not accomplished with 100 per cent efficiency because some energy is converted into heat and does no useful work as far as that particular conversion is concerned.

Resistance in a circuit may serve a number of useful purposes, but unless it has been specifically designed for heating or dissipation purposes, the energy transformed in the resistance generally serves no useful purpose.

13-7 Efficiency

Because all electric equipment contains resistance, there must always be some heat developed when current flows. Unless the equipment is to be used for producing heat, the heat due to the resistance of the equipment represents wasted energy. No electric equipment or other machine is capable of converting energy received into useful work without some loss.

The power that is furnished a machine is called its *input*, and the power received from a machine is called its *output*. The efficiency of a machine is equal to the ratio of the output to the input. That is,

$$\text{Efficiency} = \frac{\text{output}}{\text{input}} \qquad [7]$$

It is evident that the efficiency, as given in Eq. [7], is always a decimal, that is, a number less than 1. Naturally, in Eq. [7], the output and input must be expressed in the same units. Hence, if the output is expressed in kilowatts, then the input must be expressed in kilowatts; if the output is expressed in horsepower, then the input must be expressed in horsepower; etc.

EXAMPLE 6   A voltage of 110 volts across a resistor causes a current of 5 amp to flow through it. How much power is expended in the resistor?
SOLUTION   The circuit is represented in Fig. 13-7.
Given $E = 110$ volts   and $I = 5$ amp
               $P = ?$

Using Eq. [4],

$$P = EI = 110 \times 5 = 550 \text{ watts}$$

ALTERNATE SOLUTION   Find the value of the resistance and use it to solve for P. Thus, using Eq. [3],

$$R = \frac{E}{I} = \frac{110}{5} = 22 \ \Omega$$

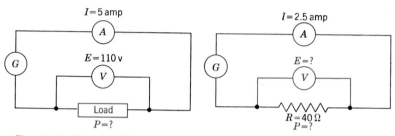

FIG. 13–7 Circuit of Example 6.   FIG. 13–8 Circuit of Example 7.

Using Eq. [5], $P = I^2 R = 5^2 \times 22 = 5 \times 5 \times 22 = 550$ watts

ALTERNATE SOLUTION   Using Eq. [6],

$$P = \frac{E^2}{R} = \frac{110^2}{22} = \frac{110 \times 110}{22} = 550 \text{ watts}$$

Solving a problem by two methods serves as an excellent check on the results, for there is little chance of making the same error twice, as is too often the case when a problem is repeated using the same method of solution.

EXAMPLE 7   A current of 2.5 amp flows through a resistance of 40 Ω.
(a) How much power is expended in the resistor?
(b) What is the potential difference across the resistor?
SOLUTION   The circuit is represented in Fig. 13–8.

Given $I = 2.5$ amp   and $R = 40 \ \Omega$
                          $P = ?$ $E = ?$

(a) $P = I^2 R = (2.5)^2 \times 40 = 2.5 \times 2.5 \times 40 = 250$ watts
(b) $E = IR = 2.5 \times 40 = 100$ volts

ALTERNATE SOLUTIONS   (a) Find E, as above, and use it to solve for P.

Thus, $P = \frac{E^2}{R} = \frac{(100)^2}{40} = \frac{100 \times 100}{40} = 250$ watts

or $P = EI = 100 \times 2.5 = 250$ watts

EXAMPLE 8   A voltage of 1.732 volts is applied across a 500-Ω resistor.
(a) How much power is expended in the resistor?
(b) How much current flows through the resistor?

SOLUTION   A diagram of the circuit is shown in Fig. 13–9.

Given $E = 1.732$ volts   and $R = 500\ \Omega$
                         $P = ?$ $I = ?$

(a) $P = \dfrac{E^2}{R} = \dfrac{(1.732)^2}{500} = \dfrac{(1.732)^2}{5 \times 10^2} = \dfrac{(1.732)^2}{5} \times 10^{-2} = 0.006$ watt

or $P = 6\,\text{mw}$

(b) $I = \dfrac{E}{R} = \dfrac{1.732}{500} = \dfrac{1.732}{5} \times 10^{-2} = 0.346 \times 10^{-2}$ amp

or $I = 3.46\,\text{ma}$

Check the foregoing solution for power by using an alternate method.

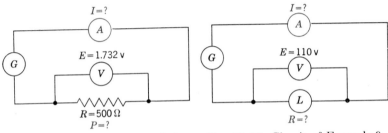

FIG. 13–9 Circuit of Example 8.   FIG. 13–10 Circuit of Example 9.

EXAMPLE 9   (a) What is the hot resistance of a 100-watt 110-volt lamp?
(b) How much current does it take?
(c) At 4 cents/kwhr, how much does it cost to operate this lamp for 24 hr?

SOLUTION   The circuit is represented in Fig. 13–10.

Given $P = 100$ watts   and $E = 110$ volts

(a) Because the power and voltage are known and the resistance is unknown,
an equation that contains these three must be used. Thus,

$$P = \frac{E^2}{R} \qquad [6]$$

Hence, $R = \dfrac{E^2}{P} = \dfrac{(110)^2}{100} = 121\ \Omega$

(b) $I = \dfrac{E}{R} = \dfrac{110}{121} = 0.909$ amp

(c) If the lamp is lighted for 24 hr, it will consume
                    $100 \times 24 = 2,400$ watt-hr $= 2.40$ kwhr

At 4 cents/kwhr the cost would be
                    $2.4 \times 4 = 9.6$ cents

ALTERNATE SOLUTION   The current may be found first by making use of the relation

$$P = EI \qquad [4]$$

which results in

$$I = \frac{P}{E} = \frac{100}{110} = 0.909 \text{ amp}$$

The resistance can now be determined by

$$R = \frac{E}{I} = \frac{110}{0.909} = 121 \ \Omega$$

The solution can be checked by

$$P = I^2R = (0.909)^2 \times 121 = 100 \text{ watts}$$

which is the power rating of the lamp as given in the example. The cost is computed as before.

EXAMPLE 10   A motor delivering 6.50 mechanical horsepower is drawing 26.5 amp from a 220-volt line.

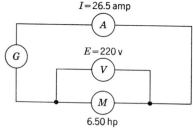

$I = 26.5$ amp

$E = 220$ v

6.50 hp

FIG. 13–11   Circuit of Example 10.

(a) How much electric power is the motor taking from the line?

(b) What is the efficiency of the motor?

(c) If power costs 3 cents/kwhr, how much does it cost to run the motor for 8 hr?

SOLUTION   A diagram of the circuit is shown in Fig. 13–11.

Given $E = 220$ volts $I = 26.5$ amp
and mechanical horsepower

$$P = 6.5 \text{ hp} = 6.5 \times 746 = 4,850 \text{ watts} = 4.85 \text{ kw}$$

(a) The power taken by the motor is

$$P = EI = 220 \times 26.5 = 5,830 \text{ watts}$$
$$= 5.83 \text{ kw}$$

(b) $\text{Efficiency} = \dfrac{\text{output}}{\text{input}} = \dfrac{4.85}{5.83} = 0.832$

$$= 83.2 \text{ per cent}$$

(c) Because the motor consumes 5.83 kw, in 8 hr it would take

$$5.83 \times 8 = 46.6 \text{ kwhr}$$

At 3 cents/kwhr, the cost would be

$$46.6 \times 0.03 = \$1.40$$

NOTE   The cost was computed in two steps for the purpose of illustrating the solution. When you have become familiar with the method, the cost should be computed in one step. Thus,

$$\text{Cost} = 5.83 \times 8 \times 0.03 = \$1.40$$

From the foregoing examples, it will be noted that computations involving power consist mainly in the applications of Ohm's law. Little trouble will be encountered if each problem is given careful thought and a systematic procedure followed for the solution as previously outlined.

PROBLEMS 13 – 2

1   10 hp = (*a*) _____watts? (*b*) _____kw?

2   37.3 kw = (*a*) _____watts? (*b*) _____ hp?

3   A certain electric soldering iron draws 1.6 amp from a 115-volt line. How much power does it consume?

4   How much power is expended in a 10-Ω resistor through which a current of 12 amp flows?

5   What is the electric horsepower of a generator that delivers a current of 50 amp at a voltage of 230 volts?

6   A voltmeter connected across a 250-Ω resistor reads 110 volts. How much power is being expended in the resistor?

7   A diesel engine is rated at 1,500 hp. What is its rating in kilowatts?

8   A wattmeter is connected in a 440-volt line ahead of a motor. When the motor is running, the wattmeter reads 1 kw. How much current is the motor taking from the line?

9   The resistance of a certain ammeter is 0.017 Ω. Determine the power expended in the ammeter when it reads 5 amp.

10   The resistance of a certain voltmeter is 250,000 Ω. Determine the power expended in the voltmeter when it is connected across a 230-volt line.

11   A type 6F6 vacuum tube, used in the output stage of a radio receiver, has a cathode-biasing resistor of 470 Ω. A voltmeter connected across the resistor reads 16.5 volts.
   (*a*) How much power is being expended in the resistor?
   (*b*) How much current flows through the resistor?

12   A type 6C5 vacuum tube is operating with a cathode-biasing resistor of 1,000 Ω through which a current of 8 ma flows.
   (*a*) How much power is being expended in the resistor?
   (*b*) What is the voltage across the resistor?

13   A voltage of 100 μv is applied across a 500-Ω resistor.
   (*a*) How much power is expended in the resistor?
   (*b*) How much current flows through the resistor?

14 An electric coffee pot that consumes 250 watts is used 20 min each day. At 3 cents/kwhr, how much will it cost to operate the coffee pot for a 30-day month?

15 A motor is delivering 15 hp. A kilowattmeter that measures the power taken by the motor reads 14.3 kw.
(a) What is the efficiency of the motor?
(b) At 2.5 cents/kwhr, how much would it cost to run the motor continuously for 5 days?

16 A 440-volt 10-hp motor has an efficiency of 75 per cent.
(a) How many kilowatts does it consume?
(b) How much current does it take from the line?
(c) At 2 cents/kwhr, how much would it cost to run this motor continuously for 1 week?

17 It requires 19.2 hp to drive a generator that delivers 50 amp at 230 volts. What is the efficiency of the generator?

18 A 25-hp motor has an efficiency of 78 per cent. How many kilowatts are required for its operation?

19 A generator delivers 100 amp at 115 volts with an efficiency of 79 per cent. How much power is lost in the generator?

20 A 230-volt 5-hp motor with an efficiency of 76 per cent is driving a radio transmitter 2,000-volt generator that has an efficiency of 74 per cent. With the motor running fully loaded
(a) How much power does the motor take from the line?
(b) How much current does the motor take?
(c) How much power will the generator deliver?
(d) How much current will the generator deliver?
(e) What is the over-all efficiency, that is, from motor input to generator output?

13 – 8   Resistances in series

So far, our studies of the electric circuit have taken into consideration but one electric component in the circuit, excluding the source of voltage. This is all very well for the purpose of becoming familiar with simple Ohm's law and power relations. However, practical circuits consist of more than one piece of equipment as far as circuit computations are concerned.

In a *series circuit* the various components comprising the circuit are so connected that the current, starting from the voltage source, must flow through each circuit component, in turn, before returning to the other side of the source.

There are three important facts concerning series circuits that must be borne in mind in order thoroughly to understand the action of such circuits and to facilitate their solution.

In a series circuit:

1   The total voltage is equal to the sum of the voltages across the different parts of the circuit.

2   The current in any part of the circuit is the same.

3   The total resistance of the circuit is equal to the sum of the resistances of the different parts.

Point 1 is practically self-evident. If the sum of all the potential differences (voltage drops) around the circuit were not equal to the applied voltage, there would be some voltage left over which would cause an increase in current. This increase in current would continue until it caused enough voltage drop across some resistance just to balance the applied voltage. Hence,

$$E_t = E_1 + E_2 + E_3 + \cdots \qquad [8]$$

Point 2 is evident, for the circuit components are connected so that the current must flow through each part in turn and there are no other paths back to the source.

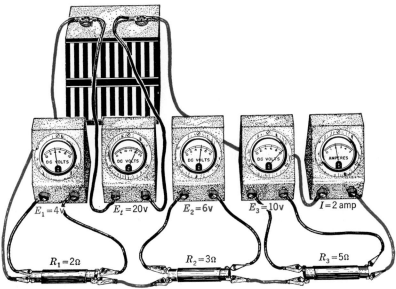

FIG. 13-12   Three resistors connected in series with a voltmeter connected across each resistor. The sum of the voltages across the resistors is equal to the battery voltage.

To some, point 3 might not be self-evident.   However, because it is agreed that the current I in Figs. 13–12 and 13–13 flows through all

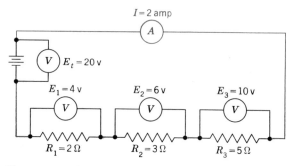

FIG. 13–13   Schematic diagram of the circuit represented in Fig. 13–12.

resistors, Eq. [8] can be used to demonstrate the truth of point 3 above.   Thus, by dividing each member of Eq. [8] by I,

$$\frac{E_t}{I} = \frac{E_1 + E_2 + E_3}{I}$$

or

$$\frac{E_t}{I} = \frac{E_1}{I} + \frac{E_2}{I} + \frac{E_3}{I}$$

Substituting R for $\frac{E}{I}$,

$$R_t = R_1 + R_2 + R_3 \qquad [9]$$

NOTE E_t and R_t are used to denote "total voltage" and "total resistance," respectively.

EXAMPLE 11   Three resistors $R_1 = 30$ Ω, $R_2 = 160$ Ω, and $R_3 = 40$ Ω are connected in series across a generator. A voltmeter connected across R_2 reads 80 volts. What is the voltage of the generator?

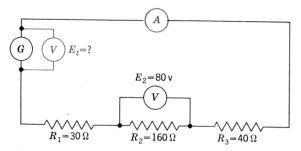

FIG. 13–14   Circuit of Example 11.

SOLUTION   Figure 13–14 is a diagram of the circuit.

$$I = \frac{E^2}{R^2} = \frac{80}{160} = 0.5 \text{ amp}$$

$$R_t = R_1 + R_2 + R_3 = 30 + 160 + 40 = 230 \ \Omega$$

$$E_t = IR_t = 0.5 \times 230 = 115 \text{ volts}$$

EXAMPLE 12   A 300-Ω relay must be operated from a 120-volt line. How much resistance must be added in series with the relay coil to limit the current through it to 250 ma?

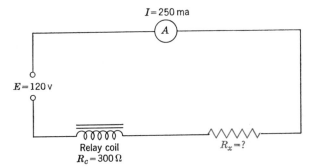

$I = 250$ ma

A

$E = 120$ v

Relay coil
$R_c = 300 \ \Omega$

$R_x = ?$

FIG. 13–15   Circuit of Example 12.

SOLUTION   The circuit is represented in Fig. 13–15. For a current of 250 ma to flow in a 120-volt circuit, the total resistance must be

$$R_t = \frac{E}{I} = \frac{120}{0.250} = 480 \ \Omega$$

Because the relay coil has a resistance of 300 Ω, the resistance to be added is

$$R_x = R_t - R_c = 480 - 300 = 180 \ \Omega$$

ALTERNATE SOLUTION   For 0.250 amp to flow through the relay coil, the voltage across the coil must be

$$E_c = IR_c = 0.250 \times 300 = 75 \text{ volts}$$

Because the line voltage is 120 volts, the voltage across the added resistance must be

$$E_x = E - E_c = 120 - 75 = 45 \text{ volts}$$

Then the value of resistance to be added is

$$R_x = \frac{E_x}{I} = \frac{45}{0.250} = 180 \ \Omega$$

EXAMPLE 13   Three resistors $R_1 = 20$ Ω, $R_2 = 50$ Ω, and $R_3 = 30$ Ω are connected in series across a generator. The current through the circuit is 2.5 amp.

(a) What is the generator voltage?
(b) What is the voltage across each resistor?
(c) How much power is expended in each resistor?
(d) What is the total power expended?

SOLUTION   The circuit is represented in Fig. 13–16.

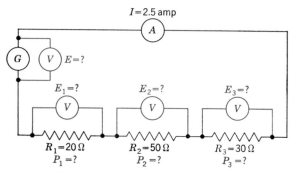

FIG. 13–16 Circuit of Example 13.

(a) $R_t = R_1 + R_2 + R_3 = 20 + 50 + 30 = 100$ Ω
                   $E = IR_t = 2.5 \times 100 = 250$ volts
(b) $E_1 = IR_1 = 2.5 \times 20 = 50$ volts
                      $E_2 = IR_2 = 2.5 \times 50 = 125$ volts
                      $E_3 = IR_3 = 2.5 \times 30 = 75$ volts
   Check: $E = E_1 + E_2 + E_3$
                          $= 50 + 125 + 75 = 250$ volts
(c) Power in R_1, $P_1 = E_1I = 50 \times 2.5 = 125$ watts
   Check: $P_1 = I^2R_1 = 2.5^2 \times 20 = 125$ watts
Power in R_2, $P_2 = E_2I = 125 \times 2.5 = 312.5$ watts
   Check: $P_2 = I^2R_2 = 2.5^2 \times 50 = 312.5$ watts
Power in R_3, $P_3 = E_3I = 75 \times 2.5 = 187.5$ watts
   Check: $P_3 = I^2R_3 = 2.5^2 \times 30 = 187.5$ watts
(d) Total power, $P_t = P_1 + P_2 + P_3$
                          $= 125 + 312.5 + 187.5 = 625$ watts
   Check: $P_t = I^2R_t = 2.5^2 \times 100 = 625$ watts

or $P_t = \dfrac{E^2}{R_t} = \dfrac{250^2}{100} = 625$ watts

PROBLEMS 13–3

1   Three resistors $R_1 = 8.38$ Ω, $R_2 = 9.35$ Ω, and $R_3 = 7.27$ Ω are connected in series across 115 volts.

(a) How much current flows in the circuit?

(b) How much power is expended in R_1?

(c) What is the voltage across R_3?

2   Three resistors $R_1 = 12.3$ Ω, $R_2 = 40.6$ Ω, and $R_3 = 18.1$ Ω are connected in series across a 230-volt generator.

(a) What is the voltage across R_3?

(b) How much power is expended in R_1?

3   A 115-volt soldering iron, which is rated at 250 watts, is to be used on a 230-volt line.

(a) How much resistance must be connected in series with the iron to limit the current to rated value?

(b) How much power will be expended in the added resistance?

4   Four lamps of equal voltage and power rating are connected in series across a 440-volt line. The current through the lamps is 909 ma.

(a) What is the resistance of each lamp?

(b) What is the power rating of each lamp?

5   A lamp of 10 Ω, a resistor of 17 Ω, and a coil of 2.1 Ω are connected in series across a generator. A voltmeter connected across the lamp reads 11 volts.

(a) How much power is expended in the coil?

(b) What is the generator voltage?

6   Three resistors R_1, R_2, and R_3 are connected in series across a 230-volt line. A voltmeter when connected across R_1 reads 24 volts; when connected across R_2, it reads 62.5 volts. $R_3 = 110$ Ω.

(a) What is the value of R_1?

(b) What is the value of R_2?

(c) How much current flows through the circuit?

(d) How much power is expended in R_1?

7   Three resistors of 10.4, 9.8, and 11.6 Ω are connected in series across a 12-volt battery. If the current through the circuit is 375 ma, what is the resistance of the connecting wires?

8   A certain broadcast tuner has been designed to use one each of the following tubes: 12BE6, 12BA6, 12AT6, and 35W4. The first three tubes require 12.6 volts for each heater (filament), and the 35W4 requires 35 volts. Since all heaters are designed for a current of 150 ma, they are to be operated in series. What value of series resistance R_s is required for operation from a 115-volt line?

9   Three resistors $R_1 = 3.8$ Ω, R_2, and R_3 are connected in series across a 120-volt generator which results in a current of 7.5 amp. The voltage across R_3 is 78 volts.

(a) What is the value of R_2?

(b) How much power is expended in the circuit?

10 Four resistors $R_1 = 72\ \Omega$, $R_2 = 100\ \Omega$, $R_3 = 56\ \Omega$, and $R_4 = 47\ \Omega$ are connected in series across a generator. The voltage across R_3 is 89.6 volts.

(a) What is the generator voltage?

(b) How much power is being supplied by the generator?

(c) What is the voltage across R_4?

13 – 9   Cathode biasing

The great majority of vacuum-tube applications require that the control grid G of the tube be maintained at a negative potential with

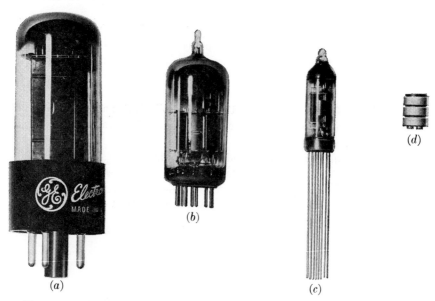

(d)

(b)

(a)   (c)

FIG. 13–17   Evolution of vacuum tubes: (a) T-9 octal base, (b) glass miniature, (c) glass subminiature, and (d) ceramic microminiature. (Shown approximately three-fourths of actual size.) (*Courtesy of General Electric Company.*)

respect to the cathode K. There are several methods of accomplishing this, and they largely depend upon the use of the tube and the circuit with which it is used. However, the most common source of bias is a resistance R_k inserted in the cathode circuit where the plate P and screen (if any) currents must flow through it. The voltage drop across this resistance is employed as a bias as illustrated in Fig. 13–20, which illustrates schematically a type 6C5 triode operating with a bias voltage of $E_g = -8$ volts. Since the plate supply voltage maintains the plate P positive with respect to the cathode K, electrons flow from cathode to plate, and these constitute the plate current I_p.

As far as the d-c circuit is concerned and therefore the bias voltage, Fig. 13-20 can be reduced to the equivalent series circuit of Fig. 13-21 wherein the signal voltage source E_s has been eliminated and the equivalent plate resistance R_p has been substituted for the cathode-to-plate electron circuit. For the purpose of illustration, the plate load resistance R_L has been eliminated from this particular example, but this cannot be done in all applications as will be shown later. In this circuit the tube is operating with a plate supply voltage of $E_b = 258$ volts, a plate voltage with respect to cathode of $E_p = 250$ volts, and a grid bias voltage with respect to cathode of $E_g = -8$ volts.

Starting at the negative source of the plate supply voltage E_b, the plate current I_p of 8 ma flows through the 1,000-Ω cathode-biasing resistor R_k, which results in a voltage of 8 volts

Fig. 13-18 Cutaway of type GL-5751 vacuum tube, shown approximately $2\frac{1}{2}$ times actual size. (*Courtesy of General Electric Company.*)

across this resistor. The polarity is such that the cathode is 8 volts positive with respect to the negative source of plate voltage, ground potential, and the grid, since all are connected together. This is the same as saying that the grid is 8 volts negative with respect to the cathode. The remaining 250 volts exists between plate P and cathode K, with the plate 250 volts positive with respect to cathode.

EXAMPLE 14   The type 6A3 triode power amplifier tube, when operating as a Class A amplifier, has a plate current of 60 ma when the plate voltage is 250 volts and the grid bias E_g is -45 volts.

(a) What value of cathode-biasing resistor R_k is necessary?

(b) How much power is consumed in the biasing resistor?

(c) Disregarding plate load resistance R_L, what is the value of the plate voltage supply E_b?

(d) How much power P_b is taken from the plate voltage supply?

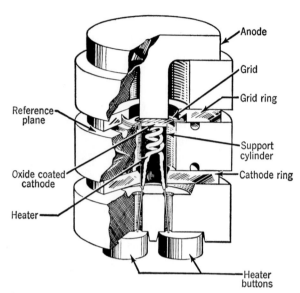

FIG. 13–19   Basic physical construction of type 6BY4 vacuum tube illustrated in Fig. 13–17d. (*Courtesy of General Electric Company.*)

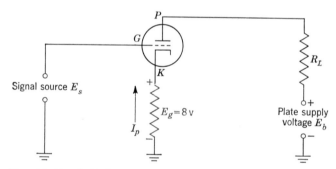

FIG. 13–20   Grid G is biased -8 volts with respect to cathode K.

SOLUTION   The circuit is shown schematically in Fig. 13–22.

(a) $$R_k = \frac{E_g}{I_p} = \frac{45}{0.060} = \frac{45}{6 \times 10^{-2}} = \frac{45}{6} \times 10^2 = 750 \ \Omega$$

(b) $$P_k = I_p{}^2 R_k = (6 \times 10^{-2})^2 \times 750 = 2.7 \text{ watts}$$

Check: $$P = \frac{E_g{}^2}{R_k} = \frac{45^2}{750} = 2.7 \text{ watts}$$

(c) $$E_b = E_p + E_g = 250 + 45 = 295 \text{ volts}$$

(d) $$P_b = E_b I_p = 17.7 \text{ watts}$$

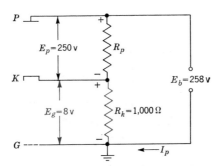

Fig. 13-21   Equivalent circuit of Fig. 13-20.

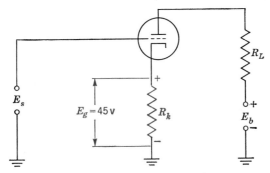

Fig. 13-22   Circuit of Example 14.

EXAMPLE 15   If the tube of Example 14 is to work into a d-c load resistance of $R_L = 2,500$ Ω, what plate supply voltage E_b will be required?

SOLUTION   The circuit is illustrated in Fig. 13-23. The voltage across the load resistance R_L is

$$E_L = I_p R_L = 0.060 \times 2,500 = 150 \text{ volts}$$

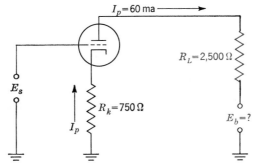

Fig. 13-23   Circuit of Example 15.

In order to maintain the original tube operating voltages, the supply voltage must be increased by 150 volts. That is,

$$E_b = 295 + 150 = 445 \text{ volts}$$

or $\qquad E_b = E_p + E_g + E_L = 250 + 45 + 150 = 445 \text{ volts}$

EXAMPLE 16   The type 6SK7 pentode has the following characteristics: Plate voltage $E_p = 250$ volts, grid bias $E_g = -3$ volts, plate current $I_p = 9.2$ ma, screen voltage $E_{sg} = 100$ volts, screen current $I_{sg} = 2.4$ ma. Disregarding the plate load resistance R_L,

(a) What value of cathode-biasing resistor is necessary?

(b) What value of series screen-grid resistor R_{sg} is needed if the screen-grid voltage is to be supplied from the positive side of the plate voltage supply?

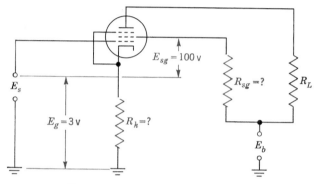

FIG. 13–24   Circuit of Example 16.

SOLUTION   The circuit is illustrated in Fig. 13–24. The control grid, which is nearest the cathode, is to be 3 volts negative with respect to cathode. The suppressor grid, which is nearest the plate, is connected directly to the cathode to suppress secondary emission. The screen grid, which is between control grid and suppressor grid, is to be operated at 100 volts positive with respect to the cathode.

(a) Since the plate current I_p and the screen current I_{sg} both flow through the cathode, the cathode current from the supply is

$$I_k = I_p + I_{sg} = 9.2 + 2.4 = 11.6 \text{ ma}$$

Then $\qquad R_k = \dfrac{E_g}{I_k} = \dfrac{3}{11.6 \times 10^{-3}} = \dfrac{30}{11.6} \times 10^2 = 259 \ \Omega$

(b) The series screen-grid dropping resistor must reduce the plate voltage of 250 to 100 volts on the screen. Therefore the voltage drop across this resistor must be

$$E = E_p - E_{sg} = 250 - 100 = 150 \text{ volts}$$

Then $\qquad R_{sg} = \dfrac{E}{I_{sg}} = \dfrac{150}{2.4 \times 10^{-3}} = \dfrac{15}{24} \times 10^4 = 62,500 \; \Omega$

PROBLEMS 13 – 4

1 The type 6A5G triode power amplifier, when operating as a Class A amplifier with a plate voltage of 300 volts, draws 11 ma of plate current when the grid bias is −10.5 volts.
   (a) What is the value of the cathode bias resistor?
   (b) Disregarding plate load resistance, what is the plate supply voltage?

2 The type 6AF5G triode, when operating as a Class A amplifier with a plate voltage of 180 volts, draws 7 ma of plate current when the grid bias is −18 volts.
   (a) What is the value of the cathode bias resistor?
   (b) How much power is expended in the bias resistor?
   (c) Disregarding plate load resistance, what is the plate supply voltage?

3 The type 12E5GT triode, when operating as a Class A amplifier with a plate voltage of 250 volts, draws 50 ma of plate current when the grid bias is −10.5 volts. The plate load resistance is 1,000 Ω.
   (a) What is the value of the cathode bias resistor?
   (b) How much power is expended in the bias resistor?
   (c) What is the plate supply voltage?
   (d) How much power is taken from the plate supply?

4 The type 14V7 high-frequency pentode, when operating as a Class A amplifier with a plate voltage of 300 volts and a screen voltage of 150 volts, draws 9.6 ma of plate current and 3.9 ma of screen current when the grid bias is −2 volts.
   (a) What is the value of the cathode bias resistor?
   (b) What is the value of the screen dropping resistor?

5 The type 6M7G pentode, when operating as a Class A amplifier with a plate voltage of 250 volts and a screen voltage of 125 volts, draws 10.5 ma of plate current and 2.8 ma of screen current when the grid bias is −2.5 volts.
   (a) What is the value of the cathode bias resistor?
   (b) How much power is expended in the bias resistor?
   (c) What is the value of the screen dropping resistor?
   (d) How much power is expended in the screen dropping resistor?
   (e) Disregarding load resistance, what is the plate supply voltage?
   (f) How much power is taken from the plate supply?

CHAPTER 14
RESISTANCE
WIRE SIZES

The effects of resistance in series circuits were discussed in the preceding chapter. However, in order to prevent confusion while the more simple relations of Ohm's law were being discussed, the nature of resistance and the resistance of wires used for connecting sources of voltage with their respective loads were not mentioned.

In the consideration of practical circuits two important features must be taken into account: the resistance of the wires between the source of power and the electric appliances that are to be furnished with power and the current-carrying capacity of these wires for a given temperature rise.

14 – 1   Resistance

There is a wide variation in the ease (conductance) of current flow through different materials. No material is a perfect conductor, and the amount of opposition (resistance) to current flow within it is governed by the specific resistance of the material, its length, cross-sectional area, and temperature. Thus, for the same material and cross-sectional area, a long conductor will have a greater resistance than a shorter one. That is, *the resistance of a conductor of uniform cross-sectional area is directly proportional to its length.* This is conveniently expressed as

$$\frac{R_1}{R_2} = \frac{L_1}{L_2} \qquad\qquad [1]$$

where R_1 and R_2 are the resistances of conductors with lengths L_1 and L_2, respectively.

EXAMPLE 1   The resistance of No. 8 copper wire is 0.641 Ω per 1,000 ft. What is the resistance of 1 mile of the wire?

SOLUTION   Given $R_1 = 0.641$ Ω, $L_1 = 1,000$ ft, and $L_2 = 1$ mile $= 5,280$ ft. $R_2 = ?$ Solving Eq. [1] for R_2,

$$R_2 = \frac{R_1 L_2}{L_1} \frac{\Omega\ \text{ft}}{\text{ft}} = \frac{0.641 \times 5,280}{1,000} \frac{\Omega\ \text{ft}}{\text{ft}} = 3.38\ \Omega$$

For the same material and length, a conductor will have more resistance than another with a larger cross-sectional area. That is, *the resistance of a conductor is inversely proportional to its cross-sectional area.* Expressed as an equation,

$$\frac{R_1}{R_2} = \frac{A_2}{A_1} \qquad\qquad [2]$$

where R_1 and R_2 are the resistances of conductors with cross-sectional areas A_1 and A_2, respectively.

Because most wires are drawn round, Eq. [2] can be rearranged into a more convenient form. For example, let A_1 and A_2 represent the cross-sectional areas of two equal lengths of round wires with diameters d_1 and d_2, respectively. Because the area A of a circle of a diameter d is given by

$$A = \frac{\pi d^2}{4}$$

then
$$A_1 = \frac{\pi d_1^2}{4}$$

and
$$A_2 = \frac{\pi d_2^2}{4}$$

Substituting in Eq. [2]
$$\frac{R_1}{R_2} = \frac{\pi d_2^2/4}{\pi d_1^2/4}$$

or
$$\frac{R_1}{R_2} = \frac{d_2^2}{d_1^2} \qquad\qquad [3]$$

Hence, the resistance of a round conductor varies inversely as the square of its diameter.

EXAMPLE 2   A rectangular conductor with a cross-sectional area of 0.01 in.² has a resistance of 0.075 Ω. What would be its resistance if the cross-sectional area were 0.02 in.²?

SOLUTION   Given $R_1 = 0.075$ Ω, $A_1 = 0.01$ in.², and $A_2 = 0.02$ in.²; $R_2 = ?$ Solving Eq. [2] for R_2,

$$R_2 = \frac{R_1 A_1}{A_2} \frac{\Omega \text{ in.}^2}{\text{in.}^2} = \frac{0.075 \times 0.01}{0.02} \frac{\Omega \text{ in.}^2}{\text{in.}^2} = 0.0375 \ \Omega$$

EXAMPLE 3   A round conductor, with a diameter of 0.25 in., has a resistance of 8 Ω. What would be its resistance if the diameter were 0.5 in.?

SOLUTION   Given $d_1 = 0.25$ in., $R_1 = 8$ Ω, and $d_2 = 0.5$ in. $R_2 = ?$ Solving Eq. [3] for R_2,

$$R_2 = \frac{R_1 d_1^2}{d_2^2} \frac{\Omega \text{ in.}^2}{\text{in.}^2} = \frac{8 \times (0.25)^2}{(0.5)^2} \frac{\Omega \text{ in.}^2}{\text{in.}^2} = 2 \ \Omega$$

Hence, if the diameter is doubled, the cross-sectional area is increased four times and the resistance is reduced to one-quarter of its original value.

PROBLEMS 14 – 1

1   Number 8 copper wire has a resistance of 0.641 Ω per 1,000 ft. What is the resistance of 2 miles of this wire?

2   The values of Prob. 1 being used, what is the resistance of 4,000 ft of No. 8 wire?

3   Number 10 copper wire has a resistance of 1.02 Ω per 1,000 ft. What is the resistance of (a) 200 ft of this wire, (b) 1 mile of this wire?

4   Number 1 wire has a resistance of approximately 0.665 Ω/mile. What is the resistance per 1,000 ft?

5   The values of Prob. 4 being used, what is the resistance of (a) 350 ft of No. 1 wire, (b) 55 ft of No. 1 wire?

6   A square conductor that is 0.50 in. on a side has a resistance of 0.0064 Ω. Another square conductor that is 0.25 in. on a side is of the same material and the same length. What is the resistance of the second conductor?

7   Number 0 copper wire, which has a diameter of 0.325 in., has a resistance of 0.100 Ω per 1,000 ft. What is the resistance of 1,000 ft of No. 7 wire which has a diameter of 0.144 in.?

8   Number 2 copper wire, which has a diameter of 0.258 in., has a resistance of 0.840 Ω/mile. What is the resistance of 800 ft of No. 6 wire, which has a diameter of 0.162 in.?

9 Number 40 copper wire has a resistance of 1,070 Ω per 1,000 ft. A coil wound with this wire was measured and found to have a resistance of 645 Ω. Find the length of wire in the coil.

10 The resistance of 50 ft of No. 20 copper wire was measured and found to be 0.52 Ω. A coil of identical wire had a resistance of 2.60 Ω. Find the length of wire in the coil.

11 It is desired to wind a milliammeter shunt having a resistance of 6.11 Ω. Number 39 enameled copper wire with a resistance of 848 Ω per 1,000 ft is available. What length of wire is required?

12 It is desired to wind a microammeter shunt having a resistance of 0.320 Ω. Number 30 enameled copper wire, with a resistance of 105 Ω per 1,000 ft is available. How much wire is required?

14 – 2   The circular mil

In the measurement of wire cross section, it is convenient to use a small unit of measurement because the diameter of a wire is usually only a small fraction of an inch. Accordingly, the diameter of a wire is expressed in terms of a unit called the *mil*, which is 1/1,000 inch. That is, there are 1,000 mils in an inch. This is easily remembered because the mil is simply a milli-inch (Sec. 11–10). For example, it is evident that using 64 mils as the diameter of No. 14 wire is more convenient than using 0.064 in.

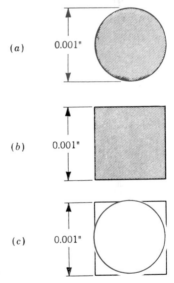

FIG. 14–1 Comparison of the circular mil and the square mil: (*a*) the circular mil, (*b*) the square mil, (*c*) circular and square mils compared.

The cross-sectional areas of round conductors are measured in terms of the circular mil. The *circular mil*, abbreviated cir mil, is the area of a circle whose diameter is 1 mil. Note that the circular mil is a unit of *area* in its own right; except for purposes of comparison, it is seldom necessary to convert wire cross sections into any other units. The relative sizes of the circular mil and the square mil are illustrated in Fig. 14–1.

The areas of circles vary as the squares of their diameters. For example, a circle whose diameter is 2 in. has four times the area of a circle having a diameter of 1 in. Similarly, the area of a circle whose diameter is 0.003 in. (3 mils) has nine times the area of a circle having a diameter of 0.001 in. (1 mil). Because, by definition, the circular mil is the area of a circle with a diameter of 1 mil, it is evident that a circle whose diameter is 3 mils must have an area of 9 cir mils. Hence the area of a circle can be expressed in circular mils by squaring the diameter, provided, however, that the diameter is expressed in mils. Conversely, if the area of a circle is expressed in circular mils, the diameter in mils can be found by extracting the square root of the area.

EXAMPLE 4   Number 10 wire has a diameter of 0.102 in. What is its circular-mil area?

SOLUTION   Given d = 0.102 in. = 102 mils.

Area = (diameter)^2 = 102^2 = 10,400 cir mils   (Sec. 11–22)

EXAMPLE 5   Number 14 wire has a cross-sectional area of 4,110 cir mils. What is the diameter?

SOLUTION   Given A = 4,110 cir mils.

Diameter = $\sqrt{\text{cir-mil area}}$ = $\sqrt{4,110}$ = 64 mils

Because the area of a circle is

$$A = \frac{\pi d^2}{4}$$

or $A = 0.7854 d^2$ square units

it follows that

Sq mils = cir mils × 0.7854   [4]

From Eq. [4],   **Cir mils = $\dfrac{\text{sq mils}}{0.7854}$**   [5]

Equations [4] and [5] are useful relations in determining the equivalence of round and rectangular conductors.

EXAMPLE 6   A bus bar is 1 in. wide and ¼ in. thick. What is its circular-mil area?

SOLUTION   Given

Width = 1 in. = 1,000 mils

Thickness = 0.25 in. = 250 mils

Area = width × thickness = 1,000 × 250 = 250,000 sq mils

Cir mils = $\dfrac{250,000}{0.7854}$ = 318,000

PROBLEMS 14 – 2

1 What is the circular-mil area of a wire 0.182 in. in diameter?

2 What is the circular-mil area of a wire 0.289 in. in diameter?

3 Find the cross-sectional area of a wire 28.5 mils in diameter.

4 Find the diameter in mils of a wire whose cross-sectional area is 254 cir mils.

5 What is the diameter in mils of a wire whose cross-sectional area is 83,690 cir mils?

6 What is the diameter in inches of a wire with a cross-sectional area of 810 cir mils?

7 A certain wire has a cross-sectional area of 33,100 cir mils. What is its area in square mils?

8 A rectangular bus bar has a cross-sectional area of 187,500 sq mils. What is its circular-mil area?

9 A wire has a cross-sectional area of 26,250 cir mils. What is the area in square inches?

10 A rectangular bus bar has a cross-sectional area of 0.50 in.^{2} Find its circular-mil area.

14 – 3   The circular-mil-foot

For the purpose of computing the resistance of wires of various areas and lengths and for comparing the resistances of wires made of different materials, it is apparent that some standardized unit of wire size is needed. Hence, the circular-mil-foot has been taken as the unit conductor. A conductor having 1 circular mil cross-sectional area and a length of 1 foot is called a *circular-mil-foot*, or a *mil-foot*, of conductor. Such a conductor is represented in Fig. 14–2.

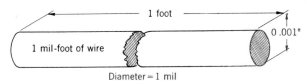

Diameter = 1 mil

FIG. 14–2   Representation of 1 cir-mil-ft of conductor.

Since the resistance of a conductor is proportional to its length and inversely proportional to the area, the resistance of any wire can be expressed by the equation

$$R = \rho \frac{l}{d^2} \quad \Omega \qquad [\,6\,]$$

where R = resistance of wire, Ω

ρ = resistance, Ω/cir-mil-ft of material composing wire

l = length of wire, ft

d = diameter of wire, mils

The factor ρ (Greek letter rho) in Eq. [6] is called the *specific resistance* or *resistivity* of the material. Thus, the specific resistance of a wire is the resistance of 1 mil-foot of that wire. Table 14–1 lists the specific resistances of a few of the materials used for conductors.

TABLE 14–1   SPECIFIC RESISTANCES AT 20°C (68°F)

Material	Ω/cir-mil-ft	Material	Ω/cir-mil-ft
Aluminum............	17.0	Lead................	132
Bismuth.............	663.	Mercury.............	565
Copper (drawn)........	10.4	Nichrome............600 to 660	
German silver.........200 to 290		Nickel...............	47
Gold................	14.7	Phosphor-bronze.......	23.7
Iron (cast)...........448 to 588		Steel................	95 to 308

EXAMPLE 7   What is the resistance at 20°C of a copper wire 250 ft long and 5.6 mils in diameter?

SOLUTION   Given l = 250 ft, d = 5.6 mils, and, from Table 14–1, ρ = 10.4 Ω. R = ? Substituting in Eq. [6],

$$R = \frac{10.4 \times 250}{5.6^2} = 82.9 \ \Omega$$

EXAMPLE 8   The resistance of a conductor 1,000 ft long and 32 mils in diameter was found to be 12 Ω at 20°C. What is the specific resistance of the wire?

SOLUTION   Given l = 1,000 ft, d = 32 mils, and R = 12 Ω. ρ = ? Solving Eq. [6] for ρ,

$$\rho = \frac{Rd^2}{l}$$

Substituting the known values, $\rho = \dfrac{12 \times 32^2}{1,000} = 12.3 \ \Omega/\text{mil-ft}$

EXAMPLE 9   A roll of copper wire was found to have a resistance of 2.54 Ω at 20°C. The diameter of the wire is 64 mils. How long is the wire?

SOLUTION   Given R = 2.54 Ω, d = 64 mils, and ρ = 10.4. l = ? Solving Eq. [6] for l,

$$l = \frac{Rd^2}{\rho}$$

Substituting the known values, $l = \dfrac{2.54 \times 64^2}{10.4} = 1,000$ ft

PROBLEMS 14-3

NOTE In the following problems, consider all wire temperatures as 20°C.

1 What is the resistance of a copper wire 400 ft long and 64 mils in diameter?

2 What is the resistance of a phosphor-bronze wire of the same dimensions as the wire in Prob. 1?

3 What is the resistance of an aluminum wire of the same dimensions as the wire in Prob. 1?

4 What is the resistance per 1,000 ft of copper wire with a diameter of 0.102 in?

5 Number 30 wire has a diameter of 0.010 in. How many feet of copper wire are required to make a resistance of 20 Ω?

6 A nichrome wire 25 ft long and 0.032 in. in diameter has a resistance of 15.3 Ω. What is the specific resistance?

7 A steel wire 100 ft long and 40 mils in diameter was measured and found to have a resistance of 6.25 Ω. What is the specific resistance of this wire?

8 A coil of copper wire was measured and found to have a resistance of 2.54 Ω and a diameter of 64 mils. What is the length of wire in the coil?

9 What is the resistance of 1 mile of the wire in Prob. 8?

10 How many miles of copper wire 0.162 in. in diameter will it take to make 5 Ω resistance?

4-4 Temperature effects

In the preceding section the specific resistance of certain materials was given at a temperature of 20°C. The reason for stating the temperature is that the resistance of all pure metals increases with a rise in temperature. The results of experiments show that over ordinary temperature ranges this variation in resistance is directly proportional to the temperature. Hence, for each degree rise in temperature above some reference value, each ohm of resistance is increased by a constant amount α, called the *temperature coefficient of resistance*. The relation between temperature and resistance can be expressed by the equation

$$R_t = R_0(1 + \alpha t) \qquad \Omega \qquad\qquad [7]$$

where R_t = resistance at a temperature of $t°C$

R_0 = resistance at 0°C

α = temperature coefficient of resistance at 0°C

The temperature coefficient for copper is 0.00427. That is, if a copper wire has a resistance of 1 Ω at 0°C, it will have a resistance of $1 + 0.00427 = 1.00427$ Ω at 1°C. The value of the temperature coefficient for copper is essentially the same as that for most of the unalloyed metals.

A more convenient relation is derived by assuming that the proportionality between resistance and temperature extends linearly to the point where copper has a resistance of 0 Ω at a temperature of -234.5°C. This results in the ratio

$$\frac{R_2}{R_1} = \frac{234.5 + t_2}{234.5 + t_1} \qquad [\,8\,]$$

where R_1 = resistance of copper in ohms at a temperature of t_1°C
       R_2 = resistance of copper in ohms at a temperature of t_2°C

EXAMPLE 10   The resistance of a coil of copper wire is 34 Ω at 15°C. What is its resistance at 70°C?
SOLUTION   Given $R_1 = 34$ Ω, $t_1 = 15$°C, and $t_2 = 70$°C. $R_2 = ?$ Solving Eq. [8] for R_2,

$$R_2 = \left(\frac{234.5 + t_2}{234.5 + t_1}\right) R_1$$

Substituting the known values,

$$R_2 = \left(\frac{234.5 + 70}{234.5 + 15}\right) \times 34 = 41.5 \ \Omega$$

The specifications for electric machines generally include a provision that the temperature of the coils, etc., when the machines are operating under a specified load for a specified time, must not rise more than a certain number of degrees. The temperature rise can be computed by measuring the resistance of the coils at room temperature and then again at the end of the test.

EXAMPLE 11   The field coils of a shunt motor have a resistance of 90 Ω at 20°C. After running the motor for 3 hr the resistance of the field coils was 146 Ω. What was the temperature of the coils?
SOLUTION   Given $R_1 = 90$ Ω, $t_1 = 20$°C, $R_2 = 146$ Ω. $t_2 = ?$ Solving Eq. [8] for t_2,

$$t_2 = \left(\frac{234.5 + t_1}{R_1}\right) R_2 - 234.5$$

Substituting the known values, $t_2 = \left(\dfrac{234.5 + 20}{90}\right) \times 146 - 234.5$

$$= 413 - 234.5 = 178.5°$$

The actual temperature rise is $t_2 - t_1 = 178.5° - 20° = 158.5°$

PROBLEMS 14 – 4

1   The resistance of a coil wound with copper wire is 3.42 Ω at 20°C. What
    will be its resistance at a temperature of 45°C?

2   The resistance of the field coils of a generator is 30 Ω at 20°C. What will
    be the resistance when the temperature has increased to 65°C?

3   What will be the resistance of the field coils of Prob. 2 at a temperature
    of −15°C?

4   The resistance of the secondary winding of a transformer was 2.50 Ω at
    20°C. After the transformer had operated under full load for 6 hr, the
    resistance of the secondary was measured and found to be 2.99 Ω. What
    was the final operating temperature?

5   The specifications for the manufacture of a motor included a provision
    that it was to operate continuously under full load with the temperature
    of the field coils not to exceed 90°C. The resistance of the coils was
    measured and found to be 25.4 Ω at a temperature of 20°C. After running
    for 24 hr the machine was shut down and the resistance of the coils meas-
    ured. Their resistance was 32.6 Ω. Did the motor meet the specifications?

14 – 5   Wire measure

Wire sizes are designated by numbers in a system known as the
American wire gauge (formerly Brown and Sharpe gauge). These
numbers, ranging from 0000, the largest size, to 40, the smallest size,
are based on a constant ratio between successive gauge numbers.
Table 5 lists the wire sizes in addition to other pertinent data.

Inspection of the wire table will reveal that the progression
formed by the wire diameters serves as an aid in remembering
relative wire sizes and the respective resistances. For example,
No. 10 wire is a convenient reference because it is nearly 1/10 in.
in diameter and has a cross-sectional area of approximately 10,000
cir mils. Moreover, its resistance is very nearly 1 Ω per 1,000 ft.
As the wire sizes become smaller, every third gauge number results
in one-half the area and, therefore, double the resistance. Hence,
No. 13 wire (three numbers from No. 10) has an area of about
5,000 cir mils and a resistance of approximately 2 Ω per 1,000 ft.
Similarly, by using additional approximations, No. 16 has an area of
2,500 cir mils with a resistance of 4 Ω per 1,000 ft, No. 19 has an area of
1,250 cir mils with a resistance of 8 Ω per 1,000 ft, etc. Conversely,
as the wire sizes become larger, every third gauge number results in
twice the circular-mil area and half the resistance. For example,
No. 7 has an approximate area of 20,000 cir mils, with a resistance of
nearly 0.5 Ω per 1,000 ft.

14 – 6   Factors governing wire size in practice

From an electrical viewpoint, three factors govern the selection of the
size of wire to be used for transmitting current:

1. The safe current-carrying capacity of the wire
2. The power lost in the wire
3. The allowable voltage variation, or the voltage drop, in the
wire

It must be remembered that the length of wire, for the purpose of
computing wire resistance and its effects, is always twice the distance
from the source of power to the load (outgoing and return leads).

EXAMPLE 12   A motor receives its power through No. 4 wire from a
generator located at a distance of 1,000 ft. The voltage across the motor is
220 volts, and the current taken by the motor is 19.8 amp. What is the
brush potential of the generator?

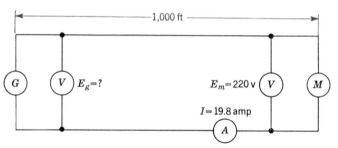

Fig. 14–3   Generator G supplying power to motor M at a distance of 1,000 ft.

SOLUTION   The circuit is represented in Fig. 14–3. Note that it consists
of a simple series circuit which can be simplified to that of Fig. 14–4. The
resistance of the 1,000 ft of No. 4 wire from the generator to the motor is
represented by R_o; reference to Table 5 shows it to be 0.253 Ω. Similarly,
the resistance from the motor back to the generator, which is represented by
R_r, is also 0.253 Ω. The voltage drop in *each* wire is

$$E = IR_o = IR_r = 19.8 \times 0.253 = 5.01 \text{ volts}$$

Since the applied voltage must equal the sum of all the voltage drops
around the circuit (Sec. 13–8), the brush potential of the generator is

$$E_g = 220 + 5.01 + 5.01 = 230.02 \text{ or } 230 \text{ volts}$$

Since the resistance out R_o is equal to the return resistance R_r, the foregoing solution is simplified by taking twice the actual wire distance for the
length of wire that comprises the resistance of the feeders. Therefore, the

length of No. 4 wire between generator and motor is 2,000 ft, which results in a line resistance R_L of

$$2 \times 0.253 = 0.506 \ \Omega$$

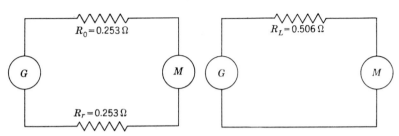

FIG. 14–4 Simplified circuit of that shown in Fig. 14–3.

FIG. 14–5 Equivalent circuit of circuits shown in Figs. 14–3 and 14–4.

The circuit can be further simplified as shown in Fig. 14–5.
Thus, the generator brush potential is

$$E_g = 220 + IR_L = 220 + (19.8 \times 0.506) = 230 \text{ volts}$$

The power lost in the line is

$$P_L = I^2 R_L = 19.8^2 \times 0.506 = 198 \text{ watts}$$

The power taken by the motor is

$$P_M = E_M I = 220 \times 19.8 = 4,356 \text{ watts} = 4.356 \text{ kw}$$

The power delivered by the generator is

$$P_G = P_L + P_M = 198 + 4,356 = 4,554 \text{ watts}$$

$$\text{Efficiency of transmission} = \frac{\text{power delivered to load}}{\text{power delivered by generator}} \qquad [\,9\,]$$

$$= \frac{4,356}{4,554} = 0.956 = 95.6 \text{ per cent}$$

The efficiency of transmission is obtainable in terms of the generator terminal voltage E_G and the voltage across the load E_L. Because

$$\text{Power delivered to load} = E_L I$$

and   Power delivered by generator $= E_G I$

substituting in Eq. [9],

$$\text{Efficiency of transmission} = \frac{E_L I}{E_G I} = \frac{E_L}{E_G} \qquad [\,10\,]$$

Substituting the voltages in Eq. [10],

$$\text{Efficiency of transmission} = \frac{220}{230} = 0.956 = 95.6 \text{ per cent}$$

PROBLEMS 14 – 5

NOTE   All wires in the following problems are copper with characteristics as listed in Table 5.

1 (a) What is the resistance of 3,000 ft of No. 00 wire?
   (b) What is its weight?

2 (a) What is the resistance of 2 miles of No. 6 wire?
   (b) What is its weight?

3 A coil of No. 8 wire weighs 100 lb.
   (a) What is the length of wire in the coil?
   (b) What is the resistance of the coil?

4 The resistance of a coil of No. 14 wire was measured and found to be 12.9 Ω.
   (a) How much does the coil weigh?
   (b) What is the length of wire in the coil?

5 A telephone cable consisting of several pairs of No. 19 wire connects two cities 45 miles apart. If a pair is short-circuited at one end, what will be the resistance of the loop thus formed?

6 A solenoid is to be wound with 1,500 turns of No. 18 wire. If the average diameter of a turn is 4.2 in., what will be the resistance?

7 Fifteen kilowatts of power is to be transmitted 500 ft from a generator that maintains a constant terminal voltage of 240 volts. If not over 5 per cent line drop is allowed, what size wire must be used?

8 A generator with a constant brush potential of 230 volts is feeding a motor 175 ft away. The feeders are No. 6 wire, and the motor current is 27.7 amp.
   (a) What would a voltmeter read if connected across the motor brushes?
   (b) What is the efficiency of transmission?

9 A motor requiring 34 amp at 230 volts is located 365 ft from a generator that maintains a constant terminal voltage of 240 volts.
   (a) What size wire must be used between generator and motor in order to supply the motor with rated current and voltage?
   (b) What will be the efficiency of transmission?

10 A 25-hp 230-volt motor is to be installed 350 ft from a generator that maintains a constant potential of 240 volts.
   (a) If the motor is 84 per cent efficient, what size wire should be used between motor and generator?
   (b) If the wire specified in (a) is used, what will be the motor voltage under rated load condition?

CHAPTER 15

SPECIAL PRODUCTS

FACTORING

In the study of arithmetic, it is necessary to memorize the multiplication tables as an aid to rapid computation. Similarly, in the study of algebra, certain forms of expressions occur so frequently that it is essential to be able to multiply, divide, or factor them by inspection.

5 – 1 Factoring

To *factor* an algebraic expression means to find two or more expressions that when multiplied will result in the original expression.

EXAMPLE 1 $2 \times 3 \times 4 = 24$. Thus, 2, 4, and 3 are some of the factors of 24.

EXAMPLE 2 $b(x + y) = bx + by$. b and $(x + y)$ are the factors of $bx + by$.

EXAMPLE 3 $(x + 4)(x - 3) = x^2 + x - 12$. The quantities $(x + 4)$ and $(x - 3)$ are the factors of $x^2 + x - 12$.

5 – 2 Prime numbers

A number that has no factor other than itself and unity is known as a *prime number*. Thus, 3, 5, 13, x, and $(a + b)$ are prime numbers.

15 – 3   The square of a monomial

The student should review the law of exponents for multiplication in Sec. 9–3.

EXAMPLE 4 $(2ab^2)^2 = (2ab^2)(2ab^2) = 4a^2b^4$

EXAMPLE 5 $(-3x^2y^3)^2 = (-3x^2y^3)(-3x^2y^3) = 9x^4y^6$

By application of the rules for the multiplication of numbers having like signs and the law of exponents, we have the following rule:

RULE   To square a monomial, square the numerical coefficient and multiply this product by the literal factors of the monomial, multiplying the exponent of each letter by 2.

15 – 4   The cube of a monomial

EXAMPLE 6 $(3a^2b)^3 = (3a^2b)(3a^2b)(3a^2b) = 27a^6b^3$

EXAMPLE 7 $(-2xy^3)^3 = (-2xy^3)(-2xy^3)(-2xy^3) = -8x^3y^9$

Note that the cube of a *positive* number is always *positive* and that the cube of a *negative* number is always *negative*. Again, by application of the rules for the multiplication of positive and negative numbers and the law of exponents, we have the following rule:

RULE   To cube a monomial, cube the numerical coefficient, multiply this product by the literal factors of the monomial, multiply the exponent of each letter by 3, and affix the same sign as the monomial.

PROBLEMS 15 – 1

Find the values of the following indicated powers:

1   $(\pi R)^2$

2   $(ab)^3$

3   $(ei^2Z^2)^3$

4   $(-6\pi^2\theta)^2$

5   $\left(3\dfrac{E}{R}\right)^2$

6   $(2\phi^3\theta^2)^3$

7   $(-3I^2R)^3$

8   $(-9e^2i)^2$

9   $\left(-5\dfrac{i^2z}{e}\right)^3$

10   $-(\omega^2\theta^3\phi)^2$

11   $-(-12x^2yz^3)^2$

12   $-(-4\pi^2rl^3)^3$

13   $(-6EI^2R)^3$

14   $(13\lambda^2fC)^2$

15   $(4\pi^2fL^2C)^3$

16   $\left(-\dfrac{3\alpha^2\beta\pi}{4\theta^2}\right)^2$

17   $-\left(\dfrac{4m^2n^2}{5}\right)^2$

18   $-\left(-\dfrac{i^2r}{3P}\right)^2$

19   $-\left(\dfrac{2}{3}\alpha^2\beta r^2\right)^3$

20   $-\left(-\dfrac{3\theta^2\phi\pi^3}{\omega^2\lambda}\right)^3$

5 – 5   The square root of a monomial

The *square root* of an expression is one of its equal factors.

EXAMPLE 8 $\sqrt{3}$ is a number such that
$$\sqrt{3} \cdot \sqrt{3} = 3$$
EXAMPLE 9 $\sqrt{n}$ is a number such that
$$\sqrt{n} \cdot \sqrt{n} = n$$

Because $(+2)(+2) = +4$
and $(-2)(-2) = +4$

it is apparent that 4 has two square roots, $+2$ and -2. Similarly, 16 has two square roots, $+4$ and -4.

In general, every number has two square roots, equal in magnitude, one positive and one negative. The positive root is known as the *principal root;* if no sign precedes the radical, the positive root is understood. Thus, in practical numerical computations, the following is understood:
$$\sqrt{4} = +2$$
and $-\sqrt{4} = -2$

In dealing with literal numbers, the values of the various factors often are unknown. Therefore, when extracting a square root we affix the double sign $\pm$ to denote "plus or minus."

EXAMPLE 10   Since $a^4 \cdot a^4 = a^8$ and $(-a^4)(-a^4) = a^8$,
then $\sqrt{a^8} = \pm a^4$
EXAMPLE 11   Since $x^2y^3 \cdot x^2y^3 = x^4y^6$ and $(-x^2y^3)(-x^2y^3) = x^4y^6$,
then $\sqrt{x^4y^6} = \pm x^2y^3$

From the foregoing examples, we formulate the following:

RULE   To extract the square root of a monomial, extract the square root of the numerical coefficient, divide the exponents of the letters by 2, and affix the $\pm$ sign.

EXAMPLE 12 $\sqrt{4a^4b^2} = \pm 2a^2b$
EXAMPLE 13 $\sqrt{\tfrac{1}{9}x^2y^6z^4} = \pm\tfrac{1}{3}xy^3z^2$

NOTE   A perfect monomial square is positive and has a perfect square numerical coefficient and only even numbers as exponents.

5 – 6   Cube root of a monomial

The *cube root* of a monomial is one of its three equal factors.

Because $(+2)(+2)(+2) = 8$

then $\qquad\qquad\qquad \sqrt[3]{8} = 2$

Similarly, $\qquad\qquad (-2)(-2)(-2) = -8$

and $\qquad\qquad\qquad \sqrt[3]{-8} = -2$

From this it is evident that the cube root of a monomial has the same sign as the monomial itself.

Because $\qquad\qquad x^2y^3 \cdot x^2y^3 \cdot x^2y^3 = x^6y^9$

then $\qquad\qquad\qquad \sqrt[3]{x^6y^9} = x^2y^3$

The above results can be stated as follows:

RULE   To extract the cube root of a monomial, extract the cube root of the numerical coefficient, divide the exponents of the letters by 3, and affix the same sign as the monomial.

EXAMPLE 14 $\qquad \sqrt[3]{8x^6y^3z^{12}} = 2x^2yz^4$

EXAMPLE 15 $\qquad \sqrt[3]{-27a^3b^9c^6} = -3ab^3c^2$

NOTE   A perfect cube monomial has a positive or negative perfect cube numerical coefficient and exponents that are exactly divisible by 3.

PROBLEMS 15 – 2

Find the value of the following:

1 $\sqrt{6^2}$	2 $\sqrt{2^2 \cdot 4^2}$	3 $\sqrt{4i^2}$
4 $\sqrt{9r^4}$	5 $\sqrt{25\lambda^2}$	6 $\sqrt{16e^2i^4}$
7 $\sqrt{36\theta^2\phi^4\omega^2}$	8 $\sqrt[3]{-27}$	9 $\sqrt[3]{(-3)^6}$
10 $\sqrt{144\alpha^2\beta^4R^8}$	11 $3\sqrt{4\theta^4}$	12 $\sqrt{100\pi^2f^2L^4}$
13 $\sqrt[3]{27^3}$	14 $\sqrt[5]{32\omega^{10}C^5}$	15 $\sqrt[3]{-216E^3I^6R^9}$
16 $\sqrt{\dfrac{16}{25}i^2r^4z^2}$	17 $\sqrt{\dfrac{64\theta^2\phi^4}{100\alpha^4\beta^6}}$	18 $\sqrt[3]{-\dfrac{27Z^3R^9X^{12}}{343\omega^6\lambda^9}}$
19 $-\sqrt[3]{-\dfrac{8i^6r^3z^3}{512e^3i^3P^6}}$	20 $\sqrt{\dfrac{49\alpha^6\beta^2\gamma^8}{144\theta^2\phi^4\pi^{10}}}$	21 $\sqrt[3]{-\dfrac{125E^6I^3Z^9}{729e^3i^6z^3}}$
22 $\sqrt[5]{\dfrac{243\pi^{10}\omega^{15}\lambda^5}{32r^5z^{10}}}$	23 $-\sqrt[3]{\dfrac{8a^3b^6c^3d^{12}}{343x^6y^3z^9}}$	24 $\sqrt{\dfrac{169r^6s^2t^4u^8}{225m^4n^2p^{10}}}$
25 $-\sqrt[3]{\dfrac{1,331\alpha^3\beta^9\gamma^{12}}{216\omega^6f^3\phi^{15}}}$		

15 – 7   **Polynomials with a common monomial factor**

Type: $\qquad\qquad a(b + c + d) = ab + ac + ad$

RULE   To factor polynomials whose terms contain a common monomial factor,

1 Determine by inspection the greatest common factor of its terms.
2 Divide the polynomial by this factor.
3 Write the quotient in parentheses preceded by the monomial factor.

EXAMPLE 16   Factor $3x^2 - 9xy^2$.

SOLUTION   The common monomial factor of both terms is $3x$.
$$\therefore 3x^2 - 9xy^2 = 3x(x - 3y^2)$$

EXAMPLE 17   Factor $2a - 6a^2b + 4ax - 10ay^3$.

SOLUTION   Each term contains the factor $2a$.
$$\therefore 2a - 6a^2b + 4ax - 10ay^3 = 2a(1 - 3ab + 2x - 5y^3)$$

EXAMPLE 18   Factor $14x^2yz^3 - 7xy^2z^2 + 35xz^5$.

SOLUTION   Each term contains the factor $7xz^2$.
$$\therefore 14x^2yz^3 - 7xy^2z^2 + 35xz^5 = 7xz^2(2xyz - y^2 + 5z^3)$$

PROBLEMS 15-3

Factor:

1 $3e + 9$

2 $\dfrac{1}{4}\theta + \dfrac{1}{8}\phi$

3 $6\alpha + \alpha\beta + 7\alpha^2$

4 $\dfrac{1}{3}\omega^2 f - \dfrac{1}{6}\omega f^2 + \dfrac{1}{9}\omega f$

5 $3R + 15I^2R$

6 $2\dfrac{E^2}{R} + 16\dfrac{E^3}{R^2} - 8\dfrac{E^2r^2}{R}$

7 $\dfrac{1}{12}\pi^4r^5 - \dfrac{1}{8}\pi^2r - \dfrac{1}{4}\pi r^3$

8 $4\pi^2f^2L^2 - 2\pi fL + 30\pi^3fL$

9 $3i^2r - 27ir^2 - 15irz$

10 $\dfrac{1}{6}\alpha^4\beta - \dfrac{1}{3}\alpha^3\beta + \dfrac{1}{9}\alpha^2\beta^2$

11 $70\theta^3\phi^2 + 28\theta^2\phi^3 - 42\theta\phi^4$

12 $\dfrac{1}{81}R^2r + \dfrac{1}{27}R^2r^3 + \dfrac{1}{18}R^4r^2$

13 $52E^2I^2Z - 39E^6I^3Z^4 + 26E^2I^3Z^4$

14 $\dfrac{1}{15}\omega\lambda^2 + \dfrac{1}{20}\omega^2\lambda^3 - \dfrac{1}{5}\omega\lambda$

15 $\dfrac{1}{6}\alpha^4\beta^2\theta^3\phi - \dfrac{1}{18}\alpha^2\beta\theta^4\phi^2 + \dfrac{1}{3}\alpha\beta\theta$

15-8 The square of a binomial

Type: $(a + b)^2 = a^2 + 2ab + b^2$

The multiplication

$$
\begin{array}{r}
a + b \\
a + b \\
\hline
a^2 + ab \\
+\, ab + b^2 \\
\hline
a^2 + 2ab + b^2
\end{array}
$$

results in the formula

$$(a + b)^2 = a^2 + 2ab + b^2$$

which can be expressed by the following rule:

RULE   To square the sum of two terms, square the first term, add twice the product of the two terms, and add the square of the second term.

EXAMPLE 19   Square $(2b + 4cd)$.

SOLUTION $(2b + 4cd)^2 = (2b)^2 + 2(2b)(4cd) + (4cd)^2$
$$= 4b^2 + 16bcd + 16c^2d^2$$

EXAMPLE 20   Let x and y be represented by lengths.   Then
$$(x + y)^2 = x^2 + 2xy + y^2$$
can be illustrated graphically as shown in Fig. 15–1.

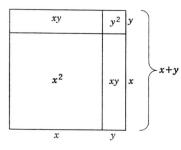

The multiplication

$$\begin{array}{r} a - b \\ a - b \\ \hline a^2 - ab \\ - ab + b^2 \\ \hline a^2 - 2ab + b^2 \end{array}$$

results in the formula

$$(a - b)^2 = a^2 - 2ab + b^2$$

FIG. 15–1   Graphical illustration of $(x + y)^2 = x^2 + 2xy + y^2$.

which can be expressed as follows:

RULE   To square the difference of two terms, square the first term, subtract twice the product of the two terms, and add the square of the second term.

EXAMPLE 21   Square $(3a^2 - 5xy)$.

SOLUTION $(3a^2 - 5xy)^2 = (3a^2)^2 - 2(3a^2)(5xy) + (5xy)^2$
$$= 9a^4 - 30a^2xy + 25x^2y^2$$

EXAMPLE 22   Let x and y be represented by lengths.   Then

$$(x - y)^2 = x^2 - 2xy + y^2$$

can be illustrated graphically as shown in Fig. 15–2. x^2 is the large square. The figure shows that the two rectangles taken from x^2 leave $(x - y)^2$. Since an amount y^2 is a part of one xy that has been subtracted from x^2 and is outside x^2, we must add it.   Hence, we obtain

$$(x - y)^2 = x^2 - 2xy + y^2$$

Practice squaring sums and differences of binomials mentally by following the foregoing rules. Proficiency in these and later methods will greatly reduce the labor in performing multiplications.

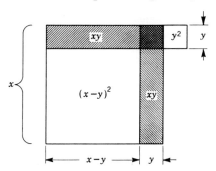

Fig. 15-2   Graphical illustration of $(x - y)^2 = x^2 - 2xy + y^2$.

PROBLEMS 15 – 4

Square the following mentally:

1 $r + 4$	2 $R - 6$	3 $Z + 5$
4 $2\omega + f$	5 $\theta + 4\phi$	6 $\lambda - 3F$
7 $3\alpha - \beta$	8 $I + 4R$	9 $3Z - X$
10 $r + 6R$	11 $3\mu - 2\gamma$	12 $\theta^2 + \phi^3$
13 $9\alpha^2 - 6\beta^2$	14 $5L^2 - 8C^2$	15 $1 + F^2$
16 $\omega^2 + 3f^3$	17 $9E^2 - 7e^2$	18 $7R + r^2$
19 $8Z^2 - 1$	20 $2\alpha^2 + 4\beta^3$	21 $6\theta\phi - \omega^2$
22 $3i^2 + 5I$	23 $5\mu^2 - 3$	24 $3L^3 + 4f^2$
25 $5r^2 - 11Z$		

Expand:

26 $(e + \frac{1}{3})^2$	27 $(\alpha - \frac{1}{2})^2$	28 $(\beta + \frac{1}{4})^2$
29 $(\mu - \frac{1}{9})^2$	30 $(R + \frac{2}{3})^2$	31 $(E - \frac{5}{8})^2$
32 $(Z + \frac{2}{7})^2$	33 $(\lambda^2 - \frac{5}{6})^2$	34 $(L^2 + \frac{4}{5})^2$
35 $(f^2 - \frac{3}{8})^2$		

15 – 9   The square root of a trinomial

In the preceding section, it was shown that

$$(a + b)^2 = a^2 + 2ab + b^2$$

and
$$(a - b)^2 = a^2 - 2ab + b^2$$

From these and other binomials that have been squared, it is evident that a trinomial is a perfect square if

1   Two terms are squares of monomials and positive.

2   The other term is twice the product of these monomials and has affixed either a plus or a minus sign.

EXAMPLE 23 $x^2 + 2xy + y^2$ is a perfect trinomial square because x^2 and y^2 are the squares of the monomials x and y, respectively, and $2xy$ is twice the product of the monomials. Therefore,

$$x^2 + 2xy + y^2 = (x + y)^2$$

EXAMPLE 24 $4a^2 - 12ab + 9b^2$ is a perfect trinomial square because $4a^2$ and $9b^2$ are the squares of $2a$ and $3b$, respectively, and the other term is $-2(2a)(3b)$. Therefore,

$$4a^2 - 12ab + 9b^2 = (2a - 3b)^2$$

RULE   To extract the square root of a perfect trinomial square, extract the square roots of the two perfect square monomials and connect them with the sign of the remaining term.

EXAMPLE 25   Supply the missing term in $x^4 + (?) + 16$ so that the three will form a perfect trinomial square.
SOLUTION   The missing term is twice the product of the monomials whose squares result in the two known terms; that is, $2(x^2)(4) = 8x^2$. Hence,

$$x^4 + 8x^2 + 16 = (x^2 + 4)^2$$

EXAMPLE 26   Supply the missing term in $25a^2 + 30ab + (?)$ so that the three will form a perfect trinomial square.
SOLUTION   The square root of the first term is $5a$. The missing term is the square of some number N such that $2(5a)(N) = 30ab$. Multiplying, we obtain $10aN = 30ab$, or $N = 3b$. Therefore,

$$25a^2 + 30ab + 9b^2 = (5a + 3b)^2$$

PROBLEMS 15 – 5

Supply the missing terms so that the three form a perfect trinomial square:

1   $i^2 + (?) + 25$ 2 $E^2 + (?) + I^2$

3   $I^2 - (?) + 36R^2$ 4 $25C^2 - (?) + 4$

5   $\theta^2 + (?) + 49\lambda^2$ 6 $16x^2 + (?) + 100y^2$

7   $81r^2 - (?) + 25R^2$ 8 $4\alpha^2 + 16\alpha + (?)$

9   $(?) - 54\alpha^2\beta + 81\beta^2$ 10 $\omega^2 + 22\omega f^2 + (?)$

11   $\dfrac{1}{4}m^2 - (?) + \dfrac{1}{9}n^2$ 12 $\dfrac{1}{16}\beta^2 + \dfrac{1}{14}\beta + (?)$

13   $\dfrac{1}{25} - \dfrac{2}{15}\alpha + (?)$ 14 $(?) + \dfrac{2}{9}xy + \dfrac{1}{9}y^2$

15   $\dfrac{1}{36}\phi^2 - \dfrac{1}{24}\phi\theta + (?)$

Extract the square roots of the following:

16 $i^2 + 12ir + 36r^2$ 17 $64\alpha^2\beta^2 - 48\alpha\beta\theta + 9\theta^2$

18 $54ab + 81b^2 + 9a^2$ 19 $100E^2 + e^2 - 20eE$

20 $84rZ + 49Z^2 + 36r^2$ 21 $\frac{1}{4} - \omega + \omega^2$

22 $\dfrac{\theta^2}{9} - \dfrac{2\theta\pi}{3} + \pi^2$ 23 $\dfrac{4}{81}x^2 + \dfrac{1}{9}y^2 - \dfrac{4}{27}xy$

24 $\dfrac{12}{35}rR + \dfrac{4}{49}R^2 + \dfrac{9}{25}r^2$ 25 $9I^2 + \dfrac{4i^2}{25} - \dfrac{12iI}{5}$

–10 Prime factors of an expression

In factoring a number, all its prime factors should be obtained. After factoring an expression once, it may be possible to factor it again.

EXAMPLE 27 Find the prime factors of $12i^2r + 12iIr + 3I^2r$.

SOLUTION $12i^2r + 12iIr + 3I^2r = 3r(4i^2 + 4iI + I^2)$
$$= 3r(2i + I)(2i + I) = 3r(2i + I)^2$$

PROBLEMS 15 – 6

Find the prime factors of the following:

1 $4a^2c + 8abc + 4b^2c$ 2 $75i^2r^2 - 90i^2rz + 27i^2z^2$

3 $6\alpha^2\theta - 12\alpha\beta\theta + 6\beta^2\theta$ 4 $36e^2E + 24eE + 4E$

5 $112x^2z^2 + 343y^2z^2 - 392xyz^2$ 6 $\dfrac{5e^2I^2}{r} + \dfrac{45e^2i^2}{r} - \dfrac{30e^2Ii}{r}$

7 $\dfrac{150eE}{R} + \dfrac{125e}{R} + \dfrac{45eE^2}{R}$ 8 $\dfrac{\beta\theta^2}{\alpha} + \dfrac{\beta}{16\alpha} - \dfrac{\beta\theta}{2\alpha}$

9 $\dfrac{\omega}{4\pi} + \dfrac{\omega f^4}{\pi} - \dfrac{\omega f^2}{\pi}$ 10 $\dfrac{252F^2fL}{C} + \dfrac{21LF^4}{C} + \dfrac{756f^2L}{C}$

–11 The product of the sum and difference of two numbers

Type: $(a + b)(a - b) = a^2 - b^2$

The multiplication of the sum and difference of two general numbers, such as

$$
\begin{array}{r}
a + b \\
a - b \\
\hline
a^2 + ab \\
\quad - ab - b^2 \\
\hline
a^2 \qquad - b^2
\end{array}
$$

results in the formula

$$(a + b)(a - b) = a^2 - b^2$$

which can be expressed by the following:

RULE   The product of the sum and difference of two numbers is equal to the difference of their squares.

EXAMPLE 28 $(3x + 4y)(3x - 4y) = 9x^2 - 16y^2$

EXAMPLE 29 $(6ab^2 + 7c^3d)(6ab^2 - 7c^3d) = 36a^2b^4 - 49c^6d^2$

PROBLEMS 15 – 7

Multiply by inspection:

1 $(R + 3)(R - 3)$ 2 $(Z - z)(Z + z)$

3 $(2I - 3r)(2I + 3r)$ 4 $(3E + e)(3E - e)$

5 $(5\alpha - 2\beta)(5\alpha + 2\beta)$ 6 $(\frac{1}{2} + \theta)(\frac{1}{2} - \theta)$

7 $\left(\dfrac{\alpha}{\beta} - \dfrac{2\gamma}{3}\right)\left(\dfrac{\alpha}{\beta} + \dfrac{2\gamma}{3}\right)$ 8 $\left(\dfrac{3I^2R}{4} + \dfrac{2E^2}{R}\right)\left(\dfrac{3I^2R}{4} - \dfrac{2E^2}{R}\right)$

9 $\left(\dfrac{2e}{5} - \dfrac{3ir}{7}\right)\left(\dfrac{2e}{5} + \dfrac{3ir}{7}\right)$ 10 $\left(\dfrac{\theta^2}{10\phi} + \dfrac{\omega}{8}\right)\left(\dfrac{\theta^2}{10\phi} - \dfrac{\omega}{8}\right)$

15 – 12   Factoring the difference of two squares

RULE   To factor the difference of two squares, extract the square root of the two squares, add the roots for one factor, and subtract the second from the first for the other factor.

EXAMPLE 30 $x^2 - y^2 = (x + y)(x - y)$

EXAMPLE 31 $9a^2c^4 - 36d^6 = (3ac^2 + 6d^3)(3ac^2 - 6d^3)$

PROBLEMS 15 – 8

Factor:

1 $I^2 - i^2$ 2 $R^2 - 16r^2$ 3 $9\alpha^2 - \beta^2$

4 $1 - E^2$ 5 $25\omega^2 - 49f^2$ 6 $4\theta^2 - 81\phi^2$

7 $4\lambda^2 - 1$ 8 $\dfrac{e^2}{36} - 49$ 9 $16 - \dfrac{\omega^2 f^2}{9}$

10 $\dfrac{1}{\lambda^2} - \dfrac{25\mu^2}{64}$ 11 $\dfrac{1}{4} - 225\beta^2$ 12 $\dfrac{1}{49}Z^2 - \dfrac{100}{z^2}$

13 $\dfrac{121F^2}{169f_1^2} - \dfrac{\omega^2}{16}$ 14 $\dfrac{E^2}{R^2} - \dfrac{Z^2}{r^2}$ 15 $\dfrac{1}{\theta^2} - \dfrac{9\phi^2}{\pi^2}$

15 – 13   The product of two binomials having a common term

Type: $(x + a)(x + b) = x^2 + (a + b)x + ab$

The multiplication

$$
\begin{array}{l}
x + a \\
x + b \\
\hline
x^2 + ax \\
 + bx + ab \\
\hline
x^2 + ax + bx + ab
\end{array}
$$

when factored, results in $x^2 + (a + b)x + ab$.

This type of formula can be expressed as follows:

RULE   To obtain the product of two binomials having a common term, square the common term, multiply the common term by the algebraic sum of the second terms of the binomials, find the product of the second terms, and add the results.

EXAMPLE 32   Find the product of $x - 7$ and $x + 5$.

SOLUTION $(x - 7)(x + 5) = x^2 + (-7 + 5)x + (-7)(+5)$
$$= x^2 - 2x - 35$$

EXAMPLE 33 $(ir + 3)(ir - 6) = i^2r^2 + (+3 - 6)ir + (+3)(-6)$
$$= i^2r^2 - 3ir - 18$$

Although the above examples have been written out in order to illustrate the method, the actual multiplication should be mental. In Example 33 above, the i^2r^2 term is written first.   Then one glances at the $+3$ and -6, notes that their sum is -3 and the product is -18, and writes down the complete product.

PROBLEMS 15 - 9

Multiply the following mentally:

1	$(x + 2)(x + 3)$	2	$(R + 1)(R + 4)$
3	$(i + 3)(i + 1)$	4	$(\theta + 6)(\theta + 4)$
5	$(E - 6)(E - 7)$	6	$(I - 3)(I - 4)$
7	$(\omega - 2)(\omega - 12)$	8	$(r - 13)(r - 3)$
9	$(\pi + 2)(\pi - 1)$	10	$(I - 7)(I + 5)$
11	$(P + 1)(P - 13)$	12	$(f - 20)(f + 3)$
13	$(\alpha + \frac{1}{3})(\alpha + 6)$	14	$(\lambda + 4)(\lambda + \frac{1}{2})$
15	$(\phi - \frac{1}{5})(\phi - 5)$	16	$(IR - \frac{1}{3})(IR - \frac{1}{6})$

17   $\left(\mu + \frac{2}{3}\right)\left(\mu - \frac{1}{3}\right)$ 18 $\left(\frac{2e}{r} - i\right)\left(\frac{2e}{r} + \frac{i}{4}\right)$

19   $\left(\frac{W}{10} + \frac{P}{5}\right)\left(\frac{W}{10} - \frac{2P}{5}\right)$ 20 $\left(\alpha\theta^2 + \frac{1}{4}\right)\left(\alpha\theta^2 - \frac{1}{2}\right)$

15 – 14   Factoring trinomials of the form $a^2 + ba + c$

A trinomial of this form can be factored if it is the product of two binomials having a common term.

RULE   To factor a trinomial of the form $a^2 + ba + c$, find two num-. bers whose sum is b and whose product is c.   Add each of them to the square root of the first term for the factors.

EXAMPLE 34   Factor $a^2 + 7a + 12$.

SOLUTION   It is necessary to find the two numbers whose product is $+12$ and whose sum is $+7$. The factors of 12 are

$$1 \times 12$$
$$2 \times 6$$
$$3 \times 4$$

The first two pairs will not do because their sums are not 7. The third pair gives the correct sum.

$$\therefore a^2 + 7a + 12 = (a + 3)(a + 4)$$

EXAMPLE 35   Factor $x^2 - 15x + 36$.

SOLUTION   Since the 36 is positive, its factors must bear the same sign; also, since -15 is negative, it follows that both factors must be negative. The factors of 36 are

$$1 \times 36$$
$$2 \times 18$$
$$3 \times 12$$
$$4 \times 9$$
$$6 \times 6$$

Inspection of these factors shows that 3 and 12 are the required numbers.

$$\therefore x^2 - 15x + 36 = (x - 3)(x - 12)$$

EXAMPLE 36   Factor $e^2 - e - 56$.

SOLUTION   Since we have -56, the two factors must have unlike signs. The sum of the factors must equal -1; therefore the negative factor of -56 must have the greater absolute value. The factors of 56 are

$$1 \times 56$$
$$2 \times 28$$
$$4 \times 14$$
$$7 \times 8$$

Since the factors 7 and 8 differ in value by 1, we have

$$e^2 - e - 56 = (e + 7)(e - 8)$$

PROBLEMS 15 – 10

Factor:

1 $r^2 + 7r + 12$

2 $\theta^2 + 2\theta + 1$

3 $f^2 - 7f + 12$

4 $e^2 - 11e + 30$

5 $\alpha^2 - 15\alpha + 56$

6 $i^2 - i - 2$

7 $R^2 + 2R - 3$

8 $\omega^2 + \omega - 56$

9 $I^2 - 6I - 55$

10 $\phi^2 - \phi - 20$

11 $\alpha^2 - 22\alpha\beta + 105\beta^2$

12 $\omega^2 + 18\omega f - 115 f^2$

13 $225 + E^2 + 30E$

14 $R^2 + 96 + 20R$

15 $\mu^2 - 117 - 4\mu$

16 $14\pi - 32 + \pi^2$

17 $I^2 - I - 72$

18 $50 + E^2 - 27E$

19 $P^2 + 160 - 26P$

20 $e^2i^2 - 2ei - 35$

15   The product of any two binomials

Type: $(ax + b)(cx + d)$

Up to the present, if it was desired to multiply $(5x - 2)$ by $(3x + 6)$, we multiplied in the following manner:

$$
\begin{array}{r}
5x - 2 \\
3x + 6 \\
\hline
15x^2 - 6x \\
+\ 30x - 12 \\
\hline
15x^2 + 24x - 12
\end{array}
$$

Note that $15x^2$ is the product of the first terms of the binomials and the last term is the product of the last terms of the binomials. Also, the middle term is the sum of the products of the first term of each binomial by the second term of the other binomial.

The above example can be written in the following manner:

$$
\begin{array}{c}
5x - 2 \\
\diagdown\diagup \\
\diagup\diagdown \\
3x + 6 \\
\hline
15x^2 + 24x - 12
\end{array}
$$

The middle term $(+24x)$ is the sum of *cross products* $(5x)(+6)$ and $(3x)(-2)$, which is obtained by multiplying the first term of each binomial by the second term of the other.

The usual method of obtaining this product is indicated by the following solution:

$$(5x - 2)(3x + 6) = 15x^2 + 24x - 12$$

RULE   For finding the product of any two binomials,
1   The first term of the product is the product of the first terms of the binomials.

2 The second term is the algebraic sum of the product of the two outer terms and the product of the two inner terms.
3 The third term is the product of the last terms of the binomials.

EXAMPLE 37   Find the product of $(4e + 7j)(2e - 3j)$.
SOLUTION   The only difficulty encountered in obtaining such products mentally is that of finding the second term.

$$(4e)(-3j) = -12ej, \ (7j)(2e) = 14ej, \ \text{and} \ (-12ej) + (14ej) = +2ej$$
$$\therefore (4e + 7j)(2e - 3j) = 8e^2 + 2ej - 21j^2$$

EXAMPLE 38   Find the product $(7r^2 + 8Z)(8r^2 - 9Z)$.
SOLUTION   1. The first term of the product is $(7r^2)(8r^2) = 56r^4$.
2. Since $(7r^2)(-9Z) = -63r^2Z$ and $(8Z)(8r^2) = 64r^2Z$, the second term is $(-63r^2Z) + (64r^2Z) = +r^2Z$.
3. The third term is $(8Z)(-9Z) = -72Z^2$.
$$\therefore \ (7r^2 + 8Z)(8r^2 - 9Z) = 56r^4 + r^2Z - 72Z^2$$

By repeated drills you should acquire enough skill so that you can readily obtain such products mentally. This type of product is frequently encountered in algebra, and the ability to multiply rapidly will save much time.

PROBLEMS 15 – 11

1	$(3i + 2)(2i + 1)$	2	$(4R + 6)(3R + 2)$
3	$(f + 2)(f - 5)$	4	$(3E - 6)(E + 3)$
5	$(7 - 3\theta)(3 - 7\theta)$	6	$(\omega + 7)(\omega - 4)$
7	$(3\lambda + 2)(3\lambda + 4)$	8	$(3e - 2)(15e + 20)$
9	$(6\omega\pi - 7)(4\omega\pi - 3)$	10	$(I + 6)(I - 9)$
11	$(\alpha - 15)(11 + \alpha)$	12	$(1 + 7\phi)(5 - 3\phi)$
13	$(4r - 7)(r + 2)$	14	$(8Z - 9)(Z + 3)$
15	$(3 + 2\beta)(9\beta + 2)$	16	$(vt - 13s)(vt + 2s)$
17	$(6F - 7f)(6F - f)$	18	$(\mu + 7\gamma)(3\mu - 2\gamma)$
19	$(5L - 5C)(L + C)$	20	$(6W - P)(3W - 5P)$
21	$(8iz + E)(iz - 8E)$	22	$(2x + 1)(x - 1)$
23	$\left(10\alpha - \dfrac{\beta}{10}\right)\left(5\alpha + \dfrac{\beta}{5}\right)$	24	$(4ei + 5I^2R)(8ei - 9I^2R)$
25	$\left(4R + \dfrac{1}{3Z}\right)\left(6R + \dfrac{1}{2Z}\right)$	26	$\left(5\theta - \dfrac{2}{3\phi}\right)\left(6\theta + \dfrac{2}{3\phi}\right)$
27	$(E + \frac{1}{4})(E + \frac{1}{2})$	28	$(0.6\omega + 2)(0.3\omega + 8)$
29	$\left(8i + \dfrac{r}{3}\right)\left(6i - \dfrac{r}{2}\right)$	30	$(3Z - 0.5R)(4Z + 0.5R)$

- 16   **Factoring trinomials of the type $ax^2 + bx + c$**

This is best illustrated by examples.

EXAMPLE 39   Factor $3a^2 + 5a + 2$.

SOLUTION   It is apparent that the two factors are binomials and the product of the end terms must be $3a^2$ and 2. Therefore the binomials to choose from are

$$(3a + 1)(a + 2)$$

and
$$(3a + 2)(a + 1)$$

However, the first factors when multiplied result in a product of $7a$ for the middle term. The second pair of factors when multiplied give a middle term of $5a$. Therefore,

$$3a^2 + 5a + 2 = (3a + 2)(a + 1)$$

EXAMPLE 40   Factor $6e^2 + 7e + 2$.

SOLUTION   Again, the end terms of the binomial factors must be chosen so that their products result in $6e^2$ and 2. Both the last terms of the factors are of like signs, for the last term of the trinomial is positive. Also, both last terms of the factors must be positive, for the second term of the trinomial is positive. One of the several methods of arranging the work is as shown below. The tentative factors are arranged as if for multiplication:

Trial factors	*Products*	
$(6e + 1)(e + 2)$	$= 6e^2 + 13e + 2$	Wrong
$(6e + 2)(e + 1)$	$= 6e^2 + 8e + 2$	Wrong
$(3e + 1)(2e + 2)$	$= 6e^2 + 8e + 2$	Wrong
$(3e + 2)(2e + 1)$	$= 6e^2 + 7e + 2$	Right

It is seen that any combination of the trial factors when multiplied results in the correct first and last term.

$$\therefore 6e^2 + 7e + 2 = (3e + 2)(2e + 1)$$

NOTE   This may seem to be a long process, but with practice, most of the factor trials can be tested mentally.

EXAMPLE 41   Factor $12i^2 - 17i + 6$.

SOLUTION   The third term of this trinomial is $+6$; therefore, its factors must have like signs. Since the second term is negative, the cross products must be negative. Then it follows that both factors of 6 must be negative.

Some of the combinations are as follows:

Trial factors	*Products*	
$(2i - 3)(6i - 2)$	$= 12i^2 - 22i + 6$	Wrong
$(2i - 2)(6i - 3)$	$= 12i^2 - 18i + 6$	Wrong

$$(3i - 3)(4i - 2) = 12i^2 - 18i + 6 \quad \text{Wrong}$$
$$(3i - 2)(4i - 3) = 12i^2 - 17i + 6 \quad \text{Right}$$
$$\therefore\ 12i^2 - 17i + 6 = (3i - 2)(4i - 3)$$

EXAMPLE 42   Factor $8r^2 - 14r - 15$.

SOLUTION   The factors of -15 must have unlike signs. The signs of these factors must be arranged so that the cross product of greater absolute value is minus, because the middle term of the trinomial is negative.

$$
\begin{array}{ll}
\textit{Trial factors} & \textit{Products} \\
(8r + 3)(r - 5) & = 8r^2 - 37r - 15 \quad \text{Wrong} \\
(4r + 5)(2r - 3) & = 8r^2 - 2r - 15 \quad \text{Wrong} \\
(4r + 3)(2r - 5) & = 8r^2 - 14r - 15 \quad \text{Right}
\end{array}
$$

EXAMPLE 43   Factor $6R^2 - 7R - 20$.

NOTE   Many students prefer the following method to that of the foregoing examples in which trial-and-error methods were used.

SOLUTION   Multiply and divide the entire expression by the coefficient of R^2. The result is

$$\frac{36R^2 - 42R - 120}{6}$$

Take the square root of the first term, which is $6R$, and let that be some other letter such as x. Then, if

$$6R = x$$

by substituting the value of $6R$ in the above expression, we obtain

$$\frac{x^2 - 7x - 120}{6}$$

This results in an expression with a numerator easy to factor. Thus,

$$\frac{x^2 - 7x - 120}{6} = \frac{(x + 8)(x - 15)}{6}$$

Substituting $6R$ for x in the last expression, we obtain

$$\frac{(6R + 8)(6R - 15)}{6}$$

Factoring the numerator,

$$\frac{2(3R + 4)3(2R - 5)}{6}$$

Canceling, $6R^2 - 7R - 20 = (3R + 4)(2R - 5)$

EXAMPLE 44 Factor $4E^2 - 8EI - 21I^2$.

SOLUTION Multiplying and dividing by the coefficient of E^2,

$$\frac{16E^2 - 32EI - 84I^2}{4}$$

Let the square root of the first term $4E = x$.

Then $\quad \dfrac{x^2 - 8Ix - 84I^2}{4} = \dfrac{(x + 6I)(x - 14I)}{4}$

Substituting for x, $\quad \dfrac{(4E + 6I)(4E - 14I)}{4}$

Factoring, $\quad \dfrac{2(2E + 3I)2(2E - 7I)}{4}$

Canceling, $\quad 4E^2 - 8EI - 21I^2 = (2E + 3I)(2E - 7I)$

PROBLEMS 15 – 12

Factor:

1 $2t^2 + 3t + 1$

3 $2\omega^2 + 9\omega + 4$

5 $9\theta^2 + 36\theta + 32$

7 $2e^2 + e - 28$

9 $6E^2 - 31E + 35$

11 $72\lambda^2 - 145\lambda + 72$

13 $15\alpha^2 - 77\alpha + 10$

15 $3f^2 - 13f + 14$

17 $2\mu^2 + \mu\phi - 28\phi^2$

2 $2L^2 + 5L + 2$

4 $3r^2 + 11r + 6$

6 $2\beta^2 - \beta - 1$

8 $12f^2 + 13f - 35$

10 $10 - 5R - 15R^2$

12 $2 - 3z - 2z^2$

14 $20 - 9x - 20x^2$

16 $24I^2 - 29IZ - 4Z^2$

18 $L^2 - LC - 240C^2$

19 $3F^2 + 23Ff + 14f^2$

21 $P^2 + 0.5PW - 0.14W^2$

23 $i^2r^2 + 0.1eir - 0.3e^2$

25 $E^2I^2 + 0.1EIP - 0.9P^2$

20 $\omega^2 - \omega\pi + \dfrac{\pi^2}{4}$

22 $\dfrac{1}{9}\alpha^2 - \dfrac{2}{3}\alpha\beta + \beta^2$

24 $3\theta^2 - \dfrac{5\theta\phi}{6} - \dfrac{\phi^2}{18}$

5 – 17 Summary

In this chapter, various cases of products and factoring have been treated separately in the different sections. Frequently, however, it becomes necessary to apply the principles underlying two or more cases to a single problem. It is very important, therefore, that you recognize the standard type of forms in order that you can apply them as needed. These are summarized in Table 15–1.

TABLE 15–1

General type	Factors	Section
$ab + ac + ad$	$a(b + c + d)$	15–7
$a^2 + 2ab + b^2$	$(a + b)^2$	15–8
$a^2 - 2ab + b^2$	$(a - b)^2$	15–8
$a^2 - b^2$	$(a + b)(a - b)$	15–12
$a^2 + (b + c)a + bc$	$(a + b)(a + c)$	15–13
$acx^2 + (bc + ad)x + bd$	$(ax + b)(cx + d)$	15–15

Problems 15–13 are included as a review of the entire chapter. If you can work all of them, you thoroughly understand the contents of this chapter. If not, a review of the doubtful parts is suggested, for a good working knowledge of special products and factoring makes it possible

1. To perform quickly many multiplications and divisions mentally
2. To solve many problems that might appear impossible of solution unless factoring is used

PROBLEMS 15–13

Find the value of:

1 $(-6I^2R)^2$

2 $(-5\alpha^2\beta^3\omega f^3)^3$

3 $\left(\dfrac{a^2bc^3d^4}{xy^3z^2}\right)^4$

4 $-\sqrt{36\theta^2\phi^4\omega^2\pi^6}$

5 $\sqrt{\dfrac{25L^2C^4M^2}{169F^4\pi^2V^2t^6}}$

6 $\sqrt[3]{-64e^3i^6E^3I^9}$

7 $-\sqrt[3]{\dfrac{27\lambda^6\mu^3a^{12}b^9}{125x^3y^9z^6}}$

8 $-\sqrt{\dfrac{225I^2P^4W^2}{121E^2R^2Z^6}}$

9 $-\sqrt[3]{-216\alpha^3\beta^3\omega^6\lambda^9}$

Factor:

10 $\omega F^2 - \omega f_o^2$

11 $\dfrac{E^2}{R_1} + \dfrac{E^2}{R_2} + \dfrac{E^2}{R_3}$

12 $0.125i^2r_1 + 0.25i^2r_2 - 0.0125i^2z$

13 $7.2\pi^2\lambda - 0.36\phi\lambda - 10.8n\lambda$

14 $\dfrac{3}{5}\alpha\beta - \dfrac{1}{5}\alpha\theta - \dfrac{2}{5}\alpha\phi$

15 $\dfrac{7\omega L}{3} - 21\omega M + \dfrac{14\omega\theta}{3}$

Find the products mentally:

16 $(E + 11)^2$

17 $(3\alpha - 6\beta^2)^2$

18 $(10E + \tfrac{2}{5})^2$

19 $(\tfrac{2}{3}\omega - 9f)^2$

20 $(0.25E - 3e)^2$

21 $(0.1IR + 0.8Z)^2$

Supply the missing terms so that the three form a trinomial square:

22 $R^2 + (?) + 36I^2$

24 $\omega^2 - 6\omega f + (?)$

23 $25\alpha^2 - (?) + 81\beta^2$

25 $(?) + 24\theta\phi + 16\phi^2$

26 $(?) - \dfrac{2}{15}LC + \dfrac{1}{25}C^2$

27 $\lambda^2 + \dfrac{4}{5}\pi\lambda + (?)$

Extract the square roots of the following:

28 $e^2 - 18e + 81$

29 $4i^2 - 12ir + 9r^2$

30 $\dfrac{\alpha^2}{4} + \alpha + 1$

31 $\theta^2 + \dfrac{\phi^2}{9} - \dfrac{2\theta\phi}{3}$

32 $\dfrac{4\mu^2}{49} + \dfrac{25\lambda^2}{36} + \dfrac{10\lambda\mu}{21}$

33 $\dfrac{12vt}{5} + 9t^2 + \dfrac{4v^2}{25}$

Find the products:

34 $(a + 3b)(a - 3b)$

35 $(6E - 4I)(6E + 4I)$

36 $\left(\dfrac{3R}{8} + \dfrac{Z}{5}\right)\left(\dfrac{3R}{8} - \dfrac{Z}{5}\right)$

37 $\left(0.6\theta - \dfrac{4}{5}\phi\right)\left(0.6\theta + \dfrac{4}{5}\phi\right)$

Factor:

38 $Z^2 - 9$

39 $81 - f^2$

40 $\alpha^2\beta^2\gamma^2 - \mu^2$

41 $0.16\pi^2v^2 - \tfrac{9}{16}t^2$

42 $0.0025\omega^2t^2 - 0.49\theta^2\phi^2$

43 $0.01L^2C^2 - 0.64R^2$

Find the quotients:

44 $\dfrac{4 - \pi^2}{2 + \pi}$

45 $\dfrac{9E^2 - 25r^2}{5r + 3E}$

46 $\dfrac{\dfrac{1}{4}\alpha^2 - \dfrac{1}{9}\beta^2}{\dfrac{1}{3}\beta + \dfrac{1}{2}\alpha}$

47 $\dfrac{0.09\omega^2 - 0.36\lambda^2}{0.3\omega - 0.6\lambda}$

48 $\dfrac{I^2 + 2IR + R^2 - 81}{I + R - 9}$

49 $\dfrac{\dfrac{9}{81}i^2 - \dfrac{25}{121}z^2}{\dfrac{5}{11}z + \dfrac{3}{9}i}$

Find the products:

50 $(\theta + 3)(\theta - 6)$

51 $(5 - Z)(7 - 4Z)$

52 $(0.1R - 3)(R + 0.25)$

53 $(0.3 + 0.5L)(0.2 + L)$

54 $(W - \tfrac{1}{2})(W + \tfrac{1}{4})$

55 $(5\mu + 8)(\tfrac{1}{4}\mu - \tfrac{1}{5})$

56 $(3P - 6W)(8P + W)$

57 $(\omega f + 3F_o)(4\omega f - 7F_o)$

58 $(0.3i - 0.05r)(6i - r)$

59 $(0.2I + 0.7R)(0.1I + 3R)$

60 $\left(6\pi - \dfrac{2t}{7}\right)\left(14\pi + \dfrac{t}{3}\right)$

61 $\left(\dfrac{3\alpha}{5} - 8\beta\right)\left(\dfrac{\alpha}{4} - 10\beta\right)$

Factor:

62 $\phi^2 - 2\phi - 15$

63 $\theta^2 - 12\theta + 32$

64 $E^2 + 0.3E + 0.02$

65 $z^2 - 0.7z - 0.3$

66 $\lambda^2 - \dfrac{\lambda}{12} - \dfrac{1}{12}$

67 $\omega^2 - \dfrac{\omega}{4} - \dfrac{1}{8}$

68 $3L^2 - 11LC - 20C^2$

69 $6P^2 - 16PW - 6W^2$

70 $3e^2 + 0.4ez - 0.15z^2$

71 $v^2 + 0.3vt - 0.1t^2$

72 $\dfrac{i^2}{81} + \dfrac{2ir}{9} + r^2$ 73 $e^2 + \dfrac{2e}{r} + \dfrac{1}{r^2}$

74 $48\omega^2 + 24\omega f + 3f^2$ 75 $13Z^2 - 13R^2$

76 $IX_L{}^2 - IX_C{}^2$ 77 $\pi^6 - 0.2\pi^3 - 0.15$

78 $4\alpha^2 - 100$ 79 $\theta^2 + 0.18\phi^2 - 0.9\theta\phi$

80 $225\alpha\beta^2 - \dfrac{16}{289}\alpha$

CHAPTER 16
FRACTIONS

Algebraic fractions play an important role in mathematics, especially in equations for electric and electronic circuits.

At this time, if you feel you have not thoroughly mastered arithmetical fractions, you are urged to review them. A good foundation in arithmetical fractions is essential, for every rule and operation pertaining to them is applicable to algebraic fractions. It is a fact that one who really knows arithmetical fractions rarely has trouble with algebraic fractions.

16 – 1   The degree of a monomial

The degree of a monomial is determined by the number of literal factors it has.

Thus, $6ab^2$ is a monomial of the third degree because $ab^2 = a \cdot b \cdot b$; $3mn$ is a monomial of the second degree. From these examples, it is seen that the degree of a monomial is the sum of the exponents of the letters.

In such an expression as $5X^2Y^2Z$ we speak of the whole term as being of the fifth degree, X and Y as being of the second degree, and Z as being of the first degree.

The above definition for the degree of a monomial does not apply to letters in a denominator.

16 – 2   The degree of a polynomial

The degree of a polynomial is taken as the degree of its term of highest degree. Thus, $3ab^2 - 4cd - d$ is of the *third* degree; $6x^2y + 5xy^2 + y^4$ is a polynomial of the *fourth* degree.

16 – 3   Highest common factor

A factor of each of two or more expressions is a *common factor* of those expressions. For example, 2 is a common factor of 4 and 6; a^2 is a common factor of a^3, $(a^2 - a^2b)$, and $(a^2x^2 - a^2y)$.

The product of all the factors common to two or more numbers, or expressions, is called their *highest common factor*. That is, the highest common factor is the expression of highest degree that will divide each of them without a remainder. It is commonly abbreviated HCF.

EXAMPLE 1   Find the HCF of

$$6a^2b^3(c + 1)(c + 3)^2 \qquad \text{and} \qquad 30a^3b^2(c - 2)(c + 3)$$

SOLUTION   6 is the greatest integer that will divide both expressions.
The highest power of a that will divide both is a^2.
The highest power of b that will divide both is b^2.
The highest power of $(c + 3)$ that will divide both is $(c + 3)$.
$(c + 1)$ and $(c - 2)$ will not divide both expressions.

$$\therefore 6a^2b^2(c + 3) = \text{HCF}$$

RULE   To determine the HCF,
1   Determine all the prime factors of each expression.
2   Take the common factors of all the expressions, giving to each the lowest exponent it has in any of the expressions.
3   The HCF is the product of all the common factors as obtained in step 2.

EXAMPLE 2   Find the HCF of
$$50a^2b^3c(x + y)^3(x - y)^4 \qquad \text{and} \qquad 75a^2bc^2(x + y)^2(x - y)$$
SOLUTION $50a^2b^3c(x + y)^3(x - y)^4 = 2 \cdot 5 \cdot 5a^2b^3c(x + y)^3(x - y)^4$
$75a^2bc^2(x + y)^2(x - y) = 3 \cdot 5 \cdot 5a^2bc^2(x + y)^2(x - y)$
$\therefore \text{HCF} = 5^2a^2bc(x + y)^2(x - y) = 25a^2bc(x + y)^2(x - y)$
EXAMPLE 3   Find the HCF of
$$e^2 + er \qquad e^2 + 2er + r^2 \qquad \text{and} \qquad e^2 - r^2$$

SOLUTION
$$e^2 + er = e(e + r)$$
$$e^2 + 2er + r^2 = (e + r)^2$$
$$e^2 - r^2 = (e + r)(e - r)$$
$$\therefore \text{HCF} = e + r$$

PROBLEMS 16-1

Find the HCF of:

1 36, 81
2 105, 75, 225
3 $16ab^2, 32a^2bc, 24a^2c$
4 $9x^2y^3, 21x^2y^2, 15xy^2$
5 $21I^2R, 56IR^2Z, 35IRZ^2$
6 $51\alpha\beta\gamma^2, 34\alpha^2\beta\gamma, 17\alpha\beta^2\gamma$
7 $30\theta\phi^2\omega^2, 42\theta^3\phi\omega^2, 35\theta^2\phi^3\omega$
8 $25F^4L^5C^2, 15F^5L^3C^7, 60F^3L^7C^6$
9 $P^2 + PW, P^2 - W^2$
10 $(\lambda + \pi)^2, \lambda^2 - \pi^2$
11 $v^2 - t^2, v^2 - 2vt + t^2, s(v - t)$
12 $2e^2 - 7e + 3, 3e^2 - 7e - 6$
13 $2i^2 + 9i + 4, 2i^2 + 11i + 5, 2i^2 - 3i - 2$
14 $6\mu^2 + 11\mu f + 3f^2, 2\mu^2 + 7\mu f + 6f^2, 2\mu^2 + 9\mu f + 9f^2$
15 $4E^2 + 14Ez + 6z^2, 2E^2 + 10Ez + 12z^2, 2E^2 + 8Ez + 6z^2$

16-4 Multiple

A number is a *multiple* of any one of its factors. For example, some of
the multiples of 4 are 8, 16, 20, and 24. Similarly, some of the
multiples of $(a + b)$ are $3(a + b)$, $a^2 + 2ab + b^2$, and $a^2 - b^2$. A
common multiple of two or more numbers is a multiple of each of them.
Thus, 45 is a common multiple of 1, 3, 5, 9, and 15.

16-5 Lowest common multiple

The smallest number that will contain each one of a set of factors is
called their *lowest common multiple*. Thus, 48, 60, and 72 are all
common multiples of 4 and 6, but the lowest common multiple of 4
and 6 is 12.

The lowest common multiple is abbreviated LCM.

EXAMPLE 4   Find the LCM of $6x^2y$, $9xy^2z$, and $30x^3y^3$.

SOLUTION
$$6x^2y = 2 \cdot 3 \cdot x^2y$$
$$9xy^2z = 3^2 \cdot xy^2z$$
$$30x^3y^3 = 2 \cdot 3 \cdot 5 \cdot x^3y^3$$

Because the LCM must contain *each* of the expressions, it must have 2, 3^2,
and 5 as factors. Also, it must contain the literal factors of highest degree, or
x^3y^3z.

$$\therefore \text{LCM} = 2 \cdot 3^2 \cdot 5 \cdot x^3y^3z = 90x^3y^3z$$

RULE   To determine the LCM of two or more expressions, determine all the prime factors of each expression.   Find the product of all the different prime factors, taking each factor the greatest number of times it occurs in any one expression.

EXAMPLE 5   Find the LCM of
$$3a^3 + 6a^2b + 3ab^2 \qquad 6a^4 - 12a^3b + 6a^2b^2 \qquad \text{and} \qquad 9a^3b - 9ab^3$$
SOLUTION
$$3a^3 + 6a^2b + 3ab^2 = 3a(a + b)^2$$
$$6a^4 - 12a^3b + 6a^2b^2 = 2 \cdot 3 \cdot a^2(a - b)^2$$
$$9a^3b - 9ab^3 = 3^2 \cdot ab(a + b)(a - b)$$
$$\therefore \text{LCM} = 2 \cdot 3^2 \cdot a^2b(a + b)^2(a - b)^2$$
$$= 18a^2b(a + b)^2(a - b)^2$$

PROBLEMS 16 – 2

Find the LCM of the following:

1   30, 35, 42

2   42, 30, 66

3   80, 48, 108

4   e^2i^2, eir

5   $2\alpha^2\beta^3$, $3\alpha\beta$, $4\alpha^3\beta^4$

6   $5\theta^2\phi$, $6\phi\omega^2$, $3\omega\phi^2$

7   $44x^3y^4z^2$, $24x^2y^3z^4$, $66x^4y^2z^3$

8   $21bc$, $4ac^2$, $7a^2b$, $6ac^3$

9   $6F^2 - 2F$, $9F^2 - 3F$

10   $Z^2 + Z$, $Z^2 - 1$

11   $E^2 - I^2$, $(E - I)^2$

12   $\pi^2 - \pi$, $\pi^3 - 9\pi^2 - 10\pi$

13   $L^2 - 5L + 4$, $L^2 - 6L + 8$

14   $8\mu^2 - 38\mu\lambda + 35\lambda^2$, $4\mu^2 - \mu\lambda - 5\lambda^2$, $2\mu^2 - 5\mu\lambda - 7\lambda^2$

15   $4v^2 - 9vt + 5t^2$, $12v^2 - 23vt + 10t^2$, $3v^2 - 5vt + 2t^2$

16 – 6   Definitions

A fraction is an indicated division.   Thus, we indicate 4 divided by 5 as $\dfrac{4}{5}$ (read four-fifths).   Similarly, X divided by Y is written $\dfrac{X}{Y}$ (read X divided by Y or X over Y).

The quantity above the horizontal line is called the *numerator* and that below the line is called the *denominator* of the fraction.   The numerator and denominator are often called the *terms* of the fraction.

16 – 7   Operations on numerator and denominator

As in arithmetic, when fractions are to be simplified or affected by one of the four fundamental operations, we find it necessary to make frequent use of the following important principles.

1   The numerator and the denominator of a fraction can be multiplied by the same number or expression, except zero, without changing the value of the fraction.

2   The numerator and the denominator can be divided by the same number or expression, except zero, without changing the value of the fraction.

EXAMPLE 6 $\dfrac{2}{3} = \dfrac{2 \times 3}{3 \times 3} = \dfrac{6}{9} = \dfrac{2}{3}$

Also, $\dfrac{6}{9} = \dfrac{6 \div 3}{9 \div 3} = \dfrac{2}{3} = \dfrac{6}{9}$

EXAMPLE 7 $\dfrac{x}{y} = \dfrac{x \cdot a}{y \cdot a} = \dfrac{ax}{ay} = \dfrac{x}{y}$

Also, $\dfrac{ax \div a}{ay \div a} = \dfrac{x}{y}$ (where $a \neq 0$)

No new principles are involved in performing these operations, for multiplying or dividing both numerator and denominator by the same number, except zero, is equivalent to multiplying or dividing the fraction by 1.

It will be noted that, in the foregoing principles, multiplication and division of numerator and denominator by zero are excluded. When any expression is multiplied by zero, the product is zero. For example, $6 \times 0 = 0$. Therefore, if we multiplied both numerator and denominator of some fraction by zero, the result would be meaningless. Thus,

$$\frac{5}{6} \neq \frac{5 \times 0}{6 \times 0} \qquad \text{because} \qquad \frac{5 \times 0}{6 \times 0} = \frac{0}{0}$$

Division by zero is meaningless. Some say that any number divided by zero results in a quotient of infinity, denoted by ∞. If this is accepted, we immediately impose a severe restriction on operations with even simple equations. For example, let us assume for the moment that any number divided by zero *does* result in infinity. Then if

$$\frac{4}{0} = \infty$$

by following Axiom 3 we should be able to multiply both sides of this equation by 0. If so, we obtain

$$4 = \infty \cdot 0$$

which we know is not sensible. Obviously, there is a fallacy existing here; therefore, we shall simply say at this time that *division by zero is not a permissible operation.*

16 – 8 Equivalent fractions

Examples 6 and 7 show that when a numerator and a denominator are multiplied or divided by the same number, except zero, we change the *form* of the given fraction but *not* its value. Therefore, two fractions having the same value but not the same form are called *equivalent fractions*.

PROBLEMS 16 – 3

Supply the missing terms:

1 $\dfrac{2}{5} = \dfrac{?}{15}$

2 $\dfrac{5}{12} = \dfrac{?}{48}$

3 $\dfrac{1}{x} = \dfrac{?}{xy}$

4 $\dfrac{3a}{7b} = \dfrac{?}{21bc}$

5 $\dfrac{v - 5}{v + 2} = \dfrac{?}{(v + 2)(v + 5)}$

6 $\dfrac{\theta + 7}{1} = \dfrac{?}{\theta - 3}$

7 $\dfrac{3}{\alpha + \beta} = \dfrac{?}{\alpha^2 + 2\alpha\beta + \beta^2}$

8 $\dfrac{3}{e - 3i} = \dfrac{?}{9i - 3e}$

9 $\dfrac{1}{2\omega - 3\lambda} = \dfrac{?}{6\omega^2 + \omega\lambda - 15\lambda^2}$

10 $\dfrac{\phi - 4}{\phi - 2} = \dfrac{?}{2\phi - \phi^2}$

11 Change the fraction $\frac{8}{32}$ into an equivalent fraction whose denominator is 8.

12 Change the fraction $\frac{3}{5}$ into an equivalent fraction whose denominator is 40.

13 Change the fraction $\dfrac{E}{\omega C}$ to an equivalent fraction whose denominator is $\omega^2 C F_1$.

14 Change the fraction $\dfrac{1}{R_1 + R_2}$ into an equivalent fraction whose denominator is $R_1^2 - R_2^2$.

15 Change the fraction $\dfrac{e}{1 - \mu\beta}$ to an equivalent fraction whose denominator is $1 - 2\mu\beta + \mu^2\beta^2$.

16 – 9 Reduction of fractions to their lowest terms

If the numerator and denominator of a fraction have no common factor other than 1, then the fraction is said to be in its lowest terms. Thus, the fractions $\dfrac{2}{3}, \dfrac{3}{5}, \dfrac{x}{y}$, and $\dfrac{x + y}{x - y}$ are in their lowest terms, for the numerator and denominator of each fraction have no common factor except 1.

The fractions $\dfrac{4}{6}$ and $\dfrac{3x}{9x^2}$ are not in their lowest terms, for $\dfrac{4}{6}$ can be reduced to $\dfrac{2}{3}$ if both numerator and denominator are divided by 2.

Similarly, $\dfrac{3x}{9x^2}$ can be reduced to $\dfrac{1}{3x}$ by dividing both numerator and denominator by 3x.

RULE To reduce a fraction to its lowest terms, factor the numerator and denominator into prime factors and cancel the factors common to both.

Cancellation as used in the rule really means that we actually *divide* both terms of the fraction by the *common factors*. Then, to reduce a fraction to its lowest terms, it is only necessary to divide both numerator and denominator by the highest common factor, which leaves an equivalent fraction.

EXAMPLE 8   Reduce $^{27}/_{108}$ to lowest terms.

SOLUTION $\dfrac{27}{108} = \dfrac{3 \cdot 3 \cdot 3}{2 \cdot 2 \cdot 3 \cdot 3 \cdot 3} = \dfrac{1}{4}$

EXAMPLE 9   Reduce $\dfrac{24x^2yz^3}{42x^2yz^2}$ to lowest terms.

SOLUTION $\dfrac{24x^2yz^3}{42x^2yz^2} = \dfrac{2 \cdot 2 \cdot 2 \cdot 3 \cdot x^2yz^3}{2 \cdot 3 \cdot 7 \cdot x^2yz^2} = \dfrac{4z}{7}$

Actually, the above solution need not have been written out, for it can be seen by inspection that the HCF of both terms of the fraction is $6x^2yz^2$, which we divide into both terms to obtain the equivalent fraction $4z/7$.

Also, in reducing fractions, we may resort to direct cancellation as in arithmetic.

EXAMPLE 10   Reduce $\dfrac{x^2 - y^2}{x^3 - y^3}$ to lowest terms.

SOLUTION $\dfrac{x^2 - y^2}{x^3 - y^3} = \dfrac{(x + y)(x - y)}{(x - y)(x^2 + xy + y^2)} = \dfrac{x + y}{x^2 + xy + y^2}$

EXAMPLE 11   Reduce to lowest terms

$$\dfrac{r^2 - R^2}{r^2 + 3rR + 2R^2}$$

SOLUTION $\dfrac{r^2 - R^2}{r^2 + 3rR + 2R^2} = \dfrac{(r + R)(r - R)}{(r + 2R)(r + R)} = \dfrac{r - R}{r + 2R}$

PROBLEMS 16 – 4

Reduce to lowest terms:

1   $^{32}\!\!/_{80}$

2   $^{36}\!\!/_{81}$

3   $^{63}\!\!/_{112}$

4   $^{78}\!\!/_{169}$

5   $^{121}\!\!/_{154}$

6   $\dfrac{6a^2bc}{12ab^2c}$

7   $\dfrac{14x^3yz^2}{49x^2y^2z}$

8   $\dfrac{45eE^3I^2}{72eE^4I}$

9   $\dfrac{i^2}{i(i-r)}$

10   $\dfrac{(Z+R)^2}{Z^2-R^2}$

11   $\dfrac{3(\alpha-\beta)}{(\alpha-\beta)^2(\alpha+\beta)}$

12   $\dfrac{\theta^2-5\theta}{\theta^2-4\theta-5}$

13   $\dfrac{3\phi^2+6\phi}{\phi^2+4\phi+4}$

14   $\dfrac{\omega^2\pi^2-16\omega^2}{\omega\pi^2+9\omega\pi+20\omega}$

15   $\dfrac{3\lambda^2+23\lambda+14}{3\lambda^2+41\lambda+26}$

16 – 10   **Signs of fractions**

As stated in Sec. 16–6, a fraction is an indicated division or an indicated quotient. Heretofore, all our fractions have been positive, but now there must be taken into account three signs in working with an algebraic fraction: the sign of the numerator, the sign of the denominator, and the sign preceding the fraction. By the law of signs in division, we have

$$+\frac{+12}{+6} = +\frac{-12}{-6} = -\frac{+12}{-6} = -\frac{-12}{+6} = +2$$

or, in general,

$$+\frac{+a}{+b} = +\frac{-a}{-b} = -\frac{+a}{-b} = -\frac{-a}{+b}$$

Careful study of the above examples will show the truths of the following important principles:

1   The sign before either term of a fraction can be changed if the sign before the fraction is changed.

2   If the signs of both terms are changed, the sign before the fraction must not be changed.

That is, we can change *any two* of the three signs of a fraction without changing its value.

It must be remembered that, when a term of a fraction is a polynomial, changing the sign of the term involves changing the sign of *each* *term* of the polynomial.

Changing the signs of both numerator and denominator, as mentioned in the second principle above, can be explained by considering both terms as multiplied or divided by -1, which, as previously explained, does not change the value of the fraction.

Multiplying (or dividing) a quantity by -1 twice does not change the value of the quantity. Hence, multiplying each of the two factors of a product by -1 does not change the value of the product. Thus,

$$(a - 4)(a - 8) = (-a + 4)(-a + 8) = (4 - a)(8 - a)$$

Also, $\quad (a - b)(c - d)(e - f) = (b - a)(d - c)(e - f)$

The validity of these illustrations should be checked by multiplication.

EXAMPLE 12   Change $-\dfrac{a}{b}$ to three equivalent fractions having different signs.

SOLUTION $-\dfrac{a}{b} = \dfrac{-a}{b} = \dfrac{a}{-b} = -\dfrac{-a}{-b}$

EXAMPLE 13   Change $\dfrac{a - b}{c - d}$ to three equivalent fractions having different signs.

SOLUTION $\dfrac{a - b}{c - d} = \dfrac{-a + b}{-c + d} = -\dfrac{-a + b}{c - d} = -\dfrac{a - b}{-c + d}$

EXAMPLE 14   Change $\dfrac{a - b}{c - d}$ to a fraction whose denominator is $d - c$.

SOLUTION $\dfrac{a - b}{c - d} = \dfrac{-a + b}{-c + d} = \dfrac{b - a}{d - c}$

PROBLEMS 16-5

Express as a positive fraction (with a positive numerator):

1 $\dfrac{-s}{v - t}$

2 $-\dfrac{-\omega F}{f - f_o}$

3 $\dfrac{-\mu E_g}{R_p + R_L}$

4 $\dfrac{-(P + W)}{I^2 R - ei}$

5 $\dfrac{-\theta - \phi}{\alpha - \beta}$

6 $\dfrac{-Ir - iR}{-E - e}$

Express as a positive fraction (with a positive denominator):

7 $\dfrac{L - C}{-R}$ 8 $\dfrac{e - E}{-(E^2 - e^2)}$

9 $-\dfrac{E + e}{-8z}$

Reduce to lowest terms:

10 $\dfrac{a - b}{b^2 - a^2}$ 11 $\dfrac{v - t}{t - v}$

12 $-\dfrac{\beta\phi - 6\alpha\phi}{36\alpha^2 - \beta^2}$ 13 $\dfrac{x^2 - 6xy + 9y^2}{9y^2 - x^2}$

14 $\dfrac{a^2 - 2ab + b^2}{b^2 - 2ba + a^2}$ 15 $\dfrac{2\lambda + \pi}{\pi^2 - 4\pi\lambda + 4\lambda^2}$

16 – 11   Common errors in working with fractions

It has been demonstrated that a fraction can be reduced to lower terms by dividing both numerator and denominator by the same number (Sec. 16–9).   Mistakes are often made by canceling parts of numerator and denominator that are *not* factors.   Take, for example,

$$\frac{5 + 2}{7 + 2} = \frac{7}{9}$$

Here is a case where both terms of the fraction are polynomials and the terms, even if alike, can never be canceled.   Thus,

$$\frac{5 + \cancel{2}}{7 + \cancel{2}} \neq \frac{5}{7}$$

because canceling terms has changed the value of the fraction.

Similarly, it would be incorrect to cancel the x's in the fraction $\dfrac{3a - x}{5c - x}$, for the x's *are not factors*.   Hence, it is apparent that $\dfrac{3a - x}{5c - x}$ cannot be reduced to lower terms, for neither term of the fraction can be factored.   It is permissible to cancel x's in the fraction $\dfrac{6x}{ax + 5x}$ because *each term* of the denominator contains x.   Or the denominator may be factored to give $\dfrac{6x}{x(a + 5)}$, the result being that the x's are a factor in both terms of the fraction.

Thus, we cannot remove, or cancel, like *terms* from the numerator and denominator of a fraction.   Only like *factors* can be removed, or canceled.

Reduce the following to mixed expressions:

21 $\dfrac{107}{15}$ 　　　　　　　　　　　　22 $\dfrac{120}{9}$

23 $\dfrac{208}{12}$ 　　　　　　　　　　　　24 $\dfrac{16a^2 - 4a + 3}{4a}$

25 $\dfrac{25\alpha^3 - 30\alpha^2 - 10\alpha - 5}{5\alpha}$ 　　26 $\dfrac{I + 7}{I + 2}$

27 $\dfrac{3R + 3}{R - 1}$ 　　　　　　　　　28 $\dfrac{i^3 - 4i}{i^3 + 5i^2 + 6i}$

29 $\dfrac{2e^2 - 7e - 1}{e - 3}$ 　　　　　　30 $\dfrac{5\omega^2 + 6\omega L + L^2}{5\omega^2 + 2\omega L - 3L^2}$

16-14 Reduction to the lowest common denominator

The *lowest common denominator* (LCD) of two or more fractions is the lowest common multiple of their denominators.

EXAMPLE 17　　Reduce $\frac{1}{3}$ and $\frac{3}{5}$ to their LCD.

SOLUTION　　The LCM of 3 and 5 is 15. To change the denominator of $\frac{1}{3}$ to 15, we must multiply the 3 by 5 (15 ÷ 3). In order not to change the value of the fraction, the numerator must also be multiplied by 5.

Hence, $$\frac{1}{3} = \frac{1}{3} \times \frac{5}{5} = \frac{5}{15}$$

For the second fraction, we must multiply the denominator by 3 in order to obtain a new denominator of 15 (15 ÷ 5). Again we must also multiply the numerator by 3 to maintain the original value of the fraction.

Hence, $$\frac{3}{5} = \frac{3}{5} \times \frac{3}{3} = \frac{9}{15}$$

EXAMPLE 18　　Reduce $\dfrac{4a^2b}{3x^2y}$ and $\dfrac{6cd^2}{4xy^2}$ to their LCD.

SOLUTION　　The LCM of the two denominators is $12x^2y^2$. This is the LCD.

For the first fraction the LCD is divided by the denominator.
That is, $$12x^2y^2 \div 3x^2y = 4y$$

Multiplying both numerator and denominator by $4y$,

$$\frac{4a^2b}{3x^2y} = \frac{4a^2b}{3x^2y} \cdot \frac{4y}{4y} = \frac{16a^2by}{12x^2y^2}$$

For the second fraction the same procedure is followed.

$$12x^2y^2 \div 4xy^2 = 3x$$

Multiplying both numerator and denominator by $3x$,

$$\frac{6cd^2}{4xy^2} = \frac{6cd^2}{4xy^2} \cdot \frac{3x}{3x} = \frac{18cd^2x}{12x^2y^2}$$

RULE   To reduce fractions to their LCD,

1   Factor each denominator into its prime factors, and find the LCM of the denominators.   This is the LCD.

2   For each fraction, divide the LCD by the denominator, and multiply both numerator and denominator by the quotient thus obtained.

EXAMPLE 19   Reduce $\dfrac{3x}{x^2 - y^2}$ and $\dfrac{4y}{x^2 - xy - 2y^2}$ to their LCD.

SOLUTION

$$\frac{3x}{x^2 - y^2} = \frac{3x}{(x + y)(x - y)}$$

$$\frac{4y}{x^2 - xy - 2y^2} = \frac{4y}{(x + y)(x - 2y)}$$

The LCM of the two denominators, and therefore the LCD, is $(x + y)(x - y)(x - 2y)$.

For the first fraction, the LCD divided by the denominator is $(x + y)(x - y)(x - 2y) \div (x + y)(x - y) = x - 2y$.

$$\therefore \frac{3x}{(x + y)(x - y)} = \frac{3x(x - 2y)}{(x + y)(x - y)(x - 2y)}$$

For the second fraction, the LCD divided by the denominator is $(x + y)(x - y)(x - 2y) \div (x + y)(x - 2y) = x - y$.

$$\therefore \frac{4y}{(x + y)(x - 2y)} = \frac{4y(x - y)}{(x + y)(x - 2y)(x - y)}$$

To check the solution, the fractions having the LCD can be changed into the original fractions by cancellation.

PROBLEMS 16–7

Reduce to equivalent fractions having their LCD:

1   $\frac{1}{4}, \frac{4}{5}, \frac{1}{3}$

2   $\frac{1}{9}, \frac{1}{2}, \frac{1}{27}$

3   $\frac{1}{10}, \frac{5}{6}, \frac{3}{8}$

4   $\frac{1}{\alpha}, \frac{1}{\beta}$

5   $\frac{\theta}{\phi}, \frac{\lambda}{\pi}$

6   $\frac{1}{E}, \frac{1}{e}, \frac{e}{E}$

7   $\frac{1}{\omega}, \frac{M}{L}, \frac{K}{C}$

8   $\frac{E^2}{R}, \frac{E}{R_1}, \frac{e^2}{r}, \frac{3e}{R}$

9 $\dfrac{2}{\theta - \phi}, \dfrac{6}{\theta + \phi}$

10 $\dfrac{3}{v - t}, \dfrac{s}{v + t}, \dfrac{t^2}{v - t}$

11 $\dfrac{7E}{2IR - 2I^2}, \dfrac{5I}{3R^2 - 3IR}$

12 $\dfrac{2}{r^2 + 3r + 2}, \dfrac{3}{r^2 - 2r - 3}$

13 $\dfrac{\alpha}{6\alpha^2 - 13\alpha\beta - 15\beta^2}, \dfrac{\beta}{\alpha^2 - 9\beta^2}$

14 $\dfrac{2\omega - 2f}{2\omega^2 - \omega f - 3f^2}, \dfrac{\omega + f}{4\omega^2 - 10\omega f + 6f^2}$

15 $\dfrac{3i}{i - r}, \dfrac{4i^2}{5(i^2 - r^2)}, \dfrac{r}{3r - 3i}, \dfrac{7r}{10(r^2 - i^2)}$

-15 Addition and subtraction of fractions

The sum of two or more fractions having the same denominator is obtained by adding the numerators and writing the result over the common denominator.

EXAMPLE 20 $\dfrac{2}{7} + \dfrac{1}{7} + \dfrac{5}{7} = \dfrac{2 + 1 + 5}{7} = \dfrac{8}{7}$

EXAMPLE 21 $\dfrac{3e}{R + r} + \dfrac{e}{R + r} + \dfrac{5e}{R + r} = \dfrac{3e + e + 5e}{R + r} = \dfrac{9e}{R + r}$

To subtract two fractions having the same denominator, subtract the numerator of the subtrahend from the numerator of the minuend and write the result over their common denominator.

EXAMPLE 22 $\dfrac{4}{5} - \dfrac{3}{5} = \dfrac{4 - 3}{5} = \dfrac{1}{5}$

EXAMPLE 23 $\dfrac{a}{x} - \dfrac{b}{x} = \dfrac{a - b}{x}$

EXAMPLE 24 $\dfrac{a}{x} - \dfrac{b - c}{x} = \dfrac{a - b + c}{x}$

Note that *the vinculum is a sign of grouping* and that, when a minus sign precedes a fraction having a polynomial numerator, all the signs in the numerator must be changed in order to complete the process of subtraction.

We have thus the following:

RULE To add or subtract fractions having unlike denominators,
1 Reduce them to equivalent fractions having their LCD.
2 Combine the numerators of these equivalent fractions, in parentheses, giving each the sign of the fraction. This is the numerator of the result.
3 The denominator of the result is the LCD.

4 Simplify the numerator by removing parentheses and combining terms.

5 Reduce the fraction to the lowest terms.

EXAMPLE 25 Simplify $\dfrac{a-5}{6x} - \dfrac{2a-5}{16x}$.

SOLUTION

$$\frac{a-5}{6x} - \frac{2a-5}{16x} = \frac{8(a-5)}{48x} - \frac{3(2a-5)}{48x}$$

$$= \frac{8(a-5) - 3(2a-5)}{48x}$$

$$= \frac{8a - 40 - 6a + 15}{48x}$$

$$= \frac{2a - 25}{48x}$$

CHECK Let $a = 6$, $x = 1$.

$$\frac{a-5}{6x} = \frac{1}{6} \qquad \frac{2a-5}{16} = \frac{7}{16}$$

$$\frac{1}{6} - \frac{7}{16} = \frac{8-21}{48} = -\frac{13}{48}$$

Also,

$$\frac{2a-25}{48} = \frac{12-25}{48} = -\frac{13}{48}$$

Solution is correct.

EXAMPLE 26 Simplify $\dfrac{x^2 - xy + y^2 - 2y^3}{x+y}$.

$$x^2 - xy + y^2 - \frac{2y^3}{x+y}$$

$$= \frac{(x+y)x^2}{x+y} - \frac{(x+y)xy}{x+y} + \frac{(x+y)y^2}{x+y} - \frac{2y^3}{x+y}$$

$$= \frac{x^3 + x^2y - x^2y - xy^2 + xy^2 + y^3 - 2y^3}{x+y} = \frac{x^3 - y^3}{x+y}$$

PROBLEMS 16 – 8

Perform the following indicated additions and subtractions:

1 $\frac{3}{4} - \frac{1}{5} + \frac{1}{3}$

2 $\frac{5}{12} + \frac{2}{3} - \frac{1}{8}$

3 $\frac{4}{7} - \frac{5}{6} + \frac{2}{9}$

4 $\dfrac{\lambda}{8} + \dfrac{3\lambda}{11} - \dfrac{5\lambda}{4}$

5 $\dfrac{3\pi}{4} - \dfrac{2\pi}{9} + \dfrac{5\pi}{18}$

6 $\dfrac{7z}{8} - \dfrac{z}{4} + \dfrac{7z}{16}$

7 $\dfrac{5}{r} - \dfrac{3}{7r}$

8 $\dfrac{4E}{3R} + \dfrac{3E}{8R} - \dfrac{17E}{48R}$

9 $\dfrac{3}{ir} - \dfrac{7}{i} + \dfrac{1}{r}$

10 $\dfrac{13}{I^2} + \dfrac{3}{R} - \dfrac{2}{3I^2R}$

11 $\quad \dfrac{7}{\omega} - \dfrac{1}{\omega C} - \dfrac{13}{\omega L} + \dfrac{1}{L}$

12 $\quad \dfrac{\alpha}{r_1} + \dfrac{\beta}{r_2} - \dfrac{\theta}{r_3}$

13 $\quad \dfrac{3e + 5}{2} + \dfrac{7e - 6}{10}$

14 $\quad \dfrac{Z - 9}{3} - \dfrac{Z + 13}{8}$

15 $\quad \dfrac{2}{f - 3} + \dfrac{3}{f + 2}$

16 $\quad \dfrac{7}{a + 4} - \dfrac{3}{a - 7}$

17 $\quad \dfrac{9}{t + 3} - \dfrac{4}{t - 3}$

18 $\quad \dfrac{3\phi}{1 - \phi^2} - \dfrac{2}{\phi + 1} + \dfrac{2}{1 - \phi}$

19 $\quad 8\mu + \dfrac{4 + 3\mu}{5\mu} + 7\mu + \dfrac{\mu - 2}{3}$

20 $\quad \dfrac{s}{t} - \dfrac{2s + t}{s - t}$

21 $\quad \dfrac{4}{c - 3} - \dfrac{2}{c^2 - 5c + 6}$

22 $\quad \dfrac{4\omega}{1 - 4\omega^2} + \dfrac{1}{2\omega - 1} + \dfrac{1}{2\omega + 1}$

23 $\quad 1 - \dfrac{L^2 - C^2}{L - C} + C + L$

24 $\quad \mu + \dfrac{\mu^2 + 5}{\mu - 4} + 4$

25 $\quad \dfrac{3E}{6R^2 - 6} - \dfrac{5E}{7R - 7}$

26 $\quad \dfrac{1}{F^2 - 11F + 30} + \dfrac{1}{F^2 - 9F + 20}$

27 $\quad \dfrac{r + R}{r - R} - \dfrac{4rR}{r^2 - R^2} - \dfrac{r - R}{r + R}$

28 $\quad \dfrac{1}{P - 1} - \dfrac{P - 2}{P + 2} + \dfrac{P - 3}{P + 2}$

29 $\quad \dfrac{1}{2ir - 5e} + \dfrac{3ir}{25e^2 - 4i^2r^2} + \dfrac{1}{2ir + 5e}$

30 $\quad 4 - \dfrac{9\omega^2 + 16}{3\omega - 4} + 3\omega$

31 $\quad \dfrac{E^2 + 2E + 4}{E + 2} - \dfrac{E^2 - 2E + 4}{2 - E}$

32 $\quad \dfrac{1}{2I + 2} + \dfrac{5}{3I - 3} + \dfrac{3I - 1}{1 - I^2}$

33 $\quad \dfrac{1}{x} - \dfrac{1}{x + y} - \dfrac{1}{y} - \dfrac{1}{x - y}$

34 $\quad \dfrac{5\alpha - 1}{\alpha^2 + 3\alpha} - \dfrac{2\alpha + 1}{\alpha^2 + 5\alpha} + \dfrac{6\alpha}{\alpha^2 + 8\alpha + 15}$

35 $\quad \dfrac{\theta^2 - \phi^2}{\theta\phi} - \dfrac{\theta\phi - \phi^2}{\theta\phi - \theta^2}$

36 $\quad \dfrac{2}{\pi^2 - \pi - 2} - \dfrac{1}{\pi^2 - 1} + \dfrac{2}{\pi^2 - 3\pi + 2}$

37 $\quad \dfrac{3 - 2\beta}{3 + 2\beta} - \dfrac{3 + 2\beta}{3 - 2\beta} + \dfrac{24\beta}{9 - 12\beta + 4\beta^2}$

38 $\quad \dfrac{7\alpha}{6\alpha^2 + 7\alpha - 3} - \dfrac{12(3\alpha + 1)}{11(4\alpha^2 + 8\alpha + 3)} + \dfrac{5(2\alpha - 3)}{11(6\alpha^2 + \alpha - 1)}$

39 $\quad \dfrac{R + 3Z}{4R^2 + 12RZ + 8Z^2} - \dfrac{R + Z}{4R^2 + 20RZ + 24Z^2} + \dfrac{R + 2Z}{R^2 + 4RZ + 3Z^2}$

40 $\quad \dfrac{3}{\theta - \phi} - \dfrac{1}{\phi + 3\theta} + \dfrac{1}{\phi - 3\theta} + \dfrac{3}{\phi + \theta}$

16 – 16   Multiplication of fractions

The methods of multiplication of fractions in algebra are identical with those in arithmetic.

The product of two or more fractions is the product of their numerators divided by the product of their denominators.

EXAMPLE 27 $\dfrac{2}{3} \times \dfrac{3}{5} = \dfrac{6}{15}$

EXAMPLE 28 $\dfrac{a}{b} \cdot \dfrac{x}{y} = \dfrac{ax}{by}$

Where a factor occurs one or more times in *any* numerator and in *any* denominator of the product of two or more fractions, it can be canceled the same number of times from both, this process resulting in the product of the given fractions in lower terms.

EXAMPLE 29   Multiply $\dfrac{6x^2y}{7b}$ by $\dfrac{21b^2c}{24xy^2}$

SOLUTION $\dfrac{6x^2y}{7b} \cdot \dfrac{21b^2c}{24xy^2} = \dfrac{3bcx}{4y}$

EXAMPLE 30   Simplify $\dfrac{2a^2 - ab - b^2}{a^2 + 2ab + b^2} \cdot \dfrac{a^2 - b^2}{4a^2 + 4ab + b^2}$

SOLUTION $\dfrac{2a^2 - ab - b^2}{a^2 + 2ab + b^2} \cdot \dfrac{a^2 - b^2}{4a^2 + 4ab + b^2}$

$= \dfrac{(2a + b)(a - b)}{(a + b)(a + b)} \cdot \dfrac{(a + b)(a - b)}{(2a + b)(2a + b)}$

$= \dfrac{(a - b)(a - b)}{(a + b)(2a + b)} = \dfrac{a^2 - 2ab + b^2}{2a^2 + 3ab + b^2}$

It is very important that you understand clearly what we are allowed to cancel in the numerators and the denominators. The *whole* of an expression is always canceled, *never one term*. For example, in the expression $\dfrac{8a}{a - 5}$, it is not permissible to cancel the a's and obtain $\dfrac{8}{-5}$. It must be remembered that the denominator $a - 5$ denotes *one quantity*. We should not cancel the a's if the expression were written $\dfrac{8a}{(a - 5)}$ because of the parentheses. However, the parentheses are not needed; for the *vinculum, which is also a sign of grouping, serves the same purpose.* We shall consider this again in the next chapter.

– 17 Division of fractions

As with multiplication, the methods of division of fractions in algebra are identical with those of arithmetic. Therefore, to divide by a fraction, invert the divisor fraction and proceed as in the multiplication of fractions.

EXAMPLE 31 $\quad \dfrac{5}{2} \div \dfrac{2}{3} = \dfrac{5}{2} \cdot \dfrac{3}{2} = \dfrac{15}{4}$

EXAMPLE 32 $\quad \dfrac{ab^2}{xy} \div \dfrac{a^2b}{xy^2} = \dfrac{ab^2}{xy} \cdot \dfrac{xy^2}{a^2b} = \dfrac{by}{a}$

EXAMPLE 33 $\quad \dfrac{x}{y} \div \left(a + \dfrac{b}{c}\right) = \dfrac{x}{y} \div \dfrac{ac + b}{c}$

$$= \dfrac{x}{y} \cdot \dfrac{c}{ac + b} = \dfrac{cx}{y(ac + b)} = \dfrac{cx}{acy + by}$$

Students often ask why we must invert the divisor and multiply by the dividend in dividing fractions. As an example, suppose we have $\dfrac{a}{b} \div \dfrac{x}{y}$. The dividend is $\dfrac{a}{b}$, and the divisor is $\dfrac{x}{y}$. Now

Quotient × divisor = dividend

Therefore, the quotient must be such a number that when multiplied by $\dfrac{x}{y}$ it will give $\dfrac{a}{b}$ as a product. Then,

$$\left(\dfrac{a}{b} \cdot \dfrac{y}{x}\right) \cdot \dfrac{x}{y} = \dfrac{a}{b}$$

Hence, the quotient is $\dfrac{a}{b} \cdot \dfrac{y}{x}$, which is the dividend multiplied by the inverted divisor.

PROBLEMS 16 – 9

Simplify:

1 $\quad \frac{2}{3} \times \frac{6}{25} \times \frac{5}{8}$

2 $\quad \frac{3}{4} \times \frac{5}{9} \times \frac{11}{15}$

3 $\quad \frac{7}{16} \times 112 \times \frac{15}{49}$

4 $\quad \frac{5}{6} \div \frac{7}{12}$

5 $\quad \frac{8}{9} \div (-\frac{3}{4})$

6 $\quad \frac{15}{32} \div \frac{3}{4} \times \frac{1}{8}$

7 $\quad \dfrac{7e^3iR}{9EZ^2} \cdot \dfrac{27EZ}{14e^2R}$

8 $\quad \dfrac{2\omega}{3\pi} \cdot \dfrac{5\pi\lambda}{6\omega\pi\lambda} \cdot \dfrac{3\lambda^2}{4\omega^2}$

9 $\dfrac{36c^3d^2}{81ab} \cdot \dfrac{a^2}{8b} \div \dfrac{15ace^5}{27b^2e^3f}$

10 $\dfrac{4E^2 - 6E}{12E + 18} \cdot \dfrac{2E^2 + 3E}{4E^3}$

11 $\dfrac{2\omega + 1}{4\omega + \omega^2} \div \dfrac{1 - 4\omega^2}{\omega^3 - 16\omega}$

12 $\dfrac{\phi - 2}{4\phi - 3\theta} \div \dfrac{\phi^2 - 4}{16\phi^2 - 9\theta^2}$

13 $\dfrac{\pi(3\alpha + 2)}{5\alpha + \beta} \cdot \dfrac{25\alpha^2 - \beta^2}{9\alpha^2\pi^2 - 4\pi^2}$

14 $\dfrac{\mu^2 - 9}{\mu^2 - 2\mu - 3} \div \dfrac{\mu^2 + 5\mu + 6}{\mu^2 - 1}$

15 $\dfrac{f - 2}{f - 3} \cdot \dfrac{f - 1}{f - 2} \div \dfrac{f - 4}{f - 3}$

16 $\dfrac{LC - C^2}{L^2 + LC} \cdot \dfrac{L + C}{L^3 - L^2C}$

17 $\dfrac{I^2 - 12I - 45}{I^2 - 6I - 27} \div \dfrac{I^2 - 14I - 15}{I^2 - 4I - 45}$

18 $\dfrac{2R^2 + 11R + 5}{4R^2 - 1} \div \dfrac{2R^2 + 13R + 15}{4R^2 - 9}$

19 $\dfrac{16i^2 - 49}{4i^2 + i - 14} \cdot \dfrac{2i^2 + 5i + 2}{2i^2 - i - 1}$

20 $\dfrac{r^2 - 9}{r^2 - r - 12} \cdot \dfrac{(r - 4)^2}{r^2 - 2r - 3}$

21 $\dfrac{P + 1}{P^2 + 5P} \div \dfrac{P^2 - P - 2}{P^2 + 2P - 8} \cdot \dfrac{P^2 - P - 20}{P^2 - 25}$

22 $\left(\dfrac{\beta^2 - 6\beta - 7}{\beta^2 - 15\beta + 56}\right)\left(\dfrac{\beta^2 - 18\beta + 80}{\beta^2 - 5\beta - 50}\right) \div \dfrac{\beta - 1}{\beta + 5}$

23 $\left(\dfrac{\omega^2 + 2\omega L + L^2}{\omega L + L^2}\right)\left(\dfrac{L^2}{\omega^2 - L^2}\right) \div \dfrac{\omega^2 - \omega L}{\omega^2 - 2\omega L + L^2}$

24 $\dfrac{\theta^2 + 2\theta}{\theta^2 - \theta - 20} \div \left(\dfrac{\theta^2 - \theta - 6}{\theta^2 - 25}\right)\left(\dfrac{5\theta + \theta^2}{\theta^2 + \theta - 12}\right)$

25 $\dfrac{64b^2c^2 - d^4}{a^2 - 4} \cdot \dfrac{(a - 2)^2}{8bc + d^2} \div \dfrac{a^2 - 4}{(a + 2)^2}$

26 $\left(1 - \dfrac{E}{R}\right)\left(\dfrac{R}{R^2 - E^2}\right)$

27 $\left(\dfrac{\pi}{\lambda} - \dfrac{\lambda}{\pi}\right) \div \left(1 - \dfrac{\lambda}{\pi}\right)$

28 $\left(4 - \dfrac{6}{E + 1}\right) \div \left(8 + \dfrac{8 - 2E}{E^2 - 1}\right)$

29 $\left(\dfrac{i^2}{R^2} - 1\right) \div \left(1 + \dfrac{i^2 + R^2}{2ir}\right)$

30 $\left(\dfrac{5F^4 + 5F^3}{F^2 - 11F + 28}\right)\left(\dfrac{4}{F^2} - \dfrac{5}{F} + 1\right)\left(1 - \dfrac{7F - 1}{F^2 - 1}\right)$

16 – 18   Complex fractions

A *complex fraction* is one whose numerator or denominator, or both, are themselves fractions. The name is an unfortunate one. There is nothing complex or intricate about such compounded fractions, as we shall see.

RULE To simplify a complex fraction, reduce both numerator and denominator to simple fractions; then perform the indicated division.

EXAMPLE 34   Simplify $\dfrac{\dfrac{1}{3} + \dfrac{1}{5}}{4 - \dfrac{1}{5}}$

SOLUTION $\dfrac{\dfrac{1}{3} + \dfrac{1}{5}}{4 - \dfrac{1}{5}} = \dfrac{\dfrac{5+3}{15}}{\dfrac{20-1}{5}} = \dfrac{\dfrac{8}{15}}{\dfrac{19}{5}} = \dfrac{8}{15} \times \dfrac{5}{19} = \dfrac{8}{57}$

EXAMPLE 35   Simplify $\dfrac{5 - \dfrac{1}{a+1}}{3 + \dfrac{2}{a+1}}$.

SOLUTION $\dfrac{5 - \dfrac{1}{a+1}}{3 + \dfrac{2}{a+1}} = \dfrac{\dfrac{5(a+1)-1}{a+1}}{\dfrac{3(a+1)+2}{a+1}} = \dfrac{\dfrac{5a+4}{a+1}}{\dfrac{3a+5}{a+1}}$

$= \dfrac{5a+4}{a+1} \cdot \dfrac{a+1}{3a+5}$

$= \dfrac{5a+4}{3a+5}$

NOTE It is evident that if the same factor occurs in both numerators of a complex fraction the factors can be canceled. Also, if a factor occurs in both denominators, it can be canceled. Thus, $(a+1)$ could have been canceled in Example 35 after reducing the numerators and denominators from mixed expressions to simple fractions.

EXAMPLE 36   Simplify $\dfrac{\dfrac{a}{b} + \dfrac{a+b}{a-b}}{\dfrac{a}{b} - \dfrac{a-b}{a+b}}$.

SOLUTION $\dfrac{\dfrac{a}{b} + \dfrac{a+b}{a-b}}{\dfrac{a}{b} - \dfrac{a-b}{a+b}} = \dfrac{\dfrac{a(a-b)+b(a+b)}{b(a-b)}}{\dfrac{a(a+b)-b(a-b)}{b(a+b)}} = \dfrac{\dfrac{a^2-ab+ab+b^2}{b(a-b)}}{\dfrac{a^2+ab-ab+b^2}{b(a+b)}}$

$= \dfrac{\dfrac{a^2+b^2}{b(a-b)}}{\dfrac{a^2+b^2}{b(a+b)}} = \dfrac{a+b}{a-b}$

PROBLEMS 16 – 10

Simplify:

1 $\dfrac{\dfrac{3}{5} - 3}{2 - \dfrac{2}{5}}$

2 $\dfrac{25 - \left(\dfrac{2}{7}\right)^2}{5 + \dfrac{2}{7}}$

3 $\dfrac{\dfrac{1}{\alpha} + \dfrac{1}{\beta}}{\dfrac{1}{\alpha} - \dfrac{1}{\beta}}$

4 $\dfrac{2 + \dfrac{3E}{4I}}{E + \dfrac{8I}{3}}$

5 $\dfrac{1}{r + \dfrac{e}{i}}$

6 $\dfrac{1 - \dfrac{\omega^2}{\lambda^2}}{1 + \dfrac{\omega^2}{\lambda^2}}$

7 $\dfrac{Z}{Z - \dfrac{E_L}{I_L}}$

8 $\dfrac{3R + \dfrac{7r}{8z}}{\dfrac{7r}{8R} + 3z}$

9 $\dfrac{\dfrac{R_1 - R_1 R_2}{R_1 + R_2}}{\dfrac{R_1 + R_1 R_2}{R_1 - R_2}}$

10 $\dfrac{\omega + 5 + \dfrac{6}{\omega}}{\dfrac{6}{\omega} + \dfrac{8}{\omega^2} + 1}$

11 $\dfrac{1}{1 - \dfrac{1 + \alpha}{\alpha - \dfrac{1}{\alpha}}}$

12 $\dfrac{1}{e - \dfrac{e^2 - 1}{e + \dfrac{1}{e - 1}}}$

13 $\dfrac{1}{I - \dfrac{1}{I + \dfrac{1}{I}}} - \dfrac{1}{I + \dfrac{1}{I - \dfrac{1}{I}}}$

14 $\dfrac{\dfrac{\theta + 1}{\theta} - \dfrac{\phi + 1}{\phi}}{\dfrac{1}{\theta} + \dfrac{1}{\phi}}$

15 $\dfrac{\dfrac{\alpha + \beta}{\alpha - \beta} + \dfrac{\alpha - \beta}{\alpha + \beta}}{\dfrac{\alpha + \beta}{\alpha - \beta} - \dfrac{\alpha - \beta}{\alpha + \beta}}$

CHAPTER 17
FRACTIONAL EQUATIONS

An equation containing a fraction in which the unknown occurs in a denominator is called a *fractional equation*. Equations of this type are encountered in many problems involving electric and radio circuits. Simple fractional equations, wherein the unknown appeared only as a factor, were studied in earlier chapters.

7 – 1   Fractional coefficients

A number of problems lead to equations containing *fractional coefficients*. This type of equation is included in this chapter because the methods of solution apply also to fractional equations.

EXAMPLE 1 $\dfrac{3x}{4} + \dfrac{3}{2} = \dfrac{5x}{8}$ and $\dfrac{x}{2} + \dfrac{x}{3} = 5$

are equations having fractional coefficients.

EXAMPLE 2 $\dfrac{60}{x} - 3 = \dfrac{60}{4x}$ and $\dfrac{x-2}{x} = \dfrac{4}{5}$

are fractional equations.

You are familiar with the methods of solving simple equations that do not contain fractions. An equation involving fractions can be changed to an equation containing no denominators and then solved as heretofore.   To accomplish this we have the following rule:

RULE   To solve an equation containing fractions,
1   First clear of fractions by multiplying every term of the equation by the LCD.   (This will permit canceling all denominators.)
2   Solve the resulting equation.

EXAMPLE 3   Given $\dfrac{5x}{12} - 13 = \dfrac{x}{18}.$ Solve for x.

SOLUTION   Given $\dfrac{5x}{12} - 13 = \dfrac{x}{18}$

M:36, the LCD, $\dfrac{36 \cdot 5x}{12} - 36 \cdot 13 = \dfrac{36x}{18}$

Canceling, $\dfrac{\overset{3}{\cancel{36}} \cdot 5x}{\cancel{12}} - 36 \cdot 13 = \dfrac{\overset{2}{\cancel{36}x}}{\cancel{18}}$

Simplifying, $15x - 468 = 2x$
Collecting terms, $13x = 468$
D:13, $x = 36$

CHECK   Substitute 36 for x in the original equation.

$$\dfrac{5 \cdot 36}{12} - 13 = \dfrac{36}{18}$$

Clearing fractions, $15 - 13 = 2$

$$2 = 2$$

EXAMPLE 4   Given $\dfrac{e - 4}{9} = \dfrac{e}{10}.$ Solve for e.

SOLUTION   Given $\dfrac{e - 4}{9} = \dfrac{e}{10}$

M:90, the LCD, $\dfrac{90(e - 4)}{9} = \dfrac{90e}{10}$

Canceling, $\dfrac{\overset{10}{\cancel{90}}(e - 4)}{\cancel{9}} = \dfrac{\overset{9}{\cancel{90}e}}{\cancel{10}}$

Simplifying, $10(e - 4) = 9e$
or $10e - 40 = 9e$
Collecting terms, $10e - 9e = 40$
or $e = 40$

CHECK   Substituting 40 for e in the original equation,

$$\dfrac{40 - 4}{9} = \dfrac{40}{10}$$

Clearing fractions, $4 = 4$

Note that when the fractions were cleared and the equation written in simplified form in the above solution, the resulting equation was

$$10(e - 4) = 9e$$

which is equivalent to multiplying each member by the denominator of the other member and expressing the resulting equation with no denominators. This is called *cross multiplication*. You will see the justification of this if each member is expressed as a fraction having the LCD. Although the method is convenient, it must be remembered that *cross multiplication is permissible only when each term of a member of an equation has the same denominator*.

PROBLEMS 17 – 1

Solve for the following:

1 $\dfrac{\alpha}{3} - \dfrac{\alpha}{4} = 1$

2 $\dfrac{\beta}{3} = \dfrac{\beta}{7} + 4$

3 $\dfrac{5\pi}{4} - 1 = \dfrac{3\pi}{4} + \dfrac{1}{2}$

4 $\omega - 1 = \dfrac{2\omega}{5} - \dfrac{7}{5}$

5 $R + \dfrac{16}{3} = \dfrac{3R}{2} + \dfrac{25}{6}$

6 $3 = \dfrac{1 + E}{2} + \dfrac{2E - 3}{3}$

7 $\dfrac{8 + 9I}{6} + \dfrac{5I - 4}{18} = 4I - 10$

8 $21 + \dfrac{3Z - 11}{16} = \dfrac{5Z - 5}{8} + \dfrac{97 - 7Z}{2}$

NOTE   If a fraction is negative, the sign of each term of the numerator must be changed after removing the denominator. Remember that *the vinculum is a sign of grouping*.

9 $\dfrac{6 - e}{4} - \dfrac{3e + 14}{3} = 1$

10 $\theta + \dfrac{3\theta - 5}{2} = 12 - \dfrac{2\theta - 4}{3}$

11 $2 - \dfrac{2i - \frac{3}{4}}{2} + \dfrac{3}{4}i = 0$

12 $r - \dfrac{7 + 4r}{6} + \dfrac{2r - 5}{10} - \dfrac{r - 4}{15} = 0$

13 $\pi - \frac{1}{5}(3\pi - 3) + 4 = \frac{1}{2}(20 - \pi) - \frac{1}{7}(6\pi - 8) + \frac{1}{5}(4\pi - 4)$

NOTE $\dfrac{1}{2}(20 - \pi) = \dfrac{20 - \pi}{2}$

14 $\dfrac{11}{3} + \dfrac{8I}{15} = \dfrac{1}{5}(20 - 4I) - \dfrac{1}{6}(2I - 1)$

15 $\dfrac{1}{4}\left(4 + \dfrac{3}{2}\alpha\right) = \dfrac{1}{7}\left(2\alpha - \dfrac{1}{3}\right) + \dfrac{31}{28}$

17 – 2   Equations containing decimals

Equations containing decimals are readily solved by first clearing the equation of the decimals. This is accomplished by multiplying both members by a power of 10 that corresponds to the largest number of decimal places appearing in any term.

EXAMPLE 5   Solve $0.75 - 0.7a = 0.26$.

SOLUTION   Given $0.75 - 0.7a = 0.26$

M:100, $75 - 70a = 26$

Collecting terms, $70a = 49$

D:70, $a = 0.7$

CHECK   Substituting 0.7 for a in the original equation,

$$0.75 - 0.7 \cdot 0.7 = 0.26$$
$$0.75 - 0.49 = 0.26$$
$$0.26 = 0.26$$

If decimals occur in any denominator, multiply both numerator and denominator of the fraction by a power of 10 that will reduce the decimals to integers.

EXAMPLE 6   Solve

$$\frac{5m - 1.33}{0.02} - \frac{m}{0.05} = 1{,}083.5$$

SOLUTION   Given

$$\frac{5m - 1.33}{0.02} - \frac{m}{0.05} = 1{,}083.5$$

Multiplying numerator and denominator of each fraction by 100,

$$\frac{500m - 133}{2} - \frac{100m}{5} = 1{,}083.5$$

The equation is then solved and checked by the usual methods.

PROBLEMS 17 – 2

Solve the following:

1   $0.5E = 1.5$

2   $0.06i = 0.03$

3   $0.6\alpha = 0.3\alpha + 1.2$

4   $0.16 - 0.09r = 0.05r - 0.12$

5   $0.027 - 0.028\beta = 0.019 - 0.016\beta$

6   $0.04 + 0.03(\theta - 7) = 0.16 + 0.02(5\theta + 1)$

7   $0.08e - 0.05(4e + 3) = -0.03 - 0.04(2e - 7)$

8   $0.018 - 0.004\pi + 0.027 + 0.009\pi - 0.003 + 0.016\pi = 0$

9   $\dfrac{0.1R}{3} + \dfrac{0.1R - 0.5}{10} = \dfrac{0.4R + 0.3}{5}$

10 $\dfrac{0.01I - 0.01}{3} - \dfrac{0.02I + 0.02}{5} = 0$

11 $\dfrac{0.2\phi - 0.5}{10} - \dfrac{0.1\phi - 0.4}{15} - \dfrac{0.4\phi + 0.7}{6} + 0.1\phi = 0$

12 $\dfrac{0.4E - 0.6}{0.06E - 0.07} = \dfrac{2E - 3}{0.3E - 0.4}$

13 $56 = \dfrac{r - 2}{0.05} - \dfrac{r - 4}{0.0625}$

14 $\dfrac{0.7(e - 1)}{0.1 - 0.5e} - \dfrac{1 - 1.4e}{0.2 + e} = 0$

15 $(3\omega + 1.25)(2\omega - 1.125) = (3\omega - 2.25)(2\omega + 1.5)$

17 – 3   Fractional equations

Fractional equations are solved in the same manner as equations containing fractional coefficients (Sec. 17–1). That is, every term of the equation must be multiplied by the LCD.

EXAMPLE 7   Solve

$$\frac{x + 2}{3x} - \frac{2x^2 + 3}{6x^2} = \frac{1}{2x}$$

SOLUTION   Given

$$\frac{x + 2}{3x} - \frac{2x^2 + 3}{6x^2} = \frac{1}{2x}$$

M:$6x^2$, the LCD, $\dfrac{6x^2(x + 2)}{3x} - \dfrac{6x^2(2x^2 + 3)}{6x^2} = \dfrac{6x^2}{2x}$

Canceling, $\dfrac{\overset{2x}{\cancel{6x^2}}(x + 2)}{\cancel{3x}} - \dfrac{\cancel{6x^2}(2x^2 + 3)}{\cancel{6x^2}} = \dfrac{\overset{3x}{\cancel{6x^2}}}{\cancel{2x}}$

Rewriting, $2x(x + 2) - (2x^2 + 3) = 3x$

Simplifying, $2x^2 + 4x - 2x^2 - 3 = 3x$

Collecting terms, $4x - 3x = 3$

or $x = 3$

CHECK   Substituting 3 for x in the original equation,

$$\frac{3 + 2}{9} - \frac{18 + 3}{54} = \frac{1}{6}$$

That is, $\dfrac{30}{54} - \dfrac{21}{54} = \dfrac{9}{54}$

EXAMPLE 8   Solve

$$\frac{8a + 2}{a - 2} - \frac{2a - 1}{3a - 6} + \frac{3a + 2}{5a - 10} + 5 = 15$$

SOLUTION   Given

$$\frac{8a + 2}{a - 2} - \frac{2a - 1}{3a - 6} + \frac{3a + 2}{5a - 10} + 5 = 15$$

Factoring denominators, $\dfrac{8a + 2}{a - 2} - \dfrac{2a - 1}{3(a - 2)} + \dfrac{3a + 2}{5(a - 2)} + 5 = 15$

M:$15(a - 2)$, the LCD,

$$\dfrac{15(a - 2)(8a + 2)}{a - 2} - \dfrac{15(a - 2)(2a - 1)}{3(a - 2)} + \dfrac{15(a - 2)(3a + 2)}{5(a - 2)}$$
$$+ 15(a - 2)(5) = 15(a - 2)(15)$$

Canceling,

$$\dfrac{15(\cancel{a - 2})(8a + 2)}{\cancel{a - 2}} - \dfrac{\overset{5}{\cancel{15}}(\cancel{a - 2})(2a - 1)}{\cancel{3}(\cancel{a - 2})} + \dfrac{\overset{3}{\cancel{15}}(\cancel{a - 2})(3a + 2)}{\cancel{5}(\cancel{a - 2})}$$
$$+ 15(a - 2)(5) = 15(a - 2)(15)$$

Rewriting,

$$15(8a + 2) - 5(2a - 1) + 3(3a + 2) + 15(a - 2)(5) = 15(a - 2)(15)$$

Simplifying, $120a + 30 - 10a + 5 + 9a + 6 + 75a - 150 = 225a - 450$

Collecting terms,

$$120a - 10a + 9a + 75a - 225a = -30 - 5 - 6 + 150 - 450$$
$$-31a = -341$$
$$a = 11$$

Check the solution by the usual method.

PROBLEMS 17 – 3

Solve the following:

1 $\dfrac{1}{2e} + \dfrac{5}{8} = \dfrac{3}{e}$

2 $\dfrac{2}{r} + \dfrac{5}{6} = 1.5$

3 $\dfrac{3}{3\alpha} + \dfrac{1}{3} - \dfrac{8}{15} = 0$

4 $\dfrac{1}{\pi} + \dfrac{2}{\pi} = 3 - \dfrac{3}{\pi}$

5 $\dfrac{4}{\beta} + \dfrac{7}{6} - \dfrac{2}{3\beta} - \dfrac{1}{\beta} = 0$

6 $\dfrac{5}{2} + \dfrac{1}{2R} = \dfrac{8}{R}$

7 $\dfrac{13 - I}{I} - \dfrac{1}{I} = \dfrac{5}{I}$

8 $\dfrac{\pi - 5}{3\pi} + \dfrac{5}{6} - \dfrac{\pi + 5}{\pi} = 0$

9 $\dfrac{5}{2} - \dfrac{i + 4}{i} = \dfrac{i - 4}{2i}$

10 $\dfrac{2}{5} - \dfrac{e + 4}{e + 1} = 0$

11 $\dfrac{r + 4}{3r} = \dfrac{3r - 8}{4r}$

12 $\dfrac{\theta}{\theta - 1} - \dfrac{3}{\theta + 1} = 1$

13 $\dfrac{4}{2E + 6} = \dfrac{3}{4E - 8}$

14 $\dfrac{R}{R + 1} + 2 = \dfrac{3R}{R + 2}$

15 $\dfrac{Z - 1}{Z + 1} - \dfrac{Z}{Z - 2} + \dfrac{4}{Z} = 0$

16 $\dfrac{3\phi + 4}{\phi + 2} - \dfrac{3\phi - 5}{\phi - 4} = \dfrac{12}{\phi^2 - 2\phi - 8}$

17 $\dfrac{3\lambda + 10}{\lambda^2 + 5\lambda + 6} + \dfrac{\lambda}{\lambda + 2} = \dfrac{\lambda}{\lambda + 3}$

18 $\dfrac{1}{4z} - \dfrac{2}{z(z - 1)} = \dfrac{1}{2(1 - z)}$

19 $\dfrac{4(9 - \beta)}{\beta^2 - 9} - \dfrac{3\beta - 2}{\beta + 3} - \dfrac{3\beta + 2}{3 - \beta} = 0$

20 $\dfrac{6}{1 - 4\alpha} = \dfrac{1}{9} - \dfrac{10}{8\alpha - 2}$

21 *A* can do a piece of work in 8 hr, and *B* can do it in 6 hr; how long will it take them to do it together?

SOLUTION   Let n = number of hours it will take them to do it together. Now *A* does $\frac{1}{8}$ of the job in 1 hr; therefore, he will do $\frac{n}{8}$ in n hr.

Also, *B* does $\frac{1}{6}$ of the job in 1 hr; therefore, he will do $\frac{n}{6}$ in n hr. Then they will do $\frac{n}{8} + \frac{n}{6}$ in n hr.

The entire job will be completed in n hr, which we may represent by $\frac{8}{8}$ or $\frac{6}{6}$ of itself, which is 1.

$$\therefore \frac{n}{8} + \frac{n}{6} = 1$$

M:24, the LCD, $3n + 4n = 24$
$$7n = 24$$
$$n = 3\frac{3}{7}\ \text{hr}$$

22 A technician can install a television transmission line in 5 hr, and his helper can do it in 8 hr. In how many hours should they be able to do it if they work together?

23 A water tank can be filled in 1 hr and 10 min if one pipe is used. If a different pipe is used, it takes 1 hr and 45 min to fill the tank. How long will it take to fill the tank if both pipes are used?

24 *A* can do a piece of work in a days, and *B* can do it in b days. Derive a general formula for the number of days it would take both together to do the work.

SOLUTION   Let x = number of days it will take both together.

Now *A* will do $\frac{x}{a}$ of the job in x days. Also, *B* will do $\frac{x}{b}$ of the job in x days.

Then $\frac{x}{a} + \frac{x}{b} = 1$

M:ab, $bx + ax = ab$
Factoring, $x(a + b) = ab$

D:$(a + b)$, $x = \dfrac{ab}{a + b}$

ALTERNATE SOLUTION   Let x = number of days it will take both together. Then $\frac{1}{x}$ = part that both together can do in 1 day, $\frac{1}{a}$ = part that *A* alone can do in 1 day, $\frac{1}{b}$ = part that *B* alone can do in 1 day.

Now, $$\frac{1}{a} + \frac{1}{b} = \frac{1}{x}$$

M :abx, $bx + ax = ab$

Factoring, $x(b + a) = ab$

D:$(a + b)$, $$x = \frac{ab}{a + b}$$

25 A can do a piece of work in a days, B in b days, and C in c days. Derive a general formula for the number of days it would take them to do it together.

26 A tank can be filled by two pipes in 3 and 5 hr, respectively. It can be emptied by the drain pipe in 6 hr. If all three pipes are open, how long will it take to fill the tank?

27 Three circuits are connected to a storage battery. Circuit 1 completely discharges the battery in 20 hr, circuit 2 in 15 hr, and circuit 3 in 12 hr. All circuits are connected to the battery in parallel. In how many hours will the battery be discharged?

28 A tank can be filled by two pipes in x and y hr, respectively, and emptied by a drain pipe in z hr. Derive a general formula for the number of hours required to fill the tank with all pipes open.

29 A bottle contains 1 gal of a mixture of equal parts of acid and water. How much water must be added to make a mixture that will be one-tenth acid?

SOLUTION   Let n = number of quarts of water to be added
                        4 qt = amount of original mixture

Then,   2 qt = amount of acid

Hence, $n + 4$ = amount of new one-tenth acid mixture

Now, $$\frac{1}{10} = \frac{\text{amount of acid}}{\text{total mixture}}$$

Then, $$\frac{1}{10} = \frac{2}{n + 4}$$

or $n = 16$ qt of water to be added

30 An engine radiator contains 6 gal of a 30 per cent alcohol solution. How much alcohol must be added to obtain a 45 per cent mixture?

31 How much metal containing 25 per cent copper must be added to 10 lb of pure copper to obtain a mixture having 50 per cent copper?

SOLUTION   Let x = desired amount of metal containing 25 per cent copper

Then, $0.25x$ = amount of copper in this metal
                  $10 + 0.25x$ = amount of copper in mixture
                       $x + 10$ = total weight of mixture

$$0.5(x + 10) = \text{amount of copper in mixture}$$
$$0.5(x + 10) = 10 + 0.25x$$
$$x = 20 \text{ lb}$$

32 How much 10 per cent nickel alloy must be added to 10 lb of 30 per cent nickel alloy to form a 12 per cent nickel alloy?

33 A fighter plane traveling at 600 mph leaves its base at 9:00 A.M. to overtake a bomber which departed from the same base at 7:00 A.M., traveling at a speed of 350 mph. How much time is required for the fighter to overtake the bomber?

34 The sum of two numbers is 300. When the larger is divided by the smaller, the quotient is 24. Find the numbers.

35 If 7 is added to a certain number and this sum is divided by 4, the quotient is 3 and the remainder is 3. Find the number.

36 The sum of two numbers is 433. When the larger is divided by the smaller, the quotient is 32 and there is a remainder of 4. Find the numbers.

37 A rope 25 ft long is cut into two pieces, one of which is two-thirds the length of the other. Find the length of each piece.

38 Divide 77 into two parts so that one part is five-sixths of the other.

39 What number must be added to both the numerator and denominator of $\frac{1}{3}$ to result in a new fraction equal to $\frac{3}{4}$?

40 The denominator of a certain fraction is 12 more than the numerator. If the numerator is increased by 2 and the denominator is increased by 6, the result is $\frac{1}{3}$. Find the fraction.

41 The denominator of a certain fraction exceeds the numerator by 27; if 9 is subtracted from both terms of the fraction, the value of the fraction becomes $\frac{1}{4}$. Find the fraction.

42 If x is added to the numerator of $\frac{2}{7}$ and 9 is added to the denominator, the result is $\frac{3}{4}$. Find x.

43 A rectangle is four times as long as it is wide. If it was 4 ft shorter and 1.5 ft wider, its area would be 11 ft² more. Find its dimensions.

44 The perimeter of a triangle is 41 in. The second side is 9 in. longer than one-third the first, and the third side is 1 in. shorter than one-half the first. Find the length of each side.

45 There are two consecutive numbers such that one-fourth of the smaller exceeds one-fifth of the greater by 1. Find the numbers.

7 – 4   Literal equations

Equations in which some or all of the numbers are replaced by letters are called *literal equations*. These were studied in Chap. 12. Having attained more knowledge of algebra, such as factoring and fractions,

we are now ready to proceed with the solution of more difficult literal
equations, or formulas. No new methods are involved in the actual
solutions—we are prepared to solve a more complicated equation
simply because we have available more tools with which to work.
Again, it is desired to point out that the ability to solve formulas is of
utmost importance.

EXAMPLE 9   Given $\dfrac{I = E}{R + r}$, solve for r.

SOLUTION   Given $I = \dfrac{E}{R + r}$

M:$(R + r)$, $I(R + r) = E$

Removing parentheses, $IR + Ir = E$

S:IR, $Ir = E - IR$

D:I, $r = \dfrac{E - IR}{I}$

EXAMPLE 10   Given $S = \dfrac{RL - a}{R - 1}$, solve for L.

SOLUTION   Given $\dfrac{RL - a}{R - 1} = S$

M:$(R - 1)$, $RL - a = S(R - 1)$

A:a, $RL = S(R - 1) + a$

D:R, $L = \dfrac{S(R - 1) + a}{R}$

EXAMPLE 11   Given $\dfrac{a}{x - b} = \dfrac{2a}{x + b}$, solve for x.

SOLUTION   Given $\dfrac{a}{x - b} = \dfrac{2a}{x + b}$

M:$(x^2 - b^2)$, the LCD, $\dfrac{(x^2 - b^2)a}{x - b} = \dfrac{(x^2 - b^2)2a}{x + b}$

Canceling, $\dfrac{\overset{x + b}{\cancel{(x^2 - b^2)}a}}{\cancel{x - b}} = \dfrac{\overset{x - b}{\cancel{(x^2 - b^2)}2a}}{\cancel{x + b}}$

Rewriting, $(x + b)a = (x - b)2a$

Removing parentheses, $ax + ab = 2ax - 2ab$

Collecting terms, $ax - 2ax = -2ab - ab$

or $-ax = -3ab$

M:-1, $ax = 3ab$

D:a, $x = 3b$

NOTE   The last two steps can be combined into one step by dividing $-ax = -3ab$ by $-a$ to obtain $x = 3b$.

CHECK   Substitute $3b$ for x in the given equation.

$$\frac{a}{3b - b} = \frac{2a}{3b + b}$$

Simplifying,
$$\frac{a}{2b} = \frac{2a}{4b}$$

or
$$\frac{a}{2b} = \frac{a}{2b}$$

PROBLEMS 17-4

Given: Solve for:

1   $v = v_o + gt$ t, v_o, g

2   $A = \frac{1}{2}h(a + b)$ h, b

3   $V = r^2(a - b)$ a

4   $a = \dfrac{W - W_1}{W - W_2}$ W, W_2

5   $\dfrac{a}{v} = \dfrac{m}{M + m}$ m, M

6   $F = 1 + \dfrac{R_{eq}}{R}$ R_{eq}, R

7   $\mu = \dfrac{g_m}{g'_m - g_m}$ g_m, g'_m

8   $\mu = \dfrac{2G_L + g_p - 2G_2}{G_2 - G_L}$ G_2

9   $m_2 = \dfrac{Fr^2}{m_1}$ F

10   $p = \dfrac{a}{1 + rt}$ a, r

11   $a = \dfrac{1}{T - t}$ T, t

12   $ax - b = 0$ a

13   $L_o = \dfrac{L_t}{1 + \alpha t}$ L_t, α

14   $\dfrac{\alpha + \theta}{\alpha - \phi} - \dfrac{3}{4} = 0$ α

15   $\theta^2 = \phi^2 + \omega^2 + 2\phi\Delta$ Δ

16   $I = \dfrac{E_g - E_t}{R}$ E_t, E_g

17   $E_b = IR + E_c$ I

18   $s = \dfrac{N(a + L)}{2}$ a, N

19   $e = \dfrac{Er}{R + r}$ r, R

20 $t = \dfrac{d(ad + 1)}{P}$ $\qquad$ a

21 $M = \dfrac{Lt + g}{t}$ $\qquad$ $L,\ g,\ t$

22 $a = \dfrac{Cb}{kb + C}$ $\qquad$ $C,\ b$

23 $V_o = \dfrac{2s - gt^2}{2t}$ $\qquad$ s

24 $L = \dfrac{sr - s + a}{r}$ $\qquad$ $a,\ s$

25 $C = Y_c p + 2m$ $\qquad$ $Y_c,\ m$

26 $L = \dfrac{c - 12D}{A}$ $\qquad$ D

27 $\dfrac{\lambda}{\pi} - \omega = \dfrac{\alpha\beta}{\pi}$ $\qquad$ π

28 $\dfrac{\theta + 2}{\phi} = \dfrac{2}{\phi} + \dfrac{1}{\Delta}$ $\qquad$ Δ

29 $L = \dfrac{WL_1 + W_g}{pA - V}$ $\qquad$ $p,\ W$

30 $b_1 = \dfrac{2A}{h} - b_2$ $\qquad$ $A,\ h$

31 $R = \dfrac{\omega^2 L^2}{Z - 1}$ $\qquad$ Z

32 $R_b = \dfrac{2p}{I_{\max}{}^2}$ $\qquad$ p

33 $s = \dfrac{r(R + EI)}{p + e}$ $\qquad$ p

34 $F = \dfrac{9C}{5} + 32$ $\qquad$ C

35 $E_g = \dfrac{I_p R_p - E_p - m}{\mu}$ $\qquad$ I_p

36 $\dfrac{1}{R_t} = \dfrac{1}{R_1} + \dfrac{1}{R_2}$ $\qquad$ $R_t,\ R_1,\ R_2$

37 $P = \dfrac{\mu E_g}{r + R_p}$ $\qquad$ r

38 $G = g_m \dfrac{R_{pg} r_p}{R_{pg} + r_p}$ $\qquad$ $g_m,\ r_p$

39 $k = \dfrac{273h}{273 + t}$ $\qquad$ $t,\ h$

40 $p = \dfrac{m}{d - L} - \dfrac{m}{d + L}$ $\qquad$ m

41 $MH\alpha = C\left(\dfrac{\pi}{2} - \alpha\right)$ $\qquad$ α

42    $\mu = \dfrac{kE_p}{E_b - kE_g}$ $E_b,\ E_g$

43    $\alpha\beta - \alpha^2 = \beta - 1$ β

44    $E'_g = \dfrac{\mu E_g - E'_p + E_p}{\mu}$ μ

45    $E_b = \sqrt{2}\,P_{ac} + E_p$ P_{ac}

46    $\dfrac{r_1}{r_1 + r_2} = \dfrac{r_3}{r_3 + r_4}$ $r_1,\ r_4$

47    $r_1 = \dfrac{ir - i_g r_g}{i + i_g}$ i_g

48    $R_1 = \dfrac{R_o(E - I_2 R_2)}{I_2(R_o + R_2)}$ I_2

49    $\dfrac{\theta}{\phi} = \beta(\theta - \omega) + \dfrac{\omega}{\phi}$ ϕ

50    $Z_c = \dfrac{e_2 \omega C r_p Z_e}{\mu e - e_2 \omega C(Z_e + r_p)}$ e_2

51    $\dfrac{Q}{p} = \dfrac{L_2 + \alpha}{100 - L_2 + \beta}$ L_2

52    $k_1 = \dfrac{3kE - E_2 k_2}{2E_2}$ E_2

53    $\dfrac{\alpha}{\omega} + \dfrac{\alpha}{\theta} + \dfrac{\alpha}{\phi} = 1$ α

54    $L_b = \dfrac{\mu e_g - i_p(r_p + R_b)}{\omega i_p}$ i_p

55    $M = \dfrac{F' x^4}{2m'(x - 3)}$ F'

56    $Z_1 = \dfrac{Ea - I_s Z_2}{I_s a^2}$ I_s

57    $\omega^2 L_p(C_p + C_o) = 1$ C_o

58    $R_p = \dfrac{e_1 Z_1}{\mu e_g - e_1}$ e_1

59    $C_{gp} = \dfrac{(C_g - C_{gf})(r_p + r_b)}{r_p + r_b + \mu R_b}$ $R_b,\ C_g$

60    $\dfrac{E_b - E_c}{\mu} = E_c + E_s \dfrac{R_p}{R_1 + R_p}$ R_1

61    $E = \dfrac{I_{\max}(R_1 R_2 + \omega^2 M^2)}{\omega M}$ $R_1,\ I_{\max}$

62    $MH = \dfrac{4\pi r^2}{T^2\left(1 + \dfrac{\alpha}{\dfrac{\pi}{2} - \alpha}\right)}$ α

63    $R_c = \dfrac{R_p(R_{gl} - R)}{R - R_{gl} - R_p}$ $R_p,\ R$

64    $L = \dfrac{0.08r^2N^2}{6r + 9d + 10l}$ d

65    $C_s = \dfrac{G_a + n^2G_s - 2\pi\beta C_a}{2\pi\beta n^2}$ β

66    $R_2 = \dfrac{Z_1(\mu e_g Z_2 - e_2 r_p)}{e_2(r_p + Z_1)}$ $Z_1,\ e_2$

67    $\mu = G_m \dfrac{\omega LQ}{1 + \dfrac{\omega LQ}{R_p} + \dfrac{\omega LQ}{R_{gl}}}$ $L,\ R_p$

68    $\dfrac{\alpha - \dfrac{\pi}{\alpha - \beta}}{\alpha + \dfrac{\pi}{\alpha - \beta}} - 1 = \dfrac{\alpha}{\beta}$ π

69    $I_p = \dfrac{R_{eq}I_c g_m{}^2}{2.5g_m + 20I_c - R_{eq}g_m{}^2}$ R_{eq}

70   The force F between two magnetic poles of strengths S_1 and S_2 at a distance of l cm is

$$F = \frac{S_1 S_2}{l^2} \quad \text{dynes}$$

When separated by a distance of 60 cm, a force of 1.5 dynes exists between them. $S_1 = 60$ units. What is the value of S_2?

71    $H = 0.4\pi NI$ oersted. A solenoid of $N = 120$ turns has a magnetic field of 300 oersteds. How much current is required to maintain this field?

72   The force of attraction between two bodies is

$$F = K\frac{W_1 W_2}{D} \quad \text{dynes}$$

If the force of attraction between two bodies $W_1 = 50$ kg and $W_2 = 150$ kg at a distance of $D = 0.05$ cm is $F = 0.01$ dyne, what is the value of the constant of gravitation K?

73   When two impedances Z_1 and Z_2 are connected in parallel, the resultant joint impedance Z_t is

$$Z_t = \frac{Z_1 Z_2}{Z_1 + Z_2} \quad \Omega$$

Solve for Z_2.

74   Using the formula of Prob. 73, what is the value of Z_1 when $Z_t = 3\ \Omega$ and $Z_2 = 6\ \Omega$?

75 $\dfrac{N_p}{N_s} = \dfrac{E_p}{E_s}$. $E_p = 100$, $N_p = 400$, and $N_s = 80$. What is the value of E_s?

76 $\dfrac{V_1}{V_2} = \dfrac{R_1}{R_2}$. $R_1 = 47.7\ \Omega$, $R_2 = 100\ \Omega$, and $V_1 = 16.2$ volts. What is the value of V_2?

77 Corresponding temperature readings in Fahrenheit degrees F can be obtained from a centigrade thermometer by the use of the formula $F = \frac{9}{5}C + 32°$, where C is the temperature in centigrade degrees. When $F = 68°$, what is the centigrade temperature?

78 Using the formula given in Prob. 77, find the temperature at which the Fahrenheit and centigrade temperatures are equal, that is, at which $F = C$.

79 $L_t = L_o + L_o \alpha t$. $L_t = 15$, $L_o = 10$, $\alpha = 8.33 \times 10^{-2}$. $t = ?$

80 $R_t = R_o(1 + 0.0042t)$. The resistance of a copper wire is $R_o = 32\ \Omega$ at 0°C. What is the temperature t when the resistance has increased to $R_t = 40\ \Omega$?

81 $P = \dfrac{LI^2}{2}$. The energy P stored in a circuit is 100 joules. If the current $I = 1.58$ amp, find the value of the coefficient of self-induction L.

82 When two capacitors C_1 and C_2 are connected in series, the resultant total capacitance can be computed by means of the equation $\dfrac{1}{C_t} = \dfrac{1}{C_1} + \dfrac{1}{C_2}$. $C_1 = 3\ \mu f$, and $C_t = 2\ \mu f$. $C_2 = ?$

83 The joint conductance $\dfrac{1}{R_t}$ mhos of three resistances R_1, R_2, and R_3 connected in parallel is expressed

$$\frac{1}{R_t} = \frac{1}{R_1} + \frac{1}{R_2} + \frac{1}{R_3}$$

Solve for R_t.

84 A lens formula is $\dfrac{1}{f} = \dfrac{1}{p} + \dfrac{1}{q}$. How much is q when $f = 50$ and $p = 133\frac{1}{3}$?

85 Using the lens equation given in Prob. 84, if the focal length $f = -40$ and the image distance $q = -20$, find the object distance p.

86 Using the formula $P = \dfrac{E^2}{R}$, (a) how is the value of P changed when E is doubled, (b) how is the value of P changed when R is doubled?

87 A source of voltage consists of n cells in parallel, each having an emf of E volts and an internal resistance of $r\ \Omega$. The current I that flows through a load of $R\ \Omega$ is given by the relation

$$I = \frac{E}{R + \dfrac{r}{n}} \quad \text{amp}$$

Solve for r and R.

88   Using the formula stated in Prob. 87, find the value of E when $r = 0.6\ \Omega$, $R = 0.9\ \Omega$, $I = 2$ amp, and $n = 4$ cells.

89   Using the formula stated in Prob. 87, find n in terms of E and I when $R = 16\ \Omega$ and $r = 0.2\ \Omega$.

90   A source of voltage consists of n cells in series, each with an emf of E volts and an internal resistance of $r\ \Omega$. The current flowing through a load of $R\ \Omega$ is given by the relation

$$I = \frac{nE}{R + nr} \quad \text{amp}$$

Solve for R and n.

91   Using the formula stated in Prob. 90, find the internal resistance r of each of 10 cells of 2.1 volts each if a current I of 2 amp flows through a load resistance $R = 4.5\ \Omega$.

92   When a signal voltage e_g is impressed on the grid of a vacuum tube which has an amplification factor of μ, the resulting plate current i_p flowing in the output circuit, which consists of the plate resistance r_p in series with the load circuit r_b, is

$$i_p = \frac{\mu e_g}{r_p + r_b} \quad \text{amp}$$

Solve for μ and r_p.

93   Using the formula stated in Prob. 92, what value of load resistance r_b is needed for a plate current of $i_p = 5$ ma when $e_g = 20$ volts, $r_p = 10{,}000\ \Omega$, and $\mu = 5$?

94   If $\mu = \left(\dfrac{M}{M + m}\right)v$, what is the value of M when $m = -67.8$, $\mu = 500$, and $v = 48$?

95   In the formula $I = \dfrac{E}{R + r}$, what is the value of R if $E = 220$ volts, $r = 4\ \Omega$, and $I = 5$ amp?

96   Does $\dfrac{IR + E}{R} = I + E$?   Explain your answer.

97   Given $I = \dfrac{E}{R_1 + R_2 + R_3}$.   Is $R_3 = \dfrac{E}{R_1 + R_2 + I}$ correct?   Explain your answer.

98   A pulley formula is $P = \dfrac{W(R - r)}{2R}$.   What is the value of r if $W = 60$, $R = 6$, and $P = 10$?

99   $V = \frac{1}{3}\pi r^2 h$ is the formula for the volume of a circular cone, where r = radius and h = height. A certain cone has twice the volume of another. Their radii are equal. How does the height of the first cone compare with that of the second?

100   $A = \dfrac{h(b_1 + b_2)}{2}$. What is the value of b_1 when $b_2 = 100$, $A = 300$, and $h = 4$?

101   $S = V_o t + \frac{1}{2}gt^2$. What is the value of the initial velocity V_o when $S = 1{,}710$ ft, $g = 32.2$, and $t = 10$ sec?

102   $F_t = \dfrac{W}{g}(V_1 - V_o)$. What is the value of V_1 when $V_o = -40$, $F_t = 155.3$, $W = 100$, and $g = 32.2$?

103   $\dfrac{a}{b} = \dfrac{a - \dfrac{x}{a-b}}{a + \dfrac{x}{a-b}} - 1$. What is the value of b when $a = 3$ and $x = 11$?

104   $\dfrac{x}{a} + \dfrac{x}{b} + \dfrac{x}{c} = 1$. What is the value of b if $x = 25$, $a = 36$, and $c = 30$?

105   The incremental plate resistance R_b of a vacuum tube is equal to the quotient obtained by dividing the plate voltage swing by the plate current swing. That is,

$$R_b = \frac{E_{\max} - E_{\min}}{I_{\max} - I_{\min}}$$

Solve for $E_{\min}$ and $I_{\max}$.

106   $I_p = \dfrac{E_p + \mu e_g + m}{R_p}$. What is the value of μ when $m = -250$, $I_p = 0.050$ amp, $e_g = 50$ volts, $E_p = 250$ volts, and $R_p = 50{,}000\ \Omega$?

107   $E = L\dfrac{I_1 - I_2}{t}$. $L = 5$ henrys, and the initial current $I_1 = 102$ amp. The induced voltage E is 1,000 volts in $t = 0.5$ sec. What is the value of the current I_2?

108   $I = C\dfrac{E_1 - E_2}{t}$. In a circuit containing a capacitor C, when the voltage changes from $E_1 = 100$ volts to $E_2 = 2$ volts in $t = 0.0294$ sec, a current of 0.05 amp flows. What is the value of the capacitor?

109   $\dfrac{r_1}{r_1 + r_2} = \dfrac{r_3}{r_3 + r_4}$. If $r_1 = 20$, what is the value of r_3 in terms of r_2 and r_4?

110   $R_a = \dfrac{R_1 R_3}{R_1 + R_2 + R_3}$. Three resistances $R_1 = 2\,\Omega$, $R_2 = 3\,\Omega$, and $R_3 = ?$ are connected in a delta circuit. One branch of the equivalent Y circuit is $R_a = 0.6\ \Omega$. Find R_3.

CHAPTER 18
OHM'S LAW
PARALLEL CIRCUITS

Most of the systems employed for the distribution of electric energy consist of parallel circuits; that is, a source of emf is connected to a pair of conductors, known as *feeders*, and various types of load are connected across these feeders. A simple distribution circuit consisting of a motor and a bank of five lamps is represented schematically in Fig. 18–1 and pictorially in Fig. 18–2. The motor and the lamps are

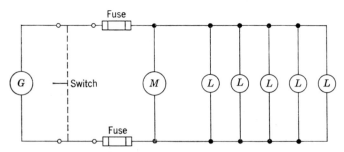

FIG. 18–1 Schematic diagram of a generator G connected to a motor M in parallel with a bank of five lamps L.

said to be in *parallel*, and it is evident that the current supplied by the generator divides between the motor and the lamps.

In this chapter you will analyze parallel circuits and solve parallel-circuit problems. The solution of a parallel circuit generally consists

To generator

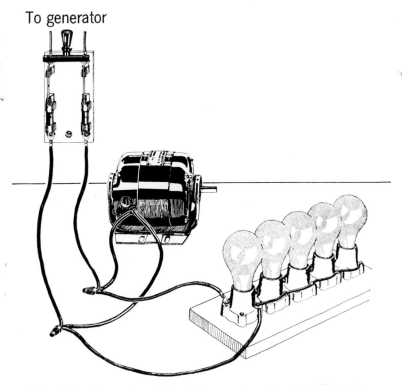

Fig. 18–2   Illustration of circuit shown schematically in Fig. 18–1.

in reducing the entire circuit to a single equivalent resistance that could replace the original circuit without any change in the supply voltage or current.

18 — 1   Two resistances in parallel

The schematic diagram of Fig. 18–3 and the accompanying circuit shown in Fig. 18–4 represent two resistors R_1 and R_2 connected in parallel across a source of voltage E. An examination of the circuit arrangement brings out two important facts:

1. The same voltage exists across the two resistors.
2. The total current I_t delivered by the generator enters the

paralleled resistors at junction a, divides between the resistors, and leaves the parallel circuit at junction b. Thus, the sum of the currents I_1 and I_2, which flow through R_1 and R_2, respectively, is equal to the total current I_t.

By making use of these facts and applying Ohm's law, it is easy to

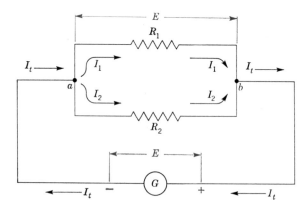

FIG. 18–3 Resistors R_1 and R_2 connected in parallel across generator G, which maintains a potential of E volts.

derive equations that show how paralleled resistances combine. From 1 above, $I_1 = \dfrac{E}{R_1}$, $I_2 = \dfrac{E}{R_2}$, and $I_t = \dfrac{E}{R_t}$, where R_t is the joint resistance of R_1 and R_2, or the total resistance of the parallel combination.

From 2 above,
$$I_t = I_1 + I_2 \qquad [1]$$

Substituting in Eq. [1] the value of the currents,
$$\frac{E}{R_t} = \frac{E}{R_1} + \frac{E}{R_2}$$

D:E,
$$\frac{1}{R_t} = \frac{1}{R_1} + \frac{1}{R_2} \qquad [2]$$

Equation [2] states that the total conductance (Sec. 11–4) of the circuit is equal to the sum of the parallel conductances of R_1 and R_2; that is,
$$G_t = G_1 + G_2 \qquad [3]$$

It is evident, therefore, that, when resistances are connected in parallel, each additional resistance represents another path (conductance) through which current will flow. Hence, increasing the number of resistances in parallel increases the total conductance of the circuit, thus decreasing the equivalent resistance of the circuit.

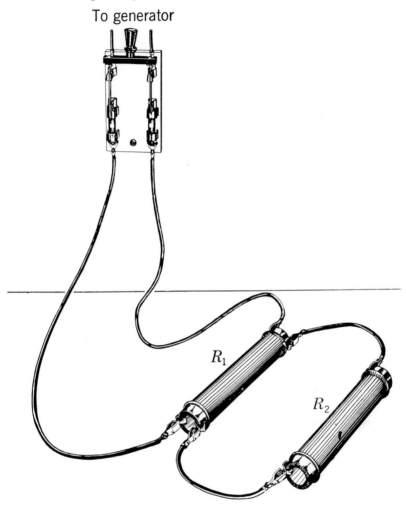

To generator

FIG. 18–4 Illustration of schematic circuit shown in Fig. 18–3.

EXAMPLE 1   What is the joint resistance of the circuit of Fig. 18–3 if $R_1 = 6 \ \Omega$ and $R_2 = 12 \ \Omega$?

SOLUTION   Given $R_1 = 6 \ \Omega$ and $R_2 = 12 \ \Omega$. $R_t = ?$

Substituting the known values in Eq. [2],

$$\frac{1}{R_t} = \frac{1}{6} + \frac{1}{12} = 0.1667 + 0.0833$$

or $$\frac{1}{R_t} = 0.250$$

Solving for R_t, $$R_t = \frac{1}{0.250} = 4.0\ \Omega$$

ALTERNATE SOLUTION   A more convenient formula for the joint resistance of two parallel resistances is obtained by solving Eq. [2] for R_t. Thus,

$$R_t = \frac{R_1 R_2}{R_1 + R_2} \qquad [\,4\,]$$

Hence, the joint resistance of two resistances in parallel is equal to their product divided by their sum.

Substituting the values of R_1 and R_2 in Eq. [4],

$$R_t = \frac{6 \times 12}{6 + 12} = \frac{72}{18} = 4.0\ \Omega$$

Thus, the paralleled resistors R_1 and R_2 are equivalent to a single resistance of 4.0 Ω. Note that the joint resistance is *less* than either of the resistances in parallel.

EXAMPLE 2   (*a*) What is the joint resistance of the circuit of Fig. 18–3 if $R_1 = 21\ \Omega$ and $R_2 = 15\ \Omega$?   (*b*) If the generator supplies 12 volts across points *a* and *b*, what is the generator (line) current?
SOLUTION

(*a*) $$R_t = \frac{R_1 R_2}{R_1 + R_2} = \frac{21 \times 15}{21 + 15} = 8.75\ \Omega$$

(*b*) $$I_t = \frac{E}{R_t} = \frac{12}{8.75} = 1.371\ \text{amp}$$

ALTERNATE SOLUTION   Since 12 volts exists across both resistors, the current through each can be found and added to obtain the total current. Thus,

Current through R_1, $$I_1 = \frac{E}{R_1} = \frac{12}{21} = 0.571\ \text{amp}$$

Current through R_2, $$I_2 = \frac{E}{R_2} = \frac{12}{15} = 0.8\ \text{amp}$$

Total current, $$I_t = I_1 + I_2 = 0.571 + 0.8 = 1.371\ \text{amp}$$

Hence, $$R_t = \frac{E}{I_t} = \frac{12}{1.371} = 8.75\ \Omega$$

From the foregoing, it is evident that R_1 and R_2 could be replaced by a single resistor of 8.75 Ω, connected between *a* and *b*, and the generator would be working under the same load conditions. Also, it is apparent that when a current enters a junction of resistors connected in parallel, the current divides between the branches in inverse proportion to their resistances; that is, the greatest current flows through the least resistance.

EXAMPLE 3   In the circuit of Fig. 18–3, $R_1 = 25\ \Omega$, $E = 220$ volts, and $I_t = 14.3$ amp. What is the resistance of R_2?

SOLUTION   Current through R_1, $I_1 = \dfrac{E}{R_1} = \dfrac{220}{25} = 8.8$ amp

Since $I_t = I_1 + I_2$
the current through R_2 is $I_2 = I_t - I_1 = 14.3 - 8.8 = 5.5$ amp

Then $R_2 = \dfrac{E}{I_2} = \dfrac{220}{5.5} = 40\ \Omega$

ALTERNATE SOLUTION $R_t = \dfrac{E}{I_t} = \dfrac{220}{14.3} = 15.4\ \Omega$

Solving Eq. [2] or [4] for R_2, $R_2 = \dfrac{R_1 R_t}{R_1 - R_t} = \dfrac{25 \times 15.4}{25 - 15.4} = 40\ \Omega$

PROBLEMS 18 – 1

1   A resistor of 8 Ω is connected in parallel with a resistor of 12 Ω. What is their joint resistance?

2   Two resistors of 75 and 50 Ω are connected in parallel. Find the equivalent resistance of the combination.

3   What is the joint resistance of 500 and 1,000 Ω connected in parallel?

4   Find the joint resistance of 5 and 750 Ω connected in parallel.

5   Find the total resistance of (a) two 50-Ω resistors connected in parallel, (b) two 10-Ω resistors connected in parallel, (c) two 1,000-Ω resistors connected in parallel.

6   State a general formula for the total resistance R_t of two equal resistances of R Ω connected in parallel.

7   In the circuit of Fig. 18–3, how much generator voltage would be required to force a total current of 9 amp through the parallel combination if $R_1 = 27.1\ \Omega$ and $R_2 = 25\ \Omega$?

8   How much power would be expended in the 27.1-Ω resistor of Prob. 7?

9   In the circuit of Fig. 18–3, $I_t = 3.75$ amp, $E = 12$ volts, and $R_1 = 16\ \Omega$. What is the resistance of R_2?

10   How much power is expended in R_1 of Prob. 9?

11   In the circuit of Fig. 18–3, $R_1 = 10,000\ \Omega$ and the current through R_2 is 20 ma. A total current of $I_t = 120$ ma flows through the parallel combination. What is the resistance of R_2?

12   How much power is expended in R_2 in Prob. 11?

13   How much power is supplied by the generator in Prob. 11?

14   In the circuit of Fig. 18–3, $E = 5,000$ volts, $I_t = 25$ ma, and the current flowing through R_2 is 10 ma. What is the resistance of R_1?

15   Under the conditions of Prob. 14, how much power is expended in R_2?

18 – 2   Three or more resistances in parallel

The procedure for deriving a general equation for the joint resistance of three or more resistances in parallel is the same as that of the preceding section. For example, Fig. 18–5 represents three resistors R_1,

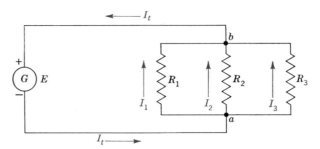

Fɪɢ. 18–5   Resistors R_1, R_2, and R_3 connected in parallel.

R_2, and R_3 connected in parallel across a source of voltage E. The total line current I_t splits at junction a into currents I_1, I_2, and I_3 which flow through R_1, R_2, and R_3, respectively. Then

$$I_1 = \frac{E}{R_1} \qquad I_2 = \frac{E}{R_2} \qquad I_3 = \frac{E}{R_3} \qquad \text{and} \qquad I_t = \frac{E}{R_t}$$

where R_t is the joint resistance of the parallel combination.

Since $$I_t = I_1 + I_2 + I_3$$

by substituting, $$\frac{E}{R_t} = \frac{E}{R_1} + \frac{E}{R_2} + \frac{E}{R_3}$$

D:E, $$\frac{1}{R_t} = \frac{1}{R_1} + \frac{1}{R_2} + \frac{1}{R_3} \qquad\qquad [5]$$

From Eq. [5], it is evident that the total conductance of the circuit is equal to the sum of the paralleled conductances of R_1, R_2, and R_3; that is,

$$G_t = G_1 + G_2 + G_3$$

In like manner, it can be demonstrated that the joint resistance R_t of any number of resistances connected in parallel is

$$\frac{1}{R_t} = \frac{1}{R_1} + \frac{1}{R_2} + \frac{1}{R_3} + \frac{1}{R_4} + \frac{1}{R_5} + \cdots$$

Or, in terms of conductances,

$$G_t = G_1 + G_2 + G_3 + G_4 + G_5 + \cdots$$

EXAMPLE 4   What is the joint resistance of the circuit of Fig. 18-5 if $R_1 = 5\ \Omega$, $R_2 = 10\ \Omega$, and $R_3 = 12.5\ \Omega$?

SOLUTION   Substituting the known values in Eq. [5],

$$\frac{1}{R_t} = \frac{1}{5} + \frac{1}{10} + \frac{1}{12.5} = 0.2 + 0.1 + 0.08$$

or

$$\frac{1}{R_t} = 0.38$$

Solving for R_t, $R_t = \dfrac{1}{0.38} = 2.63\ \Omega$

If Eq. [5] is solved for R_t, the result is

$$R_t = \frac{R_1 R_2 R_3}{R_1 R_2 + R_1 R_3 + R_2 R_3} \qquad [6]$$

It is seen that Eq. [6] is somewhat cumbersome for computing the joint resistance of three resistances connected in parallel. However, you should recognize such expressions for three or more resistances in parallel, for they will be encountered in the analysis of networks.

Finding the joint resistance of any number of resistors in parallel is facilitated by arbitrarily assuming a voltage to exist across the parallel combination. The currents through the individual branches that *would* flow if the assumed voltage were actually impressed are added to obtain the total line current. The assumed voltage divided by this total current results in the joint resistance of the combination.

The assumed voltage should always be a power of 10 in order that the slide-rule operator can make full use of the reciprocal scales. In order to avoid decimal quantities, that is, currents of less than 1 amp, the assumed voltage should be numerically greater than the highest resistance of any parallel branch.

EXAMPLE 5   Three resistances $R_1 = 10\ \Omega$, $R_2 = 15\ \Omega$, and $R_3 = 45\ \Omega$ are connected in parallel. Find their joint resistance.

SOLUTION   Assume $E_a = 100$ volts to exist across the combination.

Current through R_1, $I_1 = \dfrac{E_a}{R_1} = \dfrac{100}{10} = 10$ amp

Current through R_2, $I_2 = \dfrac{E_a}{R_2} = \dfrac{100}{15} = 6.67$ amp

Current through R_3, $I_t = \dfrac{E_a}{R_3} = \dfrac{100}{45} = 2.22$ amp

Total current, $I_t = 18.89$ amp

Joint resistance, $R_t = \dfrac{E_a}{I_t} = \dfrac{100}{18.89} = 5.3 \ \Omega$

PROBLEMS 18 – 2

1 What is the total resistance of 25, 20, and 50 Ω connected in parallel?

2 Find the resistance of 40, 16, and 50 Ω connected in parallel.

3 Find the total resistance of 500, 1,500, and 1,000 Ω connected in parallel.

4 Three resistors of 5, 1,000, and 2,000 Ω are connected in parallel. Find the joint resistance of the combination.

5 What is the equivalent resistance of 22, 15, 33, and 47 Ω connected in parallel?

6 Four resistors of 8,200, 1,500, 2,700, and 3,300 Ω are connected in parallel. What is the equivalent resistance of the combination?

7 What is the joint resistance of (a) three 20-Ω resistors connected in parallel, (b) four 20-Ω resistors connected in parallel?

8 What is the joint resistance of (a) three 100-Ω resistors connected in parallel, (b) four 100-Ω resistors connected in parallel, (c) five 100-Ω resistors connected in parallel?

9 State a general formula for the total resistance R_t of n equal resistances of R Ω connected in parallel.

10 In the circuit of Fig. 18–5, the total current I_t = 14.4 amp. R_1 = 100 Ω, R_2 = 60 Ω, and E = 240 volts. What is the resistance of R_3?

11 The values of Prob. 10 being used, what power will be expended in the circuit if an additional resistance of 20 Ω is connected across junctions a and b?

12 In the circuit of Fig. 18–5, R_1 = 16 Ω, R_2 = 4 Ω, I_3 = 4 amp, and E = 32 volts. Find (a) I_t, (b) I_1, (c) I_2, (d) R_3, (e) total power P_t.

13 In the circuit of Fig. 18–5, R_2 = 5,100 Ω, R_3 = 2,700 Ω, I_t = 0.438 amp, and I_1 = 0.152 amp. Find the value of R_1 to two significant figures.

14 In the circuit of Fig. 18–5, R_1 = R_2 = 10,000 Ω, R_3 = 5,000 Ω, and I_t = 0.40 amp. What value of resistance must be connected between junctions a and b to result in a total current of 0.50 amp?

15 A 10,000-Ω 50-watt resistor, a 15,000-Ω 100-watt resistor, and a 30,000-Ω 10-watt resistor are connected in parallel. What is the maximum permissible value of current through this parallel combination that will not exceed the rating of any resistor?

18 – 3   Compound circuits

The solution of circuits containing combinations of series and parallel branches generally consists in reducing the parallel branches to

equivalent series circuits and combining these with the series
branches. No set rules can be formulated for the solution of all types
of such circuits, but from the examples that follow you will be able to
build up your own methods of attack.

EXAMPLE 6   Find the total resistance of the circuit represented in
Fig. 18-6.

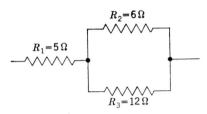

SOLUTION   Note that the parallel
branch of Fig. 18-6 is the circuit of
Example 1. Since the equivalent
series resistance of the parallel branch
is

$$\frac{R_2 R_3}{R_2 + R_3}$$

FIG. 18-6   Series-parallel circuit of
Example 6.

the circuit reduces to two resistances in series, the total resistance of which is

$$R_t = R_1 + \frac{R_2 R_3}{R_2 + R_3} = 5 + \frac{6 \times 12}{6 + 12} = 9.0 \; \Omega$$

EXAMPLE 7   Find the total resistance of the circuit represented in Fig. 18-7.

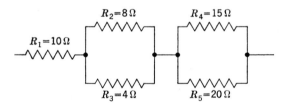

FIG. 18-7   Circuit of Example 7, consisting of one
resistance in series with two parallel branches.

SOLUTION   This circuit is similar to that shown in Fig. 18-6, with an additional parallel branch. By utilizing the expression for the joint resistance
of two resistances in parallel, the entire circuit reduces to three resistances in
series, the total resistance of which is

$$R_t = R_1 + \frac{R_2 R_3}{R_2 + R_3} + \frac{R_4 R_5}{R_4 + R_5} = 10 + \frac{8 \times 4}{8 + 4} + \frac{15 \times 20}{15 + 20} = 21.2 \; \Omega$$

EXAMPLE 8   Find the total resistance between points a and b in Fig. 18-8.

SOLUTION   Since R_2 and R_L are in series, they must be added before being
combined with R_3. Again, by utilizing the expression for the joint resistance
of two resistances in parallel, the entire circuit reduces to two resistances in
series. Thus, the total resistance is

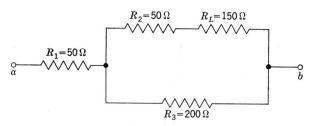

FIG. 18-8   Circuit of Example 8.

$$R_t = R_1 + \frac{R_3(R_2 + R_L)}{R_3 + (R_2 + R_L)} = 50 + \frac{200(50 + 150)}{200 + 50 + 150} = 150\ \Omega$$

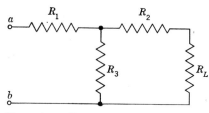

FIG. 18-9   Circuit of Example 8 illustrated in T network form.

Note that the circuit of Fig. 18-8 is identical with that of Fig. 18-9. The latter is the customary method for representing T networks, often encountered in communication circuits, where R_L is the load or receiving resistance.

EXAMPLE 9   Find the resistance between points a and b in Fig. 18-10.

SOLUTION   In many instances a circuit diagram that *appears* to be complicated can be better understood and analyzed by redrawing it in a more simplified form. For example, Fig. 18-11 represents the circuit of Fig. 18-10.

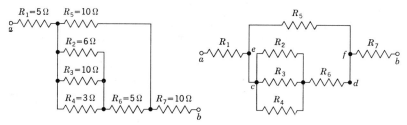

FIG. 18-10   Circuit of Example 9.   FIG. 18-11   Simplified circuit of Example 9.

First find the equivalent series resistance of the parallel group formed by R_2, R_3, and R_4; add this resistance to R_6, which will result in the resistance R_{cd} between points c and d. R_{cd} is now combined with R_5, which is in parallel, to give an equivalent series resistance R_{ef} between points e and f. The circuit is now reduced to an equivalence of R_1, R_{ef}, and R_7 in series, which are added to obtain the total resistance R_{ab} between points a and b.

The joint resistance of R_2, R_3, and R_4 is 1.67 Ω which, when added to R_6, results in a resistance $R_{cd} = 6.67$ Ω between c and d. The equivalent series resistance R_{ef} between points e and f, formed by R_{cd} and R_5 in parallel, is 4.0 Ω. Therefore the resistance R_{ab} between points a and b is

$$R_{ab} = R_1 + R_{ef} + R_7 = 19 \ \Omega$$

PROBLEMS 18-3

1   In the circuit of Fig. 18-12, $R_1 = 620 \ \Omega$, $R_2 = 150 \ \Omega$, $R_3 = 200 \ \Omega$, and $E_G = 230$ volts. What is the total current I_t of the circuit?

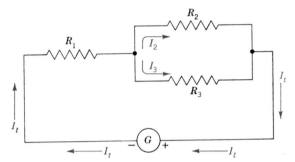

FIG. 18-12 R_1 connected in series with R_2 and R_3 in parallel.

2   In Prob. 1, how much power is expended in R_3?

3   In Prob. 1, if R_1 is short-circuited, how much power will be expended in R_2?

4   In Prob. 1, what will be the total current I_t if R_2 is open-circuited?

5   In the circuit of Fig. 18-12, $R_1 = 4,700 \ \Omega$, $R_2 = 2,200 \ \Omega$, $I_t = 58.6$ ma, and the voltage across R_3 is 74.4 volts. Find (a) E_G, (b) R_3, (c) R_t, (d) I_2, (e) I_3.

6   In Prob. 5, how much current will the generator supply if R_3 is short-circuited?

7   In the circuit of Fig. 18-12, $R_t = 7,180 \ \Omega$, $R_1 = 5,600 \ \Omega$, $E_G = 1,000$ volts, and $I_2 = 29.3$ ma. Find (a) voltage across R_1, (b) voltage across R_2, (c) resistance of R_2 to two significant figures, (d) resistance of R_3 to two significant figures, (e) total current I_t, (f) current through R_3, (g) total power expended in circuit.

8   In Prob. 7, if R_1 is short-circuited, (a) how much power will be expended in R_2, (b) how much current will flow through R_3?

9   In the circuit of Fig. 18-9, R_1, R_2, and R_3 all are 200-Ω resistors and $R_L = 600 \ \Omega$. What is the resistance between points a and b?

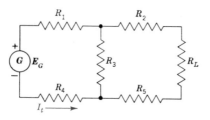

FIG. 18–13   Circuit of Prob. 10.

10   In the circuit of Fig. 18–13, R_1, R_2, R_4, and R_5 are all 150-Ω resistors, $R_3 = 1,500$ Ω, and $R_L = 600$ Ω. If a voltage of 3 volts exists across R_L, what is the total current I_t?

11   How much power is being supplied by the generator in Prob. 10?

12   If, in Prob. 10, the load resistance R_L is short-circuited, how much current will flow through R_3?

13   In the circuit of Fig. 18–14, the generator voltage $E_G = 3,500$ volts,

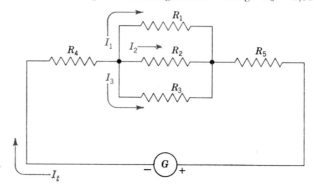

FIG. 18–14   Series-parallel circuit of Prob. 13.

$I_t = 273$ ma, $R_1 = 4,300$ Ω, $I_1 = 84.6$ ma, $R_2 = 6,800$ Ω, and $R_5 = 10,000$ Ω. Find to two significant figures (a) resistance of R_3, (b) resistance of R_4, (c) power expended in R_2.

14   In the circuit represented in Fig. 18–15, find (a) total current I_t, (b) power expended if points a and b are short-circuited.

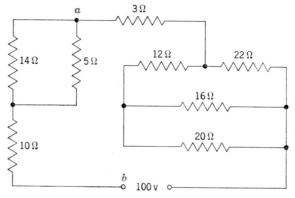

FIG. 18–15   Circuit of Prob. 14.

15   In the circuit shown in Fig. 18–16, find (a) total current I_t, (b) power
expended if points a and b are short-circuited.

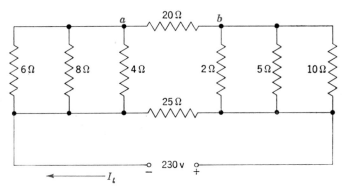

Fig. 18–16   Circuit of Prob. 15.

CHAPTER 19
METER CIRCUITS

Chapters 13 and 18 dealt with the study of Ohm's law as applied to series and parallel circuits, and in Chap. 14 consideration was given to the effects of resistance in current-carrying conductors. The principles and methods learned therein are applied in the present chapter to circuits relating to d-c instruments used for servicing electrical, radio, and other electronic equipment.

19 – 1   Direct-current instruments—basic meter movement

The most common measuring instruments used with electric and electronic circuits are the *voltmeter* and the *ammeter*. As the name implies, a voltmeter is an instrument used to measure voltage. An ammeter is a current-measuring instrument.

The great majority of meters used with direct currents employ the D'Arsonval movement illustrated in Fig. 19–1. This movement utilizes a coil of wire mounted on jeweled bearings between the pole pieces of a permanent magnet. When direct current flows through the coil, a magnetic field is set up around the coil, thereby producing a force which, in conjunction with the magnetic field of the permanent magnet, causes the coil to rotate from the no-current position. Since the arc of rotation is proportional to the amount of current passing

through the coil, a pointer
can be attached to the coil
and the deflection of the
pointer over a calibrated
scale can be used to indicate values of current.

The *sensitivity* of a current-
indicating meter is the amount
of current necessary to cause
full-scale deflection of the
pointer. For example, an instrument of wide usage is the
0–1 milliammeter illustrated
in Fig. 19–2. This meter has

FIG. 19–1   D'Arsonval meter movement. (*Courtesy of Weston Electrical
Instrument Corporation.*)

a sensitivity of 1 ma because
when a current of 1 ma flows
through the meter, the pointer
indicates full-scale deflection.
This particular meter has an
internal resistance of 55 Ω.
Other meter movements have
different sensitivities with various values of internal resistance.

–2   Multirange current meters

Instead of utilizing a number
of meters to make various
current measurements, it is
common practice to select a
meter movement with sufficient sensitivity and, with the
aid of one or more shunts, ex-

FIG. 19–2   0–1 milliammeter. (*Courtesy of Triplett Electrical Instrument
Company.*)

tend the range of the meter and therefore its usefulness. A shunt, in
this application, is a resistor that is shunted (connected in parallel)
across the meter coil as shown in Fig. 19–3.

A meter such as illustrated in Fig. 19–2, with a resistance of 55 Ω, is
connected to measure the circuit current of Fig. 19–4. In this condition the switch S is open and the meter indicates a full-scale deflection

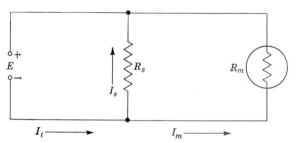

FIG. 19–3 Total current I_t consists of current I_s, which flows through shunt resistor R_s, and the meter current I_m, which flows through the coil of the meter. That is, $I_t = I_s + I_m$.

of 1 ma. In Fig. 19–5 the switch S is closed, thereby shunting the 55-Ω resistor R_s across the meter. Since the meter resistance and shunt resistance are equal, the circuit current I_t divides equally between them and the meter reads 0.5 ma.

In Fig. 19–4, with the switch open, the meter would indicate actual

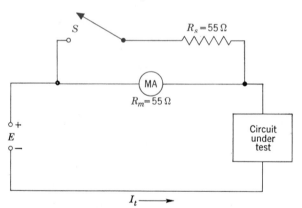

FIG. 19–4 Total current I_t flows through the milliammeter which indicates a full-scale deflection of 1 ma.

values of current. In Fig. 19–5, with the switch closed, circuit current would be obtained by multiplying the meter readings by a factor of 2 or by re-marking the scale as shown in Fig. 19–6.

EXAMPLE 1   A 0–1 milliammeter has an internal resistance of 70 Ω. Design a circuit that will allow this meter to be used as a multirange meter having the ranges 0–1, 0–10, and 0–100 ma and 0–1 amp.

SOLUTION   The circuit is shown in Fig. 19–7. The switch S is used for range selection by switching in the proper shunt resistor. In its present

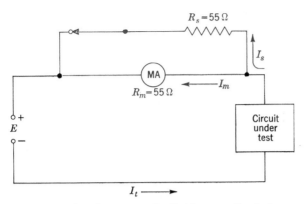

FIG. 19-5 Total current I_t divides equally between meter resistance R_m and shunt resistance R_s. $I_t = I_m + I_s = 1$ ma. $I_s = I_m = 0.5$ ma.

position no shunt resistor is used and therefore the meter is connected to measure within its basic range of 0–1 ma.

At full-scale deflection the voltage across the meter will be

$$E_m = I_t R_m = 0.001 \times 70 = 7 \times 10^{-2} \text{ volt}$$

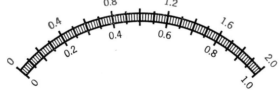

FIG. 19-6 Multirange meter scale.

Since whatever shunt resistor in use will be in parallel with the resistance of the meter R_m, the same voltage will appear across the shunt resistance. That is,

$$E_m = E_s = 7 \times 10^{-2} \text{ volt}$$

When utilizing the 0- to 10-ma range, the switch S will connect R_{s10} in parallel with the meter and therefore its internal resistance R_m. For full-scale deflection 1 ma must flow through the meter coil, which leaves 9 ma to flow through R_{s10}. For this condition the value of R_{s10} must be

$$R_{s10} = \frac{E_s}{I_s} = \frac{7 \times 10^{-2}}{9 \times 10^{-3}} = 7.78 \ \Omega$$

Similarly, when the 0- to 100-ma range is placed in operation by switching to shunt resistor R_{s100}, full-scale deflection 1 ma still must flow through the meter coil, leaving 99 ma to flow through R_{s100}. Then,

$$R_{s100} = \frac{E_s}{I_s} = \frac{7 \times 10^{-2}}{99 \times 10^{-3}} = 0.707 \ \Omega$$

Likewise, when the 0- to 1-amp (0- to 1,000-ma) range is used, 999 ma must flow through the shunt resistor for full-scale deflection.

$$\therefore R_{s1,000} = \frac{E_s}{I_s} = \frac{7 \times 10^{-2}}{999 \times 10^{-3}} = 0.0701 \ \Omega$$

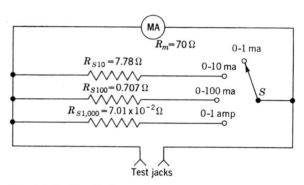

FIG. 19–7   Circuit for extending range of 0–1 milliam-meter.   Test leads from jacks are connected in series with circuit in which current is to be measured.

It will be noted that only basic Ohm's law was used in Example 1. This was done to emphasize its usefulness. Also, special seldom-used formulas are difficult to remember and handbooks for ready reference are not always available on the job. Actually, the resistance of a meter shunt can be found by using your knowledge of current distribution in parallel circuits. For the 0- to 1-ma range of Example 1, the 70-Ω meter movement must carry 1 ma and the shunt resistor must carry 9 ma. Since the shunt carries nine times the meter current, the shunt resistance must be one-ninth the resistance of the meter or $\frac{1}{9} \times 70 = 7.78 \ \Omega$.

Similarly, for the range of 0 to 100 ma, the meter movement still must carry 1 ma, leaving 99 ma to flow through the shunt. Therefore the resistance of the shunt will be $\frac{1}{99}$ the resistance of the meter move-ment, or $\frac{1}{99} \times 70 = 0.707 \ \Omega$.

Now that the principles of meter shunts are understood, it is left as an exercise for you to show that

$$R_s = \frac{R_m}{N-1} \qquad \Omega \qquad\qquad [1]$$

where R_s = shunt resistance, Ω

$\quad R_m$ = meter resistance, Ω

$\quad N$ = ratio obtained by dividing new full-scale reading by basic full-scale reading, both readings in same units

The ratio N is known as the multiplying power of the shunt resistor, that is, the factor by which the basic meter scale is multiplied when the shunt resistor R_s is connected in parallel with the meter resistance R_m. From Eq. [1],

$$N = \frac{R_m}{R_s} + 1$$

EXAMPLE 2   What factor must the scale readings be multiplied by when a resistance of 100 Ω is connected across a meter movement of 400 Ω?

SOLUTION $N = \dfrac{R_m}{R_s} + 1 = \dfrac{400}{100} + 1 = 5$

19 – 3   Shunting methods

Although mechanical details are not shown in Fig. 19–7, it is necessary to use a shorting switch in this type of circuit to avoid damage to the meter movement. When switching from one shunt to another, the new shunt must be connected before contact is broken with the shunt in use. If this is not done, the entire circuit current will flow through the meter movement while the switch is moving from one contact to another.

Another method of switching is illustrated in Fig. 19–8, whereby shunts are connected into the circuit by the two-pole rotary switch which makes connections between two sets of contacts. With this arrangement, the meter movement is protected by an open circuit when switching from one shunt to another.

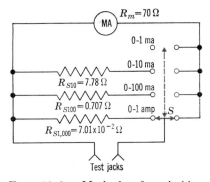

FIG. 19–8   Method of switching shunts.

Still another method of employing shunts is shown in Fig. 19–9. This is known as the *Ayrton*, or *universal*, shunt. In addition to other advantages, it provides a safe and convenient method of switching from one range to another. The total shunt resistance, which is permanently connected across the meter, generally has the same resistance as the meter movement. The value of the resistance for each range shunt can be computed by dividing the total circuit resist-

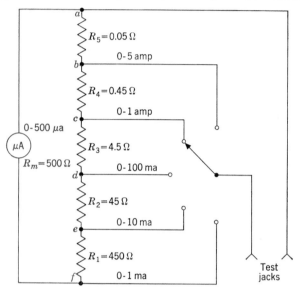

FIG. 19–9   Multicurrent test meter using universal shunt.

ance $R_{a-f} = R_m$ by the multiplying power N. For example, the 0–500 microammeter movement has a resistance R_m of 500 Ω and the total shunt resistance R_{a-f} connected across the meter is 500 Ω. When the switch is on the 0- to 1-ma position, the multiplying power N is 2.

For the 0- to 10-ma range, N would be 20 because 10 ma is 20 times the original full scale of ½ ma. Therefore, the required shunt for this range is

$$R_{a-e} = \frac{R_{a-f} + R_m}{N} = \frac{500 + 500}{20} = 50 \ \Omega$$

Since the entire shunt resistance is 500 ohms,

$$R_1 = R_{a-f} - R_{a-e} = 500 - 50 = 450 \ \Omega$$

When the switch is connected to the 0- to 100-ma range, N becomes 200 and R_1 and R_2 in series (R_{d-f}) form the shunt. That is,

$$R_{a-d} = \frac{R_{a-f} + R_m}{N} = \frac{500 + 500}{200} = 5 \ \Omega$$

Since $\qquad R_1 = 450\ \Omega$

and $\qquad R_{a-d} = 5\ \Omega$

then $\qquad R_2 = R_{a-f} - (R_1 + R_{a-d}) = 500 - (450 + 5) = 45\ \Omega$

The values of the remaining shunts are computed in the same manner.

PROBLEMS 19 – 1

1 A 0–1 milliammeter has an internal resistance of 46 Ω. What shunt resistance is required to extend the meter to 0 to 50 ma?

2 A meter movement with a sensitivity of 50 μa has an internal resistance of 1,770 Ω. How much shunt resistance is required to result in a 0- to 10-ma range?

3 The meter in Prob. 1 is being used as a multicurrent instrument. The shunt for the 0- to 100-ma range is burned out, but a spool of No. 30 enamel-covered copper wire is on hand. How much of this wire is needed to wind a substitute shunt?

4 A 0–50 microammeter has an internal resistance of 1,170 Ω. If this meter is shunted with a 130-Ω resistor, what must the meter readings be multiplied by to obtain the correct values of current?

5 It is desired to use the milliammeter illustrated in Fig. 19–2 as a multicurrent meter. What values of shunts are required for the following ranges: (a) 0 to 10 ma, (b) 0 to 50 ma, (c) 0 to 500 ma, (d) 0 to 2 amp?

6 In the circuit of Fig. 19–10 the total shunt resistance is equal to the

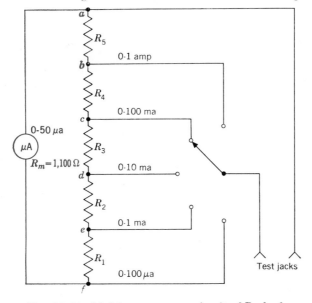

FIG. 19–10 Multicurrent meter circuit of Prob. 6.

resistance of the meter movement. Find the values of R_1, R_2, R_3, R_4, and R_5.

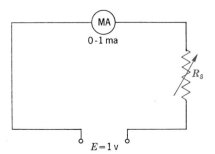

FIG. 19–11 Basic circuit of milliam-meter used to indicate voltage.

19 – 4   Voltmeters

In Fig. 19–11, a voltage of 1 volt is impressed across a circuit consisting of a 0–1 milliammeter in series with a variable resistor. The resistor is adjusted so that the circuit is limited to 1 ma; therefore the meter indicates a full-scale deflection, or a reading of 1 ma. If the resistor is unchanged and the voltage is reduced to $\frac{1}{2}$ volt, then the circuit current would be reduced to one-half its original value and the meter would read 0.5 ma. Even though the meter deflection is the result of current flow, actually the meter could be used as a 0–1 voltmeter, indicating 1 volt in the first instance and 0.5 volt when the voltage was reduced.

Similarly, if the resistor is adjusted to a higher safe value so that the application of 150 volts causes full-scale deflection, the instrument can be used as a 0–150 voltmeter. In that case voltage values would be obtained by multiplying the basic scale readings by a factor of 150 or by substituting a new scale as shown in Fig. 19–12.

EXAMPLE 3   It is desired to use the milliammeter of Fig. 19–2 as a 0–10 voltmeter. What resistance R_{mp} must be connected in series with the instrument to accomplish this?

SOLUTION   The additional series resistance is called a *multiplier* resist-

FIG. 19–12   Panel voltmeter. (*Courtesy of Weston Electrical Instrument Corporation.*)

ance, and its value must be such that when added to the resistance of the meter movement, the total resistance will limit the current through the instrument to 1 ma when 10 volts is applied. The circuit is shown in Fig.

19–13. R_{mp} is the multiplier resistance, and $R_m = 55\ \Omega$ is the resistance of the meter movement.

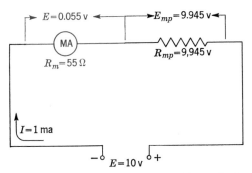

Fig. 19–13 Voltmeter circuit of Example 3.

If 10 volts is to be applied across the two series resistances as shown in Fig. 19–13, in order to limit the current to 1 ma, 0.055 volt must appear across the meter because

$$E_m = IR_m = 10^{-3} \times 55 = 0.055 \text{ volt}$$

The remaining voltage, which is $10 - 0.055 = 9.945$ volts, must appear across R_{mp}. Accordingly,

$$R_{mp} = \frac{E_{mp}}{I} = \frac{9.945}{10^{-3}} = 9,945\ \Omega$$

If a 10,000-Ω resistor is used as a multiplier, with 10 volts applied to the jacks, and if an observer could discern the difference, the voltage reading would be in error by only 0.05 volt.

EXAMPLE 4   A 0–50 microammeter, with a resistance of 1,140 Ω, is to be used as a 0–100 voltmeter. What value of multiplier resistance is needed?
SOLUTION   For full-scale deflection the voltage across the meter must be limited to

$$E_m = IR_m = 50 \times 10^{-6} \times 1,140 = 0.057 \text{ volt}$$

The remaining voltage across the multiplier is $100 - 0.057 = 99.943$ volts, which results in

$$R_{mp} = \frac{E_{mp}}{I} = \frac{99.943}{50 \times 10^{-6}} = 1,998,850\ \Omega$$

Naturally, a 2-MΩ resistor would be used.

19 – 5   Voltmeter sensitivity

The *sensitivity* of a voltmeter is expressed in the number of ohms in the multiplier for each volt of range. For example, the voltmeter of Example 3 has a range of 10 volts and a multiplier of 10,000 Ω, resulting in a sensitivity of 1,000 Ω/volt. The voltmeter of Example 4 has a sensitivity of 20,000 Ω/volt.

19 – 6   Voltmeter loading effects

The sensitivity of a voltmeter is a good indication of its accuracy. This is particularly true when measuring voltages in low-current circuits often encountered in electronic equipment. For example, a 0–150 voltmeter with a sensitivity of 200 Ω/volt would give excellent service, say as a power switchboard meter, at an economical cost. However, it would not be satisfactory for some other applications. In Fig. 19–14, two 60,000-Ω resistors are connected in series across 120 volts. In this condition, 60 volts will appear across each resistor. If the voltmeter is con-

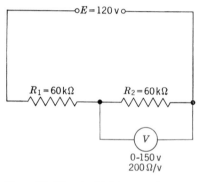

FIG. 19–15   A 30,000-Ω voltmeter connected across R_2. Total circuit current is now 1.5 ma, and the voltage across R_2 is 30 volts.

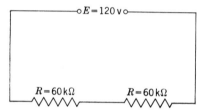

FIG. 19–14   The current through the resistors is 1 ma, and the voltage across each resistor is 60 volts.

nected across R_2 as shown in Fig. 19–15, the joint resistance R_p of R_2 and R_{mp} becomes

$$R_p = \frac{R_2 R_{mp}}{R_2 + R_{mp}} = 20,000 \ \Omega$$

The total resistance of the circuit is now

$$R_1 + R_p = 60,000 + 20,000 = 80,000 \ \Omega$$

This results in a circuit current of

$$I_t = \frac{E}{R_t} = \frac{120}{80,000} = 1.5 \times 10^{-3} \text{ amp}$$

Therefore the voltage existing across R_2 due to the shunting effect of the voltmeter is

$$E_p = I_t R_p = 1.5 \times 10^{-3} \times 20,000 = 30 \text{ volts}$$

It is left as an exercise for you to show that if the voltmeter of Example 4 is used to measure the voltage across R_2, the reading will be 59.1 volts.

9 – 7 Multirange voltmeters

Using a single multiplier provides only one voltmeter range. Similar to the usage of current-measuring instruments, it has become practice to increase the usefulness of an instrument by selecting a meter movement of sufficient sensitivity and, with the use of several multipliers, use the instrument as a multirange voltmeter. Such an arrangement is shown in Fig. 19–16.

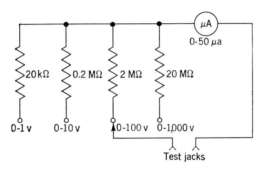

FIG. 19–16   A 0–50 microammeter used with multipliers for multirange voltmeter.

9 – 8 Ohmmeters

Owing to the fact that a change in the resistance of a circuit will cause a change in the current in that circuit, a current-measuring instrument can be calibrated to indicate values of resistance required for a given change in current. Such a calibrated instrument is called an *ohmmeter*.

In the schematic diagram of Fig. 19–17, the 0–1 milliammeter of Fig. 19–2 is connected in series with a 1.5-volt battery and a resistance of 1,445 Ω. Since the total resistance of the circuit is 1,500 Ω, if the test jacks are short-circuited, the meter will read full scale. If the short circuit is removed and a resistance R_x of 1,500 Ω is connected across the jacks, the meter will indicate half-scale deflection because now the total circuit resistance is 3,000 Ω. Therefore, at full-scale deflection the meter scale could be marked 0 Ω of external circuit resistance, and at half scale it could be marked 1,500 Ω. Similarly,

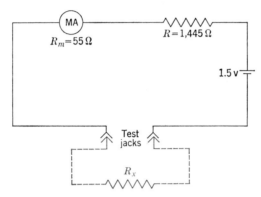

Fig. 19–17   A 0–1 milliammeter used in ohm-meter circuit.

other values of known resistance could be used to calibrate the scale throughout its range.   Also, unknown resistances can be used to calibrate the scale by making use of the relation

$$R_x = R_c \frac{I_1 - I_2}{I_2} \qquad \Omega \qquad\qquad [\,2\,]$$

where R_x = unknown resistance, Ω

R_c = circuit resistance when test jacks are short-circuited, Ω

I_1 = current when test jacks are short-circuited, amp

I_2 = current when R_x is connected in circuit, amp

Using your knowledge of Ohm's law and Axiom 5 (Sec. 12–2), derive Eq. [2].

In order to compensate for battery aging and maintain calibration, variable resistors controlled from the instrument panel are connected in ohmmeter circuits by either of two methods as illustrated in Figs. 19–18 and 19–19.   In either case the test leads are short-circuited and the resistor control is adjusted until the meter reads full scale, or 0 Ω.   An example of such a control is the "Ω ADJ" on the instrument shown in Fig. 19–20.

Since zero resistance between the test jacks results in maximum current and larger values of resistance result in less current, ohmmeter scales are marked with numbers increasing from right to left as illustrated on the ohms scale in Fig. 19–20.

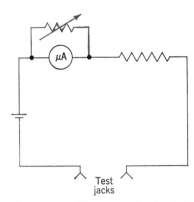

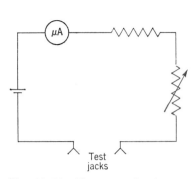

FIG. 19–18 Ohmmeter circuit with variable shunt resistance.

FIG. 19–19 Ohmmeter circuit with variable series resistance.

FIG. 19–20 Multimeter. (*Courtesy of Triplett Electrical Instrument Company.*)

In practice, the use of the ordinary ohmmeter should be limited from about one-tenth to 10 times the center-scale resistance reading because of the small deflection changes at the ends of the scale. For this reason multirange ohmmeters are employed for changing mid-scale values, and the ranges generally are designed to multiply the basic scale by some power of 10.

19 – 9   Multimeters

For the purposes of convenience and economy, meters combining the functions and desired ranges of ammeters, voltmeters, and ohmmeters are incorporated into one instrument which is called a multimeter, one type of which is illustrated in Fig. 19–20. If the test leads are plugged into the proper pin jacks and the rotary switch switched to the proper function and range, the instrument can be utilized for several functions.

PROBLEMS 19 – 2

1 In the circuit of Fig. 19–21: (*a*) What voltages are across R_1 and R_2? (*b*) A 0–100 voltmeter with a sensitivity of 1,000 Ω/volt is connected across R_1. What is the reading of the voltmeter?

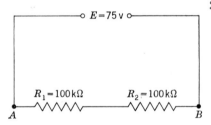

FIG. 19–21   Circuit of Probs. 1 and 2.

2 In the circuit of Fig. 19–21: (*a*) A 0–100 voltmeter with a sensitivity of 20,000 Ω/volt is connected across R_1. What is the voltmeter reading? (*b*) What will the voltmeter read if connected across points A and B? (*c*) When the voltmeter is connected across points A and B, what current flows through R_2?

3 What are the values of the multiplier resistors R_1, R_2, R_3, and R_4 in Fig. 19–22?

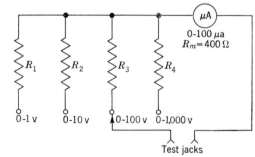

FIG. 19–22   Multirange voltmeter circuit of Prob. 3.

CHAPTER 20

VOLTAGE-DIVIDER
AND DISTRIBUTION CIRCUITS

In this chapter consideration is given to voltage-divider and two-wire electric distribution circuits. Computations involving voltages and currents in these circuits are simply applications of Ohm's law to series and parallel circuits.

The source of power for radio and television receivers, amplifiers, and similar electronic equipment generally consists of a filtered direct voltage which has been obtained from a rectified alternating voltage. For reasons of economy and design considerations, rectifier power supplies are usually designed so that only the highest voltage desired is available at the output. In most applications, however, other voltages are needed. For example, sometimes power tubes require higher voltages than do the voltage-amplifier tubes. Screen grids may require yet other voltages. Also, bias voltages are often required. These voltages can be made available from single sources of voltage by the use of *voltage dividers*.

) – 1   Voltage dividers

That several values of voltage can exist around a circuit was first demonstrated in Sec. 13–8 and Figs. 13–12 and 13–13. A similar situation exists when tapped resistors, or resistors in series, are connected across the output of a power supply as illustrated in Fig. 20–1. This represents a simple *voltage divider*.

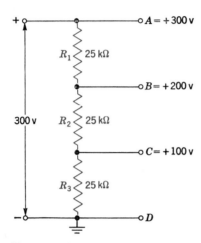

FIG. 20–1   Voltage divider consisting of three 25-kΩ resistors connected across 300-volt power supply.

Since the resistors are of equal value, one-third of the 300-volt output voltage will appear across each resistor.   Therefore, since terminal D is at zero or ground potential, terminal C will be $+100$ volts with respect to D, B will be $+200$ volts, and A will be $+300$ volts.

In addition to serving as a voltage divider, the total resistance connected across the output of a power supply generally serves as a *load resistor* and as *bleeder*. The latter serves to "bleed off" the charge of the filter capacitors after the rectifier is turned off. As a compromise between output voltage regulation and efficiency of operation, the total value of the voltage-divider resistance is designed so that the bleeder current will be about 10 per cent of the full-load current.   The bleeder current in Fig. 20–1 with no loads connected to the various voltage-divider terminals is

$$I = \frac{E}{R_1 + R_2 + R_3} = \frac{300}{75,000} = 4.00 \text{ ma}$$

The grounded point of a voltage divider is generally used as the reference point for circuit voltages supplied by the voltage divider. In Fig. 20–1, this is at grounded terminal D.

If the power-supply output voltage is grounded at no other point, the voltage divider can be grounded at an intermediate point so as to obtain both positive and negative voltages.   For example, if the voltage-divider resistors of Fig. 20–1 are grounded as shown in Fig. 20–2, the voltage relations change.   Terminal D is now -100 volts with respect to ground, B is $+100$ volts, and A is $+200$ volts.

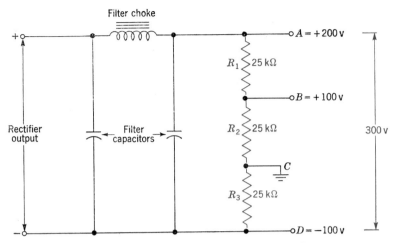

F_{IG}. 20–2   Voltage divider grounded at C.

20 – 2   Voltage dividers with loads

The voltage dividers of Figs. 20–1 and 20–2 have no loads connected to them; only the bleeder current of 4 ma flows through the voltage-divider resistors. When loads are connected to the various terminals, the resulting additional currents must be taken into consideration because these affect the operating voltages. For example, assume a load of $R_4 = 50,000\ \Omega$ connected between terminals C and D of Fig. 20–1. Under these conditions, the resistance between terminals C and D is

$$R_{CD} = \frac{R_3 R_4}{R_3 + R_4} = \frac{25,000 \times 50,000}{25,000 + 50,000} = 16,700\ \Omega$$

The total resistance between terminals A and D is

$$R_{AD} = R_1 + R_2 + R_{CD} = 66,700\ \Omega$$

resulting in a total current of

$$I_t = \frac{E}{R_{AD}} = 4.50\ \text{ma}$$

The voltage across terminals B and D is

$$E_{BD} = I_t R_{BD} = 188\ \text{volts}$$

and across terminals C and D is

$$E_{CD} = I_t R_{BD} = 75 \text{ volts}$$

The circuit is shown in Fig. 20–3.

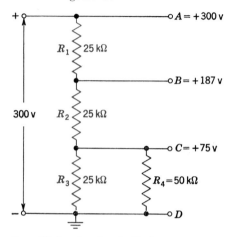

FIG. 20–3   Load of 50 kΩ connected across terminals C and D.

Show that, if an additional load of $R_5 = 50{,}000 \ \Omega$ is connected across terminals B and D, the terminal voltages would be as illustrated in Fig. 20–4.

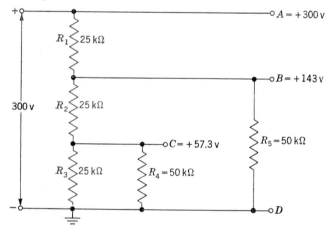

FIG. 20–4   Loads $R_4 = R_5 = 50$ kΩ connected to voltage divider.

EXAMPLE 1   Design a voltage-divider circuit for a 250-volt power supply. The connected loads are 60 ma at 250 volts and 40 ma at 150 volts. Allow a 10 per cent bleeder current.

SOLUTION   The circuit is shown in Fig. 20–5. The total load current is 100 ma; therefore the bleeder current is 10 ma, which flows through R_2. Since the voltage across R_2 is 150 volts,

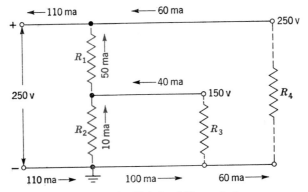

FIG. 20–5   Circuit of Example 1.

$$R_2 = \frac{150}{10 \times 10^{-3}} = 15{,}000 \ \Omega$$

The current flowing through R_1 is $40 + 10 = 50$ ma, and the voltage across R_1 is $250 - 150 = 100$ volts. Then

$$R_1 = \frac{100}{50 \times 10^{-3}} = 2{,}000 \ \Omega$$

EXAMPLE 2   What are the values of the voltage-divider resistors in Fig. 20–6 if the bleeder current is 10 per cent of the total load current?

SOLUTION   The total load current I_L is

$$I_L = 50 + 40 + 30 = 120 \text{ ma}$$

The bleeder current is

$$I_B = 0.1 \times 120 = 12 \text{ ma}$$

The complete circuit is shown in Fig. 20–7. The voltage across R_3 is 150 volts, and only the bleeder current of 12 ma flows through this resistor. Therefore

$$R_3 = \frac{150}{12 \times 10^{-3}} = 12{,}500 \ \Omega$$

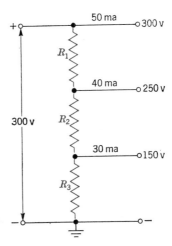

FIG. 20–6   Voltage divider of Example 2.

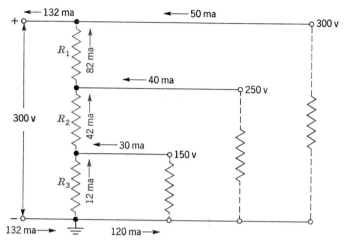

FIG. 20–7 Complete circuit of Example 2.

The 30-ma load current of the 150-volt load terminal combines with the bleeder current of 12 ma for a total of 42 ma through R_2, across which is 100 volts. Therefore

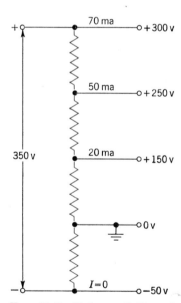

FIG. 20–8 Voltage divider of Example 3.

$$R_2 = \frac{100}{42 \times 10^{-3}} = 2,380 \ \Omega$$

Similarly, 82 ma flows through R_1, across which is 50 volts. Then

$$R_1 = \frac{50}{82 \times 10^{-3}} = 610 \ \Omega$$

NOTE Resistors $R_1 = 610$ Ω, $R_2 = 2,380$ Ω, and $R_3 = 12,500$ Ω are not readily available commercially. Try substituting standard preferred values of $R_1 = 560$ Ω, $R_2 = 2,400$ Ω, and $R_3 = 12,000$ Ω for the computed values, and determine how this would affect the loads.

EXAMPLE 3   Find the values of the voltage-divider resistors of Fig. 20–8. The −50-volt bias terminal draws no current, and the bleeder current is 10 per cent of the total load current.

SOLUTION   The total load current I_L is

$$I_L = 70 + 50 + 20 = 140 \text{ ma}$$

The bleeder current is

$$I_B = 0.1 I_L = 0.1 \times 140 = 14 \text{ ma}$$

The complete circuit is illustrated in Fig. 20-9. There is a voltage of 50 volts across R_4, and the total current of 154 ma flows through this resistor. Therefore

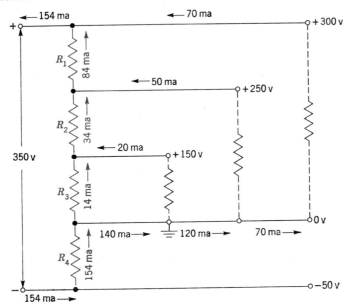

Fig. 20-9 Complete circuit of Example 3.

$$R_4 = \frac{50}{154 \times 10^{-3}} = 325 \ \Omega$$

Since R_3 carries only the bleeder current and the voltage across this resistor is 150 volts,

$$R_3 = \frac{150}{14 \times 10^{-3}} = 10,700 \ \Omega$$

In like manner,

$$R_2 = \frac{100}{34 \times 10^{-3}} = 2,940 \ \Omega$$

and

$$R_1 = \frac{50}{84 \times 10^{-3}} = 595 \ \Omega$$

As a problem, substitute the commercially available preferred values of $R_1 = 620\ \Omega$, $R_2 = 3,000\ \Omega$, $R_3 = 11,000\ \Omega$, and $R_4 = 300\ \Omega$ for the computed values, and determine how the loads would be affected.

PROBLEMS 20 – 1

1 The vertical attenuator of an oscilloscope is illustrated in Fig. 20–10. With an input voltage of 60 volts, what voltages appear between the switch positions and the input to the vertical amplifier?

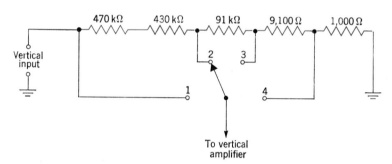

FIG. 20–10   Circuit of Prob. 1.

2 The horizontal hold control of a television receiver is shown in Fig. 20–11. What range of control voltage is available from the potentiometer to the horizontal hold control?

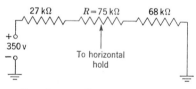

FIG. 20–11   Circuit of Prob. 2.

3 Determine the values of the voltage-divider resistors of Fig. 20–12 if a total of 180 ma is drawn from the power supply.

4 How much power is expended in the voltage divider of Fig. 20–12?

5 What are the values of the voltage-divider resistors of Fig. 20–13 if the bleeder current is 10 per cent of the total load current?

6 How much power is expended in the loads and the voltage divider of Fig. 20–13?

7 What are the values of the voltage-divider resistors of Fig. 20–14 if the bleeder current is 10 ma?

8 If the biasing resistor R_4 of Fig. 20–14 became open-circuited, what would be the voltage between terminals A and B?

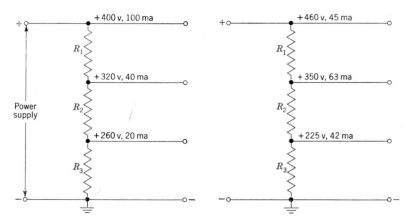

FIG. 20–12   Circuit of Probs. 3 and 4.

FIG. 20–13   Circuit of Probs. 5 and 6.

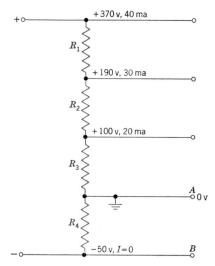

FIG. 20–14   Circuit of Probs. 7 and 8.

0 – 3   Distribution circuits

Computations involving voltages and currents of two-wire distribution circuits are simply applications of Ohm's law to series and parallel circuits.

Previous consideration of power transmission has been limited to cases where the line wires have carried current to one location only, this resulting in the same current throughout the system.   In practice, however, multiple circuits result in different currents flowing in different parts of the distribution circuit.

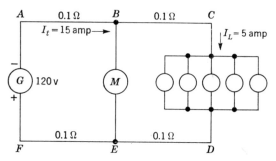

Fɪɢ. 20–15   A 120-volt generator connected to a motor and a group of lamps.

EXAMPLE 4   Figure 20–15 represents a generator, with a constant brush potential of 120 volts, delivering current to a motor and a group of lamps. The motor draws 10 amp, and each lamp takes 1 amp. Determine the voltage across the motor, the voltage across the lamps, and the power lost in the lines.

SOLUTION   It is evident that all the current supplied by the generator must flow through wires AB and EF and that voltage will be lost in forcing this current through the resistance of the wires. Such a loss is called a *line drop* or a *voltage drop*. Also, there will be a voltage drop in wires BC and DE due to the current drawn by the lamps. Listing the current distribution,

$$\text{Current in } AB = I_t = I_M + I_L = 15 \text{ amp}$$
$$\text{Current in } BC = I_L = 5 \text{ amp}$$
$$\text{Current in } DE = I_L = 5 \text{ amp}$$
$$\text{Current in } EF = I_t = 15 \text{ amp}$$

The line drops are

$$\text{Voltage drop in } AB = I_t R_{AB} = 15 \times 0.1 = 1.5 \text{ volts}$$
$$\text{Voltage drop in } BC = I_L R_{BC} = 5 \times 0.1 = 0.5 \text{ volt}$$
$$\text{Voltage drop in } DE = I_L R_{DE} = 5 \times 0.1 = 0.5 \text{ volt}$$
$$\text{Voltage drop in } EF = I_t R_{EF} = 15 \times 0.1 = \underline{1.5 \text{ volts}}$$
$$\text{Total line drop} = 4.0 \text{ volts}$$

The voltage across the motor will be the generator voltage minus the line drops in AB and EF, or

$$E_M = 120 - 1.5 - 1.5 = 117 \text{ volts}$$

The voltage across the lamps is the generator voltage minus the total line drop, or

$$E_L = 120 - 4 = 116 \text{ volts}$$

Figure 20–16 is a diagram of the circuit showing the voltage distribution. The line power loss can be computed as follows:

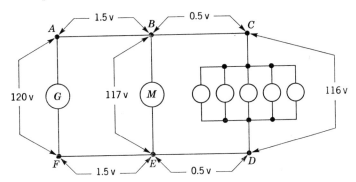

FIG. 20–16   Voltage distribution of the circuit in Fig. 20–15.

Power lost in $AB = I_t^2 R_{AB}\ = 15^2 \times 0.1 = 22.5$ watts
Power lost in $BC = I_L^2 R_{BC}\ =\ 5^2 \times 0.1 =\ \ 2.5$ watts
Power lost in $DE = I_L^2 R_{DE}\ =\ 5^2 \times 0.1 =\ \ 2.5$ watts
Power lost in $EF = I_t^2 R_{EF}\ = 15^2 \times 0.1 = \underline{22.5 \text{ watts}}$
Total line loss $= 50.0$ watts

By what other method could the line losses be computed?

EXAMPLE 5   In Fig. 20–17, motor M_1 draws 55 amp, M_2 draws 20 amp, M_3 draws 5 amp, and a lamp load represented by L draws 10 amp.   The

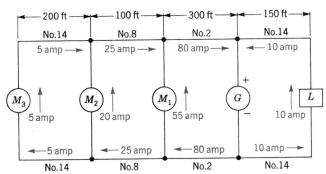

FIG. 20–17   Circuit diagram of the distribution circuit of Example 5.

generator maintains a constant brush potential of 240 volts.   Find the line drop in each part of the line, the line voltage across each motor, the voltage across the lamps, and the total power lost in the line.

SOLUTION   Total line resistances,

Between M_2 and M_3 = 400 ft of No. 14 wire = 1.03 Ω
Between M_1 and M_2 = 200 ft of No. 8 wire = 0.128 Ω
Between G and M_1 = 600 ft of No. 2 wire = 0.0954 Ω
Between G and L = 300 ft of No. 14 wire = 0.774 Ω

The line currents are

Between M_2 and M_3 = 5 amp
Between M_1 and M_2 = 25 amp
Between G and M_1 = 80 amp
Between G and L = 10 amp

Then the line drops are

Between M_2 and M_3 = 5 × 1.03 = 5.15 volts
Between M_1 and M_2 = 25 × 0.128 = 3.20 volts
Between G and M_1 = 80 × 0.0954 = 7.63 volts
Between G and L = 10 × 0.774 = 7.74 volts

The voltage across any load is equal to the generator voltage minus the line drop between the generator and the load.

Voltage across M_3 = 240 − (7.63 + 3.20 + 5.15) ≅ 224 volts
Voltage across M_2 = 240 − (7.63 + 3.2) ≅ 229.2 volts
Voltage across M_1 = 240 − 7.63 ≅ 232.4 volts
Voltage across L = 240 − 7.74 ≅ 232.3 volts

Figure 20–18 shows the distribution of voltages in the circuit.
Power losses,

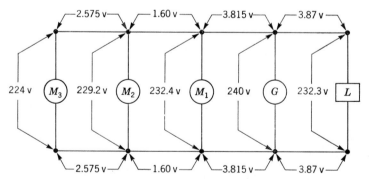

FIG. 20–18   Voltage distribution of the circuit of Fig. 20–17.

Between M_2 and $M_3 = \quad 5^2 \times 1.03 = \quad 25.8$ watts
Between M_1 and $M_2 = \quad 25^2 \times 0.128 = \quad 80 \quad$ watts
Between G and $M_1 \quad = 80^2 \times 0.0954 = 610 \quad$ watts
Between G and $L \quad \quad = \quad 10^2 \times 0.774 = \quad \underline{77.4}$ watts
Total power lost in line $= 793.2$ watts

PROBLEMS 20–2

1   In the circuit represented by Fig. 20–19, the motor draws 25 amp and each lamp draws 1 amp. The generator brush potential is 115 volts. Find (a) voltage across motor, (b) voltage across lamps, (c) power lost in lines.

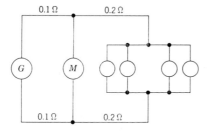

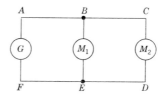

FIG. 20–19 Circuit of Probs. 1 and 2.   FIG. 20–20 Circuit of Probs. 3 and 4.

2   On the assumption that the resistances of the lamps in Prob. 1 remain constant, how much voltage will exist across them if the motor is disconnected from the line?

3   In Fig. 20–20, the distance from A to B is 200 ft, and that from B to C is 150 ft. AB and EF are No. 6 wire, and BC and DE are No. 14 wire. Motor M_1 draws 35 amp, and M_2 draws 10 amp. The generator brush potential is 230 volts. Find (a) voltage across M_1, (b) voltage across M_2, (c) power lost in lines.

4   In Fig. 20–20, the distance from A to B is 100 ft, and that from B to C is 300 ft. AB and EF are No. 10 wire, and BC and DE are No. 14 wire. Motor M_1 draws 15 amp, and M_2 draws 7.5 amp. The generator voltage is 120 volts. Find (a) voltage across M_1, (b) voltage across M_2, (c) power lost in lines.

5   The generator supplies 115 volts across points A and F

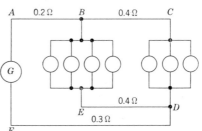

FIG. 20–21 Circuit of Probs. 5 to 8.

in Fig. 20–21. If each lamp draws 0.5 amp, find (a) voltage across group 1, (b) voltage across group 2.

6   Repeat Prob. 5, with each lamp drawing 1 amp.

7   Using the values of Prob. 5, repeat the problem, but with the wire FD disconnected from D and connected to the point E.

8   In the original circuit of Fig. 20–21, a voltmeter across the lamps of group 2 reads 110 volts. If each lamp in the circuit draws 0.75 amp, what is the generator voltage?

9   In the circuit of Fig. 20–22, motor M_1 draws 50 amp, M_2 draws 12 amp, M_3 draws 15 amp, and each lamp draws 1 amp. Find (a) voltage across M_1, (b) voltage across M_2, (c) voltage across M_3, (d) power lost in lines.

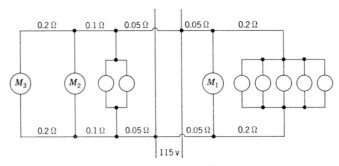

Fɪɢ. 20–22   Circuit of Prob. 9.

10   A, B, C, D, and E represent loads in Fig. 20–23. A draws 5 amp, B draws 6.5 amp, C draws 12 amp, D draws 7.5 amp, and E draws 4 amp at 100 volts. Find (a) voltage across each load, (b) generator voltage.

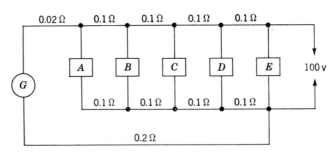

Fɪɢ. 20–23   Circuit of Prob. 10.

20 – 4   Bridge circuits

The accuracy of resistance measurements by the voltmeter-ammeter method is limited, mainly because of errors in the meters and the difficulty of reading the meters precisely. Probably the most widely

used device for precise resistance measurement is the Wheatstone
bridge, the circuit diagram of which is shown in Fig. 20–24.

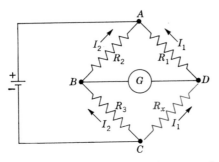

FIG. 20–24   Schematic   diagram   of
Wheatstone bridge.

Resistors R_1, R_2, and R_3 are known values, and R_x is the resistance to be measured.   In most bridges, R_1 and R_2 are adjustable in
ratios of $1:1$, $10:1$, $100:1$, etc., and R_3 is adjustable in small steps.   In
measuring a resistance, R_3 is adjusted until the galvanometer reads
zero, and in this condition the bridge is said to be "balanced."   Since
the galvanometer reads zero, it is evident that the points B and D
are exactly at the same potential; that is, the voltage drop from A to
B is the same as from A to D.   Expressed as an equation,

$$E_{AD} = E_{AB}$$

or
$$I_1 R_1 = I_2 R_2 \qquad [1]$$

Similarly, the voltage drop across R_x must be equal to that across
R_3.   Hence

$$I_1 R_x = I_2 R_3 \qquad [2]$$

Dividing Eq. [2] by Eq. [1],

$$\frac{I_1 R_x}{I_1 R_1} = \frac{I_2 R_3}{I_2 R_2}$$

$$\therefore \frac{R_x}{R_1} = \frac{R_3}{R_2} \qquad [3]$$

Equation [3] is the fundamental equation of the Wheatstone
bridge, and by solving for the only unknown R_x the value of the
resistance under measurement can be computed.

EXAMPLE 6   In the circuit of Fig. 20–24, $R_1 = 10$ Ω, $R_2 = 100$ Ω, and $R_3 = 13.9$ Ω. If the bridge is balanced, what is the value of the unknown resistance?

SOLUTION   Solving Eq. [3] for R_x, $\quad R_x = \dfrac{R_1 R_3}{R_2}$

Substituting the known values, $\qquad R_x = \dfrac{10 \times 13.9}{100} = 1.39$ Ω

Locating the point at which a telephone cable or a long control line is grounded is simplified by the use of two circuits that are modifications of the Wheatstone bridge. These are the Murray loop and the Varley loop.

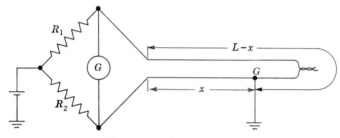

FIG. 20–25   Murray loop.

Figure 20–25 represents the method of locating the grounded point in a cable using a Murray loop. A spare ungrounded cable is connected to the grounded cable at a convenient location beyond the grounded point G. This forms a loop of length L, one part of which is the distance x from the point of measurement to the grounded point G. The other part of the loop is then $L - x$. These two parts of the loop form a bridge with R_1 and R_2, which are adjusted until the galvanometer shows no deflection. Because this results in a balanced bridge circuit,

$$\frac{R_2}{R_1} = \frac{x}{L - x} \qquad [4]$$

Solving for x,

$$x = \left(\frac{R_2}{R_1 + R_2} \right) L \qquad [5]$$

EXAMPLE 7   A Murray loop is connected as in Fig. 20–25 to locate a ground in a cable between two cities 40 miles apart. The lines forming the loop are identical. With the bridge balanced, $R_1 = 645$ Ω and $R_2 = 476$ Ω. How far is the grounded point from the test end?

SOLUTION   Substituting the known values in Eq. [5],

$$x = \left(\frac{476}{645 + 476}\right)80 = 33.97 \text{ miles}$$

If the two cables forming the loop are not the same size, the relations of Eq. [5] can be used to compute the resistance R_x of the grounded cable from the point of measurement to the grounded point. Then if R_L is the resistance of the entire loop,

$$R_x = \left(\frac{R_2}{R_1 + R_2}\right)R_L \qquad [6]$$

EXAMPLE 8   A Murray loop is connected as in Fig. 20–25. The grounded cable is No. 19 wire, and a different sized wire is used to complete the loop. The resistance of the entire loop is 126 Ω, and when the bridge is balanced, $R_1 = 342$ Ω and $R_2 = 217$ Ω. How far is the ground from the test end?
SOLUTION   Substituting the known values in Eq. [6],

$$R_x = \left(\frac{217}{342 + 217}\right)126 = 48.9 \ \Omega$$

Since No. 19 wire has a resistance of 8.21 Ω per 1,000 ft, 48.9 Ω represents 5,960 ft of wire between the test end and the grounded point.

PROBLEMS 20 – 3

1 In a Wheatstone bridge, $R_1 = 0.001$ Ω, $R_2 = 1$ Ω, and $R_3 = 28.7$ Ω. What is the value of the unknown resistance?

2 In a Wheatstone bridge, if $R_1/R_2 = 1,000$ and $R_x = 9.43$ Ω, what is the value of R_3?

3 A ground exists in one conductor of a lead-covered No. 14 pair. A Murray loop is used to locate the fault by connecting the pair together at the far end. When the bridge circuit is balanced, $R_1 = 18.7$ Ω and $R_2 = 13.2$ Ω. If the cable is 4,500 ft long, how far from the test end is the grounded point?

4 Several No. 8 wires run between two cities located 35 miles apart. One wire becomes grounded, and a Murray loop is used in one city to locate the fault by connecting two wires in the other city. When the bridge is balanced, $R_1 = 716$ Ω and $R_2 = 273$ Ω. How far from the test end is the cable grounded?

5 A No. 6 wire, which is known to be grounded, is made into a loop by connecting a wire of different size at its far end. The resistance of the loop thus formed is 5.62 Ω. When a Murray loop is connected and balanced, the value of R_1 is 16.8 Ω and that of R_2 is 36.2 Ω. How far from the test end does the ground exist?

CHAPTER 21
SIMULTANEOUS EQUATIONS

A graph is a pictorial representation of the relation existing between two or more quantities. Everyone is familiar with various types of graph or graphic chart. They are used extensively in magazines, newspapers, and trade journals and by engineers, manufacturers, and others concerned with relative values. It is difficult to conceive how the engineer could dispense with them.

The study of simultaneous linear equations provides an excellent opportunity to begin the study of graphs. Therefore, in this chapter we shall pave the way for some important and interesting topics which will follow in later chapters.

21 – 1 Solving problems by means of graphs

In many instances, problems arise involving relationships that, though readily solved by usual arithmetical or algebraic methods, are more clearly understood when solved graphically. It is also true that there are many problems which can be solved graphically with less labor then is required for the purely mathematical solutions. The following illustrative examples will show how some problems can be worked graphically:

EXAMPLE 1   Steamship A sailed from New York at 6 A.M., steaming at an average speed of 10 knots. (A knot is a measure of speed and is 1 nautical mile per hour.) The same day, at 9 A.M., steamship B sailed from New York, steering the same course as A but steaming at 15 knots. (a) How long will it take B to overtake A? (b) What will be the distance from New York at that time?

SOLUTION   Choose convenient scales on graph paper, and plot the distance in nautical miles covered by each vessel against the time in hours, as shown in Fig. 21-1. This is conveniently accomplished by making a table like Table 21-1.

It will be noted that the graphs of the two distances intersect at 90 miles, or at 3 P.M. This means the two ships will be 90 miles from New York at 3 P.M. Because they steered the same course, B overtakes A at this time and distance.

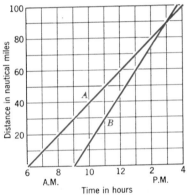

FIG. 21-1   Graph of Example 1.

TABLE 21-1

Time, hr	Distance covered by A	Distance covered by B
2	20	30
4	40	60
6	60	90
8	80	120
10	100	150

The graphic solution furnishes us with other information. For example, by measuring the vertical distance between the graphs, we can determine how far apart the ships were at any time. Thus, at 11 A.M. the ships were 20 miles apart, at 1 P.M. they were 10 miles apart, etc.

EXAMPLE 2   Ship A is 200 miles at sea, and ship B is in port. At 8 A.M., A starts toward the port, making a speed of 20 knots. At the same time, B leaves port at a speed of 30 knots to intercept A. After traveling 2 hr, B is delayed for 1 hr and 40 min at the lightship. B then continues on its course to intercept A. (a) At what time will the two ships meet? (b) How far will they be from port at that time?

SOLUTION   Figure 21-2 is a graph showing the conditions of the problem. The graph is constructed as in Example 1. A table of distances against time is made up, a convenient scale is chosen, and the points are plotted and joined with a straight line.

The intersection of the graphs shows that the two ships will meet 100 miles from port at 1 P.M. Why is there a horizontal portion in the graph of B's distance from port? If A and B continue their speeds and courses, at what time will A reach port? At what time will B arrive at A's 10 A.M. position? What will be the distance between ships at this time?

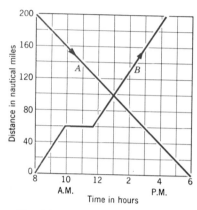

Fig. 21–2   Graph of Example 2.

PROBLEMS 21 – 1

1   A circuit consists of a 10-Ω resistor R_c connected across a variable voltage E_v. Plot the current I through the resistor against the voltage E across the resistor as E_v is varied in 10-volt steps from 0 to 120 volts. What conclusions do you draw from this graph?

2   The distance s (space) covered by a moving object is equal to the product of its velocity v and the time t during which the object is moving. That is, $s = vt$. Plot the distance in miles traveled by an automobile averaging 40 mph against time every hour from 0 to 8 hr. What conclusions do you draw from this graph?

3   A variable resistor R_v is connected across a generator that maintains a constant voltage E_c of 120 volts. Plot the current I through the resistor as its resistance is varied in 5-Ω steps from 5 to 50 Ω. What conclusions do you draw from this graph?

Solve graphically:

4   Train A leaves a city traveling at the rate of 50 mph. Two hours later train B leaves the same city, on the same track, traveling at the rate of 75 mph. (a) In how many hours will train B overtake A? (b) How far will they be from the starting point at this time? (c) How far apart are the trains 2 hr after the second starts?

5   Two men start from two places 75 miles apart and travel toward each other, the first at the rate of 5 mph and the second at the rate of 10 mph. (a) How long will it be before they meet? (b) How far will each have traveled? (c) How far are they apart 2 hr after starting? 7 hr?

6   A owns a motor that consumes 10 kwhr per day, and B owns a motor that takes 30 kwhr per day. Beginning the first day of the month, A lets his motor run continuously. B's motor runs for 1 day, is idle for 4 days, then runs for 2 days, is idle for 6 days, and then runs the rest of the month. On what days of the month will A's and B's power bill be the same?

7 The owner of a radio store decides to pay his salesmen according to either of two plans. The first plan provides for a fixed salary of $25 per week plus a commission of $3 for each radio sold. According to the second plan, a salesman may take a straight commission of $4 for each radio set. Determine at which point the second plan becomes more profitable for the salesmen.

8 A man started a savings account with a deposit of $25 and thereafter deposited $5 per week. Two weeks later, his brother started an account with $10 per week. (a) In how many weeks after the brother made his deposit will their accounts be equal? (b) During what weeks will their accounts differ by $10? (c) When will the brother's account be $100 greater?

21 – 2 Coordinate notation

Let us suppose you are standing on a street corner and a stranger asks you to direct him to some prominent building. You tell him to go four blocks east and five blocks north. By these directions, you have automatically made the street intersection a *point of reference*, or *origin*, from which distances are measured. From this point, you could count distances to any point in the city, using the blocks as a unit of distance, and pairs of directions (east, north, west, or south) for locating the various points.

To draw a graph, we had to use two lines of reference, or *axes*. These correspond to the streets meeting at right angles. Also, in fixing a point on a graph, it was necessary to locate that point by pairs of numbers. For example, when we plot distance against time, we need one number to represent the time and another number to represent the distance covered in that time.

So far, only positive numbers have been used for graphs. To restrict graphs to positive values would impose just as severe a handicap as if we were to restrict algebra to positive numbers. Accordingly, a system must be established for plotting pairs of numbers, either or both of which may be positive or negative. In so doing, a sheet of squared paper is divided into four sections, or quadrants, by drawing two intersecting axes at right angles to each other. The point O, at the intersection of the axes, is called the *origin*. The horizontal axis is generally known as the X *axis* and the vertical axis is called the Y *axis*.

There is nothing new about measuring distances along the X axis; it is the same as the basic system described in Sec. 8–5 and shown in Fig. 8–3. That is, we agree to regard distances along the X axis, to the *right* of the origin, as *positive*, and those to the *left* as *negative*. Also, distances along the Y axis are considered as *positive* if *above* the origin and *negative* if *below* the origin. In effect, we have simply added to our method of graphical representation as originally outlined in Fig. 8–3.

With this system of representation, which is called a system of *rectangular coordinates*, we are able to locate any pair of numbers regardless of the signs.

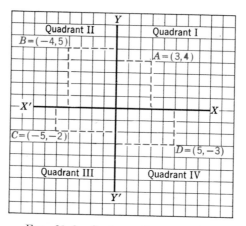

F<small>IG</small>. 21–3   System of rectangular coordinates.

E<small>XAMPLE</small> 3   Referring to Fig. 21–3,

Point A is in the first quadrant. Its x value is $+3$, and its y value is $+4$.
Point B is in the second quadrant. Its x value is -4, and its y value is $+5$.
Point C is in the third quadrant. Its x value is -5, and its y value is -2.
Point D is in the fourth quadrant. Its x value is $+5$, and its y value is -3.

Thus, every point on the surface of the paper corresponds to a pair of coordinate numbers that completely describe the point.

The two signed numbers that locate a point are called the *coordinates* of that point. The x value is called the *abscissa* of the point, and the y value is the *ordinate* of the point.

In describing a point in terms of its coordinates, the abscissa is always stated first. Thus, to locate the point A in Fig. 21–3, we write $A = (3,4)$, meaning that, to locate the point A, we count three divisions to the right of the origin along the X axis and up four divisions along the Y axis. In like manner, the point B is completely described by writing $B = (-4,5)$. Also,

$$C = (-5,-2) \quad \text{and} \quad D = (5,-3)$$

PROBLEMS 21-2

1 On a map, which lines correspond to the X axis, latitude or longitude?
2 Plot the following points: $(2,3)$, $(-6,-1)$, $(3,-7)$, $(0,-6)$, $(0,0)$, $(-8,0)$.
3 Plot the following points: $(-1.5,10)$, $(-6.5,-7.5)$, $(3.6,-4)$, $(0,2.5)$, $(6.5,8.5)$, $(3.5,0)$.

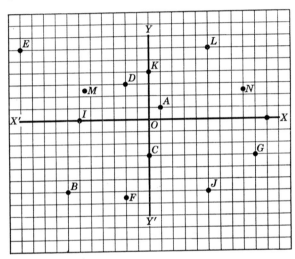

FIG. 21-4 Graph of Prob. 4.

4 Using Fig. 21-4, give the coordinates of the points A, B, C, D, E, F, G, H, I, J, K, L, M, and N.
5 Plot the following points: $A = (-1,-2)$, $B = (5,-2)$, $C = (5,4)$, $D = (-1,4)$. Connect these points in succession. What kind of figure is $ABCD$? Draw the diagonals DB and CA. What are the coordinates of the point of intersection of the diagonals?

1 – 3   Graphs of linear equations

A relation between a pair of numbers, not necessarily connected with physical quantities such as those in foregoing exercises, can be expressed by a graph.

Consider the following problem: The sum of two numbers is equal to 5. What are the numbers? Immediately it is evident there is more than one pair of numbers that will fulfill the requirements of the problem. For example, if only positive numbers are considered we have, by addition,

$$\begin{array}{cccccc} 0 & 1 & 2 & 3 & 4 & 5 \\ \underline{5} & \underline{4} & \underline{3} & \underline{2} & \underline{1} & \underline{0} \\ 5 & 5 & 5 & 5 & 5 & 5 \end{array}$$

Similarly, if negative numbers are included, we can write

$$\begin{array}{cccccc} -1 & -2 & -3 & -4 & -5 & -6 \\ \underline{+6} & \underline{+7} & \underline{+8} & \underline{+9} & \underline{+10} & \underline{+11} \\ 5 & 5 & 5 & 5 & 5 & 5 \end{array}$$

and so on, indefinitely.

Also, if fractions or decimals are considered, we have

$$\begin{array}{cccc} 1.5 & -3.75 & -1.63 & -8.36 \\ \underline{3.5} & \underline{+8.75} & \underline{+6.63} & \underline{+13.36} \\ 5 & 5 & 5 & 5 \end{array}$$

and so on, indefinitely.

It follows that there are an infinite number of pairs of numbers whose sum is 5.

Let x represent any possible value of one of these numbers, and let y represent the corresponding value of the second number. Then

$$x + y = 5$$

For any value assigned to x, we can solve for the corresponding value of y. Thus, if $x = 1$, $y = 4$. Also, if $x = 2$, $y = 3$. Likewise, if $x = -4$, $y = 9$, because, by substituting -4 for x in the equation, we obtain

$$-4 + y = 5$$
or
$$y = 9$$

In this manner, there may be obtained an unlimited number of values for x and y that satisfy the equations, some of which are listed below:

If $x =$	-6	-4	-2	0	2	4	6	8	10
Then $y =$	11	9	7	5	3	1	-1	-3	-5
Coordinates of	A	B	C	D	E	F	G	H	I

With the above pairs of numbers as coordinates the points are plotted and connected in succession as shown in Fig. 21-5. The line drawn through these points is called the *graph of the equation* $x + y = 5$.

Regardless of what pairs of numbers (coordinates) are chosen from the graph, it will be found that each pair satisfies the equation. For example, the point P has coordinates $(15, -10)$; that is, $x = 15$, and $y = -10$. These numbers satisfy the equation because $15 - 10 = 5$. Likewise, the point P_1 has coordinates $(-9, 14)$ that

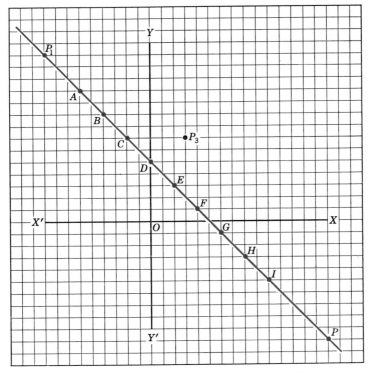

FIG. 21-5 Graph of the equation $x + y = 5$.

also satisfy the equation because $-9 + 14 = 5$. The point P_3 has coordinates $(3, 7)$. This point is not on the line, nor do its coordinates satisfy the equation, for $3 + 7 \neq 5$. The straight line, or graph, can be extended in either direction, always passing through points whose coordinates satisfy the conditions of the equation. This is as would be expected, for there are an infinite number of pairs of numbers called *solutions* that, when added, are equal to 5.

PROBLEMS 21-3

1 Graph the equation $x - y = 8$ by tabulating and plotting five pairs of values for x and y that satisfy the equation. Can a straight line be drawn

through these points? Plot the point (4,4). Is it on the graph of the equation? Do the coordinates of this point satisfy the equation? From the graph, when $x = 0$, what is the value of y? When $y = 0$, what is the value of x? Do these pairs of values satisfy the equation?

2 Graph the equation $2x + 3y = 6$ by tabulating and plotting at least five pairs of values for x and y that satisfy the equation. Can a straight line be drawn through these points? Plot the point $(-15,12)$. Is this point on the graph of the equation? Do the coordinates satisfy the equation? Plot the point $(10,-5)$. Is this point on the graph of the equation? Do the coordinates satisfy the equation? From the graph, when $x = 0$, what is the value of y? When $y = 0$, what is the value of x? Do these pairs of values satisfy the equation?

21 – 4   Summary

Each of the equations that have been plotted is of the *first degree* (Sec. 16–1) and contains *two unknowns*. From their graphs the following important facts are obtained:

1   The graph of an equation of the first degree is a straight line.
2   The coordinates of every point on the graph satisfy the conditions of the equation.
3   The coordinates of every point not on the graph do not satisfy the conditions of the equation.

Because the graph of every equation of the first degree results in a straight line, as stated under 1 above, first-degree equations are called *linear equations*. Also, because such equations have an infinite number of solutions, they are called *indeterminate* equations.

As x changes in value in such an equation, the value of y also changes. Hence, x and y are called *variables*.

21 – 5   Methods of plotting

To graph a linear equation of two variables,

1   Choose a convenient value for one variable, substitute it in the equation, and solve for the corresponding value of the other variable. This results in one solution, or one set of coordinates.
2   Choose another value and find a solution as in step 1.
3   Plot the two points whose coordinates were found in steps 1 and 2. Connect them with a straight line.
4   Check the resulting graph by solving for and plotting a third point. This third point should lie on the plotted line or its extension.

EXAMPLE 4   Graph the equation $2x - 5y = 10$.

SOLUTION   Step 1. It is convenient in plotting such an equation to first let $x = 0$, for in so doing the resulting solution will fall on the Y axis.

Then, if
$$x = 0$$
$$0 - 5y = 10$$
and
$$y = -2$$

This results in a point, which we shall call A, whose coordinates are $(0,-2)$.

   Step 2. If we now let $y = 0$, the resulting solution will fall on the X axis, for if
$$y = 0$$
$$2x - 0 = 10$$
and
$$x = 5$$

This results in another point, which we shall call B, whose coordinates are $(5,0)$.

   Step 3. Plot points A and B and connect them with a straight line as shown in Fig. 21–6.

CHECK   Choose another value for x in order to solve for a third point. Let
$$x = -10$$
Then
$$-20 - 5y = 10$$
and
$$y = -6$$

This results in point C with coordinates $(-10,-6)$ which, when plotted, falls on the graph of the equation as shown in Fig. 21–6.

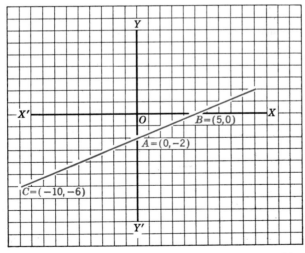

FIG. 21–6 Graph of the equation $2x - 5y = 10$.

When x was set equal to zero, the resulting point A had coordinates that located the point where the graph crossed the Y axis. This point is called the Y *intercept*. Likewise, when y was set equal to zero, the resulting point B had coordinates that located the point where the graph crossed the X axis. This point is called the X *intercept*. Not only are these easy methods of locating two points with which to graph the equation, but also these two points give us the exact location of the intercepts. These are important, as will be shown later.

PROBLEMS 21 – 4

Graph the following equations and determine the X and Y intercepts:

1 $5x + 4y = 12$ 　　　　　　　　　　2 $2x - y = 8$
3 $x - 3y = 3$ 　　　　　　　　　　　4 $2x + y = 9$

5 Plot the following equations on the same sheet of graph paper (same axes), and carefully study the results: (*a*) $x - y = -8$; (*b*) $x - y = -5$; (*c*) $x - y = 0$; (*d*) $x - y = 4$; (*e*) $x - y = 8$.

Are the graphs parallel? Note that all left members of the given equations are identical. Solve each of these equations for y and write them in a column, thus:

$$(a)\ \ y = x + 8$$
$$(b)\ \ y = x + 5$$
$$(c)\ \ y = x + 0$$
$$(d)\ \ y = x - 4$$
$$(e)\ \ y = x - 8$$

In each equation, does the last term of the right member represent the Y intercept?

When the equations are solved for y, as above, each coefficient of x is $+1$. The graphs all slant to the right because the coefficient of each x is positive. Each time an x increases one unit, note that the corresponding y increases one unit. This is because the coefficient of x in each equation is 1.

6 Plot the following equations on the same sheet of graph paper (same axes), and carefully study the results. (*a*) $4x - 2y = -30$; (*b*) $4x - 2y = -16$; (*c*) $4x - 2y = 0$; (*d*) $4x - 2y = 12$; (*e*) $4x - 2y = 30$; (*f*) $8x - 4y = 60$.

Are all the graphs parallel? Again note that all left members are identical. Does the graph of Eq. (*f*) fall on that of Eq. (*e*)? Note that (*e*) and (*f*) are *identical equations*. Why?

Solve each of these equations, except (*f*), for y, and write them in a column, thus:

(a) $y = 2x + 15$
(b) $y = 2x + 8$
(c) $y = 2x + 0$
(d) $y = 2x - 6$
(e) $y = 2x - 15$

In each equation, does the last term of the right member represent the Y intercept? When linear equations are written in this form, this last term is known as the *constant* term.

Are all the coefficients of the x's positive? This is why all the graphs slant to the right. Lines slanting in this manner are said to have *positive slopes*.

Each time an x increases or decreases one unit, note that y increases or decreases, respectively, two units. This is because the coefficient of each x is 2. If a graph has a *positive slope*, an increase or decrease in x always results in a corresponding increase or decrease in y. In these equations, each line has a slope of $+2$, the coefficient of each x.

7 Plot the following equations on the same set of axes: (a) $x + 2y = 18$; (b) $x + 2y = 10$; (c) $x + 2y = 0$; (d) $x + 2y = -14$; (e) $x + 2y = -22$; (f) $3x + 6y = -66$.

Are all the graphs parallel? How should you have known they would be parallel without plotting them?

Does the graph of (f) fall on that of (e)? How should you have known (e) and (f) would plot the same graph without actually plotting them? Solve each equation for y as in Probs. 5 and 6. Does the constant term denote the Y intercept in each case? Is the coefficient of each x equal to $-\frac{1}{2}$? The minus sign means that each graph has a *negative slope;* that is, the lines slant toward the left. Thus, when x increases, y decreases, and vice versa. The $\frac{1}{2}$ slope means that, when x varies one unit, y is changed $\frac{1}{2}$ unit. Therefore, the variations of x and y are completely described by saying the slope is $-\frac{1}{2}$.

8 Plot the following equations on the same set of axes: (a) $x - 4y = 0$; (b) $x - 2y = 0$; (c) $x - y = 0$; (d) $2x - y = 0$; (e) $4x - y = 0$; (f) $4x + y = 0$; (g) $2x + y = 0$; (h) $x + y = 0$; (i) $x + 2y = 0$; (j) $x + 4y = 0$.

Solve the equations for y, as before, and carefully analyze your results.

21–6   Variables

When two variables, such as x and y in the foregoing problems, are so related that a change in x causes a change in y, then y is said to be a *function* of x. By assigning values to x and then solving for the value of y, we make x the *independent variable* and y the *dependent variable*.

The above definitions are applicable to all types of equations and physical relations. For example, in Fig. 21–1, distance is plotted against time. The distance covered by a body moving at a constant velocity is given by

$$s = vt$$

where s = distance
v = velocity
t = time

In this equation and therefore in the resulting graph, the distance is the dependent variable because it depends upon the amount of time. The time is the independent variable, and the velocity is a constant.

Similarly, in 1 of Probs. 21–1, the formula $I = E/R$ was used to obtain values for plotting the graph. Here the resistance R is the constant, the voltage E is the independent variable, and the current I is the dependent variable.

In 3 of Probs. 21–1, the same formula $I = E/R$ was used to obtain coordinates for the graph. Here the voltage E is a constant, the resistance R is the independent variable, and the current I is the dependent variable.

From these and other examples, it is evident, as stated in Sec. 21–4, that the graph of an equation having variables of the first degree is a straight line. This fact does not apply to variables in the denominator of a fraction as in the case above where R is a variable. However, $I = E/R$ is not an equation of the first degree as far as R is concerned because, by applying the law of exponents, $I = ER^{-1}$.

It is general practice to plot the independent variable along the horizontal, or X axis, and the dependent variable along the vertical, or Y axis.

In plotting the graph of an equation, it is convenient to solve the equation for the dependent variable first. Values are then assigned to the independent variable in order to find the corresponding values of the dependent variable.

If an equation or formula contains more than two variables, after choosing the dependent variable, we must decide which one is to be the independent variable for each separate investigation, or graphing. For example, consider the formula

$$X_L = 2\pi fL$$

where X_L = inductive reactance of an inductor, ohms

f = frequency, cps

L = inductance, henrys

2π = 6.28 . . .

In this case, we can vary either the frequency f or the inductance L in order to determine the effect upon the inductive reactance X_L, but both must not be varied at the same time. Either f must be fixed at some constant value and L varied, or L must be fixed. A little thought will show the difficulty of plotting, on a plane, the variations of X_L if f and L are varied simultaneously.

21 – 7 Graphical solution of simultaneous linear equations

The graphs of the equations

$$x + 2y = 12$$

and $$3x - y = 1$$

are shown in Fig. 21–7. The point of intersection of the lines has the

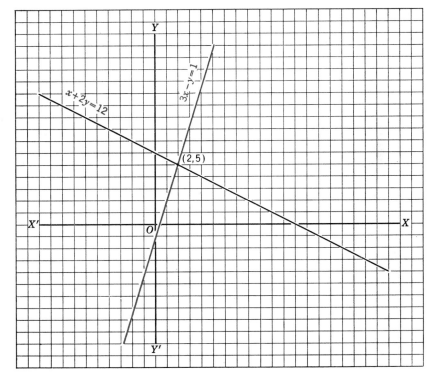

FIG. 21–7 Graph of the equations $x + 2y = 12$ and $3x - y = 1$.

coordinates $(2,5)$; that is, the x value is 2, and the y value is 5.   Now this point is on both of the graphs; it follows, therefore, that the x and y values should satisfy both equations.   Substituting 2 for x and 5 for y in each equation results in the identities

$$2 + 10 = 12$$

and $$6 - 5 = 1$$

From this it is observed that, if the graphs of two linear equations intersect, they have one common set of values for the variables, or one common solution.   These are called *simultaneous linear equations.*

Because two straight lines can intersect in only one point, there can be only one common set of values or one common solution that satisfies both equations.

Two equations, each with two variables, are called *inconsistent equations* when their plotted lines are parallel to each other.   Because parallel lines do not intersect, there is no common solution for two or more inconsistent equations.

Considerable care must be used in graphing equations, for a deviation in the graph of either equation will cause the intersection to be in the wrong place and hence will lead to an incorrect solution.

PROBLEMS 21 – 5

Solve the following pairs of equations graphically, and check by substituting the x and y values thus obtained in each pair of equations:

1	$2x + y = 9$	2	$x - 4y = 9$
	$4x - y = 6$		$2x - 2y = 6$
3	$x - 3y = -8$	4	$5x + 4y = 12$
	$3x + y = 6$		$x - 2y = 8$
5	$4\alpha + 2\beta = -2$	6	$2i - I = 8$
	$3\alpha - 2\beta = -12$		$3i + 2I = 5$
7	$r + R = 0$	8	$2E - e = 3$
	$3r + 7R = 8$		$4e + 3E = 10$
9	$2F - f = 4$	10	$\alpha + 2\beta = 6$
	$2F + 3f = 12$		$3\alpha - 2\beta = 10$

21 – 8   **Solution of simultaneous linear equations by addition and subtraction**

It has been shown in previous sections that an unlimited number of pairs of values of variables satisfy one linear equation.   Also, it can be determined graphically whether there is one pair of values, or

solution, that will satisfy two given linear equations. The solution
of two simultaneous linear equations can also be found by algebraic
methods, as illustrated in the following examples:

EXAMPLE 5   Solve the equations $x + y = 6$ and $x - y = 2$.

SOLUTION   Given $x + y = 6$ (a)

$$x - y = 2 \qquad (b)$$

Add (a) and (b), $2x = 8$ (c)

D:2 in (c), $x = 4$

Substitute this value of x in (a), $4 + y = 6$

Collecting terms, $y = 2$

The common solution for (a) and (b) is

$$x = 4 \qquad y = 2$$

CHECK   Substitute in (a), $4 + 2 = 6$

Substitute in (b), $4 - 2 = 2$

In the above example, the coefficients of y in Eqs. (a) and (b)
are the same except for signs. This being the case, y can be *eliminated* by adding these equations, which sum results in an equation in
one unknown. This method of solution is called *elimination by
addition*.

Because the coefficients of x are the same in Eqs. (a) and (b),
x could have been eliminated by subtracting either equation from
the other, an equation containing only y as a variable being the
result. This method of solution is called *elimination by subtraction*.
The remaining variable x would have been solved for in the usual
manner by substituting the value of y in either equation.

EXAMPLE 6   Solve the equations $3x - 4y = 13$ and $5x + 6y = 9$.

SOLUTION   Given $3x - 4y = 13$ (a)

$$5x + 6y = 9 \qquad (b)$$

M:3 in (a), $9x - 12y = 39$ (c)

M:2 in (b), $10x + 12y = 18$ (d)

Add (c) and (d), $19x = 57$ (e)

D:19 in (e), $x = 3$ (f)

Substitute this value of x in (a), $9 - 4y = 13$ (g)

Collecting terms, $-4y = 4$ (h)

D:-4 in (h), $y = -1$

The common solution for (a) and (b) is

$$x = 3 \qquad y = -1$$

CHECK   Substitute in (a), $9 + 4 = 13$

Substitute in (b), $15 - 6 = 9$

In the above example the coefficients of x and y in Eqs. (a) and (b) are not the same. The coefficients of y were made the same absolute value in Eqs. (c) and (d) in order to eliminate y by the method of addition.

EXAMPLE 7   Solve the equations $4a - 3b = 27$ and $7a - 2b = 31$.

SOLUTION   Given

$$4a - 3b = 27 \qquad (a)$$
$$7a - 2b = 31 \qquad (b)$$

M:7 in (a) $28a - 21b = 189 \qquad (c)$

M:4 in (b), $28a - 8b = 124 \qquad (d)$

Subtract (d) from (c), $-13b = 65 \qquad (e)$

D:-13 in (e), $b = -5 \qquad (f)$

Substitute this value of b in (a), $4a + 15 = 27 \qquad (g)$

Collecting terms, $4a = 12 \qquad (h)$

D:4 in (h), $a = 3 \qquad (i)$

The common solution for (a) and (b) is

$$a = 3 \qquad b = -5$$

CHECK   Substitute the values of the variables (a) and (b) as usual.

In the above example the coefficients of a and b in Eqs. (a) and (b) are not the same. The coefficients of a were made the same absolute value in Eqs. (c) and (d) in order to eliminate a by the method of subtraction.

RULE   To solve two simultaneous linear equations having two variables by the method of elimination by addition or subtraction,

1   If necessary, multiply each equation by a number that will make the coefficients of one of the variables of equal absolute value.

2   If these coefficients of equal absolute value have like signs, subtract one equation from the other; if they have unlike signs, add the equations.

3   Solve the resulting equation.

4   Substitute the value of the variable found in step 3 in one of the original equations, and then solve this resulting equation for the remaining variable.

5   Check the solution by substituting in both the original equations.

PROBLEMS 21 – 6

Solve for the unknowns by addition or subtraction:

1   $2E + 6e = 7$ 2 $\alpha + 4\beta = 14$

     $4E - 3e = 9$ $\alpha - 4\beta = -2$

3 $6R - r = 15$
   $2R + 5r = 21$

4 $\theta + \phi = 8$
   $\theta - \phi = 2$

5 $2I - i = 5$
   $4I + 3i = 20$

6 $s + 2t = 26$
   $4s - t = 32$

7 $9\theta + 2\phi = 34$
   $6\theta + 5\phi = -14$

8 $\alpha = 8\beta$
   $\alpha + \beta = 45$

9 $4Z - 3Z_1 = 11$
   $3Z - 2Z_1 = 9$

10 $3I - 2i = 16$
    $I + 4i = 52$

11 $9e - 4E = 16$
    $7e - 6E = -2$

12 $8R_1 - R_2 = 0$
    $3R_2 + 4R_1 = 14$

13 $2\alpha - 5\beta = 82$
    $3\alpha - 2\beta = 68$

14 $7\pi + 3\lambda = -23$
    $5\lambda + 4\pi = -23$

15 $3r_2 - 8r_1 = -20$
    $3r_1 + 8r_2 = 44$

16 $5\theta + 3\phi = -1$
    $7\phi + 3\theta = 15$

17 $3s + 7t = 50$
    $5s - 2t = 15$

18 $Z_2 + Z_1 = 21$
    $0.03Z_1 + 0.02Z_2 = 0.54$

19 $0.06a + 0.02b = 204$
    $0.05a + 0.03b = 186$

20 $\alpha + \beta = 4 \times 10^3$
    $0.06\alpha - 0.04\beta = 90$

1–9 Solution by substitution

Another common method of solution is called *elimination by substitution*.

EXAMPLE 8   Solve the equations $16x - 3y = 10$ and $8x + 5y = 18$.

SOLUTION   Given

$$16x - 3y = 10 \qquad (a)$$
$$8x + 5y = 18 \qquad (b)$$

Solve (a) for x in terms of y,

$$x = \frac{10 + 3y}{16} \qquad (c)$$

Substitute this value of x in (b),

$$8\left(\frac{10 + 3y}{16}\right) + 5y = 18 \qquad (d)$$

M:16 in (d), $$8(10 + 3y) + 80y = 288 \qquad (e)$$

Expanding (e), $$80 + 24y + 80y = 288 \qquad (f)$$

Collecting terms in (f), $$104y = 208 \qquad (g)$$

D:104 in (g), $$y = 2 \qquad (h)$$

Substitute the value of y in (a), $$16x - 6 = 10 \qquad (i)$$

Collecting terms in (i), $$16x = 16 \qquad (j)$$

D:16 in (j), $$x = 1 \qquad (k)$$

CHECK   Usual method.

Not only is the method of substitution a very useful one, but also it serves to emphasize the fact that the values of the variables are the same in both equations.

The method of solving by substitution can be stated as follows:

RULE   To solve by substitution,

1   Solve one of the equations for one of the variables in terms of the other variable.

2   Substitute the resultant value of the variable, found in step 1, in the remaining equation.

3   Solve the equation obtained in step 2 for the second variable.

4   In the simplest of the original equations, substitute the value of the variable found in step 3 and solve the resulting equation for the remaining unknown variable.

PROBLEMS 21 – 7

Solve by the method of substitution:

1   $3\alpha + 4\beta = 9$
    $5\alpha + 4\beta = 22$

2   $5E + 2e = 16$
    $3E - e = 3$

3   $4I + 3i = -1$
    $5I + i = 7$

4   $5R + r = 11$
    $3R + 2r = 8$

5   $5a + 3b = -9$
    $3a - 4b = -17$

6   $4s - 3t = 5$
    $9s - 8t = 0$

7   $3x - 4y = 17$
    $x + 3y = -3$

8   $5Z_1 - 3Z_2 = 0$
    $15Z_1 + 12Z_2 = 75$

9   $12\pi + 5\lambda = 6$
    $3\pi - 3\lambda = 10$

10   $6\alpha + 8\beta - 26 = 0$
     $5\alpha - 3\beta - 70 = 0$

11   $0.3P + 0.3W - 0.7 = 0$
     $0.9P - 0.6W - 1.6 = 0$

12   $15e - 4e_1 = 3$
     $9e - 2e_1 = 2$

13   $6I - 10i = 5$
     $14I - 15 = 15i$

14   $0.4R_1 - 0.1R_2 - 0.2 = 0$
     $0.2R_1 = 0.8 - 0.3R_2$

15   $0.2Z = 2.4Z_1$
     $0.3Z - 1.6 = 2Z_1$

16   $0.7f - 0.6F = -0.2$
     $0.9f - 0.4F = 1.6$

17   $7X_L - 6X_C - 63 = 0$
     $9X_L + 2X_C - 13 = 0$

18   $0.05\omega - 0.3\pi + 2.5 = 0$
     $0.9\omega = 9.4 - 0.04\pi$

19   $0.3\alpha + 0.2\beta + 0.9 = 0$
     $0.3\beta + 0.5\alpha + 1.9 = 0$

20   $0.3\theta + 0.04\phi = 1.66$
     $0.3\phi + 0.02\theta - 1.3 = 0$

21 – 10   Solution by comparison

In this method, we solve for the value of the same variable in each equation in terms of the other variable and place these values equal to each other. This forms an equation having only one unknown.

EXAMPLE 9   Solve the equations $x - 4y = 14$ and $4x + y = 5$.

SOLUTION   Given $x - 4y = 14$ (a)

                            $4x + y = 5$ (b)

Solve (a) for x in terms of y, $\qquad\qquad x = 14 + 4y \qquad\qquad (c)$

Solve (b) for x in terms of y, $\qquad\qquad x = \dfrac{5 - y}{4} \qquad\qquad (d)$

Equating the values of x in (c) and (d), $\quad 14 + 4y = \dfrac{5 - y}{4} \qquad (e)$

M:4 in (e), $\qquad\qquad\qquad\qquad\qquad 56 + 16y = 5 - y \qquad\qquad (f)$

Collecting terms in (f), $\qquad\qquad\qquad 17y = -51 \qquad\qquad\qquad (g)$

D:17 in (g), $\qquad\qquad\qquad\qquad\qquad y = -3$

Substitute the value of y in (a), $\qquad x + 12 = 14$

Collecting terms, $\qquad\qquad\qquad\qquad x = 2$

CHECK   Usual method.

PROBLEMS 21 – 8

Solve by the comparison method:

1 $3E + e = 14$ 2 $I + 3i = 11$
   $E + 2e = 13$ $4I + 7i = 29$

3 $6\alpha + 17\beta = 35$ 4 $52\omega - 15\pi = 80$
   $14\alpha - 3\beta = 39$ $39\omega - 8\pi = 99$

5 $5R + 7Z - 74 = 0$ 6 $13\theta - 8\phi - 1 = 0$
   $5Z - 7R = 0$ $5\phi = 8\theta$

7 $R_t + 3R_1 - 25 = 0$ 8 $3x = 7y + 19$
   $4R_1 + R_t - 31 = 0$ $2x - 9 = y$

9 $15e = 201 - 93e_1$ 10 $28Z_1 = 199 + 27Z_2$
   $15e_1 + 93e - 123 = 0$ $21Z_1 - 50Z_2 - 60 = 0$

– 11 Fractional form

Simultaneous linear equations having fractions with numerical denominators are readily solved by first clearing the fractions from the equations and then solving by any method the student considers most convenient.

EXAMPLE 10   Solve the equations $\dfrac{x}{4} + \dfrac{y}{3} = \dfrac{7}{12}$ and $\dfrac{x}{2} - \dfrac{y}{4} = \dfrac{1}{4}$

SOLUTION   Given $\qquad\qquad\qquad \dfrac{x}{4} + \dfrac{y}{3} = \dfrac{7}{12} \qquad\qquad (a)$

$\qquad\qquad\qquad\qquad\qquad\qquad \dfrac{x}{2} - \dfrac{y}{4} = \dfrac{1}{4} \qquad\qquad (b)$

M:12, the LCD, in (a), $\qquad 3x + 4y = 7$

M:4, the LCD, in (b), $\qquad 2x - y = 1$

This results in equations containing no fractions. Inspection of these shows that solution by addition is most convenient. The solution is

$$x = 1 \qquad y = 1$$

PROBLEMS 21 – 9

Solve the following equations:

1   $\dfrac{\alpha}{4} - \dfrac{\beta}{5} = 2$

$\alpha - \beta = 5$

2   $\dfrac{\theta}{2} - \dfrac{\phi}{4} - 1 = 0$

$\dfrac{5\theta}{3} = \dfrac{3\phi}{2} - 2$

3   $\omega - \dfrac{5\pi}{6} = 8$

$\dfrac{5\omega}{6} - \pi - 3 = 0$

4   $\dfrac{R}{3} + r - 34 = 0$

$3r = R$

5   $0.9E_1 - 5.7 + 0.4E = 0$

$E = \dfrac{E_1}{2} + \dfrac{1}{2}$

6   $\dfrac{2Z}{7} + \dfrac{5Z_1}{3} - 7 = 0$

$6Z = 14Z_1$

7   $\dfrac{2\mu}{9} = \dfrac{R_p}{9} - 2$

$\dfrac{\mu}{4} + \dfrac{R_p}{5} = 1$

8   $\dfrac{\omega - 2}{5} = \dfrac{10 - \omega}{3} + \dfrac{F - 10}{4}$

$\dfrac{F + 2}{6} - \dfrac{2\omega + F}{32} = \dfrac{\omega + 13}{16}$

9   $\dfrac{\alpha - \beta}{8} = \dfrac{\alpha + 1}{10} = \dfrac{3\beta - 5}{2}$

10   $3\theta - 37 - 7\phi = \dfrac{\phi}{4} + \dfrac{\theta}{3} = 0$

21 – 12   Fractional equations

Where variables occur in denominators, it is sometimes easier to solve without clearing the equations of fractions.

EXAMPLE 11   Solve the equations $\dfrac{5}{x} - \dfrac{6}{y} = -\dfrac{1}{2}$

$\dfrac{2}{x} - \dfrac{3}{y} = -1$

SOLUTION   Given

$$\dfrac{5}{x} - \dfrac{6}{y} = -\dfrac{1}{2} \qquad (a)$$

$$\dfrac{2}{x} - \dfrac{3}{y} = -1 \qquad (b)$$

M:2 in (a),

$$\dfrac{10}{x} - \dfrac{12}{y} = -1 \qquad (c)$$

M:5 in (b),

$$\dfrac{10}{x} - \dfrac{15}{y} = -5 \qquad (d)$$

Subtract (d) from (c),

$$\dfrac{3}{y} = 4$$

$$y = \tfrac{3}{4}$$

Substitute $\tfrac{3}{4}$ for y in (b),

$$\dfrac{2}{x} - 4 = -1$$

Collecting terms,

$$\frac{2}{x} = 3$$

$$\therefore x = \tfrac{2}{3}$$

CHECK   Usual method.

PROBLEMS 21 – 10

Solve the following equations:

1 $\dfrac{1}{\alpha} + \dfrac{1}{\beta} = \dfrac{5}{6}$

   $\dfrac{1}{\alpha} - \dfrac{1}{\beta} = \dfrac{1}{6}$

2 $\dfrac{9}{\theta} - \dfrac{5}{\phi} = 2$

   $\dfrac{3}{\phi} + \dfrac{5}{\theta} = 30$

3 $\dfrac{5}{R} = 5$

   $\dfrac{2}{R} - 3r = 0$

4 $\dfrac{1}{I} + \dfrac{1}{i} = \dfrac{4}{15}$

   $\dfrac{3}{I} + \dfrac{2}{i} = \dfrac{19}{15}$

5 $\dfrac{15}{E} + \dfrac{3}{E_1} = 4$

   $\dfrac{6}{E_1} + \dfrac{5}{E} = 3$

6 $\dfrac{4}{Z - 1} = \dfrac{3}{1 - Z_1}$

   $\dfrac{5}{2Z_1 - 5} - \dfrac{7}{2Z - 39} = 0$

7 $\dfrac{x - 3}{y + 1} - \dfrac{x - 6}{y - 2} = 0$

   $\dfrac{x + y - 5}{x - y + 1} = 3$

8 $\dfrac{\omega + 3\pi}{\pi - \omega} = \dfrac{1}{3}$

   $\dfrac{\omega}{4} - \dfrac{1}{6} = \dfrac{\omega - 2\pi}{6}$

9 $\dfrac{3\alpha + \beta - 3}{2\beta - \alpha} + \dfrac{1}{11} = 0$

   $\dfrac{\alpha + \beta - 2}{\alpha - \beta} = -\dfrac{1}{3}$

10 $\dfrac{r - r_1}{3} = r - (r_1 + 2)$

    $\dfrac{2r}{5} - (r_1 - 1) = 1$

– 13   Literal equations in two unknowns

The solution of literal simultaneous equations involves no new methods of solution. In general, it will be found that the addition or subtraction method will suffice for most cases.

EXAMPLE 12   Solve the equations $ax + by = c$ and $mx + ny = d$.

SOLUTION   Given

$$ax + by = c \qquad (a)$$
$$mx + ny = d \qquad (b)$$

First eliminate x.

M:m in (a), $amx + bmy = cm$ (c)

M:a in (b), $amx + any = ad$ (d)

Subtract (d) from (c). $bmy - any = cm - ad$ (e)

Factoring (e), $y(bm - an) = cm - ad$ (f)

D:$(bm - an)$ in (f), $y = \dfrac{cm - ad}{bm - an}$

Now go back to (a) and (b), and eliminate y.

M:n in (a),	$anx + bny = cn$	(g)
M:b in (b),	$bmx + bny = bd$	(h)
Subtract (h) from (g).	$anx - bmx = cn - bd$	(i)
Factoring (i),	$x(an - bm) = cn - bd$	(j)

D:$(an - bm)$ in (j), $x = \dfrac{cn - bd}{an - bm} = \dfrac{bd - cn}{bm - an}$

EXAMPLE 13   Solve the equations

$$\frac{a}{x} + \frac{b}{y} = \frac{1}{xy}$$

$$\frac{c}{x} + \frac{d}{y} = \frac{1}{xy}$$

SOLUTION   Given

$$\frac{a}{x} + \frac{b}{y} = \frac{1}{xy} \tag{a}$$

$$\frac{c}{x} + \frac{d}{y} = \frac{1}{xy} \tag{b}$$

First eliminate y, although it makes no difference which variable is eliminated first.

M:xy, the LCD, in (a),	$ay + bx = 1$	(c)
M:xy, the LCD, in (b),	$cy + dx = 1$	(d)
M:c in (c),	$acy + bcx = c$	(e)
M:a in (d),	$acy + adx = a$	(f)
Subtract (f) from (e),	$bcx - adx = c - a$	(g)
Factoring (g),	$x(bc - ad) = c - a$	(h)

D:$(bc - ad)$ in (h), $x = \dfrac{c - a}{bc - ad}$

Now go back to (a) and (b) to eliminate x, and find

$$y = \frac{b - d}{bc - ad}$$

PROBLEMS 21 – 11

Solve for α and β:

1 $3\beta + \alpha = C$
   $2\alpha - \beta = C$

2 $\alpha - \beta = 5\omega$
   $\alpha + \beta = \pi$

3 $\theta\beta + \phi\alpha = \phi$
   $\theta\alpha + \phi\beta = \theta$

4 $\dfrac{5Z}{\beta} - ZR + \dfrac{3R}{\alpha} = 0$

   $ZR - \dfrac{5R}{\beta} = \dfrac{3Z}{\alpha}$

Solve for R and r:

5 $aR - br = a - b$
   $aR + br = a + b$

6 $\dfrac{2\omega}{R} + \dfrac{3\pi}{r} - 5 = 0$

   $\dfrac{7\pi}{r} = 12 - \dfrac{5\omega}{R}$

7 $I_1R + I_2r - I_1x - I_2y = 0$ 8 $R + r = Z_1$
   $I_2R + I_1r - I_2x - I_1y = 0$ $IR - ir = Z_2$

— 14 Equations containing three unknowns

In the preceding examples and problems, two equations were necessary to solve for two unknown variables. For problems involving three variables, three equations are necessary. The same methods of solution apply.

EXAMPLE 14   Solve the equations $2x + 3y + 5z = 0$ (a)
                                      $6x - 2y - 3z = 3$ (b)
                                      $8x - 5y - 6z = 1$ (c)

SOLUTION   Choose a variable to be eliminated. Let it be x.

M:3 in (a), $6x + 9y + 15z = \quad 0$ (d)
                                      $6x - 2y - 3z = \quad 3$ (b)
Subtract (b) from (d). $11y + 18z = -3$ (e)
M:4 in (a), $8x + 12y + 20z = \quad 0$ (f)
                                      $8x - 5y - 6z = \quad 1$ (c)
Subtract (c) from (f), $17y + 26z = -1$ (g)

This gives Eqs. (e) and (g) in two variables y and z. Solving them, we obtain $y = 3$, $z = -2$.
Substitute these values into (a), $2x + 9 - 10 = 0$ (h)
Collecting terms, $2x = 1$ (i)
D:2 in (i), $x = \frac{1}{2}$

CHECK   Substitute the values of the variables in the equations.

PROBLEMS 21 – 12

Solve:

1   $a + 2b + c = 7$ 2 $x + y + 2z = 3$
    $2a + b + 2c = 2$ $2x + y + z = 16$
    $a + 3b + 4c = 14$ $x + 2y + z = 9$

3   $\alpha + \beta + \gamma = 6$ 4 $2Z + 3R + 6r = 70$
    $\alpha + \beta - \gamma = 0$ $3Z + 2R - r = 20$
    $\alpha - \beta + \gamma = 2$ $Z - R + 6r = 41$

5   $s - \dfrac{t}{7} = 8$ 6 $10I - 4i + I_1 = 5$
                                        $4I - i + 3I_1 = 11$
    $t - \dfrac{r}{2} = 10$ $3I + 6i - 2I_1 = 9$

    $5r - s = 30$

7　　$e - 2E + e_1 = 0$
　　　$e - E + 2e_1 = -11$
　　　$2e - E + e_1 = -9$

8　$\dfrac{1}{\alpha} + \dfrac{1}{\beta} + \dfrac{1}{\gamma} = \dfrac{1}{3}$

　　$\dfrac{1}{\alpha} - \dfrac{1}{\beta} - \dfrac{1}{\gamma} = -\dfrac{5}{3}$

　　$\dfrac{1}{\beta} - \dfrac{1}{\gamma} - \dfrac{1}{\alpha} = \dfrac{25}{3}$

9　　$E_1 - 2E_2 + E_3 = \beta$
　　　$E_1 + E_2 + 2E_3 = \gamma$
　　　$2E_1 - E_2 + E_3 = \alpha$

10　$\dfrac{1}{R_2} - \dfrac{1}{R_3} - \dfrac{1}{R_1} = \beta$

　　$\dfrac{1}{R_1} - \dfrac{1}{R_2} - \dfrac{1}{R_3} = \alpha$

　　$\dfrac{1}{R_3} - \dfrac{1}{R_1} - \dfrac{1}{R_2} = \gamma$

21 – 15　Methods of solution

In working a problem involving more than one unknown, it is convenient to solve it by setting up a system of simultaneous equations according to the statements of the problem.

EXAMPLE 15　When a certain number is increased by one-third of another number, the result is 23. When the second number is increased by one-half of the first number, the result is 29. What are the numbers?

SOLUTION　　Let x = first number, y = second number.

Then　　　　　$x + \dfrac{1}{3}y = 23$　　　　　　　　　　　　　　　(a)

Also,　　　　　$y + \dfrac{1}{2}x = 29$　　　　　　　　　　　　　　　(b)

Solving the equations, we obtain $x = 16$, $y = 21$.

CHECK　　When 16, the first number, is increased by ⅓ of 21, we have

$$16 + 7 = 23$$

When 21, the second number, is increased by ½ of 16, we have

$$21 + 8 = 29$$

EXAMPLE 16　Two airplanes start from Omaha at the same time. The plane traveling west has a speed of 80 mph faster than the one traveling east. At the end of 4 hr they are 1,600 miles apart. What is the speed of each plane?

SOLUTION　　Let x = rate of plane flying west, y = rate of plane flying east.

Then　　　　　　　$x - y = 80$　　　　　　　　　　　　　　　(a)
Since　　　　Rate × time = distance

then $4x$ = distance traveled by plane flying west
and $4y$ = distance traveled by plane flying east
Hence, $4x + 4y = 1,600$ (b)

Solving Eqs. (a) and (b), we obtain

$$x = 240 \text{ mph}$$
$$y = 160 \text{ mph}$$

CHECK   Substitute these values into the statements of the example.

Often it is possible to derive a formula from known data and thereby eliminate terms which are not desired or cannot be used conveniently in some investigation.

EXAMPLE 17   The effective voltage E of an alternating voltage is equal to 0.707 times its maximum value E_m. That is,

$$E = 0.707E_m \qquad [1]$$

Also, the average value E_{av} is equal to 0.637 times the maximum value. That is,

$$E_{av} = 0.637E_m \qquad [2]$$

It is desired to express the effective value E in terms of the average value E_{av}.

SOLUTION E_m must be eliminated.

Solving Eq. [1] for E_m, $E_m = \dfrac{E}{0.707}$

Solving Eq. [2] for E_m, $E_m = \dfrac{E_{av}}{0.637}$

By Axiom 5, $\dfrac{E}{0.707} = \dfrac{E_{av}}{0.637}$

Solving for E, $E = 1.11E_{av} \qquad [3]$

Equation [3] shows that the effective value of an alternating voltage is 1.11 times its average value.

EXAMPLE 18   You know that in a d-c circuit $P = EI$, also that $P = I^2R$. Derive a formula for E in terms of I and R.

SOLUTION   It is evident that P must be eliminated. Because both equations are equal to P, we can equate them (Axiom 5) and obtain

$$EI = I^2R$$
D:I, $E = IR \qquad [4]$

EXAMPLE 19   The quantity of electricity Q, in coulombs, in a capacitor is equal to the product of the capacitance C and the applied voltage E. That is,

$$Q = CE \qquad [5]$$

The total voltage across capacitors C_a and C_b connected in series is $E = E_a + E_b$. Find C in terms of C_a and C_b.

SOLUTION   Solve for E, E_a, and E_b. Thus

$$E = \frac{Q}{C}$$

$$E_a = \frac{Q}{C_a}$$

and $$E_b = \frac{Q}{C_b}$$

Then, since $$E = E_a + E_b$$

By substitution $$\frac{Q}{C} = \frac{Q}{C_a} + \frac{Q}{C_b}$$

D:Q, $$\frac{1}{C} = \frac{1}{C_a} + \frac{1}{C_b}$$

M:CC_aC_b, the LCD $$C_aC_b = CC_b + CC_a$$

Transposing, $$CC_a + CC_b = C_aC_b$$

D:$(C_a + C_b)$ $$C = \frac{C_aC_b}{C_a + C_b} \qquad [6]$$

This is the formula for the resultant capacitance C of two capacitors C_a and C_b connected in series.

PROBLEMS 21 – 13

1 The sum of two voltages is E volts, and their difference is e volts. Find the voltages.

2 Find two numbers whose sum is 25 and whose difference is 13.

3 If 1 is added to both terms of a fraction, its value becomes $\frac{3}{5}$, and if 3 is subtracted from both terms of the fraction, its value becomes $\frac{1}{3}$. Find the fraction.

4 Fifty resistors and 50 capacitors cost $10.50, and 80 capacitors and 30 resistors cost $12.30. Find the cost of each resistor and capacitor.

5 In a right triangle the acute angles are complementary. (Two angles whose sum is one right angle, or 90°, are said to be complementary angles.) Find the angles if their difference is 47°.

6 The difference between the two acute angles of a right triangle is $\theta°$. Find the angles.

7   A takes 5 hr longer than B to walk 36 miles, but if he doubles his pace, he takes 1 hr less than B. Find their rates of walking.

8   $v = gt$ and $s = \frac{1}{2}gt^2$. Solve for v in terms of s and t.

9   $A = \frac{1}{2}sh$ and $h = \frac{s\sqrt{3}}{2}$. Solve for A in terms of s.

10   $C = \frac{Q}{V}$ and $W = \frac{QV}{2}$. Solve for W in terms of C and Q.

11   $I = \frac{E}{R}$ and $P = I^2R$. $P = 2.7$ kw and $E = 180$ volts. Find the current I and the resistance R.

12   $v = \frac{s}{t}$ and $f = \frac{mv^2}{2s}$. Solve for t in terms of m, v, and f.

13   $\mu = \Delta e_b/\Delta e_c$, $r_p = \Delta e_b/\Delta i_b$, and $g_m = \Delta i_b/\Delta e_c$. Solve for μ in terms of g_m and r_p.

14   $R = 2D_L fL$ and $Q = \frac{2\pi fL}{R}$. Solve for D_L in terms of π and Q.

15   $R = \omega LQ$, $Q = \frac{\omega L}{r}$, and $\omega^2 = \frac{1}{LC}$. Solve for R in terms of L, C, and r.

16   $I = \frac{E}{R}$ and $I_1 = \frac{E}{R + R_1}$. Solve for R in terms of R_1, I, I_1.

17   $Q = It$ coulombs and $I = CE/t$ amp. Solve for Q in terms of C and E.

18   Given $P = EI$ watts, $I = E/R$ Ω, and $H = 0.24I^2Rt$ cal. Solve for H in terms of P and t.

19   Using the relations given in Prob. 18, find the voltage E necessary to produce $H = 720$ cal in a time $t = 10$ sec when the heater resistance $R = 300$ Ω.

20   Given $\alpha R_1 + \beta R_2 = \gamma$ and $\theta R_1 + \phi R_2 = \omega$. Solve for R_1 and R_2.

21   Given $I_a R_a = I_b R_b$ and $I_a R_c = I_b R_x$. Solve for R_x in terms of R_a, R_b, and R_c.

22   Given $I_a R_a = I_b R_b$, $\frac{Q_a}{C_a} = \frac{Q_b}{C_b}$, $I_a = \frac{Q_a}{t}$, and $I_b = \frac{Q_b}{t}$. Show that $\frac{R_a}{R_b} = \frac{C_b}{C_a}$.

23   $I_p = \mu E_g/(R + R_p)$ and $E_p = I_p R$. $\mu = 50$, $E_g = 5$ volts, $R = R_p = 10$ kΩ. Find the value of E_p.

24   Given $E = I_x(R + R_x)$, $E = I_a(R + R_a)$, and $E = IR$.

Show that
$$R_x = R_a \times \frac{\dfrac{I - I_x}{I_x}}{\dfrac{I - I_a}{I_a}}$$

25 Given three star-delta transformation equations:

$$R_a = \frac{R_1 R_3}{R_1 + R_2 + R_3}$$

$$R_b = \frac{R_1 R_2}{R_1 + R_2 + R_3}$$

and
$$R_c = \frac{R_2 R_3}{R_1 + R_2 + R_3}$$

Solve for R_1, R_2, and R_3 in terms of R_a, R_b, and R_c.

CHAPTER 22
GENERATOR, MOTOR, BATTERY
CIRCUITS

In order to avoid confusion in previous discussions of electric circuits, all sources of emf have been considered as sources of constant potential, and nothing has been said regarding their internal resistances. However, electric appliances which produce electric energy, as well as those which consume energy, have a certain amount of internal resistance which materially affects their operation. The application of Ohm's law to a few of the fundamental cases is dealt with in this chapter.

2 – 1   Electromotive force of a generator

A *generator* is a machine that converts mechanical energy into electrical energy. Essentially, it consists of a large number of conductors, which are carried on an armature, rotating in a magnetic field. *The electromotive force of a generator*, which is induced in the rotating conductors, is the total voltage developed by the generator armature. However, this total voltage is not all available for doing useful work in a circuit external to the generator, for some of it is used in overcoming the resistance of the armature. The voltage actually supplied to the external circuit is known as the terminal voltage; that is,

$$\text{Terminal voltage} = \text{emf} - \text{internal voltage drop}$$

22 – 2 Types of generator

Generators are divided into three types: *series, shunt,* and *compound.*

A *series* generator is one in which the armature, field, and load are in series as illustrated in Fig. 22–1. The field consists of a few turns of heavy wire and must be capable of carrying the load current. The voltage of a series generator is usually controlled by a rheostat connected across the field.

A *shunt* generator consists of a field, wound with a large number of turns of small wire, connected in shunt (parallel) with the armature as illustrated in Fig. 22–2. The voltage of a shunt generator is

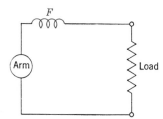

FIG. 22–1 Series generator.

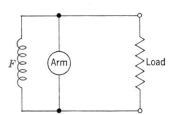

FIG. 22–2 Shunt generator.

usually controlled by a rheostat connected in series with the field.

A *compound* generator has both a series field and a shunt field. Two methods of field connections are used in compound generators. Figure 22–3 represents a *short-shunt* generator, and Fig. 22–4 represents a *long-shunt* generator.

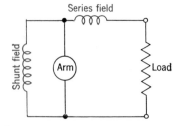

FIG. 22–3 Short-shunt generator.

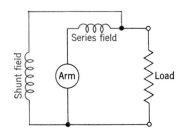

FIG. 22–4 Long-shunt generator.

EXAMPLE 1   A series generator is delivering 85 amp to a load. The armature resistance is 0.06 Ω, and the field resistance is 0.04 Ω. A voltmeter connected across the generator terminals reads 230 volts. (*a*) What is the emf of the generator? (*b*) How much power is expended in the generator?

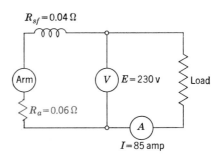

SOLUTION   Figure 22–5 is a diagram of the circuit. The armature resistance is denoted by R_a.

The voltage drop across the series field is

$$E_f = IR_{sf} = 85 \times 0.04 = 3.4 \text{ volts}$$

FIG. 22–5   Circuit of Example 1.

The voltage drop due to the resistance of the armature is

$$E_a = IR_a = 85 \times 0.06 = 5.1 \text{ volts}$$

Since the emf of the generator is the total voltage developed,

$$\text{emf} = 230 + 3.4 + 5.1 = 238.5 \text{ volts}$$

Power expended in series field $= I^2R_{sf} = 85^2 \times 0.04 = 289$ watts
Power expended in armature $\ = I^2R_a \ = 85^2 \times 0.06 = 433.5$ watts
Total power expended in the generator $= 722.5$ watts

EXAMPLE 2   A short-shunt compound generator is delivering 60 amp to a load. The armature resistance is 0.08 Ω, the resistance of the series field is 0.05 Ω, and the resistance of the shunt field is 118 Ω. A voltmeter connected across the generator terminals reads 115 volts. (*a*) What is the shunt-field current? (*b*) What is the emf of the generator? (*c*) How much power is expended in the generator?

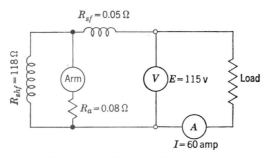

FIG. 22–6   Circuit of Example 2.

SOLUTION   Figure 22–6 is a diagram of the circuit.
The voltage drop across the series field is

$$E_{sf} = IR_{sf} = 60 \times 0.05 = 3.0 \text{ volts}$$

The same voltage exists across the armature and shunt field and is equal to the voltage across the generator terminals plus the voltage drop across the series field, or

$$E_{shf} = E + E_{sf} = 115 + 3 = 118 \text{ volts}$$

Then the current through the shunt field is

$$I_{shf} = \frac{E_{shf}}{R_{shf}} = \frac{118}{118} = 1.0 \text{ amp}$$

Since the armature must supply the current for the shunt field, the armature current is

$$I_a = I + I_{shf} = 60 + 1 = 61 \text{ amp}$$

Then the voltage drop across the armature resistance is

$$E_a = I_a R_a = 61 \times 0.08 = 4.88 \text{ volts}$$

Since the emf is the total voltage developed,

$$\text{emf} = E + E_{sf} + E_a = 115 + 3.0 + 4.88 = 122.88 \text{ volts}$$

Power expended in shunt field $= I_{shf}^2 R_{shf}$ $= 1.0^2 \times 118 = 118$ watts
Power expended in series field $= I^2 R_{sf}$ $\quad= 60^2 \times 0.05 = 180$ watts
Power expended in armature $\quad= I_a^2 R_a$ $\quad\quad= 61^2 \times 0.08 = \underline{298}$ watts
Total power expended in generator $= 596$ watts

EXAMPLE 3   A 50-kw long-shunt compound generator maintains a voltage of 220 volts across its output terminals. The armature resistance is 0.02 Ω, the shunt-field resistance is 200 Ω, and the series-field resistance is 0.04 Ω. At rated output, (a) what is the emf of the generator, (b) how much power is lost in the machine, (c) how much power does the generator develop?
SOLUTION   Figure 22–7 is a diagram of the circuit.

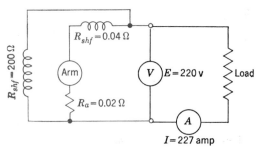

FIG. 22–7 Circuit of Example 3.

Load current,
$$I = \frac{P}{E} = \frac{50,000}{220} = 227 \text{ amp}$$

Shunt-field current,
$$I_{shf} = \frac{E}{R_{shf}} = \frac{220}{200} = 1.1 \text{ amp}$$

Armature current,
$$I_a = I + I_{shf} = 227 + 1.1 = 228.1 \text{ amp}$$

Drop across series field,
$$E_{sf} = I_a R_{sf} = 228.1 \times 0.04 = 9.124 \text{ volts}$$

Drop across armature resistance,
$$E_a = I_a R_a = 228.1 \times 0.02 = 4.562 \text{ volts}$$

Generator emf,
$$\begin{aligned} \text{emf} &= E + E_{sf} + E_a \\ &= 220 + 9.124 + 4.562 = 233.7 \text{ volts} \end{aligned}$$

Power lost in shunt field,
$$P_{shf} = I_{shf}^2 R_{shf} = 1.1^2 \times 200 = 242 \text{ watts}$$

Power lost in series field,
$$P_{sf} = I_a^2 R_{sf} = 228^2 \times 0.04 = 2,080 \text{ watts}$$

Power lost in armature,
$$P_a = I_a^2 R_a = 228^2 \times 0.02 = 1,040 \text{ watts}$$

Total power lost in generator,
$$P_G = 242 + 2,080 + 1,040 = 3,362 \text{ watts}$$

Total power developed,
$$P_t = 50,000 + 3,362 = 53,362 \text{ watts}$$

As a check, the total power can be found by multiplying the electromotive force by the armature current.

In the foregoing examples, some of the significant figures have been carried beyond the customary three for the purposes of illustration.

22–3 Voltage regulation

From the preceding examples, it is apparent that the amount of current drawn by the load will affect the generator terminal voltage. Whether the terminal voltage is increased or decreased by an increase in load current depends upon the type of generator and the method employed for voltage control. The *voltage regulation* of a generator is often used as a figure of merit of the machine; that is, if a generator is able to maintain a nearly constant terminal voltage within its capacity, it is said to have good regulation. Expressed as an equation,

Percentage of regulation

$$= \frac{\text{no-load voltage} - \text{rated-load voltage}}{\text{rated-load voltage}} \times 100$$

EXAMPLE 4   A generator, while delivering full load, has a terminal voltage of 230 volts and a no-load terminal voltage of 240 volts. What is the percentage of regulation?

SOLUTION $\text{Regulation} = \dfrac{240 - 230}{230} = 4.35 \text{ per cent}$

PROBLEMS 22 – 1

1   A series generator has a field resistance of 0.024 Ω and an armature resistance of 0.036 Ω. The load current is 125 amp, and a voltmeter connected across the generator terminals reads 230 volts. (*a*) What is the emf of the generator? (*b*) How much power is lost in the armature?

2   A series generator with an armature resistance of 0.032 Ω and a field resistance of 0.018 Ω is delivering 23 amp to a load resistance of 10 Ω. If the total resistance of the feeders is 0.4 Ω, find (*a*) the emf of the generator, (*b*) total power developed by the generator, (*c*) voltage across generator terminals.

3   A shunt generator with an armature resistance of 0.025 Ω and a field resistance of 80 Ω is delivering 150 amp to a load at a brush potential (terminal voltage) of 230 volts. (*a*) What is the emf of the generator? (*b*) What is the total power developed by the generator?

4   A shunt generator with an armature resistance of 0.04 Ω and a field resistance of 100 Ω is delivering 50 amp to a load resistance of 4.3 Ω. Each feeder is 500 ft long and consists of No. 0 wire. (*a*) What is the emf of the generator? (*b*) What is the generator terminal voltage? (*c*) What is the total power developed by the generator?

5   A compound long-shunt generator delivers 276 kw at a terminal voltage of 230 volts. The shunt field resistance is 115 Ω, the series field resistance is 0.02 Ω, and the armature resistance is 0.025 Ω. What is the emf of the generator?

6   A compound short-shunt generator delivers 125 amp to its load. A voltmeter connected across the generator terminals reads 120 volts. The series field resistance is 0.015 Ω, the shunt field resistance is 125 Ω, and the armature resistance is 0.02 Ω. What is the emf of this generator?

7   At full load the terminal voltage of a generator is 117 volts. When the load is disconnected, the terminal voltage is 121 volts. What is the percentage regulation?

8 The no-load terminal voltage of a generator is 240 volts. When the generator is delivering full load, the terminal voltage is 234 volts. What is the percentage regulation?

22 – 4 Motors

A *motor* is a machine that converts electric energy into mechanical energy. Direct-current motors, like generators, are classified with respect to their field and armature connections and are divided into the same three types, series, shunt, and compound. When connected to a suitable source of voltage, d-c generators will run as motors; when driven by mechanical means, d-c motors will function as generators.

Since the armature resistance of most motors is a small fraction of an ohm, it is evident that something other than the ohmic resistance of the armature limits the current when the motor is in operation. The conductors of a rotating motor armature cut the lines of force of the field in the same manner as the armature of a generator. This results in an emf being induced in the motor armature that is of opposite polarity to the voltage applied to the motor. Hence, the motor emf known is the counter emf of the motor. Then the net voltage acting on the armature of a shunt motor is equal to the difference between the applied voltage and the counter emf. The counter emf of a motor can be found by running it as a generator at rated speed and measuring the emf developed with a voltmeter.

EXAMPLE 5   The armature resistance of a shunt motor is 0.05 Ω, the armature current is 25 amp, and the voltage is 230 volts. Find the counter emf of the motor.

SOLUTION   The voltage drop across the armature resistance is

$$E_a = I_a R_a = 25 \times 0.05 = 1.25 \text{ volts}$$

Since counter emf = line voltage − drop across armature resistance,

$$\text{Counter emf} = 230 - 1.25 = 228.75 \text{ volts}$$

EXAMPLE 6   If full line voltage was applied to the motor of Example 5 at standstill, how much current would flow through the armature?

SOLUTION $$I_a = \frac{E}{R_a} = \frac{230}{0.05} = 4{,}600 \text{ amp}$$

This illustrates the necessity of starting resistances.

EXAMPLE 7   A shunt motor is taking a total of 21.4 kw from a 230-volt line.   454 watts is lost in the armature.   If the resistance of the field is 100 Ω, find (a) line current, (b) field current, (c) armature resistance, (d) counter emf of motor.

SOLUTION   (a) Since $P = EI$

the line current is $I_L = \dfrac{P_t}{E_L} = \dfrac{21,400}{230} = 93.0$ amp

(b) The field current is $I_f = \dfrac{E_L}{R_f} = \dfrac{230}{100} = 2.3$ amp

(c) The armature current is

$$I_a = I_L - I_f = 93.0 - 2.30 = 90.7 \text{ amp}$$

Since $P = I^2R$

the armature resistance is $R_a = \dfrac{P_a}{I_a^2} = \dfrac{454}{90.7^2} = 0.0552$ Ω

(d)   Counter emf $= E_L - I_aR_a$
$$= 230 - (90.7 \times 0.0552) = 225 \text{ volts}$$

PROBLEMS 22 – 2

1   A shunt motor with an armature resistance of 0.075 Ω is running across a 117-volt line.   If the armature current is 40 amp, find the emf of the motor.

2   How much current would flow through the armature of the motor of Prob. 1 if the motor at standstill were connected directly across the line?

3   How much resistance must be connected in series with the armature of Prob. 1 to limit the armature starting current to 50 amp?

4   A shunt motor is drawing 40 amp from a 220-volt line.   The shunt field resistance is 125 Ω, and the armature resistance is 0.04 Ω.   Find the counter emf of the motor.

5   How much current will flow if the motor of Prob. 4 at standstill is connected directly across the line?

6   How much resistance must be connected in series with the armature of Prob. 4 to limit the armature starting current to 75 amp?

7   A shunt motor has a counter emf of 215 volts.   Two amp flows through the shunt field, which has a resistance of 110 Ω.   The armature resistance is 0.05 Ω.   (a) What is the line voltage?   (b) What is the total current drawn by the motor?   (c) How much resistance must be connected in series with the armature to limit the starting current to 150 amp?

8   A shunt motor is drawing 15 kw from the line, and 242 watts is lost in the shunt field, which has a resistance of 80 Ω.   The armature loss is 490 watts.   Find (a) the field current, (b) counter emf of the motor, (c) armature resistance, (d) line voltage.

9   The motor of Prob. 8 is developing 17 hp.   What is its efficiency?

10 A 6-hp shunt motor is taking 5.25 kw from the line.   Two hundred and ninety-four watts is lost in the shunt field, which has a resistance of 180 Ω.   The armature loss is 93 watts.   Find (*a*) the field current, (*b*) armature resistance, (*c*) counter emf of motor, (*d*) line voltage, (*e*) efficiency of motor, (*f*) resistance in series with armature needed to limit armature starting current to 1.5 times its running current.

− 5   Batteries

A *battery* is a device for converting chemical energy into electric energy.   The word "battery" is taken to mean two or more *cells* connected to each other, although a single cell is often referred to as a battery.

Figure 22–8 represents a circuit by which the voltage existing across the cell can be read with the resistance connected across the battery or with the resistance disconnected from the circuit.

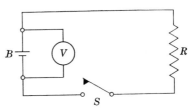

The emf of a cell is the total amount of voltage developed by the cell.   For all practical purposes the emf of a cell can be read with a high-resistance voltmeter con-

FIG. 22–8   High-resistance voltmeter used for measuring electromotive force of cell.

nected across the cell when it is not supplying current to any other circuit, as is the case with the switch S open, in Fig. 22–8.

When a cell supplies current to an external circuit, as with the switch closed, in Fig. 22–8, it will be found that the voltmeter no longer reads the open-circuit voltage (emf) of the cell.   The reason for this is that part of the emf is used in forcing current through the resistance of the cell and the remainder is used in forcing current through the external circuit.   Expressed as an equation,

$$E = E_t + Ir \qquad [1]$$

where E is the emf of the cell or group of cells and E_t is the voltage measured across the terminals while forcing a current I through the internal resistance r.   Since I also flows through the external circuit of resistance R, Eq. [1] can be written

$$E = IR + Ir$$

or $\qquad\qquad E = I(R + r) \qquad [2]$

EXAMPLE 8   A cell whose internal resistance is 0.15 Ω delivers 0.50 amp to a resistance of 2.85 Ω. What is the emf of the cell?

SOLUTION   Given $r = 0.15$ Ω, $R = 2.85$ Ω, and $I = 0.50$ amp.

From Eq. [2], $E = 0.50(2.85 + 0.15) = 1.5$ volts

EXAMPLE 9   Figure 22–9 represents a cell with an emf of 1.2 volts and an internal resistance r of 0.2 Ω connected to a resistance R of 5.8 Ω. How much current flows in the circuit?

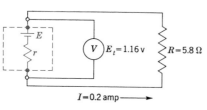

FIG. 22–9 Circuit of Example 9.

SOLUTION   Solving Eq. [2] for the current,

$$I = \frac{E}{R + r} \qquad [3]$$

$$= \frac{1.2}{5.8 + 0.2} = 0.2 \text{ amp}$$

Note the significance of Eq. [3]. It says that the current which flows in a circuit is proportional to the emf of the circuit and inversely proportional to the *total* resistance of the circuit. This is Ohm's law for the *complete circuit*.

EXAMPLE 10   A cell with an emf of 1.6 volts delivers a current of 2 amp to a circuit of 0.62 Ω. What is the internal resistance of the cell?

SOLUTION   Solving Eq. [2] for the internal resistance,

$$r = \frac{E - IR}{I} \qquad [4]$$

$$= \frac{1.6 - 2 \times 0.62}{2} = 0.18 \text{ Ω}$$

Note the significance of Eq. [4]. It says that a voltage equal to $E - IR$ is sending the current *I* through the internal resistance *r*.

Since Eq. [4] can be rearranged to

$$r = \frac{E}{I} - R$$

and $$\frac{E}{I} = R_t$$

Eq. [4] can be written $r = R_t - R$

or $$R_t = R + r \qquad [5]$$

Equation [5] states simply that the resistance of the entire circuit is equal to the resistance of the external circuit plus the internal resistance of the source of the emf.

22 – 6   Cells in series

If n identical cells are connected in series, the emf of the combination will be n times the emf of each cell. Similarly, the total internal resistance of the circuit will be n times the internal resistance of each cell. By modifying Eq. [2], the expression for the current through an external resistance of R Ω is

$$I = \frac{nE}{R + nr} \qquad [6]$$

EXAMPLE 11   Six cells, each with an emf of 2.1 volts and an internal resistance of 0.1 Ω, are connected in series, and a resistance of 3.6 Ω is connected across the combination. (a) How much current flows in the circuit? (b) What is the terminal voltage of the group?

SOLUTION   Figure 22–10 is a diagram of the circuit. The resistance nr represents the total internal resistance of all cells in series.

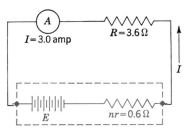

FIG.   22–10   Circuit of Example 11.

(a) $I = \dfrac{nE}{R + nr} = \dfrac{6 \times 2.1}{3.6 + 6 \times 0.1} = 3.0$ amp

(b) The terminal voltage of the group is equal to the total emf minus the voltage drop across the internal resistance. From Eq. [1],

$$E_t = nE - Inr = 6 \times 2.1 - 3 \times 6 \times 0.1 = 10.8 \text{ volts}$$

Since the terminal voltage exists across the external circuit, a more simple relation is

$$E_t = IR = 3 \times 3.6 = 10.8 \text{ volts}$$

22 – 7   Cells in parallel

If n identical cells are connected in parallel, the emf of the group will be the same as the emf of one cell and the internal resistance of the group will be equal to the internal resistance of one cell divided by the number of cells in parallel, that is, to r/n. By modifying

Eq. [2], the expression for the current through an external resistance of R ohms is

$$I = \frac{E}{R + \dfrac{r}{n}}$$ [7]

EXAMPLE 12   Three cells, each with an emf of 1.4 volts and an internal resistance of 0.15 Ω, are connected in parallel, and a resistance of 1.35 Ω is connected across the group.   (a) How much current flows in the circuit? (b) What is the terminal voltage of the group?

SOLUTION   Figure 22–11 is a diagram of the circuit.   The resistance r/n represents the internal resistance of the group.

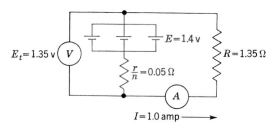

FIG. 22–11   Circuit of Example 12.

(a) $I = \dfrac{E}{R + \dfrac{r}{n}} = \dfrac{1.4}{1.35 + \dfrac{0.15}{3}} = 1.0 \text{ amp}$

(b) $E_t = IR = 1.0 \times 1.35 = 1.35 \text{ volts}$

PROBLEMS 22 – 3

1   The emf of a cell is 1.5 volts, and its internal resistance is 0.2 Ω.   When current is supplied to a circuit, the voltage drop across the internal resistance of the cell is 0.3 volt.   (a) What is the terminal voltage? (b) How much current flows in the circuit?

2   A cell whose emf is 1.4 volts and internal resistance is 0.2 Ω is supplying 1.5 amp to a circuit.   (a) What is the resistance of the external circuit? (b) How much power is lost in the cell?

3   A cell that is delivering 0.25 amp has an internal resistance of 0.5 Ω. If the emf of the cell is 1.6 volts, (a) what is the terminal voltage, (b) what is the resistance of the external circuit, (c) how much power is expended in the cell, (d) how much power is the cell delivering to the external circuit?

4   A high-resistance voltmeter reads 2.0 volts when placed across a cell that is connected to no other circuit.   When the cell is delivering 5 amp to a

circuit, the voltmeter indicates a terminal voltage of 1.1 volts. (*a*) What is the internal resistance of the cell? (*b*) What is the resistance of the external circuit? (*c*) What is the total power developed? (*d*) How much current would flow if the cell were short-circuited?

5 A cell with an emf of 2.0 volts and an internal resistance of 0.1 Ω is connected to a load consisting of a variable resistance. Plot the power delivered to the load as the load resistance is varied in 0.01-Ω steps from 0.05 to 0.15 Ω. What conclusion do you draw from this graph?

6 Six cells are connected in series to a load of 8.4 Ω. Each cell has an emf of 1.5 volts, and the internal resistance of each cell is 0.1 Ω. (*a*) What is the circuit current? (*b*) How much power is expended in the battery? (*c*) What current would flow if the cells were short-circuited?

7 If the cells of Prob. 6 are connected in parallel, how much power will be dissipated in the load resistor?

8 Twelve cells are connected in series. The emf of each cell is 1.4 volts, and the internal resistance per cell is 0.75 Ω. How much power will be expended in a resistance of 1.5 Ω connected across the group of cells?

9 If the cells of Prob. 8 are connected in parallel, how much current will flow through the load resistance?

10 Twelve identical cells are connected so that there are four series groups, each with three cells, connected in parallel as shown in Fig. 22–12. The emf of each cell is 1.6 volts, with an internal resistance of 0.2 Ω. If $R = 0.85 \Omega$, (*a*) how much current will flow through R, (*b*) how much power is dissipated in each cell?

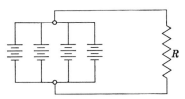

FIG. 22–12   Circuit of Prob. 10.

11 The cells of Prob. 10 are arranged so that there are two cells per series groups (six groups in parallel). (*a*) How much power is dissipated in R? (*b*) How much current flows through each cell?

12 Each cell of a six-cell storage battery has an emf of 2.0 volts and an internal resistance of 0.01 Ω. The battery is to be charged from a 14-volt line. (*a*) How much resistance must be connected in series with the battery to limit the charging current to 15 amp? (*b*) What current would flow if the battery were disconnected from the charging circuit and short-circuited?

13 Sixteen storage batteries of three cells each are to be charged in series from a 115-volt line. Each cell has an emf of 2.1 volts and an internal resistance of 0.02 Ω. (*a*) How much resistance must be connected in series with the battery to limit the charging current to 10 amp? (*b*) How

much power is required for the entire circuit?   (*c*) How much power is dissipated in the series charging resistance?   (*d*) What current would flow if the batteries were disconnected from the charging circuit and short-circuited?

EXAMPLE 13   Six identical cells connected in series deliver 4 amp to a circuit of 2.7 Ω.   When two of the same cells are connected in parallel, they deliver 5 amp to an external resistance of 0.375 Ω.   What are the emf and internal resistance of each cell?

SOLUTION   Let

$$E = \text{emf of each cell}$$
$$r = \text{internal resistance of each cell}$$
$$I = \text{current in external circuit}$$
$$R = \text{resistance of external circuit}$$

For the series connection, $6E = $ emf of six cells in series

and $6r = $ internal resistance of six cells in series

Substituting in Eq. [2], $6E = 4(2.7 + 6r) = 10.8 + 24r$ (*a*)

For the parallel connection, $E = $ emf of cells in parallel

and $\dfrac{r}{2} = $ internal resistance of two cells in parallel

Substituting in Eq. [2], $E = 5\left(0.375 + \dfrac{r}{2}\right)$

or $2E = 3.75 + 5r$ (*b*)

Solve Eqs. (*a*) and (*b*) simultaneously to obtain

$$E = 2.0 \text{ volts}$$

and $r = 0.05 \ \Omega$

14   Ten identical cells connected in series send a current of 3 amp through a 1-Ω circuit.   When three of these cells are connected in parallel, they send a current of 6 amp through an external resistance of 0.1 Ω.   What are the emf and internal resistance of each cell?

15   Five cells connected in series send a current of 5 amp through a resistance of 0.4 Ω.   When four of these cells are connected in parallel, they send 1 amp through 1.35 Ω.   What are the emf and internal resistance of each cell?

16   Twelve cells in series, each with an emf of 2.0 volts, send a certain current through a 2.4-Ω circuit.   The same current flows through a 0.24-Ω circuit when five of these cells are connected in parallel.   What are the values of the current and the internal resistance of each cell?

17   A cell with an internal resistance of 0.035 Ω sends a current of 3 amp through an external circuit.   Another cell, with the same emf but with an internal resistance of 0.385 Ω, sends a current of 2 amp through the

external circuit when substituted for the first cell. What are the emf
of the cells and the resistance of the external circuit?

18   A cell sends a current of 20 amp through an external circuit of 0.04 Ω.
When the resistance of the external circuit is increased to 3.96 Ω, the
current is 0.4 amp. What are the emf and internal resistance of the
cell?

CHAPTER 23
EXPONENTS AND RADICALS

In earlier chapters, examples and problems have been limited to those containing exponents and roots that consisted of integers. In this chapter the study of exponents and radicals is extended to include new operations that will enable you to solve electrical formulas and equations of a type hitherto omitted. In addition, new ideas are introduced that will be of fundamental importance in the study of alternating currents.

23 – 1   Fundamental laws of exponents

As previously explained, if n is a positive integer, a^n means that a is to be taken as a factor n times. Thus, a^4 is defined as being a shortened form of notation for the product $a \cdot a \cdot a \cdot a$. The number a is called the *base*, and the number n is called the *exponent*.

For the purpose of review, the fundamental laws for the use of *positive-integer exponents* are listed below:

$$a^m \cdot a^n = a^{m+n} \qquad\qquad \text{(Sec. 9–3)} \quad [\,1\,]$$
$$a^m \div a^n = a^{m-n} \quad \text{(when } n < m) \qquad \text{(Sec. 9–9)} \quad [\,2\,]$$
$$= \frac{1}{a^{n-m}} \quad \text{(when } n > m)$$
$$(a^m)^n = a^{mn} \qquad\qquad \text{(Sec. 10–11)} \quad [\,3\,]$$

$$(ab)^m = a^m b^m \qquad \text{(Sec. 10-12)} \quad [4]$$

$$\left(\frac{a}{b}\right)^m = \frac{a^m}{b^m} \qquad (b \neq 0) \qquad\qquad\qquad [5]$$

23-2 Zero exponent

If a^0 is to obey the law of exponents for multiplication as stated under [1] of the preceding article, then

$$a^m \cdot a^0 = a^{m+0} = a^m$$

Also, if a^0 is to obey the law of exponents for division, then

$$\frac{a^m}{a^0} = a^{m-0} = a^m$$

Therefore, the zero power of any number, except zero, is defined as being equal to 1, for 1 is the only number that, when used to multiply another number, does not change the value of the multiplicand.

23-3 Negative exponents

If a^{-n} is to obey the multiplication law, then

$$\frac{a^n}{a^n} = a^{n-n} = a^0 = 1$$

In Sec. 9-11, it was shown that a *factor* can be transferred from one term of a fraction to the other if the sign of its exponent is changed.

PROBLEMS 23-1

Making use of the five fundamental laws of exponents, write the results of the indicated operations:

1 $x^5 \cdot x^3$	2 $e^2 \cdot e^4$
3 $y^3 \cdot y^5$	4 $a^2 \cdot a^7$
5 $\alpha^x \cdot \alpha^y$	6 $\beta^{3e} \cdot \beta^{2e}$
7 $e^\alpha \cdot e^\beta$	8 $\theta^{r+s} \cdot \theta^{r-s}$
9 $a^8 \div a^3$	10 $b^{10} \div b^3$
11 $\phi^{2n} \div \phi^n$	12 $\pi^{x+3} \div \pi^2$
13 $\gamma^{x+y} \div \gamma^{x-y}$	14 $(E^2)^4$
15 $(r^3)^5$	16 $(z^2 Z^3)^2$
17 $(i^3 I^4 R)^3$	18 $(f\alpha)^2$
19 $(f^2)^\alpha$	20 $(\omega^2 f^2 F^{2\theta})^2$
21 $(-\alpha^n \beta^x \pi^y)^3$	22 $(-e^3 I^2 Z^2)^4$
23 $\left(\dfrac{E^2}{R}\right)^3$	24 $\left(\dfrac{L^2}{C}\right)^{2\alpha}$

25 $\left(\dfrac{f^2}{\omega F}\right)^{3\theta}$ 26 $\left(\dfrac{\theta^{2e}}{\phi^{2\pi}}\right)^{n}$

27 $\left(\dfrac{-r^3}{r_a}\right)^{3}$ 28 $\left(\dfrac{I^2}{-i^4}\right)^{3}$

29 $\left(\dfrac{\gamma^{2m}}{\gamma^{2m}}\right)^{4}$ 30 $\left(\dfrac{x^{2r}}{y^{2s}}\right)^{3t}$

Express with positive exponents:

31 $L^{-4} \cdot C^{-3}$ 32 $z^{-1}Z^{-2}$

33 $x^{-a}y^{-2}$ 34 $6b^{-3}$

35 $3^{-2}\theta^2\phi^{-3}$ 36 $(4\omega F)^{-2e}$

37 $\dfrac{\pi^{-2}\beta}{e^3}$ 38 $\dfrac{r^2R^2}{3Z^{-2}}$

39 $\dfrac{4i^{-2}I^{-1}}{6e^{-1}}$ 40 $\dfrac{\gamma^2}{3(2z)^{-3}}$

23 – 4 Fractional exponents

The meaning of a base affected by a fractional exponent is established by methods similar to those employed in determining meanings for zero or negative exponents. If we assume that Eq. [1] of Sec. 23–1 holds for fractional exponents, we should obtain, for example,

$$a^{\frac{1}{2}} \cdot a^{\frac{1}{2}} = a^{\frac{1}{2}+\frac{1}{2}} = a^1 = a$$

Also, $$a^{\frac{1}{3}} \cdot a^{\frac{1}{3}} \cdot a^{\frac{1}{3}} = a^{\frac{1}{3}+\frac{1}{3}+\frac{1}{3}} = a^1 = a$$

That is, $a^{1/2}$ is one of two equal factors of a, and $a^{1/3}$ is one of three equal factors of a. Therefore, $a^{1/2}$ is the square root of a, and $a^{1/3}$ is the cube root of a. Hence,

$$a^{\frac{1}{2}} = \sqrt{a}$$

and $$a^{\frac{1}{3}} = \sqrt[3]{a}$$

Likewise, $$a^{\frac{2}{3}} \cdot a^{\frac{2}{3}} \cdot a^{\frac{2}{3}} = a^{\frac{2}{3}+\frac{2}{3}+\frac{2}{3}} = a^{\frac{6}{3}} = a^2$$

Hence, $$(a^{\frac{2}{3}})^3 = a^2$$

or $$a^{\frac{2}{3}} = \sqrt[3]{a^2}$$

In a fractional exponent, the denominator denotes the root and the numerator denotes the power of the base.

In general, $$a^{\frac{m}{n}} = \sqrt[n]{a^m}$$

EXAMPLE 1 $a^{\frac{3}{5}} = \sqrt[5]{a^3}$

EXAMPLE 2 $-8^{\frac{1}{3}} = \sqrt[3]{-8} = -2$

PROBLEMS 23 – 2

Find the values of:

1   $9^{\frac{1}{2}}$ 2 $(-8)^{\frac{1}{3}}$

3   $-(-64)^{\frac{1}{3}}$ 4 $16^{\frac{1}{2}}$

5   $(-125a^3b^6)^{\frac{1}{3}}$ 6 $(f^5F^{10})^{\frac{1}{5}}$

7   $(L^4C^6)^{\frac{5}{4}}$ 8 $\left(\dfrac{64\alpha^6}{\beta^3}\right)^{\frac{1}{3}}$

9   $(i^3z^9)^{\frac{2}{6}}$ 10 $(a^3x^9y^6)^{\frac{2}{3}}$

Express with radical signs:

11   $3^{\frac{1}{3}}$ 12 $2^{\frac{2}{3}}$

13   $5\gamma^{\frac{1}{2}}$ 14 $(9\phi)^{\frac{1}{2}}$

15   $\alpha^{\frac{3}{2}}\beta^{\frac{2}{3}}$ 16 $\omega^{\frac{3}{4}}F^{1.5}$

Express with fractional exponents:

17   $\sqrt[3]{r^4}$ 18 $\sqrt{R^5}$

19   $4\sqrt[3]{8I}$ 20 $\sqrt[4]{16L^3C^4}$

21   $6\theta\sqrt[3]{\pi^2}$ 22 $9\sqrt[4]{\gamma^5}$

23   $b^2\sqrt[3]{f^4}$ 24 $3s\sqrt[3]{v^2l^2}$

25   $\sqrt[4]{a^3b^5}$

23 – 5   Radicand

The meaning of the radical sign was explained in Sec. 7–11. The number under the radical sign is called the *radicand*.

23 – 6   Simplification of radicals

The form in which a radical expression is written can be changed without altering its numerical value. Such changes are desirable for many reasons. For example, addition of several fractions containing different radicals in the denominators would be more difficult than addition with the radicals removed from the denominators. Similarly, it will be shown later that

$$\frac{1}{\sqrt{3}} = \frac{\sqrt{3}}{3}$$

It is apparent that the value to several decimal places could be computed more easily from the second fraction than from the first.

Because we are chiefly concerned with radicals involving a square root, only this type will be considered.

23 – 7   Removing a factor from the radical

Since, in general, $\sqrt{ab} = \sqrt{a} \cdot \sqrt{b}$, the following is evident:

RULE   A radicand can be separated into two factors, one of which is the greatest perfect square it contains.   The square root of this factor can then be written as the coefficient of a radical of which the other factor is the radicand.

EXAMPLE 3 $\sqrt{27} = \sqrt{9 \cdot 3} = \sqrt{9} \cdot \sqrt{3} = 3\sqrt{3}$

EXAMPLE 4 $\sqrt{8} = \sqrt{4 \cdot 2} = \sqrt{4} \cdot \sqrt{2} = 2\sqrt{2}$

EXAMPLE 5 $\sqrt{75} = \sqrt{25 \cdot 3} = \sqrt{25} \cdot \sqrt{3} = 5\sqrt{3}$

EXAMPLE 6 $\sqrt{200a^5b^3c^2d} = \sqrt{100a^4b^2c^2} \cdot \sqrt{2abd} = 10a^2bc\sqrt{2abd}$

PROBLEMS 23 – 3

Simplify by removing factors from the radicand:

1	$\sqrt{24}$	2	$\sqrt{27}$	3	$\sqrt{12}$
4	$\sqrt{99}$	5	$\sqrt{48}$	6	$\sqrt{50}$
7	$\sqrt{72}$	8	$\sqrt{98}$	9	$\sqrt{63}$
10	$\sqrt{20x^2}$	11	$\sqrt{54s^2t^2}$	12	$\sqrt{32I^2R}$
13	$4\sqrt{40i^2Z^3}$	14	$3\theta\sqrt{81\theta^2\phi}$	15	$2\sqrt{72\pi^3F^2}$
16	$3\sqrt{63r^3z^2}$	17	$8e^2\sqrt{96e^3E^2L}$	18	$3\sqrt{108\alpha^2\beta^4}$
19	$3\sqrt{128\omega^2f^3c^4}$	20	$2\gamma^2\sqrt{18s^3v^2t^2}$		

23 – 8   **Simplifying radicals containing fractions**

Since

$$\sqrt{\frac{4}{9}} = \frac{2}{3} \quad \text{and} \quad \frac{\sqrt{4}}{\sqrt{9}} = \frac{2}{3}$$

then

$$\sqrt{\frac{4}{9}} = \frac{\sqrt{4}}{\sqrt{9}}$$

Also,

$$\sqrt{\frac{16}{25}} = \frac{4}{5} \quad \text{and} \quad \frac{\sqrt{16}}{\sqrt{25}} = \frac{4}{5}$$

then

$$\sqrt{\frac{16}{25}} = \frac{\sqrt{16}}{\sqrt{25}}$$

Or, in general terms,

$$\sqrt{\frac{a}{b}} = \frac{\sqrt{a}}{\sqrt{b}}$$

The above relation permits simplification of radicals containing fractions by removing the radical from the denominator.   This process, by which the denominator is made a rational number, is called *rationalizing the denominator*.

RULE   To rationalize the denominator,

1   Multiply both numerator and denominator by a number that will make the resulting denominator a perfect square.

2 Simplify the resulting radical by removing factors from the radicands.

EXAMPLE 7 $\qquad \sqrt{\dfrac{2}{5}} = \sqrt{\dfrac{2}{5} \cdot \dfrac{5}{5}} = \sqrt{\dfrac{10}{25}} = \dfrac{\sqrt{10}}{\sqrt{25}} = \dfrac{\sqrt{10}}{5}$

EXAMPLE 8 $\qquad \sqrt{\dfrac{1}{2}} = \sqrt{\dfrac{1}{2} \cdot \dfrac{2}{2}} = \sqrt{\dfrac{2}{4}} = \dfrac{\sqrt{2}}{\sqrt{4}} = \dfrac{\sqrt{2}}{2}$

EXAMPLE 9 $\qquad \dfrac{3}{\sqrt{6}} = \dfrac{3}{\sqrt{6}} \cdot \dfrac{\sqrt{6}}{\sqrt{6}} = \dfrac{3\sqrt{6}}{6} = \dfrac{1}{2}\sqrt{6}$

EXAMPLE 10 $\qquad \sqrt{\dfrac{3a}{5x}} = \sqrt{\dfrac{3a}{5x} \cdot \dfrac{5x}{5x}} = \sqrt{\dfrac{15ax}{25x^2}} = \dfrac{\sqrt{15ax}}{\sqrt{25x^2}} = \dfrac{1}{5x}\sqrt{15ax}$

PROBLEMS 23-4

Simplify the following:

1 $\sqrt{\dfrac{1}{5}}$
2 $\sqrt{\dfrac{1}{3}}$
3 $\sqrt{\dfrac{3}{5}}$

4 $\sqrt{\dfrac{5}{6}}$
5 $\sqrt{\dfrac{2}{3}}$
6 $\sqrt{\dfrac{5}{8}}$

7 $\dfrac{20}{\sqrt{5}}$
8 $\dfrac{14}{\sqrt{7}}$
9 $\dfrac{9\sqrt{6}}{\sqrt{3}}$

10 $\sqrt{\dfrac{4}{9\alpha}}$
11 $\dfrac{1}{\sqrt{\beta}}$
12 $\sqrt{\dfrac{\theta}{\phi}}$

13 $\omega\sqrt{\dfrac{f}{\omega}}$
14 $E\sqrt{\dfrac{1}{E}}$
15 $\dfrac{Z}{e}\sqrt{\dfrac{e}{Z}}$

16 $\sqrt{\dfrac{\mu^2}{3}}$
17 $\dfrac{s}{t}\sqrt{\dfrac{4t}{5s}}$
18 $\sqrt{\dfrac{r+R}{r-R}}$

19 $\sqrt{F^2 - \left(\dfrac{F}{5}\right)^2}$
20 $\sqrt{C^2 + \left(\dfrac{C}{7}\right)^2}$

23-9 Addition and subtraction of radicals

Terms that are the same except in respect to their coefficients are called *similar terms*. Likewise, *similar radicals* are defined as those having the same index and the same radicand and differing only in their coefficients. For example, $-2\sqrt{5}$, $3\sqrt{5}$, and $\sqrt{5}$ are similar radicals.

Similar radicals can be added or subtracted in the same way that similar terms are added or subtracted.

EXAMPLE 11 $3\sqrt{6} - 4\sqrt{6} - \sqrt{6} + 8\sqrt{6} = 6\sqrt{6}$

EXAMPLE 12 $\sqrt{12} + \sqrt{27} = 2\sqrt{3} + 3\sqrt{3} = 5\sqrt{3}$

EXAMPLE 13

$$\sqrt{48x} + \sqrt{\frac{x}{3}} + \sqrt{3x} = 4\sqrt{3x} + \frac{1}{3}\sqrt{3x} + \sqrt{3x} = \frac{16}{3}\sqrt{3x}$$

If the radicands are not alike and cannot be reduced to a common radicand, then the radicals are dissimilar terms and addition or subtraction can only be indicated. Thus the following statement can be made:

RULE   To add or subtract radicals,

1   Reduce them to their simplest form.

2   Combine similar radicals and indicate the addition or subtraction of those which are dissimilar.

PROBLEMS 23 – 5

Simplify:

1   $\sqrt{2} - 3\sqrt{2}$ 2 $5\sqrt{2} - \sqrt{8}$

3   $4\sqrt{5} - 3\sqrt{20}$ 4 $\sqrt{28} - \sqrt{63}$

5   $I\sqrt{2} - i\sqrt{2} + 3\sqrt{2}$ 6 $\mu\sqrt{\mu} + \sqrt{9\mu} - \sqrt{4\mu^3}$

7   $\sqrt{75} + \sqrt{4/3} - \sqrt{12 \frac{3}{25}}$ 8 $2\sqrt{99} - 5\sqrt{176} + \sqrt{44}$

9   $8\sqrt{2} - 6\sqrt{1/8} + 2\sqrt{1/2}$ 10 $\sqrt{112} - \sqrt{63} + 3\sqrt{1/7}$

11   $3\sqrt{\dfrac{1}{15}} - \sqrt{\dfrac{4}{15}} + 4\sqrt{\dfrac{3}{5}}$ 12 $x - \sqrt{\dfrac{3x^2}{4}}$

13   $4\sqrt[3]{16} - 2\sqrt{8}$ 14 $a\sqrt{abc} + ac\sqrt{\dfrac{b}{ac}}$

15   $\sqrt{\dfrac{\alpha + \beta}{\alpha - \beta}} - \sqrt{\dfrac{\alpha - \beta}{\alpha + \beta}}$

23 – 10   Multiplication of radicals

Obtaining the product of radicals is the inverse of removing a factor, as will be shown in the following examples:

EXAMPLE 14 $3\sqrt{3} \cdot 5\sqrt{4} = 15\sqrt{3 \cdot 4} = 15 \cdot 2\sqrt{3} = 30\sqrt{3}$

EXAMPLE 15

$$4\sqrt{3a} \cdot 2\sqrt{6a} = 8\sqrt{3a \cdot 6a} = 8\sqrt{18a^2} = 8\sqrt{9 \cdot 2a^2} = 24a\sqrt{2}$$

EXAMPLE 16   Multiply $3\sqrt{2} + 2\sqrt{3}$ by $4\sqrt{2} - 3\sqrt{3}$.

SOLUTION

$$3\sqrt{2} + 2\sqrt{3}$$
$$4\sqrt{2} - 3\sqrt{3}$$
$$\overline{24 \quad + 8\sqrt{6}}$$
$$\quad - 9\sqrt{6} - 18$$
$$\overline{24 \quad - \sqrt{6} - 18 = 6 - \sqrt{6}}$$

PROBLEMS 23-6

Find the indicated products:

1 $\sqrt{8} \cdot \sqrt{5}$

2 $\sqrt{2} \cdot 3\sqrt{8}$

3 $2\sqrt{5} \cdot \sqrt{15}$

4 $\sqrt{21} \cdot 4\sqrt{14}$

5 $3\sqrt{12} \cdot 8\sqrt{24}$

6 $5\sqrt{32} \cdot 2\sqrt{54}$

7 $\sqrt{2\frac{2}{3}} \cdot \sqrt{2\frac{7}{8}}$

8 $\omega\sqrt{\pi^3} \cdot \pi^2\sqrt{\omega}$

9 $\sqrt{4s^3} \cdot 3\sqrt{s}$

10 $(6 + \sqrt{3})(6 - \sqrt{3})$

11 $(7 + \sqrt{2})^2$

12 $\sqrt{(e - ir)^2}$

13 $(3\sqrt{2} + 5\sqrt{3})(\sqrt{2} + 3\sqrt{3})$

14 $(\sqrt{L} - \sqrt{L - 3})^2$

15 $\dfrac{4}{3}\sqrt{\dfrac{t^3}{2v^4}} \cdot \dfrac{3}{t}\sqrt{\dfrac{v^2}{t}}$

16 $(\sqrt{\lambda + 1} - \sqrt{\lambda - 1})^2$

17 $\dfrac{\gamma}{2}(\sqrt{2} - 1)^2$

18 $\sqrt{\theta^2 - \left(\dfrac{\theta\sqrt{3} - 2\theta}{3}\right)^2}$

19 $\left(\dfrac{\pi}{3} - \dfrac{\pi\sqrt{3}}{6}\right)^2$

20 $\dfrac{1}{3}\sqrt[5]{\dfrac{z^2}{i^2}} \cdot \dfrac{1}{2}\sqrt{\dfrac{i}{z}}$

23-11 Division

An indicated root whose value is irrational but whose radicand is rational is called a *surd*. Thus, $\sqrt[3]{3}$, $\sqrt{2}$, $\sqrt[4]{5}$, $\sqrt{3}$, etc., are surds. If the indicated root is the square root, then the surd is called a *quadratic surd*. For example, $\sqrt{2}$, $\sqrt{5}$, $\sqrt{6}$, $\sqrt{15}$ are quadratic surds. Then, by extending the definition, such expressions as $3 + \sqrt{2}$ and $\sqrt{3} - 6$ are called *binomial quadratic surds*.

It is important that you become proficient in the multiplication and division of binomial quadratic surds. One method of solving a-c circuits, which will be discussed later, makes wide use of these particular operations. Multiplication of such expressions was covered in the preceding section. However, a new method is necessary for division.

Consider the two expressions $a - \sqrt{b}$ and $a + \sqrt{b}$. They differ only in the sign between the terms. These expressions are *conjugates;* that is, $a - \sqrt{b}$ is called the conjugate of $a + \sqrt{b}$, and $a + \sqrt{b}$ is called the conjugate of $a - \sqrt{b}$. Remember this meaning of "conjugate," for it has the same meaning with reference to certain circuit characteristics.

To divide a number by a binomial quadratic surd, rationalize the divisor (denominator) by multiplying both dividend (numerator) and divisor by the conjugate of the divisor.

EXAMPLE 17 $\dfrac{1}{3 + \sqrt{2}} = \dfrac{3 - \sqrt{2}}{(3 + \sqrt{2})(3 - \sqrt{2})} = \dfrac{3 - \sqrt{2}}{7}$

EXAMPLE 18 $\dfrac{1}{3\sqrt{3} - 1} = \dfrac{3\sqrt{3} + 1}{(3\sqrt{3} - 1)(3\sqrt{3} + 1)} = \dfrac{3\sqrt{3} + 1}{26}$

EXAMPLE 19 $\dfrac{3 - \sqrt{2}}{4 + \sqrt{2}} = \dfrac{(3 - \sqrt{2})(4 - \sqrt{2})}{(4 + \sqrt{2})(4 - \sqrt{2})} = \dfrac{14 - 7\sqrt{2}}{14} = \dfrac{2 - \sqrt{2}}{2}$

NOTE   In each of the foregoing examples the resulting denominator is a rational number. In general, the product of two conjugate surd expressions is a rational number. This important fact is widely used in the solution of a-c problems.

PROBLEMS 23 – 7

Perform the indicated divisions:

1 $\dfrac{2}{2 - \sqrt{3}}$ 2 $\dfrac{3}{5 + \sqrt{2}}$ 3 $\dfrac{7}{3 - \sqrt{5}}$

4 $\dfrac{5}{\sqrt{6} + 4}$ 5 $\dfrac{6}{3 - 3\sqrt{3}}$ 6 $\dfrac{9}{2\sqrt{5} + 8}$

7 $\dfrac{\sqrt{2} - 3\sqrt{6}}{\sqrt{2} + 2\sqrt{6}}$ 8 $\dfrac{\sqrt{i} - I}{I + \sqrt{i}}$ 9 $\dfrac{\sqrt{\phi} + \sqrt{\gamma}}{\sqrt{\phi} - \sqrt{\gamma}}$

10 $\dfrac{\sqrt{s} - t + \sqrt{s}}{\sqrt{s} - t - \sqrt{s}}$

23 – 12   Indicated square roots of negative numbers

So far, in the removal of factors from radicands, all the radicands have been positive numbers. Also, we have extracted the square roots of positive numbers only. How shall we proceed to factor negative radicands, and what is the meaning of the square root of a negative number?

According to our laws for multiplication, no number multiplied by itself or raised to any even power will produce a negative result. For example, what does $\sqrt{-25}$ mean when we know of no number that when multiplied by itself will produce -25?

The indicated square root of a negative number is known as an *imaginary number*. It is probable that this name was assigned before mathematicians could visualize such a number and that the word "imaginary" was originally used to distinguish such numbers from the so-called "real numbers" previously studied. In any event, calling such a number imaginary might be considered unfortunate, because in working with circuits such numbers become very real in the physical sense. For example, if you get across a large capacitor that is highly charged, you are likely to be killed by some of these "imaginary" volts. This will be discussed later.

To avoid the difficulty of operations with the indicated square roots of negative numbers, or imaginary numbers, it becomes necessary to introduce a new type of number. That is, we agree that every imaginary number can be expressed as the product of a positive number and $\sqrt{-1}$.

EXAMPLE 20 $\qquad \sqrt{-25} = \sqrt{(-1)25} = \sqrt{-1}\,\sqrt{25} = \sqrt{-1} \cdot 5$

As a convenient form of notation, mathematicians indicate $\sqrt{-1}$ by the letter i. In electrical formulas, however, this letter is used to denote current. Therefore, in order to avoid confusion we indicate $\sqrt{-1}$ by the the letter j, commonly called *the operator j*.

EXAMPLE 21 $\qquad \sqrt{-16} = \sqrt{(-1)16} = \sqrt{-1}\sqrt{16} = \sqrt{-1} \cdot 4 = j4$

EXAMPLE 22 $\qquad \sqrt{-X^2} = \sqrt{(-1)X^2} = \sqrt{-1}\sqrt{X^2} = \sqrt{-1} \cdot X = jX$

EXAMPLE 23 $\qquad -\sqrt{-4X^2} = -\sqrt{(-1)4X^2} = -\sqrt{-1}\sqrt{4X^2}$
$$= -\sqrt{-1} \cdot 2X = -j2X$$

PROBLEMS 23 – 8

Express the following, using the operator j:

1 $\sqrt{-25}$ 2 $\sqrt{-4}$ 3 $\sqrt{-49}$

4 $-\sqrt{-36}$ 5 $-\sqrt{-169\omega^2}$ 6 $-\sqrt{-5}$

7 $\sqrt{-\omega^2 L^2}$ 8 $-\sqrt{-\dfrac{1}{\omega^2 C^2}}$ 9 $-3\sqrt{-27}$

10 $\sqrt{\dfrac{-4}{49}}$ 11 $-\sqrt{\dfrac{-16}{36}}$ 12 $\sqrt{\dfrac{-32}{25}}$

13 $-\sqrt{-45\frac{4}{5}}$ 14 $-\sqrt{-\alpha^2\beta}$ 15 $-\sqrt{-\dfrac{E^2}{R}}$

23 – 13   Representation of numbers affected by *j*

So far in our studies, we have represented numbers graphically whenever possible. This method is an advantageous one, because if we can visualize a diagram or graph every time we come in contact with certain types of numbers and equations, we shall have a better understanding of the manner in which quantities vary. How shall we represent numbers affected by the operator j?

Since, in general, $\sqrt{a}$ is such a number that $\sqrt{a} \cdot \sqrt{a} = a$, it follows that the square root of any number, when multiplied by itself, will result in the given number (radicand). If we are to accept this definition, then $\sqrt{-1}\,\sqrt{-1} = -1$. This result brings us back to familiar ground, for in Fig. 8–3 we established a basis for representing positive and negative numbers. Also, in Sec. 9–2 and in Figs. 9–3 and 9–4, it was pointed out that multiplication or division by -1 caused a directed number to rotate 180°. Then, if we multiply some number by -1 twice, we get full 360° rotation of the number, or back to where it started from. This, of course, is equivalent to multiplying the number by $+1$.

With the above in mind, it is reasonable to assume that multiplying some number by $\sqrt{-1}$, or j, would cause rotation only halfway to 180°, or to 90°, because, if we multiplied by j twice, we should expect to end up 180° from the initial line, for, as previously shown,

$$\sqrt{-1} \cdot \sqrt{-1} = -1$$

That is,
$$j \cdot j = -1$$

or
$$j^2 = -1$$

Therefore, we agree to represent all directed numbers affected by the operator j as lying along a line drawn 90° from the line that

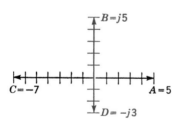

we use to represent positive and negative numbers. This is illustrated in Fig. 23–1.

The horizontal line on which we plot positive and negative numbers is called the axis of *reals*. The vertical line on which we plot numbers having $+j$ or $-j$ as a coefficient is called the axis of *imaginaries*.

Fig. 23–1   Representation of numbers affected by operator j.

It is customary to think of numbers affected by $+j$ as having been rotated in a counterclockwise direction as shown in Fig. 23–2. Also, we think of numbers having $-j$ as a coefficient as having been rotated in a clockwise direction as shown in Fig. 23–3.

Actually, the direction we consider the number to have been rotated in makes no difference, for the final position will be the

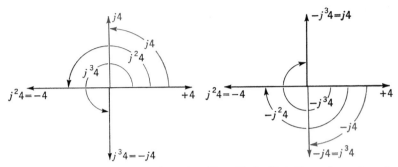

FIG. 23-2 Rotation of numbers in counterclockwise direction.

FIG. 23-3 Rotation of numbers in clockwise direction.

same. The truth of this statement can be justified by the following considerations:

$$\sqrt{-1} \cdot \sqrt{-1} = -1$$

That is,
$$j \cdot j = -1$$
$$\therefore j^2 = -1$$

Also,
$$\sqrt{-1} \cdot \sqrt{-1} \cdot \sqrt{-1} = -1 \cdot \sqrt{-1} = -j$$

That is,
$$j \cdot j \cdot j = j^3$$
$$\therefore j^3 = -j$$

Also,
$$\sqrt{-1} \cdot \sqrt{-1} \cdot \sqrt{-1} \cdot \sqrt{-1}$$
$$= (\sqrt{-1} \cdot \sqrt{-1})(\sqrt{-1} \cdot \sqrt{-1}) = (-1)(-1) = 1$$

That is,
$$j \cdot j \cdot j \cdot j = j^4$$
$$\therefore j^4 = 1$$

Similarly, it can be shown that successive multiplication by each $+j$ rotates the number 90° in a counterclockwise direction.

If we consider successive multiplication by $-j$, we have

$$(-\sqrt{-1})(-\sqrt{-1}) = -1$$

That is,
$$(-j)(-j) = j^2$$
$$\therefore (-j)^2 = -1$$

Also,
$$(-\sqrt{-1})(-\sqrt{-1})(-\sqrt{-1}) = (-1)(-\sqrt{-1}) = \sqrt{-1}$$

That is,
$$(-j)(-j)(-j) = (j^2)(-j) = (-1)(-j) = j$$
$$\therefore (-j)^3 = j$$

To demonstrate that $(-j)^4 = 1$ and $1/j = -j$ is left as a problem for you.

To summarize, it is seen that j is simply an operator for the purpose of rotating a directed number 90°, regardless of the value of that number. A $+j$ is considered as denoting counterclockwise rotation, and $-j$ denotes clockwise rotation. j is commonly referred to as the "complex operator." Actually, there is nothing complex about it.

23 – 14   Complex numbers

If a "real" number is united to an "imaginary" number by a plus or a minus sign, the expression thus obtained is called a *complex number*. Thus, $3 - j4$, $a + jb$, $R + jX$, etc., are complex numbers. At this time, we shall consider, not their graphical representation, but simply how to perform the four fundamental operations algebraically.

23 – 15   Addition and subtraction of complex numbers

Combining a real number with an imaginary number cannot be accomplished by the usual methods of addition and subtraction. These processes can only be expressed. For example, if we have the complex number $5 + j6$, this is as far as we can simplify it at this time. We should not attempt to add 5 and $j6$ arithmetically, for these two numbers are at right angles to each other, and such an operation would be meaningless. However, we *can* add and subtract complex numbers by treating them as ordinary binomials.

EXAMPLE 24   Add $3 + j7$ and $4 - j5$.
SOLUTION $3 + j7$
                           $\underline{4 - j5}$
                           $7 + j2$

EXAMPLE 25   Subtract $-15 - j6$ from $-5 + j8$.
SOLUTION $-\ 5 + j\ 8$
                           $\underline{-15 - j\ 6}$
                           $10 + j14$

PROBLEMS 23 – 9

Find the indicated sums:

1   $4 + j9$
    $\underline{3 + j9}$

2   $15 + j10$
    $\underline{3 - j12}$

3   $25 - j3$
    $\underline{3 - j7}$

4   $-75 + j40$
    $\underline{16 + j14}$

5   $67 - j176$
    $\underline{34 + j176}$

6     $-\ j39$
    $\underline{14 + j23}$

7 to 12 Subtract the lower complex number from the upper in each of the above problems.

– 16 Multiplication of complex numbers

As in addition and subtraction, complex numbers are treated as ordinary binomials when multiplied. However, when writing the result, we must not forget that $j^2 = -1$.

EXAMPLE 26   Multiply $4 - j7$ by $8 + j2$.

SOLUTION

$$
\begin{array}{r}
4 - j\ 7 \\
8 + j\ 2 \\
\hline
32 - j56 \\
+ j\ 8 - j^2 14 \\
\hline
32 - j48 - j^2 14
\end{array}
$$

Since $j^2 = -1$, the product is $32 - j48 - (-1)(14) = 32 - j48 + 14$
$$= 46 - j48$$

EXAMPLE 27   Multiply $7 + j3$ by $6 + j2$.

SOLUTION

$$
\begin{array}{r}
7 + j\ 3 \\
6 + j\ 2 \\
\hline
42 + j18 \\
+ j14 + j^2 6 \\
\hline
42 + j32 + j^2 6 = 36 + j32
\end{array}
$$

– 17 Division of complex numbers

As in the division of binomial quadratic surds, we simplify an indicated division by rationalizing the denominator in order to obtain a "real" number as divisor (Sec. 23–11). This is accomplished by multiplying by the conjugate in the usual manner.

EXAMPLE 28

$$\frac{10}{1 + j2} = \frac{10(1 - j2)}{(1 + j2)(1 - j2)} = \frac{10(1 - j2)}{1 - j^2 4} = \frac{10(1 - j2)}{5} = 2(1 - j2)$$

EXAMPLE 29

$$\frac{5 + j6}{3 - j4} = \frac{(5 + j6)(3 + j4)}{(3 - j4)(3 + j4)} = \frac{15 + j38 + j^2 24}{9 - j^2 16} = \frac{-9 + j38}{25}$$

EXAMPLE 30

$$\frac{a + jb}{a - jb} = \frac{(a + jb)(a + jb)}{(a - jb)(a + jb)} = \frac{a^2 + j2ab + j^2 b^2}{a^2 - j^2 b^2} = \frac{a^2 + j2ab - b^2}{a^2 + b^2}$$

PROBLEMS 23 – 10

Find the indicated products:

1 $(2 + j3)(4 + j2)$ 2 $(3 + j4)(5 - j6)$

3 $(6 - j9)(8 - j3)$ 4 $(1 + j1)(1 - j1)$
5 $(\alpha + j\beta)(\alpha + j\beta)$ 6 $(R + j\omega Z)(R - j\omega Z)$

Find the quotients:

7 $\dfrac{3}{1 - j3}$ 8 $\dfrac{6}{1 - j1}$

9 $\dfrac{6 + j7}{6 - j7}$ 10 $\dfrac{1 - j1}{1 + j1}$

11 $\dfrac{5}{5 + j5}$ 12 $\dfrac{3 - j8}{2 - j4}$

13 $\dfrac{2}{2 - jX}$ 14 $\dfrac{\alpha - j\beta}{\alpha + j\beta}$

15 $\dfrac{R + j\omega X}{R - j\omega X}$

23 – 18   Radical equations

An equation in which the unknown occurs in a radicand is called an
irrational or *radical equation*. To solve such an equation, arrange it
in such a manner that the radical is the only term in one member of
the equation. Then eliminate the radical by squaring each member of
the equation.

EXAMPLE 31   Given $\sqrt{3x} = 6$; solve for x.
SOLUTION $\sqrt{3x} = 6$
Squaring, $3x = 36$
D: 3, $x = 12$
CHECK   Substituting 12 for x in the given equation,
$$\sqrt{3 \cdot 12} = 6$$
$$\sqrt{36} = 6$$
$$6 = 6$$

EXAMPLE 32   Given $\sqrt{2x + 3} = 7$; solve for x.

SOLUTION $\sqrt{2x + 3} = 7$
Squaring, $2x + 3 = 49$
S:3, $2x = 46$
D:2, $x = 23$
CHECK $\sqrt{2 \cdot 23 + 3} = 7$
$$\sqrt{49} = 7$$
$$7 = 7$$

EXAMPLE 33   The time for one complete swing of a simple pendulum is
given by

$$t = 2\pi \sqrt{\frac{L}{g}}$$

where t = time, sec
$\qquad L$ = length of pendulum
$\qquad g$ = force due to gravity
Solve the equation for g and for L.

SOLUTION $\qquad$ Given $\qquad\qquad t = 2\pi \sqrt{\dfrac{L}{g}}$ $\qquad\qquad\qquad$ (a)

Squaring (a), $\qquad\qquad\qquad t^2 = 4\pi^2 \dfrac{L}{g}$ $\qquad\qquad\qquad$ (b)

M:g in (b), $\qquad\qquad\qquad gt^2 = 4\pi^2 L$ $\qquad\qquad\qquad$ (c)

D:t^2 in (c), $\qquad\qquad\qquad g = \dfrac{4\pi^2 L}{t^2}$ $\qquad\qquad\qquad$ (d)

Rewrite (c), $\qquad\qquad\qquad 4\pi^2 L = gt^2$ $\qquad\qquad\qquad$ (e)

D:$4\pi^2$ in (e), $\qquad\qquad\qquad L = \dfrac{gt^2}{4\pi^2}$

EXAMPLE 34 $\qquad$ Given $E = I_p Z_p + j\omega M I_s$ and $I_s Z_s = -j\omega M I_p$. Show that

$$E = I_p \left[Z_p + \frac{(\omega M)^2}{Z_s} \right]$$

SOLUTION $\qquad$ Since I_s does not appear in the final equation, it must be eliminated. Solving the given equations for I_s,

$$I_s = \frac{E - I_p Z_p}{j\omega M} \qquad\qquad\qquad (a)$$

$$I_s = \frac{-j\omega M I_p}{Z_s} \qquad\qquad\qquad (b)$$

Equating the right members of (a) and (b),

$$\frac{E - I_p Z_p}{j\omega M} = \frac{-j\omega M I_p}{Z_s}$$

M:$j\omega M$ $\qquad\qquad\qquad E - I_p Z_p = \dfrac{-j^2\omega^2 M^2 I_p}{Z_s}$

Substituting -1 for j^2 in the right member,

$$E - I_p Z_p = \frac{\omega^2 M^2 I_p}{Z_s}$$

A:$I_p Z_p$, $\qquad\qquad\qquad E = I_p Z_p + \dfrac{(\omega M)^2 I_p}{Z_s}$

Factoring the right member, $\quad E = I_p \left[Z_p + \dfrac{(\omega M)^2}{Z_s} \right]$

PROBLEMS 23 – 11

Solve the following:

$\quad$ 1 $\quad \sqrt{i} = 3$ $\qquad\qquad\qquad\qquad$ 2 $\quad \sqrt{r} = 5$
$\quad$ 3 $\quad \sqrt{\lambda} = 2$ $\qquad\qquad\qquad\qquad$ 4 $\quad \sqrt{\mu} + 3 = 9$

5   $\sqrt{E} - 6 = 10$ 6 $\sqrt{Z} - 2 = 6$

7   $\sqrt{F} - 3 = 13$ 8 $3\sqrt{\pi + 4} - 8 = 16$

9   $\sqrt{\dfrac{6}{e}} = 6$ 10 $\sqrt{\dfrac{3f - 2}{4}} = 2$

11   $3\sqrt{5\phi - 4} = 2\sqrt{3\phi + 24}$

12   $r = \sqrt{\dfrac{mm'}{F}}.$ Solve for F.

13   $V = \sqrt{\dfrac{2K}{m}}.$ Solve for K and m.

14   $V = \sqrt{2gh}.$ What is the value of h when V is 600 and $g = 32.2$?

15   $G_a = 1/\sqrt{G_1 R_{eq}}.$ Solve for R_{eq}.

16   $R_t = \dfrac{r}{\sqrt{d_0/d_1 - 1}}.$ Solve for d_0/d_1.

17   At an altitude of h ft above the sea or level ground, the distance d in
     miles that a person can see an object is $d = \sqrt{\dfrac{3h}{2}}.$ How high must one
     be to see an object 9 miles away?

18   The circumference c of a circle of area A is $c = 2\sqrt{\pi A}.$ $\pi = 3.14.$
     What is the area of a circle whose circumference is 12.56 in.?

19   At a resonant frequency of f cps, the inductive reactance X_L of a circuit
     of L henrys is $X_L = \omega L$ Ω. The capacitive reactance X_C of the circuit
     with a capacitance of C farads is $X_C = \dfrac{1}{\omega C}$ Ω. $\omega = 2\pi f$.   At the
     resonant frequency $X_L = X_C$. Solve for the resonant frequency in
     terms of π, L, C.

20   Using the formula for the resonant frequency derived in Prob. 19,
     find the value of L when $f = 1.40 \times 10^6$ and $C = 2.50 \times 10^{-10}$.

21   Using the formula derived in Prob. 19, find the value of C when
     $f = 6.00 \times 10^6$ and $L = 1.50 \times 10^{-8}$.

22   Show that $KE_p^{\frac{3}{2}} = KE_p \sqrt{E_p}$. This is a convenient relation for the
     slide-rule operator.

23   $f = \dfrac{1}{2\pi\sqrt{\dfrac{LC_aC_b}{C_a + C_b}}}.$ Solve for C_a.

24   Using the formula of Prob. 23, find the value of C_b if $f = 2.00 \times 10^6$,
     $L = 3.50 \times 10^{-7}$, and $C_a = 3.50 \times 10^{-8}$.

25   $L = \dfrac{1}{\omega}\sqrt{g_m{}^2 + \omega^2 C^2}.$ Solve for ω.

26   In a line through which a current I flows, the power P_m existing in the
     magnetic field around the line is $\dfrac{LI^2}{2}$ watts, where L is the inductance

per unit length. An equal power P_e exists in the electrostatic field of

the line equal to $\dfrac{CE^2}{2}$ watts, where C is capacitance of the line per

unit length. If the surge impedance Z_o of the line is $\dfrac{E}{I}$ Ω, show that

$$Z^o = \sqrt{\frac{L}{C}}.$$

27 $T = 2\pi\sqrt{\dfrac{\gamma R_2 C}{R_1 + R_2}}$ and $\sqrt{LC} = \dfrac{T}{2\pi}$. Solve for L in terms of γ, R_1, and R_2.

28 $G_a = \sqrt{G_1 + \dfrac{G_1}{R_{eq} + \dfrac{G_L}{g_m{}^2}}}$. Solve for $g_m{}^2$.

CHAPTER 24

QUADRATIC EQUATIONS

In previous chapters the study of equations has been limited mainly to those which contained the unknown quantity in the first degree. This chapter concerns itself with equations of the second degree, which are called quadratic equations.

24 – 1   Definitions

In common with polynomials (Sec. 16–2), the degree of an equation is defined as the degree of the term of highest degree in it. Thus, if an equation contains the square of the unknown quantity and no higher degree, it is an equation of the second degree, or a *quadratic equation*.

A quadratic equation that contains terms of the second degree only of the unknown is called a *pure quadratic equation*. For example,

$$x^2 = 25 \qquad R^2 - 49 = 0 \qquad 3x^2 = 12 \qquad ax^2 + c = 0$$
$$5x^2 + 2y^2 = 20$$

are pure quadratic equations.

A quadratic equation that contains terms of *both* the first and the second degree of the unknown is called an *affected* or a *complete quadratic equation*. Thus, $x^2 + 3x + 2 = 0$, $3x^2 + 11x = -2$,

$ax^2 + bx + c = 0$, etc., are affected, or complete, quadratic equations.

When a quadratic equation is solved, values of the unknown are found that will satisfy the conditions of the equation.

A value of the unknown that will satisfy the equation is called a *solution* or a *root* of the equation.

4 – 2   Solution of pure quadratic equations

As stated in Sec. 15–5, every number has two square roots, equal in magnitude but of opposite sign. Hence, all quadratic equations have two roots. In pure quadratic equations, the absolute values of the roots are equal but of opposite sign. The roots of complete quadratics are discussed in Sec. 24–3.

EXAMPLE 1   Solve the equation $x^2 - 16 = 0$.

SOLUTION   Given $x^2 - 16 = 0$
A:16, $x^2 = 16$
$\sqrt{}$ (see note below), $x = \pm 4$

CHECK   Substituting in the equation either $+4$ or -4 for the value of x, because either squared results in $+16$, we have

$$(\pm 4)^2 - 16 = 0$$
or $$16 - 16 = 0$$

NOTE   Hereafter, the radical sign will mean "take the square root of both members of the previous or designated equation."

EXAMPLE 2   Solve the equation $5R^2 - 89 = 91$.

SOLUTION   Given $5R^2 - 89 = 91$
A:89, $5R^2 = 180$
D:5, $R^2 = 36$
$\sqrt{}$, $R = \pm 6$
CHECK $5(\pm 6)^2 - 89 = 91$
                 $5 \times 36 - 89 = 91$
                    $180 - 89 = 91$
                        $91 = 91$

EXAMPLE 3   Solve the equation

$$\frac{I + 4}{I - 4} + \frac{I - 4}{I + 4} = \frac{10}{3}$$

SOLUTION   Given $$\frac{I + 4}{I - 4} + \frac{I - 4}{I + 4} = \frac{10}{3}$$

Clearing fractions,

$$3(I + 4)(I + 4) + 3(I - 4)(I - 4) = 10(I - 4)(I + 4)$$

Expanding,

$$3I^2 + 24I + 48 + 3I^2 - 24I + 48 = 10I^2 - 160$$

Collecting terms, $-4I^2 = -256$

D:-4, $I^2 = 64$

$\checkmark$, $I = \pm 8$

CHECK   By the usual method.

PROBLEMS 24 – 1

Solve the following:

1 $I^2 - 36 = 0$	2 $t^2 - 16 = 0$
3 $e^2 + 40 = 209$	4 $\lambda^2 - 0.16 = 0$
5 $3\mu^2 + 63 = 210$	6 $\theta^2 + 3.14 = 3.1625$
7 $E^2 - \frac{9}{49} = 0$	8 $4\gamma^2 - 9 = 0$
9 $5\phi^2 - 0.12 = 0.68$	10 $3C^2 = 1\frac{1}{3}$

11 $3(f + 5) - f(f - 1) - 4f = 0$

12 $\dfrac{L - 3}{L + 3} + \dfrac{L + 3}{L - 3} - 1 = \dfrac{28}{L^2 - 9}$

13 $\dfrac{4\alpha^2 - 9\alpha - 90}{3\alpha} - \dfrac{\alpha - 6}{2} = 0$

14 $5(3\beta - 10) + 3\beta(6\beta - 5) = 0$

15 $Z^2 + 2 = \dfrac{(Z - 1)^3 - Z + 24}{Z + 2}$

24 – 3 Complete quadratic equations—solution by factoring

As an example, let it be assumed that all that is known about two expressions x and y is that $xy = 0$. We know that it is impossible to find the value of either unless the value of the other is known. However, we do know that, if $xy = 0$, *either $x = 0$ or $y = 0$*, for the product of two numbers can be zero if, and only if, one of them is zero.

EXAMPLE 4   Solve the equation $x(5x - 2) = 0$.

SOLUTION   Here we have the product of two numbers x and $(5x - 2)$, equal to zero, and in order to satisfy the equation one of them must be equal to zero. Therefore, $x = 0$ or $5x - 2 = 0$. Solving the latter equation,

$$x = \tfrac{2}{5}$$

Hence, $x = 0$ *or* $x = \tfrac{2}{5}$

CHECK   If $x = 0$, $x(5x - 2) = 0(5 \cdot 0 - 2) = 0(-2) = 0$

If $x = \tfrac{2}{5}$, $x(5x - 2) = \tfrac{2}{5}(5 \cdot \tfrac{2}{5} - 2) = \tfrac{2}{5}(2 - 2) = 0$

It is evident that the roots of a complete quadratic may be of unequal absolute value and may or may not have the same signs.

It is incorrect to say $x = 0$ *and* $x = \frac{2}{5}$, for x cannot be equal to both 0 and $\frac{2}{5}$ at the same time. This will be more apparent in the following examples.

EXAMPLE 5   Solve the equation $(x - 5)(x + 3) = 0$.

SOLUTION   Again, we have the product of two numbers $(x - 5)$ and $(x + 3)$, equal to zero. Hence, either $(x - 5) = 0$ *or* $(x + 3) = 0$.

$$\therefore x = 5 \quad or \quad x = -3$$

CHECK   If $x = 5$, $(x - 5)(x + 3) = (5 - 5)(5 + 3) = 0(8) = 0$

If $x = -3$, $(x - 5)(x + 3) = (-3 - 5)(-3 + 3) = (-8)0 = 0$

EXAMPLE 6   Solve the equation $x^2 - x - 6 = 0$.

SOLUTION   Given $x^2 - x - 6 = 0$

Factoring $(x - 3)(x + 2) = 0$

Then, if $x - 3 = 0$, $x = 3$

Also, if $x + 2 = 0$, $x = -2$

$$\therefore x = 3 \ or \ -2$$

CHECK   If $x = 3$, $x^2 - x - 6 = 3^2 - 3 - 6 = 9 - 3 - 6 = 0$

If $x = -2$, $x^2 - x - 6 = (-2)^2 - (-2) - 6 = 4 + 2 - 6 = 0$

EXAMPLE 7   Solve the equation $(E - 3)(E + 2) = 14$.

SOLUTION   Given $(E - 3)(E + 2) = 14$

Expanding, $E^2 - E - 6 = 14$

S:14, $E^2 - E - 20 = 0$

Factoring, $(E - 5)(E + 4) = 0$

Then, if $E - 5 = 0$, $E = 5$

Also, if $E + 4 = 0$, $E = -4$

$$\therefore E = 5 \ or \ -4$$

CHECK   If $E = 5$, $(E - 3)(E + 2) = (5 - 3)(5 + 2) = (2)(7) = 14$

If $E = -4$, $(E - 3)(E + 2) = (-4 - 3)(-4 + 2)$

$$= (-7)(-2) = 14$$

PROBLEMS 24-2

Solve by factoring:

1   $e^2 + 5e + 6 = 0$

2   $\lambda^2 - 8\lambda + 12 = 0$

3   $f^2 - 4f = 45$

4   $\mu^2 = 15\mu - 54$

5   $r^2 = 63 - 2r$

6   $\alpha^2 + 50 = 27\alpha$

7   $R^2 + R = 72$

8   $I^2 + 160 - 26I = 0$

9   $\dfrac{5\phi - 7}{7\phi - 5} = \dfrac{\phi - 5}{2\phi - 13}$

10   $\dfrac{3}{\theta} + 1 = \theta - \dfrac{3}{\theta}$

11   $24 = \dfrac{1}{E^2} + \dfrac{2}{E}$

12   $\dfrac{6}{I - 8} - 1 = \dfrac{2}{I - 3}$

13 $\dfrac{7}{F-3} - \dfrac{1}{2} = \dfrac{F-2}{F-4}$ 14 $1 + \dfrac{L+2}{L+3} = \dfrac{36}{(L+3)^2}$

15 $\dfrac{5}{\beta+1} + \dfrac{\beta}{2\beta+4} - \dfrac{8}{\beta+2} = 0$

24 – 4 Solution by completing the square

Some quadratic equations are not readily solved by factoring. Frequently such quadratic equations are readily solved by another method known as *completing the square*.

In Probs. 15–5, missing terms were supplied in order to form a perfect trinomial square. This is the basis for the method of completing the square. For example, in order to make a perfect square of the expression $x^2 + 10x$, 25 must be added as a term to obtain $x^2 + 10x + 25$, which is the square of the quantity $x + 5$.

EXAMPLE 8   Solve the equation $x^2 - 10x - 20 = 0$.

SOLUTION   Inspection of the given equation shows that it cannot be factored with integral numbers. Therefore the solution will be accomplished by the method of completing the square.

Given $x^2 - 10x - 20 = 0$
A:20, $x^2 - 10x = 20$

Squaring one-half the coefficient of x and adding to both members,

$$x^2 - 10x + 25 = 20 + 25$$

Collecting terms, $x^2 - 10x + 25 = 45$
Factoring, $(x - 5)^2 = 45$
$\sqrt{}$, $x - 5 = \pm 6.71$
S:5, $x = 5 \pm 6.71$
or $x = 11.71 \ or \ -1.71$

The above answers are correct to three significant figures. The values of x are more precisely stated by maintaining the radical sign in the final roots. That is, if

$$(x - 5)^2 = 45$$
$\sqrt{}$, $x - 5 = \pm\sqrt{45}$
or $x - 5 = \pm 3\sqrt{5}$
A:5, $x = 5 \pm 3\sqrt{5}$
That is, $x = 5 + 3\sqrt{5} \ or \ 5 - 3\sqrt{5}$

EXAMPLE 9   Solve the equation $3x^2 - x - 1 = 0$.

SOLUTION   Given $3x^2 - x - 1 = 0$
D:3 (because the coefficient of x^2 must be 1),

$$x^2 - \tfrac{1}{3}x - \tfrac{1}{3} = 0$$

Transposing the constant term,

$$x^2 - \tfrac{1}{3}x = \tfrac{1}{3}$$

Squaring one-half the coefficient of x and adding to both members,

$$x^2 - \tfrac{1}{3}x + \tfrac{1}{36} = \tfrac{1}{3} + \tfrac{1}{36}$$

Collecting terms, $\qquad x^2 - \tfrac{1}{3}x + \tfrac{1}{36} = \tfrac{13}{36}$

Factoring, $\qquad\qquad (x - \tfrac{1}{6})^2 = \tfrac{13}{36}$

$\sqrt{}$, $\qquad\qquad\qquad x - \dfrac{1}{6} = \pm \dfrac{\sqrt{13}}{6}$

$$\therefore x = \frac{1 + \sqrt{13}}{6} \ or \ \frac{1 - \sqrt{13}}{6}$$

To summarize the method, we have the following:

RULE To solve by completing the square,

1 If the coefficient of the square of the unknown is not 1, divide both members of the equation by the coefficient.

2 Transpose the constant terms (those not containing the unknown) to the right member.

3 Find one-half the coefficient of the unknown of the first degree; square the result; add this square to both members of the equation. This makes the left member a perfect trinomial square.

4 Take the square root of both members of the equation, writing $\pm$ sign before the square root of the right member.

5 Solve the resulting simple equation.

PROBLEMS 24 – 3

Solve by completing the square:

1 $s^2 + 4s - 12 = 0$ $\qquad\qquad$ 2 $v^2 + 35 + 12v = 0$

3 $\gamma^2 = 60 + 4\gamma$ $\qquad\qquad$ 4 $\theta^2 + 11\theta + 24 = 0$

5 $\pi^2 = 30 - \pi$ $\qquad\qquad$ 6 $z^2 + 10z + 15 = 0$

7 $E^2 = 9E + 11$ $\qquad\qquad$ 8 $3R^2 = 44R - 121$

9 $12\gamma^2 = 29\gamma - 14$ $\qquad\qquad$ 10 $7\phi - 2 = 3\phi^2$

11 $15 - 8\lambda^2 = 19\lambda$ $\qquad\qquad$ 12 $6 - \dfrac{3}{\mu} = \dfrac{5}{\mu^2}$

13 $6\beta(2\beta + 1) = 7 - 6\beta^2$ $\qquad\qquad$ 14 $\dfrac{21\alpha^3 - 16}{3\alpha^2 - 4} - 5 = 7\alpha$

15 $\dfrac{1}{2Z} - \dfrac{Z^2 + 25}{7Z} - 4 - Z = 0$

24 – 5 Standard form

Any quadratic equation can be written in the general form

$$ax^2 + bx + c = 0$$

This is called the *standard form* of the quadratic equation. Written this way, *a* represents the coefficient of the term containing x^2, *b* represents the coefficient of the term containing *x*, and *c* represents the constant term. Note that all terms of the equation, when written in standard form, are in the left member of the equation.

EXAMPLE 10   Given $2x^2 + 5x - 3 = 0$. In this equation, $a = 2$, $b = 5$, and $c = -3$.

EXAMPLE 11   Given $R^2 - 5R - 6 = 0$. In this equation, $a = 1$, $b = -5$, and $c = -6$.

EXAMPLE 12   Given $9E^2 - 25 = 0$. In this equation, $a = 9$, $b = 0$, and $c = -25$.

24 – 6 Deriving a formula for solving any quadratic equation

Because the standard form $ax^2 + bx + c = 0$ represents *any* quadratic equation, it follows that the roots of $ax^2 + bx + c = 0$ represent the roots of *any* quadratic equation. Therefore, if the standard quadratic equation can be solved for the unknown, the values, or roots, thereby obtained will serve as a formula for finding the roots of *any* quadratic equation.

This formula is derived by solving the standard form by the method of completing the square as follows:

Given $\qquad\qquad\qquad ax^2 + bx + c = 0$

Divide by *a* (Rule 1): $\qquad x^2 + \dfrac{bx}{a} + \dfrac{c}{a} = 0$

Transpose the constant term (Rule 2):

$$x^2 + \frac{bx}{a} = -\frac{c}{a}$$

Add the square of one-half the coefficient of *x* to both members (Rule 3).

$$x^2 + \frac{bx}{a} + \frac{b^2}{4a^2} = \frac{b^2}{4a^2} - \frac{c}{a}$$

Factor the left member, and add terms in right member:

$$\left(x + \frac{b}{2a}\right)^2 = \frac{b^2 - 4ac}{4a^2}$$

Take the square root of both members:

$$x + \frac{b}{2a} = \pm \frac{\sqrt{b^2 - 4ac}}{2a}$$

Subtract $\frac{b}{2a}$:
$$x = -\frac{b}{2a} \pm \frac{\sqrt{b^2 - 4ac}}{2a}$$

Collect terms of right member:

$$x = \frac{-b \pm \sqrt{b^2 - 4ac}}{2a}$$

This equation is known as the quadratic formula.

Instead of attempting to solve a quadratic equation by factoring or by completing the square, we now make use of this general formula. Upon becoming proficient in the use of the formula, you will find this method a convenience.

EXAMPLE 13   Solve the equation $5x^2 + 2x - 3 = 0$.

SOLUTION   Comparing this equation with the standard form

$$ax^2 + bx + c = 0$$

we have $a = 5$, $b = 2$, and $c = -3$. Substituting in the quadratic formula

$$x = \frac{-b \pm \sqrt{b^2 - 4ac}}{2a} = \frac{-2 \pm \sqrt{2^2 - 4 \cdot 5 \cdot (-3)}}{2 \cdot 5}$$

Hence,
$$x = \frac{-2 \pm \sqrt{64}}{10}$$

$$= \frac{-2 \pm 8}{10} = \frac{-2 + 8}{10} \text{ or } \frac{-2 - 8}{10}$$

$$\therefore x = \tfrac{3}{5} \text{ or } -1$$

Check by substituting the values of x in the given equation.

NOTE   It must be remembered that the expression $\sqrt{b^2 - 4ac}$ is the square root of the *quantity* $(b^2 - 4ac)$ *taken as a whole.*

EXAMPLE 14   Solve the equation $\dfrac{3}{5 - R} = 2R$.

SOLUTION   Clearing the fractions results in $2R^2 - 10R + 3 = 0$. Comparing this equation with the standard form $ax^2 + bx + c = 0$, we have $a = 2$, $b = -10$, and $c = 3$. Substituting in the quadratic formula

$$x = \frac{-b \pm \sqrt{b^2 - 4ac}}{2a}$$

$$R = \frac{-(-10) \pm \sqrt{(-10)^2 - 4 \cdot 2 \cdot 3}}{2 \cdot 2}$$

Hence,
$$R = \frac{10 \pm \sqrt{76}}{4}$$

Factoring the radicand,

$$R = \frac{10 \pm 2\sqrt{19}}{4}$$

Dividing both terms of the fraction by 2,

$$R = \frac{5 \pm \sqrt{19}}{2} = \frac{5 + \sqrt{19}}{2} \quad \text{or} \quad \frac{5 - \sqrt{19}}{2}$$

$$\therefore R = 4.68 \text{ or } 0.320$$

These final answers are correct to three significant figures. Check the solution by the usual method.

PROBLEMS 24 – 4

Solve the following, using the quadratic formula:

1 $\pi^2 = 3\pi - 2$
2 $6 + x = x^2$
3 $E^2 = 168 + 2E$
4 $48 = L^2 - 22L$
5 $10 - 9t = 7t^2$
6 $\lambda^2 = 6.3\lambda - 1.8$
7 $4\gamma - 2 = \gamma^2$
8 $\phi^2 + \phi = 1$
9 $\theta + \dfrac{1}{\theta} - \dfrac{5}{2} = 0$
10 $1 - \mu = \dfrac{\mu - 2}{\mu}$
11 $1 + \dfrac{2}{\omega + 3} = \dfrac{3}{\omega - 2}$
12 $\dfrac{R^2}{9} = \dfrac{35}{4} - \dfrac{R}{3}$
13 $1 + \dfrac{2Z + 5}{3Z + 5} = \dfrac{3Z - 5}{2Z - 5}$
14 $\dfrac{1}{F + 2} - \dfrac{15}{8} = \dfrac{2}{F - 2}$
15 $6 = \dfrac{C - 2}{C + 2} - \dfrac{C - 1}{C + 1}$

24 – 7   Graphical solution of quadratic equations

The graphs of quadratic equations can be plotted in a manner similar to the straight-line graphs of Chap. 21.   Because the quadratic equations with which we are concerned in this section contain only one unknown, or variable, it becomes necessary to express these equations in terms of another variable in order to plot values using both X and Y axes.   For example, the equation

$$x^2 - 10x + 16 = 0$$

could not be plotted in its present form because the equation contains no dependent variable.   Therefore, we agree to set such quadratic equations equal to y, which will represent the dependent variable.   That is, for the above equation,

$$y = x^2 - 10x + 16$$

The equation in this form can be plotted, because, for every value assigned to x, there will be corresponding values of y.

EXAMPLE 15   Graph the equation $x^2 - 10x + 16 = 0$.

SOLUTION   Setting the equation equal to y,

$$y = x^2 - 10x + 16$$

Make a table of the values of y corresponding to assigned values of x, as shown:

If $x =$	0	1	3	4	5	6	7	8	9	10
Then $x^2 =$	0	1	9	16	25	36	49	64	81	100
$10x =$	0	10	30	40	50	60	70	80	90	100
$x^2 - 10x =$	0	-9	-21	-24	-25	-24	-21	-16	-9	0
$\therefore y = x^2 - 10x + 16 =$	16	7	-5	-8	-9	-8	-5	0	7	16

Plotting the corresponding values of x and y as pairs of coordinates and drawing a smooth curve through the points result in the graph shown in Fig. 24–1.

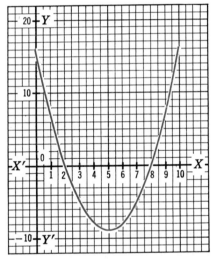

FIG. 24-1   Graph of the equation $y = x^2 - 10x + 16$.

From the figure, it is apparent that the graph has two X intercepts at $x = 2$ and $x = 8$. That is, when $y = 0$, the graph crosses the X axis at $x = 2$ and $x = 8$. This is to be expected, for when $y = 0$, the given equation $x^2 - 10x + 16 = 0$ can be solved algebraically to obtain $x = 2$ or 8. Hence, it is evident that the points at which the graph crosses the X axis denote the values of x when $y = 0$, which are the roots of the equation.

Another interesting fact regarding this graph is that the curve goes through a *minimum value*. Suppose it is desired to solve for the coordinates of the point of minimum value. First, if the equation is changed to standard form, we obtain $a = 1$, $b = -10$, and $c = 16$. If the value of $-b/2a$ is computed, the result is the x value, or abscissa, of the minimum point on the curve. That is,

$$x = -\frac{b}{2a} = -\frac{-10}{2 \times 1} = \frac{10}{2} = 5$$

Substituting this value of x in the original equation,

$$y = x^2 - 10x + 16$$
$$y = 5^2 - 10 \times 5 + 16 = -9$$

Thus, the point $(5, -9)$ is where the curve passes through a minimum value. That is, the dependent variable y is a minimum and equal to -9 when x, the independent variable, is equal to 5.

Every quadratic function of the form $ax^2 + bx + c = 0$ has a curve of this general shape. Such a curve is called a *parabola*. The parabola opens *upward* if a is positive and *downward* if a is negative.

EXAMPLE 16   Graph the equation $27 - 3x - 4x^2 = 0$.

SOLUTION   Equating $y = 27 - 3x - 4x^2$ and assigning values to x results in a table of values, as shown:

If $x =$					−4	−3	−2	−1	0	1	2	3
Then $3x =$					−12	−9	−6	−3	0	3	6	9
$27 - 3x =$					39	36	33	30	27	24	21	18
$x^2 =$					16	9	4	1	0	1	4	9
$4x^2 =$					64	36	16	4	0	4	16	36
$\therefore y = 27 - 3x - 4x^2 =$					−25	0	17	26	27	20	5	−18

Plotting the corresponding values of x and y as pairs of coordinates and drawing a smooth curve through them result in the graph shown in Fig. 24–2.

From the graph of the equation, it is observed:

1. The roots (solution) of the equation are denoted by the X intercepts.

These are $x = -3$ and $x = 2.25$. These can be checked algebraically to obtain

$$27 - 3x - 4x^2 = 0$$

Factoring, $$(3 + x)(9 - 4x) = 0$$
$$x = -3 \text{ or } 2.25$$

2. The parabola opens *downward* because the coefficient of x^2 is negative. $(a = -4.)$

3. Because the parabola opens downward, the graph goes through

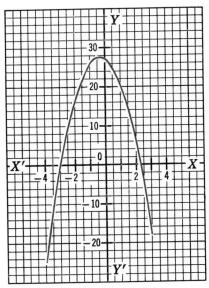

FIG. 24–2   Graph of the equation
$y = 27 - 3x - 4x^2$.

a *maximum* value. The point of maximum value is found in the same manner as the minimum point of Example 15. That is,

$$x = \frac{-b}{2a} = \frac{-(-3)}{2(-4)} = -\frac{3}{8}$$

Substituting $-\frac{3}{8}$ for x in the original equation,
$$y = 27 - 3(-\tfrac{3}{8}) - 4(-\tfrac{3}{8})^2 = 27.6$$

Thus, the dependent variable y is a maximum and equal to 27.6 when x, the independent variable, is equal to $-\frac{3}{8}$.

EXAMPLE 17   Graph the equations

(a) $y = x^2 - 8x + 12$
(b) $y = x^2 - 8x + 16$
(c) $y = x^2 - 8x + 20$

SOLUTION   As before, make up a table of y values for each equation, corresponding to assigned values of x. Using these x and y values as pairs of coordinates, plot the graphs of the equations. These graphs are shown in Fig. 24–3.

The coefficients of the equations are the same except for the values of the constant term c.

From the graphs of the equations, it is observed that

1. The curve of (a) intercepts the X axis at $x = 2$ and $x = 6$, and the roots of the equation are thus denoted as $x = 2$ or 6. This checks with the algebraic solution.

2. The curve of (b) just *touches* the X axis at $x = 4$. Solving (b) algebraically shows that the roots are *equal*, both roots being 4.

3. The curve of (c) does not intersect or touch the X axis. Solving (c) algebraically results in the "imaginary" roots $x = 4 \pm j2$.

4. All curves pass through minimum values at points having equal x values. This is as expected, for the x value of a maximum or a minimum is given by $x = -b/2a$, and these values are equal in each of the given equations.

5. Checking the y values of the minima, it is seen that they must be affected by the constant terms, for, as previously mentioned, the other coefficients of the equations are the same.

24 – 8 The discriminant of a quadratic equation

The quantity under the radical in the quadratic formula ($b^2 - 4ac$) is called the *discriminant* of the quadratic equation. The two roots of the equation are

$$x = \frac{-b + \sqrt{b^2 - 4ac}}{2a} \quad \text{and} \quad x = \frac{-b - \sqrt{b^2 - 4ac}}{2a}$$

Now, if $b^2 - 4ac = 0$, it is apparent that the two roots are equal. Also, if $b^2 - 4ac$ is *positive*, each of the roots is a *real* number. But if $b^2 - 4ac$ is *negative*, the roots are *imaginary*. Therefore, there is a direct relationship between the value of the discriminant and the roots, and hence the graph, of a quadratic equation.

For example, the discriminants of the equations of Example 17 in the preceding article are

$$b^2 - 4ac = (-8)^2 - 4 \cdot 1 \cdot 12 = 16$$
$$b^2 - 4ac = (-8)^2 - 4 \cdot 1 \cdot 16 = 0$$
$$b^2 - 4ac = (-8)^2 - 4 \cdot 1 \cdot 20 = -16$$

Upon checking these values with the curves of Fig. 24–3, and also the values of the discriminants found in the preceding exercises with their respective curves, it is evident that the roots of a quadratic equation are

1. Real and unequal if and only if $b^2 - 4ac$ is positive.

2. Real and equal if and only if $b^2 - 4ac = 0$

3. Imaginary and unequal if and only if $b^2 - 4ac$ is negative

4. Rational if and only if $b^2 - 4ac$ is a perfect square

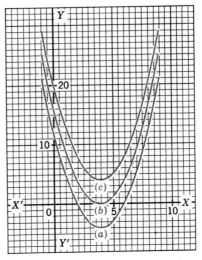

FIG. 24–3 Graphs of the equations of Example 17.

24 – 9 Maximum and minimum conditions

As previously stated, in the general quadratic equation $ax^2 + bx + c = 0$, the relation $x = -b/2a$ gives the value of the independent variable x at which the dependent variable y will be maximum or minimum. Then by substituting this value of x, the independent variable, in the equation the corresponding value of y can be obtained. Also, it has been shown that the function will be maximum if a, the coefficient of x^2, is negative because the curve opens downward. Similarly, if the coefficient of x^2 is positive, the curve will pass through a minimum because the curve opens upward.

This knowledge facilitates the solutions of many problems that heretofore would have involved considerable labor.

EXAMPLE 18   A source of emf E, with an internal resistance r, is connected to a load of variable resistance R. What will be the value of R with respect to r when maximum power is being delivered to the load?

SOLUTION   The circuit can be represented as shown in Fig. 24–4. By Ohm's law, the current flowing through the circuit is

$$I = \frac{E}{r + R} \qquad (a)$$

The power delivered to the external circuit is

$$P = VI = I^2R \qquad (b)$$

where V is the terminal voltage of the source and is

$$V = E - Ir \qquad (c)$$

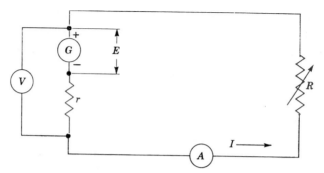

FIG. 24–4   Circuit of Example 18.

Now the terminal voltage V will decrease as the current I increases. There-fore, the power P supplied to the load is a function of the two variables V and I. Substituting Eq. (c) in Eq. (b),

$$P = (E - Ir)I = EI - I^2r$$

that is,
$$P = -rI^2 + EI \qquad (d)$$

Equation (d) is a quadratic in I, where $a = -r$ and $b = E$. Then, since, for maximum conditions, $I = -b/2a$,

$$I = \frac{-b}{2a} = \frac{-E}{2(-r)} = \frac{E}{2r} \qquad (e)$$

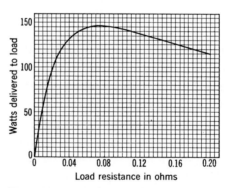

FIG. 24–5   Power delivered to load plotted against load resistance.

which is the value of the current through the circuit when maximum power is being delivered to the load. Substituting Eq. (e) in Eq. (a),

$$\frac{E}{2r} = \frac{E}{r + R} \qquad (f)$$

Solving Eq. (f) for R,
$$R = r \qquad (g)$$

Equation (g) shows that maximum power will be delivered to any load when the resistance of that load is equal to the internal resistance of the source of emf. This is one of the important concepts in electronics engineering. For example, we are concerned with obtaining maximum power output from several types of power amplifier. This is accomplished when the amplifier load resistance matches the plate resistance of the associated vacuum tube. Also, maximum power is delivered to an antenna circuit when the impedance of the antenna is made to match that of the transmission line that feeds it.

In Fig. 24–5, power delivered to the load is plotted against values of the load resistance R_L when a storage battery is used, with an emf E of 6.6 volts and an internal resistance $r = 0.075$ Ω. The circuit is as shown in Fig. 24–6.

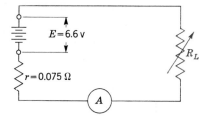

It is apparent that, when the battery or any other source of emf is delivering maximum power, half the power is lost within the battery. Under these conditions, therefore, the efficiency is 50 per cent.

Fig. 24–6 Load resistance R_L is varied to obtain power values plotted in Fig. 24–5.

PROBLEMS 24 – 5

1 Graph the following equations all on the same sheet with the same axes:
   (a) $x^2 - 6x - 16 = 0$. (b) $x^2 - 6x - 7 = 0$. (c) $x^2 - 6x = 0$.
   (d) $x^2 - 6x + 5 = 0$. (e) $x^2 - 6x + 9 = 0$. (f) $x^2 - 6x + 12 = 0$.
   (g) $x^2 - 6x + 15 = 0$. Does changing the constant term change only the vertical positions of the graphs and the solutions of the equations? Do all graphs pass through minimum values at the same value of x?
2 Solve the foregoing equations algebraically. Do these solutions check with the graphs of the equations?
3 Compute the discriminant for each equation. Do you see any connection between these values and the graph?
4 Compute the minimum value of the dependent variable y for each equation. Do these values check with the graphs?
5 What do you see from the graphs when x is equal to zero?

24 – 10 Summary

Several methods are available for solving quadratic equations.

All quadratic equations can be solved by factoring, by completing the square, by use of the quadratic formula, or by graphical methods. However, some of these methods involve unnecessary work for certain forms or types of quadratic equation; therefore one tries to choose the most convenient method for a particular equation. For example, pure quadratic equations are readily solved merely by reducing the equation to its simplest form and extracting the square root of both members of the equation in order to obtain the two roots, which are equal in absolute value but of opposite sign (Sec. 24–2).

In practical problems involving complete quadratic equations the numerical coefficients are such that you will seldom be able to solve the equation readily by factoring. Also, solution by completing the square sometimes can become a chore. Probably the most widely used method is solution by use of the quadratic formula, which, if you forget it, can be found in most handbooks and put to use whenever needed.

Solution by graphical methods allows you to visualize the variation of quantities and serves as a check to computations. In any event, through solving many problems, you will develop your own methods of attack.

In solving problems involving quadratic equations, care must be used because two answers (roots) are obtained. In all cases both roots will satisfy the mathematics of the equation, but in some cases only one root will satisfy the conditions of the problem. Therefore, we reject the obviously impossible or the impractical answers and retain the ones that are consistent with the physical conditions of the problem.

EXAMPLE 19   The square of a certain number plus four times the number is 12. Find the number.

SOLUTION   Let x = the number

Then x^2 = the square of the number

and $4x$ = four times the number

From the problem $x^2 + 4x = 12$

S:12, $x^2 + 4x - 12 = 0$

Factoring, $(x + 6)(x - 2) = 0$

Then $x = -6$ or 2

Both roots satisfy the equation and the condition of the problem; therefore both answers are correct.

EXAMPLE 20   Find the dimensions of a right triangle if its hypotenuse is 40 ft and the base exceeds the altitude by 8 ft.

SOLUTION   In any right triangle, Fig. 24–7, $c^2 = a^2 + b^2$. Since
$$c = 40$$
and $$a = b - 8$$
then $$1,600 = (b - 8)^2 + b^2$$
Are both the roots of this equation consistent with the physical conditions
of the problem?

EXAMPLE 21   The emf of a storage battery is 6.3 volts, and its internal
resistance is 0.015 Ω. The battery is used
to drive a dynamotor that requires 300
watts. What current will the battery deliver to the dynamotor, and what will be
the voltage reading across the battery terminals while supplying this current?

SOLUTION   The circuit is represented
in Fig. 24–8.

Let P = power consumed by dynamotor =
        300 watts

E_B = voltage across battery terminals
        when dynamotor is delivering
        300 watts

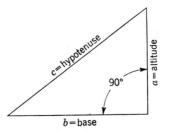

FIG. 24–7   In any right triangle $c^2 = a^2 + b^2$.

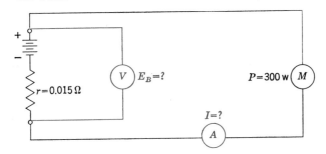

FIG. 24–8   Circuit of Example 21.

Since $$I = \frac{P}{E_B}$$

then $$I = \frac{300}{E_B}$$

Now $E_B = 6.3 - rI$

Substituting for r, $E_B = 6.3 - 0.015I$

Substituting for I, $E_B = 6.3 - 0.015 \left(\frac{300}{E_B}\right)$

Multiplying, $E_B = 6.3 - \dfrac{4.5}{E_B}$

Clearing fractions, $E_B{}^2 = 6.3\,E_B - 4.5$

Transposing, $E_B{}^2 - 6.3E_B + 4.5 = 0$

This equation is a quadratic in E_B; hence, $a = 1$, $b = -6.3$, and $c = 4.5$. Substituting these values in the quadratic formula,

$$E_B = \frac{-(-6.3) \pm \sqrt{(-6.3)^2 - 4 \cdot 1 \cdot 4.5}}{2 \cdot 1}$$

or

$$E_B = \frac{6.3 \pm \sqrt{21.7}}{2}$$

$$\therefore E_B = 5.48 \text{ volts or } 0.82 \text{ volt}$$

$$I = \frac{300}{E_B} = \frac{300}{5.48} = 54.7 \text{ amp}$$

Why was 5.48 volts chosen instead of 0.82 volts in the above solution?

PROBLEMS 24 – 6

1. Compute the discriminant and tell what it shows in each of these equations: (a) $3x^2 - 4x + 5 = 0$;   (b) $4x^2 - 20x + 25 = 0$; (c) $2x^2 - 6x - 3 = 0$.

2. Find two positive consecutive numbers whose product is 528.

3. The sum of a certain number and its reciprocal is $2\frac{9}{10}$. Find the number.

4. Can the sides of a right triangle ever be consecutive even integers? If so, find these integers.

5. Find the dimensions of a rectangle whose area is 6,624 ft² if the sum of its length and width is 165 ft.

6. Separate 182 into two parts so that one part is the square of the other.

7. One number is 7 less than another number, and the sum of their squares is 1,225. Find the numbers.

8. Given $H = ND^2/2.53$. Solve for D.

9. Given $P = kE^2/nR$. Solve for E. If k and n are doubled and P and R are held constant, what happens to E?

10. $R_t = \dfrac{r}{\left(\dfrac{d_o}{d_i}\right)^2} - 1$.   Solve for $\dfrac{d_o}{d_i}$.

11. $P = \dfrac{R(r^2 + x^2)}{r(Rr + Xx)}$.   Solve for r and x.

12. The following relations exist in the Wien bridge:

$$\omega^2 = \frac{1}{R_1 R_2 c_1 c_2} \quad \text{and} \quad \frac{c_1}{c_2} = \frac{R_b - R_2}{R_a R_1}$$

Solve for c_1 and c_2 in terms of resistance components and ω.

13. Kinetic energy (KE) is equal to one-half the product of mass m in pounds and velocity v in feet per second squared; that is, $KE = \frac{1}{2}mv^2$ ft-poundals. Find the value of v when $KE = 1.1 \times 10^6$ ft-poundals and $m = 2.2$ lb.

14 A ball rolls down a slope and travels a distance $d = 6t + t^2/2$ ft in t sec. Solve for t.

15 The distance s through which an object will fall in t sec is $s = \frac{1}{2}gt^2$ ft, where $g = 32.2$ ft/sec². The velocity v attained after t sec is $v = gt$ f/sec. Solve for the velocity in terms of g and s.

16 If an object is thrown straight upward vertically with a velocity of v f/sec, its height t sec later is $h = vt - 16t^2$ ft. If a shell was fired upward with a velocity of 1,500 f/sec, and neglecting air resistance, (a) at what time would its height be 7,100 ft on the way up, (b) at what time would its height be 7,100 ft on the way down, (c) what maximum height would it attain?

17 Using the formula for height in Prob. 16, derive an equation for maximum height attained for any initial velocity v.

18 In an a-c series circuit containing resistance R in ohms and inductance L in henrys, the current I can be computed by the formula

$$I = \frac{E}{\sqrt{R^2 + \omega^2 L^2}} \quad \text{amp}$$

where E is the voltage in volts across the circuit. Find the value of R to three significant figures if $E = 117$ volts, $I = 1.17$ amp, $L = 0.159$ henry, $\omega = 2\pi f$, and $f = 60$ cycles.

19 In an a-c circuit of R Ω resistance and X Ω reactance, the impedance is

$$Z = \sqrt{R^2 + X^2} \quad \Omega$$

Find the value of the reactance of $R = 30$ Ω and $Z = 50$ Ω.

20 The susceptance of an a-c circuit containing R Ω resistance and X Ω reactance is

$$b = \frac{X}{R^2 + X^2} \quad \text{mhos}$$

Find the value of R to three significant figures when $b = 0.016$ mho and $X = 4$ Ω.

21 A generator with an emf of 120 volts and an internal resistance of 0.10 Ω is delivering 2.5 kw to a load through two No. 0 feeders that are 1,500 ft long. What is the voltage across the load?

22 A generator with an emf of 240 volts and an internal resistance of 0.25 Ω is delivering 5 kw to a load through two No. 8 feeders that are 500 ft long. What is the generator terminal voltage?

23 Find the two combinations of resistance of R_2 and R_3 that will satisfy the circuit conditions of Fig. 24-9.

24 The circuit conditions as shown in Fig. 24-10 existed when the generator G was supplying current to the circuit. When the generator was dis-

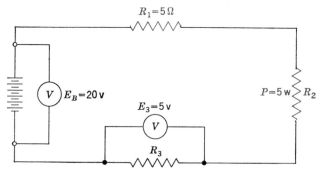

FIG. 24–9   Circuit of Prob. 23.

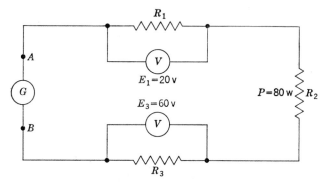

FIG. 24–10   Circuit of Prob. 24.

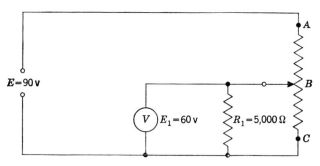

FIG. 24–11   Circuit of Prob. 25.

connected, an ohmmeter connected between points A and B read 60 Ω.
(a) What was the circuit current? (b) What was the generator voltage?
(c) What is the value of each resistor?

25 In the circuit of Fig. 24–11, the resistor ABC represents a potentiometer
with a total resistance (A to C) of 25,000 Ω. $R_1 = 5,000$ Ω across which

is 60 volts. (a) What is the resistance from A to B? (b) How much current flows from B to C?

26 What are the meter readings in the circuit of Fig. 24-12?

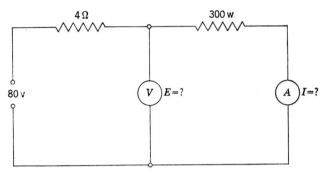

FIG. 24-12   Circuit of Prob. 26.

27 When two capacitors C_1 and C_2 are connected in series, the total capacitance C_t of the combination is always less than either of the two capacitors. That is,

$$C_t = \frac{C_1 C_2}{C_1 + C_2}$$

Suppose we have a tuning capacitor that varies from 200 to 300 $\mu\mu$f; that is, it has a *change* in capacitance of 100 $\mu\mu$f. What value of fixed capacitor should be connected in series with the tuning capacitor to limit the total *change* of circuit capacitance to 50 $\mu\mu$f?

CHAPTER 25
KIRCHHOFF'S LAWS

An understanding of Kirchhoff's laws, plus the ability to apply them in analyzing circuit conditions, will give you a better insight into the behavior of circuits. Furthermore, you will be able to solve circuit problems that with only a knowledge of Ohm's law would be very difficult in some cases and impossible in others.

25 – 1   Direction of current flow

As stated in Sec. 13–1, the most generally accepted concept of an electric current is that it consists of a motion of electrons from a negative toward a more positive point in a circuit. That is, a positively charged body is taken to be one that is deficient in electrons, whereas a negatively charged body carries an excess of electrons. When the two are joined by a conductor, electrons flow from the negative charge to the positive charge. Hence, if two such points in a circuit are *maintained* at a difference of potential, a *continuous* flow of electrons, or current, will take place from negative to positive. Therefore, in the consideration of Kirchhoff's laws, current will be considered as flowing from the negative terminal of a source of emf, through the external circuit, and back to the positive terminal of the source. Thus, in Fig. 25–1, the current flows away from the negative terminal of the battery, through R_1 and R_2, and back to the positive terminal of the battery. Note that point b is positive with respect to point a and that point d is positive with respect to point c.

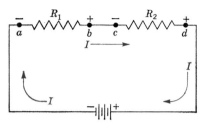

FIG. 25-1 Current I shown flowing from $-$ to $+$.

25 – 2 Statement of Kirchhoff's laws

In 1847, G. R. Kirchhoff extended Ohm's law by two important statements which have become known as Kirchhoff's laws. These laws can be stated as follows:

1 The algebraic sum of the currents at any junction of conductors is zero.

That is, at any point in a circuit, there is as much current flowing away from the point as there is flowing toward it.

2 The algebraic sum of the emfs and voltage drops around any closed circuit is zero.

That is, in any closed circuit, the applied emf is equal to the voltage drops around the circuit.

These laws are straightforward and need no proof here, for the first is self-evident from the study of parallel circuits, and the second was stated in different words in Sec. 13–8. When properly applied, they enable one to set up equations for any circuit and solve for the unknown circuit components, voltages, or currents as required.

25 – 3 Application of second law to series circuits

The second law is considered first because of its applications to problems with which you are already familiar.

Figure 25–2 represents a 20-volt generator connected to three series resistors. The validity of Kirchhoff's second law was demonstrated in Sec. 13–8; that is, in any closed circuit the applied emf is equal to the sum of the voltage drops around the circuit. Thus, neglecting the internal resistance of the generator and the resistance of the connecting wires in Fig. 25–2,

$$E = IR_1 + IR_2 + IR_3 \qquad [1]$$

or $\qquad\qquad 20 = 2I + 3I + 5I$

Hence, $\qquad\qquad I = 2\,\text{amp}$

Equation [1] is satisfactory for a circuit containing one source of emf. By considering the circuit from a different viewpoint,

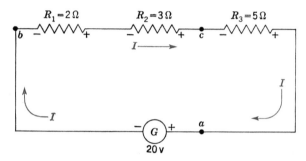

Fɪɢ. 25–2 The sum of the voltage drops across the resistors is equal to the applied voltage.

however, the voltage relations around the circuit become more understandable. For example, by starting at any point in the circuit, such as point *a*, we proceed completely around the circuit in the direction of current flow, remembering that when current passes through a resistance there is a voltage drop that represents a loss and therefore is subtractive. Also, in going around the circuit, sources of emf represent a gain in voltage if they tend to aid current flow and therefore are additive. By this method, according to the second law, the algebraic sum of all emfs and voltage drops around the circuit is zero. For example, in starting at point *a* in Fig. 25–2 and proceeding around the circuit in the direction of current flow, the first thing encountered is the positive terminal of a source of emf of 20 volts. Because this causes current to flow in the direction we are going, it is written +20. This is easily remembered, for the positive terminal was the first one encountered; therefore, write it plus. Next comes R_1, which is responsible for a *drop* in voltage due to the current *I* passing through it. Hence, this voltage drop is written $-IR_1$ or $-2I$, for R_1 is known to be 2 Ω. R_2 and R_3 are treated in a similar manner because both represent voltage *drops*. This completes the trip around the circuit, and by equating the algebraic sum of the emf and voltage drops to zero,

$$20 - 2I - 3I - 5I = 0 \qquad [2]$$

or $$I = 2 \text{ amp}$$

Note that Eq. [2] is simply a different form of Eq. [1]. If the polarities of the sources of emf are marked, they will serve as an aid in remembering whether to add or subtract. In going around the circuit, if the first terminal of a source of emf is positive, it is added; if negative, the emf is subtracted.

The point at which to start around the circuit is purely a matter of choice, for the algebraic sum of all voltages around the circuit is equal to zero. For example, starting at point b,

$$-2I - 3I - 5I + 20 = 0$$
$$I = 2 \text{ amp}$$

Starting at point c,

$$-5I + 20 - 2I - 3I = 0$$
$$I = 2 \text{ amp}$$

EXAMPLE 1   Find the amount of current flowing in the circuit represented in Fig. 25–3 if the internal resistance of battery E_1 is 0.3 Ω, that of E_2 is 0.2 Ω, and that of E_3 is 0.5 Ω.

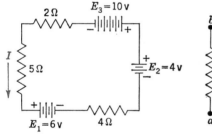

FIG. 25–3 Circuit of Example 1.

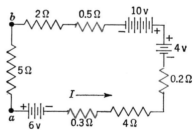

FIG. 25–4 Circuit of Example 1 illustrating internal resistances of the batteries.

SOLUTION   Figure 25–4 is a diagram of the circuit in which the internal resistances are represented in red as an aid in setting up the circuit equation. Beginning at point a and going around the circuit in the direction of current flow,

$$6 - 0.3I - 4I - 0.2I - 4 + 10 - 0.5I - 2I - 5I = 0$$

Hence, $$I = 1 \text{ amp}$$

In more complicated circuits the direction of the current is often in doubt. However, this need cause no confusion, for the direction of current flow can be *assumed* and the circuit equation written in the usual manner. If the current results in a negative value when the equation is solved, the negative sign denotes that the assumed direction was wrong. As an example, let it be assumed that the current in the circuit of Fig. 25-4 flows in the direction from *a* to *b*. Then, starting at point *a* and going around the circuit in the assumed direction,

$$- 5I - 2I - 0.5I - 10 + 4 - 0.2I - 4I - 0.3I - 6 = 0$$
$$I = -1 \text{ amp}$$

As stated above, the minus sign shows that the assumed direction of the current was wrong; therefore, the current flows in the direction from *b* to *a*.

PROBLEMS 25 – 1

Solve the following problems by using Kirchhoff's second law:

1   Three resistors $R_1 = 2\ \Omega$, $R_2 = 2.75\ \Omega$, and $R_3 = 3\ \Omega$ are connected across a 6-volt battery whose internal resistance is 0.25 Ω. How much current flows in the circuit?

2   Four resistors $R_1 = 27\ \Omega$, $R_2 = 10\ \Omega$, $R_3 = 68\ \Omega$, and $R_4 = 43\ \Omega$ are connected in series across a 12-volt battery whose internal resistance is 0.4 Ω. How much current flows in the circuit?

3   Three resistors $R_1 = 68\ \Omega$, $R_2 = 22\ \Omega$, and $R_3 = 15\ \Omega$ are connected in series across a generator whose internal resistance is 2.1 Ω. If 1.12 amp flows through the circuit, what is the generator terminal voltage?

4   What is the value of R_4 in Fig. 25-5?

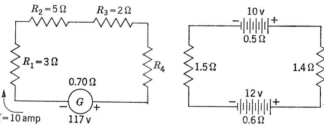

Fig. 25–5   Circuit of Prob. 4.   Fig.   25–6   Circuit   of
Prob. 7.

5   A motor that draws 16 amp at 234 volts is connected to a generator through two No. 8 copper feeders, each of which is 500 ft long. What is the generator terminal voltage?

6   A generator with a terminal voltage of 117 volts is supplying 63 amp to a load through two feeders each 1,500 ft long. If the feeders are No. 0 copper, what is the voltage across the load?

7   (a) How much current flows in the circuit of Fig. 25–6?   (b) What is the emf of the 12-volt battery?

8   (a) How much current flows in the circuit of Fig. 25–7?   (b) What is the emf of the generator?

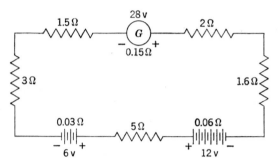

FIG. 25–7   Circuit of Prob. 8.

9   A current of 5 amp flows through the circuit of Fig. 25–8.   What is the value of R?

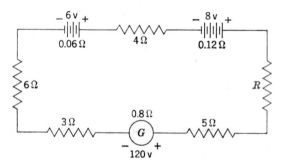

FIG. 25–8   Circuit of Prob. 9.

10   How much current flows in the circuit of Fig. 25–9?

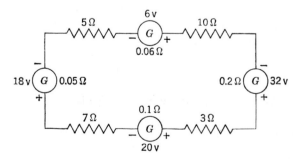

FIG. 25–9   Circuit of Prob. 10.

25 – 4 Simple applications of both laws

Although the circuits of the following examples can be solved by Ohm's law, they are included here because you are familiar with such circuits. No trouble will be encountered in solving circuits that appear to be complicated if you understand the applications of Kirchhoff's laws to simple circuits, for all circuits are combinations of the fundamental series and parallel circuits.

EXAMPLE 2   A generator supplies 7 amp to two resistances of 40 and 30 Ω connected in parallel. Neglecting the internal resistance of the generator and the resistance of the connecting wires, what is the generator voltage and the current through each resistance?

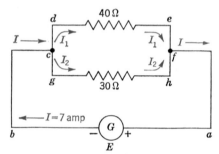

FIG. 25–10   Circuit of Example 2.

SOLUTION   Figure 25–10 is a diagram of the circuit. From our knowledge of parallel circuits, it is evident that the line current I divides at junction c into the branch currents I_1 and I_2. Similarly, I_1 and I_2 combine at junction f to form the line current I. Therefore,

$$I = I_1 + I_2$$

which is the same as $I - I_1 - I_2 = 0$ [3]

These are algebraic expressions for Kirchhoff's first law and, when used in conjunction with the second law, facilitate solution of circuits.

Upon starting at the point a and going around the circuit in the direction of current flow, the equation for the voltages around path $abcdefa$ is

$$E - 40I_1 = 0$$

$$I_1 = \frac{E}{40}$$ [4]

The equation for the voltages around path $abcghfa$ is

$$E - 30I_2 = 0$$

$$I_2 = \frac{E}{30}$$ [5]

Substituting the known values in Eq. [3],

$$7 - \frac{E}{40} - \frac{E}{30} = 0$$

$$E = 120 \text{ volts}$$

$I_1 = 3$ amp and $I_2 = 4$ amp are found from Eqs. [4] and [5], respectively.

EXAMPLE 3   Two 6-volt batteries, each with an internal resistance of 0.05 Ω, are connected in parallel to a load
resistance of 9.0 Ω. How much cur-
rent flows through the load resistance?

SOLUTION   Figure 25-11 is a diagram of the circuit. In the circuit,
two identical sources of emf are connected in parallel to supply the line
current I to the load resistance.
Again,

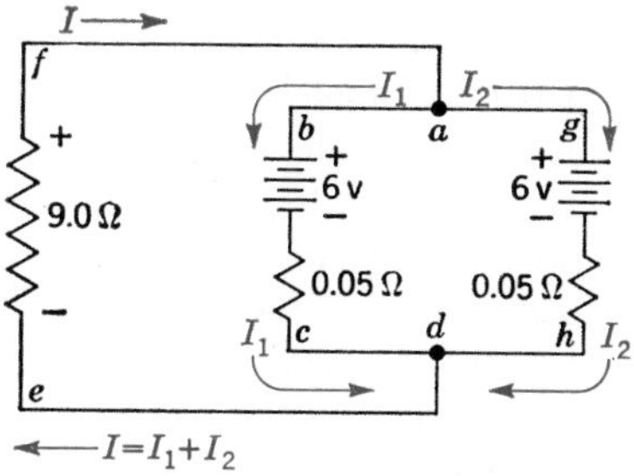

$$I = I_1 + I_2$$

or $I - I_1 - I_2 = 0$

FIG. 25-11   Circuit of Example 3.

Starting at junction a, the equation for the voltages around path $abcdefa$ is

$$6 - 0.05I_1 - 9I = 0$$

Solving for I_1, $I_1 = 120 - 180I$ [6]

Starting at junction a, the equation for the voltages around path $aghdefa$ is

$$6 - 0.05I_2 - 9I = 0$$

Solving for I_2, $I_2 = 120 - 180I$ [7]

As would be expected, I_1 and I_2 are equal. Substituting the values of I_1 and I_2
in Eq. [3],

$$I - (120 - 180I) - (120 - 180I) = 0$$

Hence, $I = 0.6648$ amp

The foregoing solution assumes three unknowns I, I_1, and I_2. However, in
writing the equations for the voltages around any path, only two unknowns
can be used, for $I = I_1 + I_2$. Thus, around path $abcdefa$,

$$6 - 0.05I_1 - 9(I_1 + I_2) = 0$$

Collecting terms, $9.05I_1 + 9I_2 = 6$ [8]

Voltages around path $aghdefa$,

$$6 - 0.05I_2 - 9(I_1 + I_2) = 0$$

Collecting terms, $9I_1 + 9.05I_2 = 6$ [9]

Since Eqs. [8] and [9] are simultaneous equations, they can be solved for I_1 and I_2. Hence,

$$I_1 = 0.3324 \text{ amp}$$
and
$$I_2 = 0.3324 \text{ amp}$$
$$I = I_1 + I_2 = 0.6648 \text{ amp}$$

PROBLEMS 25–2

1 A generator supplies 4.6 amp to two resistors of 75 and 40 Ω connected in parallel. What is the voltage across the resistors?

2 A battery supplies 7.75 amp to three resistors of 7, 16, and 14 Ω connected in parallel. What is the voltage across the resistors?

3 A generator, with an internal resistance of 0.05 Ω, supplies 15.2 amp to three resistors of 8, 4, and 10 Ω connected in parallel. What is the generator terminal voltage?

4 A battery supplies 9.7 amp to four resistors of 110, 50, 100, and 200 Ω connected in parallel. What is the voltage across the resistors?

5 (a) What is the value of the current in the circuit of Fig. 25–12? (b) How much power is expended in each of the batteries?

6 How much power would be expended in each battery in the circuit of Fig. 25–12 if the load resistance was changed from 10 to 0.5 Ω?

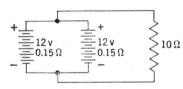

FIG. 25–12 Circuit of Prob. 5.

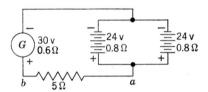

FIG. 25–13 Circuit of Probs. 7 and 8.

7 (a) What is the generator current in the circuit of Fig. 25–13? (b) In what direction does the current flow?

8 (a) What is the value of the generator current in the circuit of Fig. 25–13 if the generator terminal voltage is decreased to 12 volts? (b) In what direction does the current flow?

25 – 5 Three-wire distribution systems

Three-wire distribution systems are widely used for both d-c and a-c systems. A three-wire system may receive its energy either from a three-wire generator or from two generators of equal voltage connected in series. In either case, in solving such circuits, it is convenient to consider the three-wire system as receiving its energy from two

generators as illustrated in Fig. 25–14. The wire that is connected
at the junction between the generators is called the *neutral* wire because, when *equal* loads are connected at the same point between the
outside wires and the neutral wire, the latter carries no current.

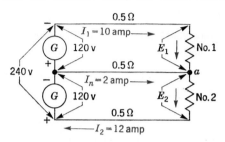

FIG. 25–14   Circuit of Example 4.

EXAMPLE 4   In the three-wire system represented in Fig. 25–14, load 1
draws 10 amp and load 2 draws 12 amp. If the terminal voltage of each
generator is 120 volts, determine the voltage across each load.

SOLUTION   Label the direction and amount of each current as in Fig.
25–14. Thus a current I_1 of 10 amp, due to load 1, flows *toward* junction a.
Also, $I_n = 2$ amp, in the neutral wire, flows *toward* junction a in order to
make a total of $I_2 = 12$ amp for load 2. This latter current flows *away*
from junction a. By assigning positive values for currents flowing toward
the junction and a negative value for the current leaving the junction,

$$I_1 + I_n - I_2 = 0$$

Substituting values, $10 + 2 - 12 = 0$

which checks according to Kirchhoff's first law.

Let E_1 and E_2 be the voltages across loads 1 and 2, respectively. Then,
starting at the positive terminal of each generator and going around the
corresponding closed circuit in the direction of load current, the voltage
equations are

For generator G_1, $120 - (10 \times 0.5) - E_1 + (2 \times 0.5) = 0$ [10]

$$E_1 = 116 \text{ volts}$$

For generator G_2, $120 - (2 \times 0.5) - E_2 - (12 \times 0.5) = 0$ [11]

$$E_2 = 113 \text{ volts}$$

In Eq. [10] the difference of potential due to the resistance of
the neutral wire was *added* because the path around the circuit
was against the direction of current in the neutral wire. In Eq. [11]
this difference of potential was *subtracted* because the path around
the circuit was in the direction of the current and therefore represented a voltage drop.

In dealing with three-wire distribution systems, it is well to remember that the difference between the currents in the outside wires flows in the neutral wire and that its direction is the same as that of the smaller of the currents in the outside wires. This is demonstrated in Fig. 25–14.

EXAMPLE 5   Figure 25–15 represents a three-wire distribution circuit in which loads 1, 2, 3, and 4 consist of lamps, each of which draws 1 amp. In

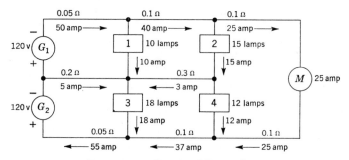

FIG. 25–15   Circuit of Example 5.

addition, a motor M, which draws 25 amp, is connected across the outside wires. Determine the voltage across each group of lamps and the voltage across the motor.

SOLUTION   First determine the amount and direction of the currents in all the wires of the system. This is conveniently accomplished by starting with the load at the end of the line and working back toward the generator until the currents in the outside wires are determined. From these, the neutral-wire currents are found. Thus, starting with the motor M of Fig. 25–15, it is apparent that the outside wires from loads 2 and 4 will carry 25 amp. Because load 2 draws 15 amp, the outside wire between loads 1 and 2 must carry this current plus the motor current, or $15 + 25 = 40$ amp. Similarly, load 1 draws 10 amp which must be carried by the outside wire between generator G_1 and load 1, in addition to the 40 amp drawn by load 2 and the motor, or $10 + 40 = 50$ amp. In like manner, the currents in the other outside wires are found, and their direction is marked. Then, because the neutral wire must supply the difference in currents between outside wires, the neutral current for each section is found, the direction being that of the smallest current in the outside wires. The work can then be checked by Kirchhoff's first law: There must be as much current flowing away from a junction as there is current flowing toward it.

Let E_1, E_2, E_3, E_4, and E_M represent the voltages across loads 1, 2, 3, 4, and M, respectively. Equations can now be written for the closed loops in the circuit.

Loop containing G_1 and load 1,

$$120 - (50 \times 0.05) - E_1 + (5 \times 0.2) = 0$$
$$E_1 = 118.5 \text{ volts}$$

Loop containing loads 1 and 2,

$$E_1 - (40 \times 0.1) - E_2 - (3 \times 0.3) = 0$$

Substituting for E_1 $\qquad 118.5 - 4 - E_2 - 0.9 = 0$
$$E_2 = 113.6 \text{ volts}$$

Loop containing G_2 and load 3,

$$120 - (5 \times 0.2) - E_3 - (55 \times 0.05) = 0$$
$$E_3 = 116.25 \text{ volts}$$

Loop containing loads 3 and 4,

$$E_3 + (3 \times 0.3) - E_4 - (37 \times 0.1) = 0$$

Substituting for E_3, $\qquad 116.25 + 0.9 - E_4 - 3.7 = 0$
$$E_4 = 113.45 \text{ volts}$$

Loop containing loads 2, 4, and M,

$$E_2 - (25 \times 0.1) - E_M - (25 \times 0.1) + E_4 = 0$$

Substituting for E_2 and E_4,
$$113.6 - 2.5 - E_M - 2.5 + 113.45 = 0$$
$$E_M = 222.05 \text{ volts}$$

CHECK   Voltage equation for outer loop containing motor,

$$120 + 120 - (50 \times 0.05) - (40 \times 0.1) - (25 \times 0.1) - E_M - (25 \times 0.1)$$
$$- (37 \times 0.1) - (55 \times 0.05) = 0$$
$$E_M = 222.05 \text{ volts}$$

PROBLEMS 25-3

1   In Fig. 25–16, each generator has a terminal voltage of 122 volts. The resistance of each feeder is 0.08 Ω, load A draws 50 amp, and load B draws 38 amp. (*a*) What is the voltage across load A? (*b*) What is the voltage across load B? (*c*) What is the total power supplied by both generators?

2   In Fig. 25–16, there is 110 volts across each load. The resistance of each feeder is 0.2 Ω, load A draws 30 amp, and load B draws 60 amp. (*a*) What is the terminal voltage of generator G_A? (*b*) What is the terminal voltage of generator G_B? (*c*) How much power is supplied by generator G_A?

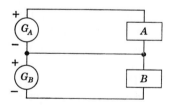

Fig. 25–16   Circuit of Probs. 1 to 4.

3   In Fig. 25–16, generator G_A has a terminal voltage of 117 volts, and the
     voltage across load B is 117 volts. The resistance of each outside feeder
     is 0.1 Ω, and the resistance of the neutral feeder is 0.2 Ω. Load A draws
     30 amp, and load B draws 20 amp. (*a*) What is the terminal voltage of
     generator G_B? (*b*) How much power is dissipated in load A?

4   In Fig. 25–16, each generator has an emf of 130 volts and an internal
     resistance of 0.25 Ω. The resistance of each outside feeder is 0.2 Ω,
     and the resistance of the neutral wire is 0.1 Ω. Load A draws 25 amp
     and B draws 30 amp. (*a*) What is the voltage across load A? (*b*) How
     much power is dissipated in load B? (*c*) What is the terminal voltage
     of generator G_A?

5   In Fig. 25–16, the power dissipated by load A is 7.39 kw and a voltmeter
     connected across this load reads 211 volts. Load B dissipates 7.24 kw,
     and a voltmeter connected across this load reads 213 volts. The gen-
     erators are located 1 mile from the loads, and the feeders are No. 0
     copper wire. What are the terminal voltages of the generators?

6   In the circuit of Fig. 25–17, each lamp draws 1 amp and the terminal
     voltage of each generator is 120 volts. (*a*) Determine the voltage
     across each group of lamps. (*b*) What is the total power expended in
     the circuit?

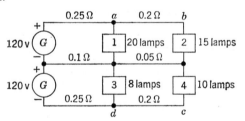

F<small>IG</small>. 25–17   Circuit of Probs. 6 to 8.

7   In the circuit of Fig. 25–17, disconnect lamp group 4. (*a*) Determine
     the voltages across the remaining groups of lamps. (*b*) What is the
     total power expended in the circuit?

8   In the original circuit of Fig. 25–17, connect a motor load of 20 amp
     across lamp group 3. (*a*) How much power is dissipated in lamp
     group 1? (*b*) Determine the voltages across each group of lamps.

9   The generators of Fig. 25–18 connect to their loads through No. 2
     copper feeders. Motor M_1, which draws 12 amp, and lamp bank 1,
     which draws 15 amp, are located 2,000 ft from the generators. Lamp
     bank 2, which draws 20 amp, and motors M_2 and M_3, each of which
     draws 12 amp, are located 3,000 ft from the generators. (*a*) Determine
     the voltage across motor M_1. (*b*) Determine the voltage across lamp
     bank 1. (*c*) Determine the voltage across lamp bank 2. (*d*) Determine

the voltage across motor M_2. (e) How much power is expended by
motor M_2?

10 Lamp bank 2 of the circuit of Fig. 25–18 is disconnected. (a) Determine
the voltage across lamp bank 1. (b) What is the total power expended
in the circuit?

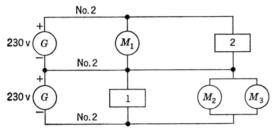

Fig. 25–18   Circuit of Probs. 9 and 10.

– 6 Further applications of Kirchhoff's laws

In previous examples and problems if two sources of emf were
connected to the same circuit, the values of emf and internal resistance have been equal. However, there are many types of circuits
that contain more than one source of power, each with a different
emf and different internal resistance.

EXAMPLE 6   Figure 25–19 represents two batteries connected in parallel
supplying current to a resistance of 2 Ω. One battery has an emf of 6 volts
with an internal resistance of 0.15 Ω, and the other battery has an emf of 5
volts with an internal resistance of 0.05 Ω. Determine the current through
the batteries and the current in the external circuit. Neglect the resistance
of the connecting wires.

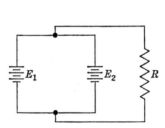

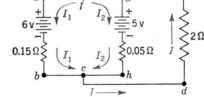

Fig. 25–19   Circuit of Example 6.

Fig. 25–20   Circuit of Example 6
labeled with known values.

SOLUTION   Draw a diagram of the circuit representing the internal resistance of the batteries, and label the circuit with all the known values as
shown in Fig. 25–20. Label the unknown currents, and mark the direction
each current is assumed to flow.

There are three currents of unknown value in the circuit, I_1, I_2, and the current I which flows through the external circuit. However, because $I = I_1 + I_2$, the unknown currents can be reduced to two unknowns by considering a current of $(I_1 + I_2)$ amp flowing through the external circuit.

For the path $abcdefa$, $6 - 0.15I_1 - 2(I_1 + I_2) = 0$

Collecting terms, $2.15I_1 + 2I_2 = 6$ [12]

For the path $ghcdefg$, $5 - 0.05I_2 - 2(I_1 + I_2) = 0$

Collecting terms, $2I_1 + 2.05I_2 = 5$ [13]

Equations [12] and [13] are simultaneous equations that, when solved, result in

$$I_1 = 5.64 \text{ amp}$$

and $$I_2 = -3.07 \text{ amp}$$

The negative sign of the current I_2 denotes that this current is flowing in a direction opposite to that assumed. The value of the line current is

$$I = I_1 + I_2 = 5.64 + (-3.07) = 2.57 \text{ amp}$$

Try checking this solution by changing the direction of I_2 in Fig. 25–20 and rewriting the voltage equations accordingly, remembering that now, at junction f, for example, $I + I_2 - I_1 = 0$. This will demonstrate that it is immaterial which way the arrows point, for the signs preceding the current values, when found, determine whether or not the assumed directions are correct. As previously mentioned, however, it must be remembered that going through a resistance in a direction opposite to the current arrow represents a voltage (rise) which must be added, whereas going through a resistance in the same direction of the current arrow represents a voltage (drop) which must be subtracted.

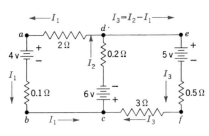

FIG. 25–21   Circuit of Example 7.

EXAMPLE 7   Figure 25–21 represents a network containing three unequal sources of emf. Find the current flowing in each branch.

SOLUTION   Assume a direction for each of the unknown currents I_1, I_2, and I_3, and label them as shown in the circuit diagram.

Although three unknown currents are involved, they can be reduced to two unknowns by expressing one current in terms of the other two. This is accomplished by applying Kirchhoff's first law to some junction such as c. By considering current flow toward a junction as positive and that flowing away from a junction as negative,

$$I_1 + I_3 - I_2 = 0$$
$$I_3 = I_2 - I_1 \qquad [14]$$

Since there are now only two unknown currents I_1 and I_2, Kirchhoff's second law may be applied to any two different closed loops in the network.

For path *abcda*, $\qquad\qquad 4 - 0.1I_1 + 6 - 0.2I_2 - 2I_1 = 0$

Collecting terms, $\qquad\qquad\qquad\qquad 2.1I_1 + 0.2I_2 = 10 \qquad\qquad$ [15]

For path *efcde*,

$$5 - 0.5(I_2 - I_1) - 3(I_2 - I_1) + 6 - 0.2I_2 = 0$$

Collecting terms, $\qquad\qquad\qquad\qquad 3.5I_1 - 3.7I_2 = -11 \qquad\qquad$ [16]

Equations [15] and [16] are simultaneous equations that, when solved, result in

$$I_1 = 4.109 \text{ amp}$$

and $\qquad\qquad\qquad\qquad I_2 = 6.860 \text{ amp}$

Substituting in Eq. [14], $\quad I_3 = 6.860 - 4.109 = 2.751 \text{ amp}$

The assumed directions of current flow are correct because all values are positive.

The solution can be checked by applying Kirchhoff's second law to a path not previously used. When the current values are substituted in the equation for this path, an identity should result. Thus, for path *adefcba*,

$$2I_1 + 5 - 0.5(I_2 - I_1) - 3(I_2 - I_1) + 0.1I_1 - 4 = 0$$

Collecting terms, $\qquad\qquad\qquad 5.6I_1 - 3.5I_2 = -1 \qquad\qquad$ [17]

The substitution of the numerical values of I_1 and I_2 in Eq. [17] verifies the solution within reasonable limits of accuracy.

−7   Outline for solving networks

In common with all other problems, the solution of a circuit or a network should not be started until the conditions are analyzed and it is clearly understood what is to be found. Then a definite procedure should be adopted and followed until the solution is completed.

In order to facilitate solutions of networks by means of Kirchhoff's laws, the following procedure is suggested:

1   Draw a large, neat diagram of the network, arranging the circuits so that they appear in their simplest form.

2   Letter the diagram with all the known values such as sources of emf, currents, and resistances. Carefully mark the polarities of the known emfs.

3   Assign a symbol to each unknown quantity.

4   Indicate with arrows the assumed direction of current flow in each branch of the network. The number of unknown currents can be reduced by assigning a direction to all but one of the unknown

currents at a junction. Then, by Kirchhoff's first law, the remaining current can be expressed in terms of the others.

5   Using Kirchhoff's second law, set up as many equations as there are unknowns to be determined. In order that each equation contain some relation that has not been expressed in another equation, each circuit path followed should cover some part of the circuit not used for other paths.

6   Solve the resulting simultaneous equations for the values of the unknown quantities.

7   Check the values obtained by substituting them in a voltage equation that has been obtained by following a circuit path not previously used.

PROBLEMS 25 – 4

1   In the circuit of Fig. 25–22, (a) how much current flows through R_3, (b) how much power is expended in R_2?

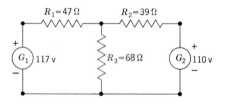

FIG. 25–22   Circuit of Probs. 1 and 2.

2   In the circuit of Fig. 25–22, R_3 becomes short-circuited. (a) How much current flows through the short circuit? (b) How much power is supplied by generator G_1?

3   In the circuit of Fig. 25–23, (a) how much current flows through R_4 (b) how much current flows through the batteries when R is open-circuited and in what direction?

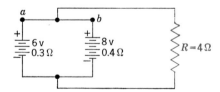

FIG. 25–23   Circuit of Probs. 3 and 4.

4   In the original circuit of Fig. 25–23, R is shunted by a resistor of 1 Ω. (a) How much power is expended in the shunting resistor? (b) What is the terminal voltage of the 6-volt battery?

5 In the circuit of Fig. 25–24, if the internal resistance of the generator
   is neglected, (a) how much power is being supplied by the generator,
   (b) what is the voltage across R?

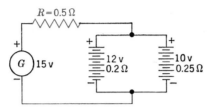

FIG. 25–24 Circuit of Probs. 5 and 6.

6 In the circuit of Fig. 25–24, the generator has an internal resistance of
   0.15 Ω. If the connections of the generator are reversed, (a) how much
   power will be dissipated in R, (b) what will be the terminal voltage of
   the 10-volt battery?

7 In the circuit of Fig. 25–25, (a) how much power is dissipated in R_4,
   (b) what is the voltage across R_1?

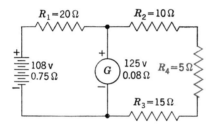

FIG. 25–25 Circuit of Probs. 7 and 8.

8 If R_1 is short-circuited in the circuit of Fig. 25–25, (a) what is the
   voltage across R_4, (b) how much power is dissipated in the battery?

9 In the circuit of Fig. 25–26, battery A has an emf of 114 volts and an
   internal resistance of 1.5 Ω. Battery B has an emf of 108 volts and an

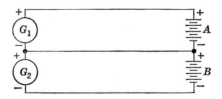

FIG. 25–26 Circuit of Prob. 9.

internal resistance of 1 Ω. Each generator has an emf of 122 volts and
an internal resistance of 0.05 Ω. The resistance of each feeder is 0.02 Ω.

(a) How much current flows through battery A?

(b) How much power is expended in battery B?

10   In the circuit of Fig. 25–27, (a) how much power is expended in R_5, (b) how much power is expended in generator G_2?

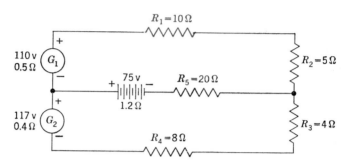

FIG. 25–27   Circuit of Probs. 10 and 11.

11   If the connections of the battery are reversed in Fig. 25–27, (a) what is the voltage across R_5, (b) how much power is expended in the entire circuit?

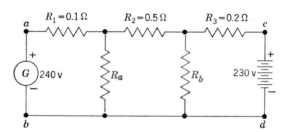

FIG. 25–28   Circuits of Probs. 12, 13, and 14.

12   Figure 25–28 represents a bank of batteries supplying power to loads R_a and R_b, with R_1, R_2, and R_3 representing the lumped line resistance. R_b is disconnected and R_a draws 50 amp.   Neglecting the internal resistance of the generator and batteries, (a) what is the voltage across R_2, (b) how much current is flowing in the batteries, and in what direction is it flowing?

13   R_b is connected in the circuit of Fig. 25–28 and draws 75 amp.   If R_a draws 50 amp, (a) what is the voltage across R_b, (b) how much power is expended in R_2?

14   In the circuit of Fig. 25–28, the loads are adjusted until R_a draws 150 amp and R_b draws 25 amp.   How much power is lost in R_2?

─ 8   Equivalent star and delta circuits

EXAMPLE 8   Determine the currents through the branches of the network of Fig. 25–29, and find the equivalent resistance between points a and c.

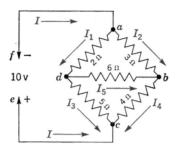

FIG. 25–29   Circuit of Example 7.

SOLUTION   Assume directions for all the currents, and label them on the figure.

By Kirchhoff's second law,

Path $efabce$,	$10 - 3I_2 - 4I_4 = 0$	[18]
Path $efadce$,	$10 - 2I_1 - 5I_3 = 0$	[19]
Path $abda$,	$-3I_2 + 6I_5 + 2I_1 = 0$	[20]
Path $dbcd$,	$-6I_5 - 4I_4 + 5I_3 = 0$	[21]
Path $abcda$,	$-3I_2 - 4I_4 + 5I_3 + 2I_1 = 0$	[22]

By Kirchhoff's first law,

Junction a,	$I - I_1 - I_2 = 0$	$\therefore I = I_1 + I_2$	[23]
Junction b,	$I_2 + I_5 - I_4 = 0$	$\therefore I_4 = I_2 + I_5$	[24]
Junction c,	$I_4 + I_3 - I = 0$	$\therefore I = I_3 + I_4$	[25]
Junction d,	$I_1 - I_5 - I_3 = 0$	$\therefore I_3 = I_1 - I_5$	[26]

Substituting I_4 from Eq. [24] in Eq. [18]

$$10 - 3I_2 - 4(I_2 + I_5) = 0$$

or
$$7I_2 + 4I_5 = 10 \qquad [27]$$

Substituting I_3 from Eq. [26] in Eq. [19],

$$10 - 2I_1 - 5(I_1 - I_5) = 0$$

or
$$7I_1 - 5I_5 = 10 \qquad [28]$$

Substituting I_4 from Eq. [24] and I_3 from Eq. [26] in Eq. [21],

$$-6I_5 - 4(I_2 + I_5) + 5(I_1 - I_5) = 0$$

or
$$5I_1 - 4I_2 - 15I_5 = 0 \qquad [29]$$

Solving Eqs. [27], [28], and [29] simultaneously,

$$I_1 = 1.540 \text{ amp}$$
$$I_2 = 1.339 \text{ amp}$$
$$I_5 = 0.1562 \text{ amp}$$

Substituting these values in equations not used before,

$$I_3 = 1.383 \text{ amp}$$
$$I_4 = 1.496 \text{ amp}$$

By Eq. [23], $I = I_1 + I_2 = 1.540 + 1.339 = 2.879 \text{ amp}$

The equivalent resistance between points a and c is

$$\frac{E}{I} = \frac{10}{2.879} = 3.47 \ \Omega$$

By expressing the branch currents in terms of other currents and labeling the circuit accordingly, this problem can be solved with a smaller number of equations. This is left as a problem for you.

You will note, from the solution of Example 7, that the solution by Kirchhoff's laws of networks containing such configurations can become complicated. There are many cases, however, where such networks can be replaced with more convenient equivalent circuits.

The three resistors R_1, R_2, and R_3 in Fig. 25–30a are said to be connected in *delta* (Greek letter Δ). R_a, R_b, and R_c in Fig. 25–30b are connected in *star*, or Y.

If these two circuits are to be made equivalent, then the resistance between terminals A and B, B and C, and A and C must be the same in each circuit. Hence, in Fig. 25–30a the resistance from A to B is

$$R_{AB} = \frac{R_1(R_2 + R_3)}{R_1 + R_2 + R_3} \qquad [30]$$

In Fig. 25–30b the resistance from A to B is

$$R_{AB} = R_a + R_b \qquad [31]$$

Equating Eqs. [30] and [31],

$$R_a + R_b = \frac{R_1 R_2 + R_1 R_3}{R_1 + R_2 + R_3} \qquad [32]$$

Similarly, $$R_b + R_c = \frac{R_1 R_2 + R_2 R_3}{R_1 + R_2 + R_3} \qquad [33]$$

and $$R_a + R_c = \frac{R_1R_3 + R_2R_3}{R_1 + R_2 + R_3}$$ [34]

Equations [32], [33], and [34] are simultaneous and, when solved, result in

$$R_a = \frac{R_1R_3}{R_1 + R_2 + R_3} = \frac{R_1R_3}{\Sigma R_\Delta}$$ [35]

$$R_b = \frac{R_1R_2}{R_1 + R_2 + R_3} = \frac{R_1R_2}{\Sigma R_\Delta}$$ [36]

and $$R_c = \frac{R_2R_3}{R_1 + R_2 + R_3} = \frac{R_2R_3}{\Sigma R_\Delta}$$ [37]

Since Σ (Greek letter sigma) is used to denote "the summation of,"

$$\Sigma R_\Delta = R_1 + R_2 + R_3$$

EXAMPLE 9   In Fig. 25-30a, $R_1 = 2\ \Omega$, $R_2 = 3\ \Omega$, and $R_3 = 5\ \Omega$. What are the values of the resistances in the equivalent Y circuit of Fig. 25-30b?

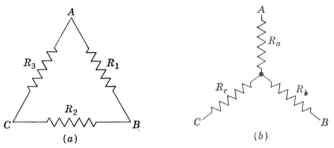

FIG. 25-30 (a) Resistors connected in delta. (b) Resistors connected in star on Y.

SOLUTION $\Sigma R_\Delta = 2 + 3 + 5 = 10\ \Omega$

Substituting in Eq. [35], $R_a = \dfrac{2 \times 5}{10} = 1\ \Omega$

Substituting in Eq. [36], $R_b = \dfrac{2 \times 3}{10} = 0.6\ \Omega$

Substituting in Eq. [37], $R_c = \dfrac{3 \times 5}{10} = 1.5\ \Omega$

EXAMPLE 10   Determine the equivalent resistance between points a and c in the circuit of Fig. 25-31a.

SOLUTION   Convert one of the delta circuits of Fig. 25-31a to its equivalent Y circuit. Thus, for the delta abd,

$$\Sigma R_\Delta = 3 + 6 + 2 = 11\ \Omega$$

The equivalent Y resistances which are shown in Fig. 25–31b are

$$R_a = \frac{3 \times 2}{11} = 0.545 \ \Omega$$

$$R_b = \frac{3 \times 6}{11} = 1.64 \ \Omega$$

and

$$R_c = \frac{2 \times 6}{11} = 1.09 \ \Omega$$

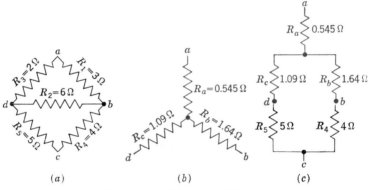

(a)   (b)   (c)

FIG. 25–31   Circuits of Example 9.

The equivalent Y circuit is connected to the remainder of the network as shown in Fig. 25–31c and is solved as an ordinary series-parallel combination.

Thus,

$$R_{ac} = R_a + \frac{(R_c + R_5)(R_b + R_4)}{R_c + R_5 + R_b + R_4}$$

$$= 0.545 + \frac{(1.09 + 5)(1.64 + 4)}{1.09 + 5 + 1.64 + 4} = 3.47 \ \Omega$$

Note that the values of Fig. 25–31 are the same as those of Fig. 25–29.

The equations for converting a Y circuit to its equivalent delta circuit are obtained by solving Eqs. [35], [36], and [37] simultaneously.   This results in

$$R_1 = \frac{\Sigma R_Y}{R_c} \qquad\qquad [\,38\,]$$

$$R_2 = \frac{\Sigma R_Y}{R_a} \qquad\qquad [\,39\,]$$

and

$$R_3 = \frac{\Sigma R_Y}{R_b} \qquad\qquad [\,40\,]$$

where

$$\Sigma R_Y = R_a R_b + R_b R_c + R_a R_c$$

A convenient method for remembering the $\Delta - Y$ and $Y - \Delta$ conversions is illustrated in Fig. 25-32.

In converting from Δ to Y, each equivalent Y resistance is equal to the product of the two *adjacent* Δ resistances divided by the summation of the Δ resistances. For example, R_1 and R_3 are adjacent to R_a; therefore,

$$R_a = \frac{R_1 R_3}{\Sigma R_\Delta}$$

In converting from Y to Δ, each equivalent Δ resistance is found by dividing ΣR_Y by the *opposite* Y resistance. For example, R_1 is opposite R_c; therefore, $R_1 = \Sigma R_Y / R_c$.

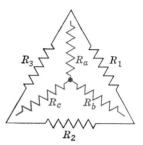

Fig. 25-32   Resistance equivalents.

PROBLEMS 25-5

1   In the Δ circuit of Fig. 25-30a, $R_1 = 15$ Ω, $R_2 = 20$ Ω, and $R_3 = 10$ Ω. Determine the resistances of the equivalent Y circuit.

2   In the Δ circuit of Fig. 25-30a, $R_1 = 9.4$ Ω, $R_2 = 15.7$ Ω, and $R_3 = 11.8$ Ω. Determine the resistances of the equivalent Y circuit.

3   In the Δ circuit of Fig. 25-30a, $R_1 = R_2 = R_3 = 100$ Ω. Determine the resistances of the equivalent Y circuit.

4   In the Y circuit of Fig. 25-30b, $R_a = 8$ Ω, $R_b = 15$ Ω, and $R_c = 10$ Ω. Determine the resistances of the equivalent Δ circuit.

5   In the Y circuit of Fig. 25-30b, $R_a = 3.20$ Ω, $R_b = 2.80$ Ω, and $R_c = 2.24$ Ω. Determine the resistances of the equivalent Δ circuit.

6   In the Y circuit of Fig. 25-30b, $R_a = R_b = R_c = 100$ Ω. Determine the resistances of the equivalent Δ circuit.

7   In the circuit of Fig. 25-33, $R_1 = 20$ Ω, $R_2 = 10$ Ω, $R_3 = 15$ Ω, $R_4 = 12$ Ω, $R_5 = 8$ Ω, and $E = 32$ volts. What is the value of I?

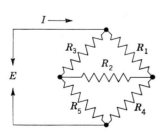

Fig. 25-33   Circuit of Probs. 7 to 12.

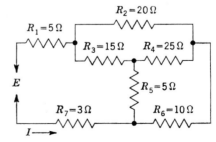

Fig. 25-34   Circuit of Probs. 13, 14, and 15.

8 How much current flows through R_5 in Prob. 7?

9 How much current is flowing in R_2 of Prob. 7?

10 In the circuit of Fig. 25–33, $R_1 = 10 \, \Omega$, $R_2 = 5 \, \Omega$, $R_3 = 25 \, \Omega$, $R_4 = 20 \, \Omega$, $R_5 = 50 \, \Omega$, and $E = 100$ volts. What is the value of I?

11 How much current is flowing in R_2 of Prob. 10?

12 In the circuit of Fig. 25–33, $R_1 = 2 \, \Omega$, $R_3 = 6 \, \Omega$, $R_4 = 3.8 \, \Omega$, $R_5 = 1.4 \, \Omega$, $E = 15.5$ volts, and $I = 5$

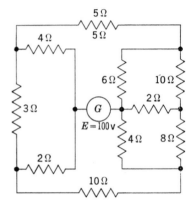

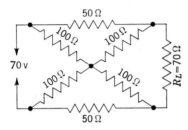

Fig. 25–35 Circuit of Prob. 16.   Fig. 25–36 Circuit of Prob. 17.

amp. What is the resistance of R_2?

13 Determine the value of the current I in the circuit of Fig. 25–34 if $E = 117$ volts.

14 How much current flows in R_3 in the circuit of Fig. 25–34?

15 How much current flows in R_6 in the circuit of Fig. 25–34?

16 How much current flows through the load resistance R_L in Fig. 25–35?

17 How much current does the generator G supply to the circuit of Fig. 25–36?

CHAPTER 26
ANGLES

This chapter deals with the study of angles as an introduction to the branch of mathematics called *trigonometry*. The word "trigonometry" is derived from two Greek words meaning "measurement" or "solution" of triangles.

Trigonometry is both algebraic and geometric in nature. It is not confined to the solution of triangles but forms a basis for more advanced subjects in mathematics. A knowledge of the subject paves the way for a clear understanding of a-c and related circuits.

26 – 1   Angles

In trigonometry, we are concerned primarily with the many relations that exist among the sides and angles of triangles. In order to understand the meaning and measurement of angles, it is essential that you thoroughly understand these corelations.

An angle is formed when two straight lines meet at a point. In Fig. 26–1a, lines OA and OX meet at the point O to form the angle AOX. Similarly, in Fig. 26–1b, the angle BOX is formed by lines OB and OX meeting at the point O. This point is called the *vertex* of the angle, and the two lines are called the *sides* of the angle. The size, or magnitude, of an angle is a measure of the difference in directions of the sides. Thus, in Fig. 26–1, angle *BOX* is a larger angle than *AOX*. The lengths of the sides of an angle have no bearing on the size of the angle.

In geometry it is customary to denote an angle by the symbol ∠.

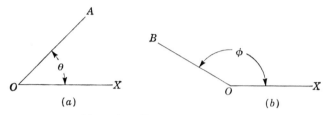

(*a*)   (*b*)

Fig. 26–1   Formation of angles.

If this notation is used, angle *AOX* would be written ∠*AOX*.

An angle is also denoted by the letter at the vertex or by a supplementary letter placed inside the angle. Thus, angle *AOX* is correctly denoted by ∠*AOX*, ∠*O*, or ∠*θ*. Also, *BOX* could be written ∠*BOX*, ∠*O*, or ∠*ϕ*.

If equal angles are formed when one straight line intersects another, the angles are called *right angles*. In Fig. 26–2, angles *XOY*, *ϕ*, *X'OY'*, and *α* are all right angles.

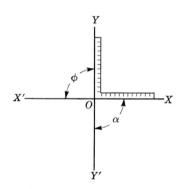

An *acute angle* is an angle that is less than a right angle. In Fig. 26–3*a*, ∠*α* is an acute angle.

An *obtuse angle* is an angle that is greater than a right angle. In Fig. 26–3*b*, ∠*β* is an obtuse angle.

Two angles whose sum is one right angle are called *complementary* angles. Either one is said to be the "complement" of the other. Thus, in Fig.

Fig. 26–2   Right angles.

26–3*c*, angles *ϕ* and *θ* are complementary angles; *ϕ* is the complement of *θ*, and *θ* is the complement of *ϕ*.

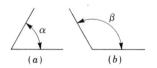   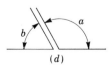

(*a*)   (*b*)   (*c*)   (*d*)

Fig. 26–3   (*a*) Acute angle, (*b*) obtuse angle, (*c*) complementary angles, and (*d*) supplementary angles.

Two angles whose sum is two right angles (a straight line) are called *supplementary angles*. Either one is said to be the "supplement" of the other. Thus, in Fig. 26–3d, angles b and a are supplementary angles; b is the supplement of a, and a is the supplement of b.

6 – 2 Generation of angles

In the study of trigonometry, it becomes necessary to extend our concept of angles beyond the geometric definitions stated in Sec. 26–1. An angle should be thought of as being generated by a line (line segment or half ray) that starts in a certain initial position and rotates about a point called the *vertex* of the angle until it stops at its final position. The original position of the rotating line is called the *initial side* of the angle, and the final position is called the *terminal side* of the angle.

An angle is said to be in *standard position* when its vertex is at the origin of a system of rectangular coordinates and its initial side extends in the positive direction along the X axis. Thus, in Fig. 26–4,

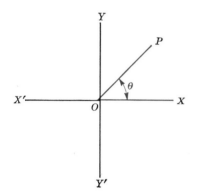

Fig. 26–4 Angle θ in standard position.

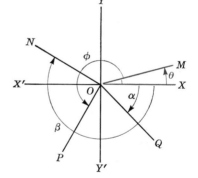

Fig. 26–5 Generation of angles.

the angle θ is in standard position. The vertex is at the origin, and the initial side is on the positive X axis. The angle has been generated by the line OP revolving, or sweeping, from OX to its final position.

An angle is called a *positive angle* if it is generated by a line revolving counterclockwise. If the generating line revolves clockwise, the angle is called a *negative angle*. In Fig. 26–5, all angles are in standard position. θ is a positive angle that was generated by the line OM revolving counterclockwise from OX. ϕ is also a positive angle whose terminal side is *OP*. α is a negative angle that was generated by the line *OQ* revolving in a clockwise direction from the initial side *OX*. β is also a negative angle whose terminal side is *ON*.

If the terminal side of an angle that is in standard position lies in the first quadrant, then that angle is said to be *an angle in the first quadrant*, etc. Thus, θ in Fig. 26–4 and θ in Fig. 26–5 are in the first quadrant. Similarly, in Fig. 26–5, β is in the second quadrant, φ is in the third quadrant, and α is in the fourth quadrant.

26 – 3   The sexagesimal system

There are several systems of angular measurement. The three most commonly used are the right angle, the circular (or natural) system, and the sexagesimal system. The right angle is almost always used as a unit of angular measure in plane geometry and is constantly used by builders, surveyors, etc. However, for the purposes of trigonometry, it is an inconvenient unit because of its large size.

The unit most commonly used in trigonometry is the *degree*, which is one-ninetieth of a right angle. The degree is defined as that angle formed by $\frac{1}{360}$ part of a revolution of the angle-generating line. The degree is divided into 60 equal parts called *minutes*, and the minute into 60 equal parts called *seconds*. The word "sexagesimal" is derived from a Latin word pertaining to the number 60.

Instead of dividing the degrees into minutes and seconds, we shall divide them decimally for convenience. For example, instead of expressing an angle of 43 degrees 36 minutes as 43°36′, we write 43.6°.

The actual measurement of an angle consists in finding how many degrees and a decimal part of a degree there are in the angle. This can be accomplished with a fair degree of accuracy by means of a *protractor*, which is an instrument for measuring or constructing angles.

To measure an angle *XOP*, as in Fig. 26–6, place the center of the

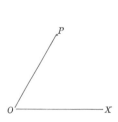

FIG. 26–6   Angle to be measured.

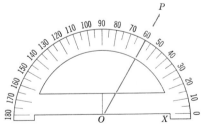

FIG. 26–7   Using protractor to measure angle *XOP*.

protractor indicated by O at the vertex of the angle with, say, the line OX coinciding with one edge of the protractor as shown in Fig. 26–7. The magnitude of the angle, which is 60°, is indicated where the line OP crosses the graduated scale.

To construct an angle, say 30° from a given line OX, place the center of the protractor on the vertex O. Pivot the protractor about this point until OX is on a line with the 0° mark on the scale. In this

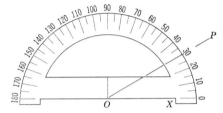

FIG. 26–8 Using protractor to construct angle.

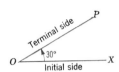

FIG. 26–9 Angle of 30°.

position, 30° on the scale now marks the terminal side OP as shown in Figs. 26–8 and 26–9.

26 – 4 Angles of any magnitude

In the study of trigonometry, it will be necessary to extend our concept of angles in order to include angles greater than 360°, either positive or negative. Thinking of an angle being generated, as explained in Sec. 26–2, permits consideration of angles of any size, for the generating line can rotate from its initial position in a positive or negative direction so as to produce an angle of any size, even greater than 360°. Figure 26–10 illustrates how an angle of +750° is generated. However, for the purpose of ordinary computation, we consider such an angle to be in the same quadrant as its terminal side with a magnitude equal to the remainder after the largest multiple of 360° it will contain has

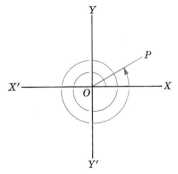

FIG. 26–10 Generation of 750° angle.

been subtracted from it. Thus, in Fig. 26–10, the angle is in the first quadrant and, geometrically, is equal to 750° − 720° = 30°.

PROBLEMS 26 – 1

1   What is the complement of (a) 22°, (b) 67°, (c) 49°, (d) 100°, (e) 275°,
    (f) −80°?

2   What is the supplement of (a) 27°, (b) 105°, (c) 215°, (d) 270°, (e) 330°,
    (f) −78°?

3   Construct two complementary angles each in standard position on the
    same pair of axes.

4   Construct two supplementary angles each in standard position on the
    same pair of axes.

5   Using a protractor, construct the following angles, placing them in
    standard position on rectangular coordinates. Indicate by arrows the
    direction and amount of rotation necessary to generate these angles:
    (a) 45°, (b) 140°, (c) 215°, (d) 310°, (e) 455°, (f) −50°, (g) −215°,
    (h) −300°, (i) −375°, (j) −840°.

6   Through how many degrees does the minute hand of a clock turn in
    (a) 25 min, (b) 50 min?

7   Through how many right angles does the minute hand of a clock turn
    from 10:15 A.M. to 3:45 P.M. of the same day?

8   How many degrees per minute do (a) the second hand, (b) the minute
    hand, and (c) the hour hand of a clock rotate?

9   A motor armature has a speed of 2,400 rpm. What is its angular velocity
    (speed) in degrees per second?

10 The shaft of the motor armature in Prob. 9 is directly connected to a
    pulley 15 in. in diameter. What is the pulley-rim speed in feet per
    second?

26 – 5   The circular, or natural, system

The circular, or natural, system of angular measurement is sometimes
called *radian measure* or *π measure*. The unit of measure is the *radian*.

A radian is an angle that, when placed with its vertex at the center
of a circle, intercepts an arc equal in length to the radius of the circle.
Thus, in Fig. 26–11, if the length of the arc AP equals the radius of the
circle, then angle AOP is equal to 1 radian. Figure 26–12 shows a
circle divided into radians.

The circular system of measure is used extensively in electrical and
electronics formulas and is almost universally used in the higher
branches of mathematics.

From geometry, it is known that the circumference of a circle is
given by the relation

$$C = 2\pi r \qquad\qquad [1]$$

where r is the radius of the circle. Dividing both sides of Eq. [1] by r,

$$\frac{C}{r} = 2\pi \qquad [2]$$

Now Eq. [2] says simply that the ratio of the circumference to the radius is 2π. That is, the length of the circumference is 2π times

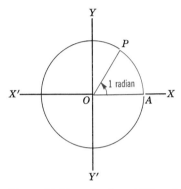

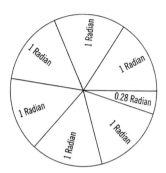

FIG. 26–11   Angle $AOP = 1$ radian.

FIG. 26–12   Circle divided into radians.

longer than the radius. Therefore, a circle must contain 2π radians. Also, since the circumference subtends 360°, it follows that

$$2\pi \text{ radians} = 360°$$
$$\pi \text{ radians} = 180°$$

or $\qquad$ **1 radian** $= \dfrac{180°}{\pi} = \textbf{57.2959°} \cong \textbf{57.3°} \qquad$ [3]

From Eq. [3], the following is evident:

To reduce radians to degrees, multiply the number of radians by 57.3°.

If absolute accuracy is desired, multiply by $180°/\pi$.

To reduce degrees to radians, multiply the number of degrees by 0.01745.

If absolute accuracy is desired, multiply by $\pi/180°$.

Several types of slide rule have gauge marks at 57.3 on scales C and D denoted by R (for radians). These marks are a convenience in converting from radians to degrees. Since 0.01745 is the reciprocal of 57.3, the former number will be found on the reciprocal scales opposite the R gauge marks. Similarly, if 180 on scale CF is set to π on DF,

0.01745 will appear on scale D opposite the index of scale C. In this manner the rule is set up for multiplication by 0.01745.

EXAMPLE 1   Reduce 1.7 radians to degrees.
SOLUTION   1 radian $= 57.3°$
Hence,   1.7 radians $= 1.7 \times 57.3 = 97.4°$

EXAMPLE 2   Convert 15.6° to radians.
SOLUTION $1° = 0.01745$ radian
Hence, $15.6° = 15.6 \times 0.01745 = 0.272$ radian

PROBLEMS 26 – 2

1 Express the following angles in radians: (a) 60°, (b) 120°, (c) 205°, (d) 15°, (e) 306°, (f) 2°.

2 Express the following angles in degrees: (a) 3 radians, (b) 0.4 radian, (c) $3\pi/4$ radians, (d) $1/\pi$ radian, (e) 0.08 radian, (f) $2\pi/3$ radians.

3 Express in terms of π the number of radians in the following angles: (a) 30°, (b) 45°, (c) 315°, (d) 135°, (e) 240°, (f) 720°.

4 Through how many radians does the second hand of a clock turn from 7:05 A.M. to 8:15 A.M. of the same day?

5 Through how many radians does the hour hand of a clock turn in 50 min?

6 What is the angular velocity, in radians per second, of (a) the second hand, (b) the minute hand, and (c) the hour hand of a clock?

7 The speed of a motor armature is 1,800 rpm. What is its angular velocity in radians per second?

8 A radar antenna rotates 6 rpm. What is its angular velocity in radians per second?

9 A radar antenna has an angular velocity of π radians/sec. What is its speed of rotation in revolutions per minute?

10 What is the approximate angular velocity of the earth in radians per minute?

26 – 6   Similar triangles

Two triangles are said to be *similar* when their corresponding angles are equal. That is, similar triangles are identical in shape but may not be the same size. The important characteristic of similar triangles is that a direct proportionality exists between corresponding sides. The three triangles of Fig. 26–13 have been constructed so that their corresponding angles are equal. Therefore, the three triangles are similar, and their corresponding sides are proportional. This leads to the proportions

$$\frac{AB}{AC} = \frac{DE}{DF} = \frac{GH}{GI} \qquad \frac{BC}{AB} = \frac{EF}{DE} = \frac{HI}{GH} \cdots$$

As an example, if $AB = 0.5$ in., $DE = 1$ in., and $GH = 1.5$ in., then DF is twice as long as AC and GI is three times as long as AC. Similarly, HI is three times as long as BC, and EF is twice as long as BC.

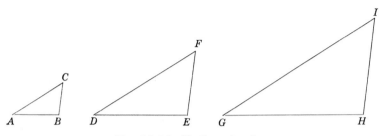

Fig. 26-13 Similar triangles.

The properties of similar triangles are used extensively in measuring distance, such as the distances across bodies of water or other obstructions or the heights of various objects. In addition, the relation between similar triangles forms the very basis of trigonometry.

Since the sum of the three angles of any triangle is 180°, it follows that if two angles of a triangle are equal to two angles of another triangle, the third angle of one must also be equal to the third angle of the other. Therefore, two triangles are similar if two angles of one are equal to two angles of the other.

If the numerical values of the necessary parts of a triangle are known, the triangle can be drawn to scale with the use of compasses, protractor, and ruler. The completed figure can then be measured with protractor and ruler to obtain the numerical values of the unknown parts. This is conveniently accomplished on squared paper.

PROBLEMS 26 – 3

1 The sides of a triangle are 16, 12, and 20 ft. The shortest side of a similar triangle is 3 ft. How long are the other two sides of the second triangle?

2 Two triangles are similar. The sides of the first are 17, 12, and 24 cm. The longest side of the second triangle is 360 mm. How long are the other two sides of the second triangle?

NOTE In the following problems the sides and angles of all triangles will be as represented in Fig. 26-14. That is, the angles will be represented by

the capital letters A, B, and C, and the sides opposite these angles will be
the corresponding letters a, b, and c.

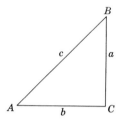

FIG. 26–14 Triangle
for Probs. 3 to 10.

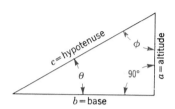

FIG. 26–15 Right triangle.

Solve the following by graphical methods:

3 $a = 4$, $B = 36.9°$, $C = 90°$

4 $a = 18$, $b = 24$, $c = 30$

5 $C = 11$, $A = 80°$, $B = 20°$

6 $c = 4.75$, $A = 110°$, $B = 36°$

7 $A = 33.8°$, $C = 46.2°$, $b = 17.7$

8 $C = 90°$, $a = 4.95$, $B = 4.95$

9 $c = 10$, $b = 20$, $A = 49.1°$

10 $b = 35$, $c = 35$, $B = 60°$

26 – 7 The right triangle

If one of the angles of a triangle is a right angle, the triangle is called a
right triangle. Then, since the sum of the angles of any triangle
is 180°, a right triangle contains one right angle and two acute angles.
Also, the sum of the acute angles must be 90°. This relation enables
us to find one acute angle when the other is given. For example, in
the right triangle shown in Fig. 26–15, if $\theta = 30°$, then $\phi = 60°$.

Since all right angles are equal, if an acute angle of one right
triangle is equal to an acute angle of another right triangle, the two
triangles are similar.

The side of a right triangle opposite the right angle is called the
hypotenuse. Thus, in Fig. 26–15, the side c is the hypotenuse. When
a right triangle is in standard position as in Fig. 26–15, the side a is
called the *altitude* and the side b is called the *base*.

Another very important property of a right triangle is that the
square of the hypotenuse is equal to the sum of the squares of the
other two sides. That is,

$$c^2 = a^2 + b^2$$

This relation provides a means of computing any one of the three sides if two sides are given.

EXAMPLE 3   A chimney is 130 ft high. What is the length of its shadow at a time when a vertical post 5 ft high casts a shadow that is 7 ft long?

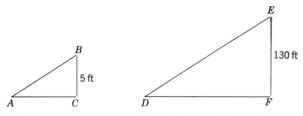

FIG. 26-16   Similar right triangles of Example 3.

SOLUTION BC in Fig. 26-16 represents the post, and EF represents the stack. Because the rays of the sun strike both chimney and post at the same angle, right triangles ABC and DEF are similar. Then, since

$$\frac{DF}{AC} = \frac{EF}{BC}$$

by substituting,

$$\frac{DF}{7} = \frac{130}{5}$$

or

$$DF = 182 \text{ ft}$$

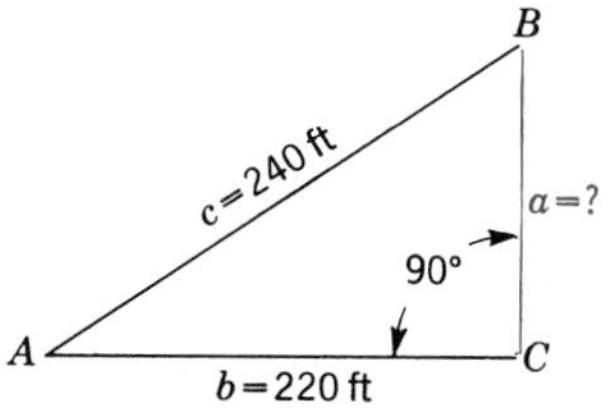

EXAMPLE 4   What is the length of a in the triangle of Fig. 26-17?

SOLUTION   Given $c^2 = a^2 + b^2$.

Transposing, $a^2 = c^2 - b^2$

$\sqrt{\ }$, $a = \sqrt{c^2 - b^2}$

Substituting, $a = \sqrt{240^2 - 220^2} = \sqrt{9,200}$

$$\therefore a = 95.9 \text{ ft}$$

FIG. 26-17   Right triangle of Example 4.

PROBLEMS 26 – 4

In the following right triangles, solve for the indicated elements:

1   $a = 24$, $b = 18$, $A = 53.1°$. Find c and B.
2   $c = 58$, $b = 15$, $B = 15°$. Find a and A.
3   $a = 18$, $c = 80$, $A = 13°$. Find b and B.
4   A bomber flies north at the rate of 650 knots and another west at 600 knots. If both start from the same place at the same time, how far apart will they be in 3 hr?
5   In Fig. 26-18, if $AC = 12$ ft, $BC = 16$ ft, and $AE = 6$ ft, find the length of DE.

6 In Fig. 26–18, AD = 15 ft, DB = 10 ft, and BC = 20 ft. What is the length of AE?

7 In Fig. 26–18, AE = 13 ft, EC = 8 ft, and AB = 31 ft. What is the length of DE?

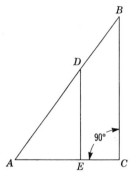

Fig. 26–18 Similar right triangles of Probs. 5, 6, and 7.

8 The top of an antenna tower is 125 ft above level ground. The tower is to be guyed 20 ft from its top to a point on the ground 80 ft from the base of the tower. What is the length of the guy?

9 A television antenna tower casts a shadow 500 ft long at a time when a yardstick, held upright with one end touching the ground, casts a shadow 2 ft long. What is the height of the tower?

10 The tower in Prob. 9 is to be guyed 200 ft from its top to a point on level ground 200 ft from the base of the tower. What will be the length of the guy?

CHAPTER 27
TRIGONOMETRIC FUNCTIONS

In the preceding chapter, it was shown that plane geometry furnishes two important properties of right triangles. These are

$$A + B = 90°$$
and
$$a^2 + b^2 = c^2$$

The first relation makes it possible to find one acute angle when the other is known. By means of the second, any one side can be computed if the other two sides are known. These relations, however, furnish no methods for computing the magnitude of an acute angle when two sides are given. Also, using these relations, we cannot compute two sides of a right triangle if the other side and one acute angle are given. With only this amount of knowledge, we should be forced to resort to actual measurement by graphical methods.

The results obtained by such methods are unsuitable for use in many problems, for even with the greatest care and large-scale drawings the degree of accuracy is definitely limited. It is evident, therefore, that certain other relations are needed in which the sides of a right triangle and the angles are united. Such relations form the foundation of trigonometry.

27 – 1   Trigonometric ratios of acute angles

In Fig. 27–1, let θ be one of the acute angles of the right triangle ABC. If the three sides of the triangle are used, two at a time, six ratios can be expressed. These ratios are

$$\frac{a}{c} \quad \frac{b}{c} \quad \frac{a}{b} \quad \frac{b}{a} \quad \frac{c}{b} \quad \text{and} \quad \frac{c}{a}$$

and have been assigned the following names:

a/c is called the *sine* of the angle θ, written sin θ.
b/c is called the *cosine* of the angle θ, written cos θ.
a/b is called the *tangent* of the angle θ, written tan θ.
b/a is called the *cotangent* of the angle θ, written cot θ.
c/b is called the *secant* of the angle θ, written sec θ.
c/a is called the *cosecant* of the angle θ, written csc θ.

These definitions for any acute angle are readily remembered, regardless of the position of the right triangle, if we take into account the positions of two sides of the triangle with respect to the acute angle under consideration. Thus, in Fig. 27–2, b is called the *adjacent side*

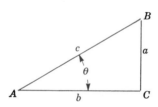

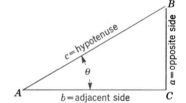

Fɪɢ. 27–1   Right triangle for determining trigonometric ratios.

Fɪɢ. 27–2   Sides of right triangle with respect to angle θ.

of θ, and a is called the *opposite side*. The trigonometric functions (ratios) can be defined in terms of these sides as follows:

$$\sin \theta = \frac{\text{opposite side}}{\text{hypotenuse}} = \frac{a}{c} \qquad \cos \theta = \frac{\text{adjacent side}}{\text{hypotenuse}} = \frac{b}{c}$$

$$\tan \theta = \frac{\text{opposite side}}{\text{adjacent side}} = \frac{a}{b} \qquad \cot \theta = \frac{\text{adjacent side}}{\text{opposite side}} = \frac{b}{a}$$

$$\sec \theta = \frac{\text{hypotenuse}}{\text{adjacent side}} = \frac{c}{b} \qquad \csc \theta = \frac{\text{hypotenuse}}{\text{opposite side}} = \frac{c}{a}$$

These definitions should be memorized so thoroughly that you can tell instantly any ratio of either acute angle of a right triangle, regardless of its position.

The sine, cosine, and tangent are the ratios most frequently used in practical work. If these are carefully learned, the others are easily remembered because they are reciprocals, as is shown in the section following.

The fact that the numerical value of any one of the trigonometric functions (ratios) depends only upon the magnitude of the angle θ is of fundamental importance. This is established from a consideration of Fig. 27–3. The angle θ is generated by the line AD revolving about the point A. From the points B, B', and B'', perpendiculars are let fall to the initial line, or adjacent side, AX. These form similar triangles ABC, $AB'C'$, and $AB''C''$ because all are right triangles having a common acute angle θ (Sec. 26–7). Hence,

$$\frac{BC}{AB} = \frac{B'C'}{AB'} = \frac{B''C''}{AB''}$$

Each of these ratios defines the sine of θ. Similarly, it can be shown that this property is true for each of the other functions. Therefore, the size of the right triangle is immaterial, for only the *relative* lengths of the sides are of importance.

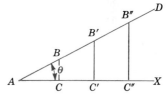

Fig. 27–3 The values of the functions depend only on the size of the angle.

Each one of the six ratios will change in value whenever the angle changes in magnitude. Thus, it is evident that the ratios are really functions of the angle under consideration. If the angle is considered to be the independent variable, then the six functions (ratios) and the relative lengths of the sides of the triangles are dependent variables.

EXAMPLE 1   Calculate the functions of the angle θ in the right triangle of Fig. 27–1 if $a = 6$ in. and $c = 10$ in.

SOLUTION   Since $c^2 = a^2 + b^2$,

then $$b = \sqrt{c^2 - a^2} = \sqrt{100 - 36} = \sqrt{64} = 8 \text{ in.}$$

Applying the definitions of the six functions,

$$\sin \theta = \tfrac{6}{10} = \tfrac{3}{5} \qquad \cos \theta = \tfrac{8}{10} = \tfrac{4}{5}$$
$$\tan \theta = \tfrac{6}{8} = \tfrac{3}{4} \qquad \cot \theta = \tfrac{8}{6} = \tfrac{4}{3}$$
$$\sec \theta = \tfrac{10}{8} = \tfrac{5}{4} \qquad \csc \theta = \tfrac{10}{6} = \tfrac{5}{3}$$

What would be the values of the above functions if $a = 6$ meters, $b = 8$ meters, and $c = 10$ meters?

27 – 2   Reciprocal relations of the functions

As a result of the definitions of the trigonometric functions, the following reciprocal relations exist:

$$\sin \theta = \frac{a}{c} = \frac{1}{\dfrac{c}{a}} = \frac{1}{\csc \theta} \qquad \csc \theta = \frac{c}{a} = \frac{1}{\dfrac{a}{c}} = \frac{1}{\sin \theta}$$

$$\cos \theta = \frac{b}{c} = \frac{1}{\dfrac{c}{b}} = \frac{1}{\sec \theta} \qquad \sec \theta = \frac{c}{b} = \frac{1}{\dfrac{b}{c}} = \frac{1}{\cos \theta}$$

$$\tan \theta = \frac{a}{b} = \frac{1}{\dfrac{b}{a}} = \frac{1}{\cot \theta} \qquad \cot \theta = \frac{b}{a} = \frac{1}{\dfrac{a}{b}} = \frac{1}{\tan \theta}$$

The cosecant, secant, and cotangent should always be thought of as the reciprocals of the sine, cosine, and tangent, respectively.

By noting the sequence of the phrases "opposite side" and "adjacent side," it is seen that they replace each other in the definitions for sine and cosine, tangent and cotangent, and secant and cosecant. Furthermore, it will be noted that if the reciprocals of the six functions are taken in the order given, the same six appear in the opposite order. Figure 27–4 will serve as an aid in remembering these relations.

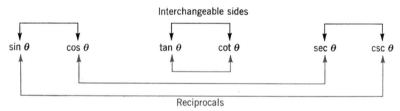

Interchangeable sides

sin θ   cos θ   tan θ   cot θ   sec θ   csc θ

Reciprocals

FIG. 27–4   Relations existing between functions.

27 – 3   Functions of complementary angles

By applying the definitions of the six functions to the angle ϕ in Fig. 27–5 and noting the positions of the adjacent and opposite sides for this angle, we obtain

$$\sin \phi = \frac{\text{opposite side}}{\text{hypotenuse}} = \frac{b}{c} \qquad \cos \phi = \frac{\text{adjacent side}}{\text{hypotenuse}} = \frac{a}{c}$$

$$\tan \phi = \frac{\text{opposite side}}{\text{adjacent side}} = \frac{b}{a} \qquad \cot \phi = \frac{\text{adjacent side}}{\text{opposite side}} = \frac{a}{b}$$

$$\sec \phi = \frac{\text{hypotenuse}}{\text{adjacent side}} = \frac{c}{a} \qquad \csc \phi = \frac{\text{hypotenuse}}{\text{opposite side}} = \frac{c}{b}$$

Upon comparing these with the original definitions given for the triangle of Fig. 27–2, the following relations appear:

$$\sin \phi = \cos \theta \qquad \cos \phi = \sin \theta$$
$$\tan \phi = \cot \theta \qquad \cot \phi = \tan \theta$$
$$\sec \phi = \csc \theta \qquad \csc \phi = \sec \theta$$

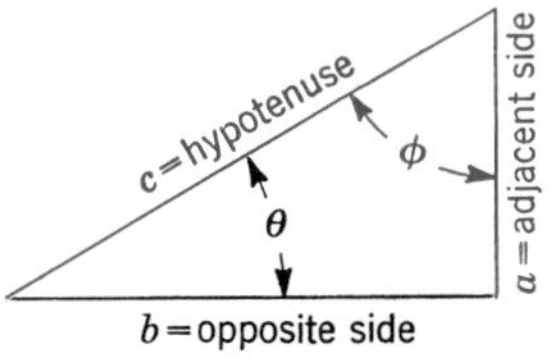

FIG. 27–5 Right triangle for determining functions of angle ϕ.

Since $\phi = 90° - \theta$, the above relations can be written

$$\sin (90° - \theta) = \cos \theta \qquad \cos (90° - \theta) = \sin \theta$$
$$\tan (90° - \theta) = \cot \theta \qquad \cot (90° - \theta) = \tan \theta$$
$$\sec (90° - \theta) = \csc \theta \qquad \csc (90° - \theta) = \sec \theta$$

The above can be stated in words as follows: *A function of an acute angle is equal to the cofunction of its complementary angle.* This enables us to find the function of every acute angle greater than 45° if we know the functions of all angles less than 45°. For example, sin 56° = cos 34°, tan 63° = cot 27°, cos 70° = sin 20°, etc.

27–4 Construction of an angle when one function is given

When the trigonometric function of an acute angle is given, the angle can be constructed geometrically by using the definition for the given function. Also, the magnitude of the resulting angle can be measured by the use of a protractor.

EXAMPLE 2   Construct the acute angle whose tangent is $\%_{10}$.

SOLUTION   Erect perpendicular lines AC and BC, preferably on cross-sectional paper. Measure off 10 units along AC and 9 units along BC. Join A and B, thus forming the right triangle ABC. tan $A = \%_{10}$; therefore, A is the required angle. Measuring A with a protractor shows it to be an angle of approximately 42°. The construction is shown in Fig. 27–6.

EXAMPLE 3   Find by construction the acute angle whose cosine is $\frac{3}{4}$.

SOLUTION   Erect perpendicular lines AC and BC. Measure off three units along AC (letting three divisions of the cross-sectional paper be equal to one unit for greater accuracy). With A as a center and with a radius of four units, draw an arc to intersect the perpendicular at B. Connect A and

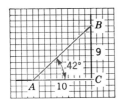

FIG. 27–6 Construction of acute angle with tangent of $\%_{10}$.

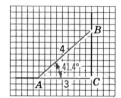

FIG. 27–7 Construction of acute angle with cosine of ¾.

B. cos *A* = ¾; therefore *A* is the required angle. Measuring *A* with a protractor shows it to be an angle of approximately 41.4°. The construction is shown in Fig. 27–7.

PROBLEMS 27 – 1

1   In Fig. 27–8, write the values of the trigonometric functions for the angles θ and ϕ in terms of ratios of the sides *a*, *b*, and *c*.

2   In Fig. 27–9, (*a*) sin α = ?   (*b*) sin β = ?   (*c*) cot β = ?   (*d*) sec α = ?   (*e*) tan α = ?

3   In Fig. 27–9, (*a*) *OP/OR* = tan ?   (*b*) *PR/PO* = sec ?   (*c*) *OR/PR* = cos ?   (*d*) *OP/RP* = sin ?   (*e*) *PR/RO* = csc ?

4   The three sides of a right triangle are 3, 4, and 5.   Let α be the acute angle opposite the side 4, and let β be the other acute angle.   Write the six functions of α and β.

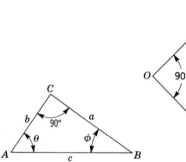

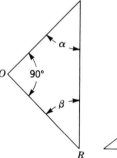

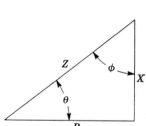

FIG. 27–8   Right triangle of Prob. 1.

FIG. 27–9   Right triangle of Probs. 2 and 3.

FIG. 27–10   Right triangle of Probs. 5, 6, and 7.

5   In Fig. 27–10, if *X* = *R*, find the six functions of θ.

6   In Fig. 27–10, if *R* = ½ *Z*, find the sine, cosine, and tangent of θ.

7   In Fig. 27–10, if *X* = 2*R*, find the sine, cosine, and tangent of ϕ.

8   (*a*) sin θ = ½, csc θ = ?   (*b*) sec α = 3, cos α = ?   (*c*) cot β = 4⁄5, tan β = ?   (*d*) cos ϕ = ⅔, sec ϕ = ?   (*e*) tan ϕ = 10, cot ϕ = ?   (*f*) csc α = 5, sin α = ?

9   The three sides of a right triangle are 5, 12, and 13.   Write the six functions of the largest acute angle.

10   Write the other functions of an acute angle whose tangent is ¾.

11   In a right triangle, *c* = 5 in. and cos *A* = 4⁄5.   Construct the triangle, and write the functions of the angle *B*.

12 State which of the following is greater if $\theta \neq 0°$ and is less than 90°:
(a) sin θ or tan θ, (b) cos θ or cot θ, (c) sec θ or tan θ, (d) csc θ or cot θ.

27 – 5   Functions of any angle

In the preceding chapter the concepts of angles were extended to include angles in any quadrant and either positive or negative. So

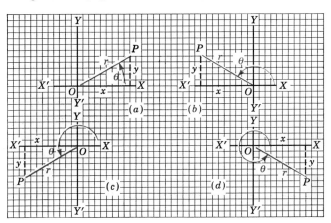

FIG. 27–11   Radius vector r generating angles.

far, the trigonometric functions have applied to acute angles only, but we are now ready to consider the functions of any angle. In Fig. 27–11, the line r is revolving about the origin of the rectangular coordinate system in a counterclockwise (positive) direction. This line, which generates the angle θ, is known as the *radius vector*. The initial side of θ is the positive X axis, and the terminal side is the radius vector. If a perpendicular is let fall from any point P along the radius vector, in any of the quadrants, a right triangle xyr will be formed with r as a hypotenuse of constant unit length and with x and y having lengths equal to the respective coordinates of P.

We then define the trigonometric functions of θ as follows:

$$\sin\theta = \frac{y}{r} = \frac{\text{ordinate}}{\text{radius}} \qquad \cos\theta = \frac{x}{r} = \frac{\text{abscissa}}{\text{radius}}$$

$$\tan\theta = \frac{y}{x} = \frac{\text{ordinate}}{\text{abscissa}} \qquad \cot\theta = \frac{x}{y} = \frac{\text{abscissa}}{\text{ordinate}}$$

$$\sec\theta = \frac{r}{x} = \frac{\text{radius}}{\text{abscissa}} \qquad \csc\theta = \frac{r}{y} = \frac{\text{radius}}{\text{ordinate}}$$

Since the values of the six trigonometric functions are entirely independent of the position of the point P along the radius vector, it follows that they depend only upon the position of the radius vector, or the size of the angle. Therefore, for every angle, there is one, and only one, value of each function.

27 – 6   Sign of the functions

The signs of the functions of angles in various quadrants are very important. If you remember the signs of the abscissas (x values) and the ordinates (y values) in the four quadrants, you will encounter no trouble.

For angles in the first quadrant, as shown in Fig. 27–11a, the x and y values are positive. Since the length of the radius vector r is always considered positive, it is evident that all functions of angles in the first quadrant are positive. For angles in the second quadrant, as shown in Fig. 27–11b, the x values are negative and the y values are positive. Therefore the sine and its reciprocal are positive, and the other four functions are negative. Similarly, the signs of all the functions can be checked from their definitions as given in the preceding section. Table 27–1 should be verified.

TABLE 27 – 1

Quadrant	$\sin \theta$	$\cos \theta$	$\tan \theta$	$\cot \theta$	$\sec \theta$	$\csc \theta$
I	+	+	+	+	+	+
II	+	−	−	−	−	+
III	−	−	+	+	−	−
IV	−	+	−	−	+	−

If the proper signs for the sine and cosine are fixed in mind, the other signs will be remembered because of an important relation

$$\frac{\sin \theta}{\cos \theta} = \frac{y/r}{x/r} = \frac{y}{x}$$

Since

$$\tan \theta = \frac{y}{x}$$

then

$$\frac{\sin \theta}{\cos \theta} = \tan \theta$$

If the sine and cosine have like signs, the tangent is positive, and if they have unlike signs, the tangent is negative. Because the signs of the sine, cosine, and tangent always agree with their respective reciprocals, the cosecant, secant, and cotangent, the signs for the latter are obtainable from the signs of the sine and cosine as outlined above. Figure 27–12 will serve as an aid in remembering the signs.

II   Y   I

$\dfrac{+\sin}{-\cos} = -\tan$ $\dfrac{+\sin}{+\cos} = +\tan$

X'————————————————X

$\dfrac{-\sin}{-\cos} = +\tan$ $\dfrac{-\sin}{+\cos} = -\tan$

III   Y'   IV

Fɪɢ. 27–12 Signs of functions in quadrants.

PROBLEMS 27 – 2

In what quadrant or quadrants is θ for each of the following conditions?

1. $\sin \theta$ is positive.
2. $\cos \theta$ is positive.
3. $\sin \theta$ is negative.
4. $\tan \theta$ is negative.
5. $\cos \theta$ is negative.
6. $\sin \theta$ positive, $\cos \theta$ negative.
7. $\tan \theta$ and $\sin \theta$ both positive.
8. $\cot \theta$ negative, $\cos \theta$ negative.
9. $\tan \theta$ negative, $\cos \theta$ positive.
10. All functions of θ are positive.
11. $\tan \theta = 6$.
12. $\cos \theta = -\frac{3}{4}$.
13. Is there an angle whose cosine is negative and whose secant is positive?
14. Find the value of $(\sin \theta - \csc \theta)/(\cot \theta - \sec \theta)$ when $\tan \theta = \frac{3}{4}$.

Give the signs of the sine, cosine, and tangent of each of the following angles:

15. $29°$
16. $192°$
17. $130°$
18. $307°$
19. $-130°$
20. $\dfrac{\pi}{4}$
21. $\dfrac{-2\pi}{3}$

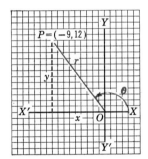

Fɪɢ. 27–13 Diagram of Prob. 22.

Find the value of the radius vector r for each of the following positions of P, and then find the trigonometric functions of the angle θ ($\angle XOP$). Keep answers in fractional form.

22. $(-9,12)$

ꜱᴏʟᴜᴛɪᴏɴ   Draw the radius vector r from O to $P = (-9,12)$ as shown in Fig. 27–13. Hence, θ is an angle in the second quadrant, with a side adjacent having an x value of -9 and a side opposite with a y value of 12.

Then $\qquad r = \sqrt{x^2 + y^2} = \sqrt{(-9)^2 + (12)^2} = 15$

Hence, by definition,

$$\sin \theta = \frac{y}{r} = \frac{12}{15} = \frac{4}{5} \qquad \cos \theta = \frac{x}{r} = \frac{-9}{15} = -\frac{3}{5}$$

$$\tan \theta = \frac{y}{x} = \frac{12}{-9} = -\frac{4}{3} \qquad \cot \theta = \frac{x}{y} = \frac{-9}{12} = -\frac{3}{4}$$

$$\sec \theta = \frac{r}{x} = \frac{15}{-9} = -\frac{5}{3} \qquad \csc \theta = \frac{r}{y} = \frac{15}{12} = \frac{5}{4}$$

23 $(12, -5)$

SOLUTION   Draw the radius vector r from O to P as shown in Fig. 27–14.

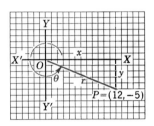

FIG. 27–14   Diagram of Prob. 23.

θ is an angle in the fourth quadrant, with a side adjacent having an x value of 12 and a side opposite with a y value of -5.

Then $r = \sqrt{x^2 + y^2} = \sqrt{12^2 + (-5)^2} = 13$

Hence, by definition,

$$\sin \theta = \frac{y}{r} = -\frac{5}{13} \qquad \cos \theta = \frac{x}{r} = \frac{12}{13}$$

$$\tan \theta = \frac{y}{x} = -\frac{5}{12} \qquad \cot \theta = \frac{x}{y} = -\frac{12}{5}$$

$$\sec \theta = \frac{r}{x} = \frac{13}{12} \qquad \csc \theta = \frac{r}{y} = -\frac{13}{5}$$

24 $(8,6)$ **25** $(4,5)$ **26** $(-4,3)$

27 $(-5,-3)$ **28** $(6,-5)$ **29** $(5,5)$

30 $(-6,-8)$

27 – 7   Computation of the functions

Tables have been computed giving the values of the functions of angles. However, there are a few important angles whose functions are obtainable from definite geometric relations. Because these angles occur so frequently in practical work, their functions are derived here.

27 – 8   Functions of 45°

Construct a right triangle with the angle θ equal to 45° and the length of the opposite side a equal to one unit as shown in Fig. 27–15. Then, by construction, $\phi = 45°$ and $b = 1$ unit. Since

$$a^2 + b^2 = c^2$$

$$c = \sqrt{a^2 + b^2} = \sqrt{1+1} = \sqrt{2}$$

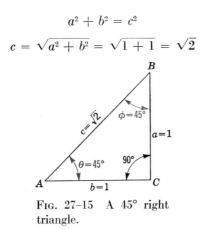

Fig. 27–15 A 45° right triangle.

From the definitions of Sec. 27–1,

$$\sin 45° = \frac{a}{c} = \frac{1}{\sqrt{2}} = \frac{1}{2}\sqrt{2} \qquad \cos 45° = \frac{b}{c} = \frac{1}{\sqrt{2}} = \frac{1}{2}\sqrt{2}$$

$$\tan 45° = \frac{a}{b} = \frac{1}{1} = 1 \qquad \cot 45° = \frac{b}{a} = \frac{1}{1} = 1$$

$$\sec 45° = \frac{c}{b} = \frac{\sqrt{2}}{1} = \sqrt{2} \qquad \csc 45° = \frac{c}{a} = \frac{\sqrt{2}}{1} = \sqrt{2}$$

– 9 Functions of 60° and 30°

Construct an equilateral triangle, making the length of each side equal to two units as ABD in Fig. 27–16. From B, draw BC perpen-

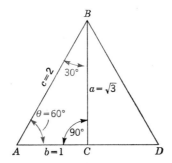

Fig. 27–16 Equilateral triangle divided into two equal right triangles.

dicular to AD. Therefore, BC bisects AD at C, making b equal to one unit. Then, in the *right* triangle ABC, $\theta = 60°$, $b = 1$, $c = 2$. Since

$$a^2 + b^2 = c^2$$

$$a = \sqrt{c^2 - b^2} = \sqrt{4 - 1} = \sqrt{3}$$

From the definitions of Sec. 27–1,

$$\sin 60° = \frac{a}{c} = \frac{\sqrt{3}}{2} = \frac{1}{2}\sqrt{3} \qquad \cos 60° = \frac{b}{c} = \frac{1}{2}$$

$$\tan 60° = \frac{a}{b} = \frac{\sqrt{3}}{1} = \sqrt{3} \qquad \cot 60° = \frac{b}{a} = \frac{1}{\sqrt{3}} = \frac{1}{3}\sqrt{3}$$

$$\sec 60° = \frac{c}{b} = \frac{2}{1} = 2 \qquad \csc 60° = \frac{c}{a} = \frac{2}{\sqrt{3}} = \frac{2}{3}\sqrt{3}$$

Since an angle of 30° is the complement of an angle of 60°, the functions of 30° are equal to the corresponding cofunctions of 60°. Therefore,

$$\sin 30° = \tfrac{1}{2}$$
$$\cos 30° = \tfrac{1}{2}\sqrt{3}$$
$$\tan 30° = \tfrac{1}{3}\sqrt{3}$$
$$\cot 30° = \sqrt{3}$$
$$\sec 30° = \tfrac{2}{3}\sqrt{3}$$
$$\csc 30° = 2$$

The sine and cosine of 30, 45, and 60° are easily remembered from the following table:

θ	30°	45°	60°
$\sin \theta$	$\tfrac{1}{2}\sqrt{1}$	$\tfrac{1}{2}\sqrt{2}$	$\tfrac{1}{2}\sqrt{3}$
$\cos \theta$	$\tfrac{1}{2}\sqrt{3}$	$\tfrac{1}{2}\sqrt{2}$	$\tfrac{1}{2}\sqrt{1}$

27 – 10   Functions of 0°

For an angle of 0°, the initial and terminal sides are both on OX. At any distance a from O, choose the point P as shown in Fig. 27–17. Then the coordinates of P are $(a,0)$. That is, the x value is equal to a units, and the y value is zero. Since the radius vector r is equal to a, by definition,

$$\sin 0° = \frac{y}{r} = \frac{0}{r} = 0 \qquad \cos 0° = \frac{x}{r} = \frac{a}{a} = 1$$

$$\tan 0° = \frac{y}{x} = \frac{0}{a} = 0 \qquad \cot 0° = \frac{x}{y} = \frac{a}{0} = \infty$$

$$\sec 0° = \frac{r}{x} = \frac{a}{a} = 1 \qquad \csc 0° = \frac{r}{y} = \frac{a}{0} = \infty$$

By $a/0 = \infty$ is meant the value of a/y as y approaches zero without limit. Thus, as y gets nearer and nearer to zero, a/y gets larger and larger. Therefore, a/y is said to *approach* infinity as y approaches zero. However, $a/0$ does not actually result in a quotient of infinity, for division by zero is meaningless.

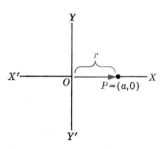

FIG. 27–17 $\theta = 0°$, $x = a$, and $y = 0$.

Determining the functions of 90, 180, and 270° is accomplished by the same method as that used for 0°. These are left as problems for you.

— 11   Line representation of the functions

By representing the functions as lengths of lines, we are able to obtain a mental picture of the manner in which the functions vary as the radius vector r revolves and generates angles. Since we are primarily concerned with the sine, cosine, and tangent, only these functions will be represented graphically.

In Fig. 27–18 the radius vector r, with a length of one unit, is revolving about the origin generating the angle θ. Then, in each of the four quadrants,

$$\sin \theta = \frac{BC}{r} = \frac{BC}{1} = BC \qquad \text{and} \qquad \cos \theta = \frac{OC}{r} = \frac{OC}{1} = OC$$

It is evident *that the sine of an angle can be represented by the ordinate (y value) of any point where the end of the radius vector coincides with the circumference of the circle.* Hence, the length BC represents $\sin \theta$ in all quadrants, as shown in Fig. 27–18. Note that the ordinate gives both the sign and the magnitude of the sine in any quadrant. Thus, in quadrants I and II, $\sin \theta = +0.6$; in quadrants III and IV, $\sin \theta = -0.6$. That is, when the radius vector is above the X axis, the ordinate and therefore the sine are positive. When the radius vector is below the X axis, the ordinate and therefore the sine are negative.

Similarly, *the cosine of an angle can be represented by the abscissa (x value) of any point where the end of the radius vector coincides with the circumference of the circle.* Hence, the length OC represents cos θ in all quadrants, as shown in Fig. 27–18. The abscissa gives both the sign and the magnitude of the cosine in any quadrant. Thus, in quadrants

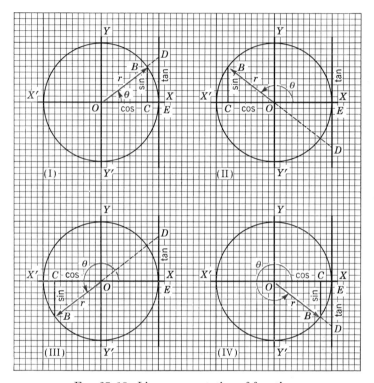

Fig. 27–18 Line representation of functions.

I and IV, cos θ = +0.8; in quadrants II and III, cos θ = −0.8. That is, when the radius vector is to the right of the Y axis, the abscissa and therefore the cosine are positive. When the radius vector is to the left of the Y axis, the abscissa, and therefore the cosine, are negative.

In Fig. 27–18, the radius vector has been extended to intersect the tangent line DE which has been drawn tangent to the circle at the positive X axis. Since by construction, DE is perpendicular to OX, OBC and ODE are similar right triangles, for they have a common acute angle BOC. From the similar triangles,

$$\frac{BC}{OC} = \frac{DE}{OE}$$

Then, in each of the four quadrants,

$$\tan \theta = \frac{BC}{OC} = \frac{DE}{OE} = \frac{DE}{1} = DE$$

From the above, it is evident that *the tangent of an angle can be represented by the ordinate (y value) of any point where the extended radius vector intersects the tangent line.* The ordinate gives both the sign and the magnitude of the tangent in any quadrant. Thus, in quadrants I and III, $\tan \theta = +0.75$; in quadrants II and IV, $\tan \theta = -0.75$.

– 12 Variation of the functions

As the radius vector r starts from OX and revolves about the origin in a positive (counterclockwise) direction, the angle θ is generated and varies in magnitude continuously from 0 to 360° through the four quadrants. Figure 27–19 illustrates the manner in which the sine, cosine, and tangent vary as the angle θ changes in value.

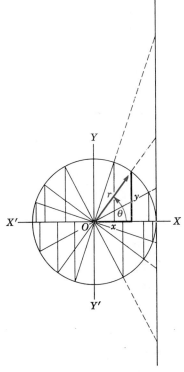

Quadrant I. As θ increases from 0° to 90°,

  x is positive and decreases from r to 0.
  y is positive and increases from 0 to r.

Therefore,

  $\sin \theta = y/r$ is *positive* and increases from 0 to 1.
  $\cos \theta = x/r$ is *positive* and decreases from 1 to 0.
  $\tan \theta = y/x$ is *positive* and increases from 0 to ∞.

Quadrant II. As θ increases from 90° to 180°,

  x is negative and decreases from 0 to $-r$.
  y is positive and decreases from r to 0.

Fig. 27–19 Lengths of lines showing variations of $\sin \theta$, $\cos \theta$, and $\tan \theta$.

Therefore,

  sin $\theta = y/r$ is *positive* and decreases from 1 to 0.
  cos $\theta = x/r$ is *negative* and decreases from 0 to -1.
  tan $\theta = y/x$ is *negative* and increases from $-\infty$ to 0.

  Quadrant III. As θ increases from $180°$ to $270°$,

x is negative and increases from $-r$ to 0.
y is negative and decreases from 0 to $-r$.

Therefore,

  sin $\theta = y/r$ is *negative* and decreases from 0 to -1.
  cos $\theta = x/r$ is *negative* and increases from -1 to 0.
  tan $\theta = y/x$ is *positive* and increases from 0 to ∞.

  Quadrant IV. As θ increases from $270°$ to $360°$,

x is positive and increases from 0 to r.
y is negative and increases from $-r$ to 0.

Therefore,

  sin $\theta = y/r$ is *negative* and increases from -1 to 0.
  cos $\theta = x/r$ is *positive* and increases from 0 to 1.
  tan $\theta = y/x$ is *negative* and increases from $-\infty$ to 0.

Students often become confused in comparing the variations of the functions, when represented as lines, with their actual numerical value. For example, in quadrant II as the angle θ increases from 90 to 180°, we say that cos θ *decreases* from 0 to $-r$. Actually, the abscissa representing the cosine is getting *longer;* confusion results from not remembering that a negative number is always less than zero. The *lengths* of the lines representing the functions, when compared with the radius vector, indicate only the *magnitude* of the function. The position of the lines, with respect to the X or Y axis, specifies the signs of the functions.

PROBLEMS 27 – 3

1   What is the least value sin θ may have?
2   What is the least value cos θ may have?
3   What is the greatest value csc θ may have in the first quadrant?
4   What is the greatest value sec θ may have in the fourth quadrant?
5   Can the secant and cosecant have values between -1 and $+1$?

CHAPTER 28

TABLES OF FUNCTIONS

For the purpose of making computations, it is evident that a table of trigonometric functions would be helpful. Such a table could be made by computing the functions of all angles by graphical methods. However, this would be laborious, and the resulting functions would not be accurate.

Fortunately, mathematicians have calculated the values of the trigonometric functions by the use of advanced mathematics and have tabulated the results. These tables are known as *tables of natural functions* to distinguish them from *tables of the logarithms of the functions*. In Table 7 of the Appendix are arranged the natural functions of angles for every one-tenth of a degree from 0 to 90°.

28 – 1 Given an angle—to find the desired function

How to use the table of natural functions is best illustrated by examples.

When the angle is given in the tables

EXAMPLE 1   Find the sine of 36.7°.

SOLUTION   The angle 36° is in the left column of the table. The sine of 36.7° is read in the sin row and in the column headed 0.7°. It is 0.5976.

$$\therefore \ \sin 36.7° = 0.5976$$

EXAMPLE 2   Find the cosine of 7.9°.

SOLUTION   The angle 7° is in the left column of the table. The cosine of 7.9° is read in the cos row and in the column headed 0.9°. It is 0.9905.

$$\therefore \cos 7.9° = 0.9905$$

EXAMPLE 3   Find the tangent of 79.1°.

SOLUTION   Opposite 79° in the tan row and in the column headed 0.1°, read 5.1929.

$$\therefore \tan 79.1° = 5.1929$$

When the angle is not given in the tables

EXAMPLE 4   Find the sine of 26.42°.

SOLUTION   Since 26.42° is between 26.4° and 26.5°, its sine value must be between sin 26.4° and sin 26.5°. Hence,

$$\sin 26.5° = 0.4462$$
$$\sin 26.4° = \underline{0.4446}$$
$$\text{Difference} = 0.0016$$

The *tabular difference* between these sines is 0.0016, and it is apparent that an increase of 0.1° from 26.4° causes the sine value to increase 0.0016. Therefore an increase from 26.4° to 26.42°, which is an increase of 0.02°, must increase the sine value 0.2 as much. Hence, the increase in the sine value is $0.0016 \times 0.2 = 0.00032$.

$$\therefore \sin 26.42° = 0.4446 + 0.00032 = 0.44492$$

The sine of 26.42°, as written above, is another good example of how the retention of decimals might easily convey a false impression of accuracy. The tables from which the sine values were taken are correct to four significant figures. Therefore, any sine value found by interpolation cannot be correct beyond four significant figures. Thus it is correct to write

$$\sin 26.42° = 0.4449$$

EXAMPLE 5   Find the cosine of 53.77°.

SOLUTION $\cos 53.7° = 0.5920$
$$\cos 53.8° = \underline{0.5906}$$
$$\text{Difference} = 0.0014$$

Since the value of the cosine *decreases* 0.0014 as the angle increases 0.1° from 53.7°, a subtraction must be made when interpolating. Then the decrease in the cosine value is $0.0014 \times 0.7 = 0.00098$.

$$\cos 53.77° = 0.5920 - 0.00098 = 0.59102$$
or $\cos 53.77° = 0.5910$

EXAMPLE 6   Find the tangent of 48.13°.

SOLUTION   tan 48.2° = 1.1184
                 tan 48.1° = 1.1145
                 Difference = 0.0039

Since the value of the tangent increases 0.0039 as the angle increases 0.1°
from 48.1°, then the increase of 0.03° will cause the tangent to increase
$0.0039 \times 0.3 = 0.00117$.

$$\therefore \tan 48.13° = 1.1145 + 0.00117 = 1.11567$$
or $\tan 48.13° = 1.1157$

PROBLEMS 28 – 1

1 Find the sine, cosine, and tangent of (a) 27°, (b) 79°, (c) 6.7°, (d) 61.5°,
   (e) 1.3°.
2 Find the sine, cosine, and tangent of (a) 15°, (b) 85.4°, (c) 71.1°, (d) 0.5°,
   (e) 23.3°.
3 Find the sine, cosine, and tangent of (a) 2.6°, (b) 58.8°, (c) 29.9°, (d) 40.1°,
   (e) 78.2°.
4 Find the sine, cosine, and tangent of (a) 7.49°, (b) 10.27°, (c) 25.75°,
   (d) 37.55°, (e) 2.14°.
5 Find the sine, cosine, and tangent of (a) 53.18°, (b) 49.11°, (c) 69.93°,
   (d) 47.72°, (e) 73.36°.

28 – 2   Inverse trigonometric functions

Frequently some form of notation is needed in order to express an
angle in terms of one of its functions. For example, in Sec. 27–4,
Example 2 dealt with an angle whose tangent was $\frac{9}{10}$. Similarly, in
Example 3 of the same section, we considered an angle whose cosine
was $\frac{3}{4}$.

If $\sin \theta = x$, then θ is an angle whose sine is x. It has been agreed to
express such a relation by the notation

$$\theta = \sin^{-1} x \qquad \text{or} \qquad \theta = \arcsin x$$

Both are read "θ is equal to the angle whose sine is x" or "the inverse
sine of x." For example, the tangent of 37.2° is 0.7590. Stated as an
inverse function, this would be written

$$37.2° = \arctan 0.7590$$

Similarly, in the case of a right triangle labeled as in Fig. 27–1, we
should write $\theta = \arctan a/b$, $\theta = \arccos b/c$, etc. In this book, we
shall not use the notation "$\theta = \sin^{-1} x$," for we prefer not to use an

exponent when no exponent is intended. Although this form of notation is used in a number of texts, the student will find that nearly all recent mathematics and engineering texts are using the "$\theta = \arcsin x$" form of notation. Because more advanced mathematics employs trigonometric functions affected by exponents, it is evident that confusion would eventually result from utilizing the other notation for specifying the inverse functions.

28 – 3   Given a function—to find the corresponding angle

As in Sec. 28-1 the use of the tables is best illustrated by examples.

When the function is given in the tables

EXAMPLE 7   Find the angle whose sine is 0.2351.

SOLUTION   Find 0.2351 in the sin row. In the degrees column opposite the sin row in which 0.2351 is located, read 13°. The column in which 0.2351 is located is the 0.6° column. Thus, 0.2351 is the sine of 13.6°. This could be written

$$13.6° = \arcsin 0.2351$$

EXAMPLE 8   Find θ if $\cos \theta = 0.0332$.

SOLUTION   Since the given cosine value is a very small number, we deduce that the corresponding angle must be large. Here is another example where a knowledge of how the functions vary is an asset because it saves time in looking up angles whose functions are given.

In the degrees column opposite the cos row in which 0.0332 is located, read 88°. 0.0332 is in the 0.1° column. Thus, 0.0332 is the cosine of 88.1°. This can be written

$$\cos 88.1° = 0.0332$$

or $$88.1° = \arccos 0.0332$$

EXAMPLE 9   Find θ if $\theta = \arctan 1.1423$.

SOLUTION   Since $\tan 45° = 1$ and the tangent value increases as the angle increases, it is evident that θ is somewhat larger than 45°. This knowledge enables one to begin searching for the given tangent value somewhere near its location.

In the degrees column opposite the tan row in which 1.1423 is located, read 48°. 1.1423 is in the 0.8° column. Thus, 1.1423 is the tangent of 48.8°. That is,

$$48.8° = \arctan 1.1423$$

When the function is not given in the tables

EXAMPLE 10   Find θ if $\theta = \arcsin 0.4452$.

SOLUTION   Examination of the table shows that 0.4452 is not given exactly in the sine values. Therefore we find the two consecutive sine values between which the given sine value lies. These are 0.4446 and 0.4462, which are the sines of 26.4° and 26.5°, respectively. Tabulating,

$$\begin{array}{r} \sin 26.5° = 0.4462 \\ \sin 26.4° = \underline{0.4446} \\ \text{Difference} = 0.0016 \end{array}$$

The *tabular difference* between these sine values is 0.0016, and it is apparent that an increase of 0.1° from 26.4° causes the sine value to increase 0.0016. Now the given sine value is 0.0006 larger than the sine of the smaller angle taken from the table (0.4452 − 0.4446 = 0.0006).
Then, since

$$\frac{\text{Increase}}{\text{Difference}} = \frac{0.0006}{0.0016} = \frac{3}{8}$$

the given sine value is $\frac{3}{8}$, or 0.375, of the way from 0.4446 to 0.4462. Therefore, we assume that θ is three-eighths, or 0.375, of the way from 26.4° to 26.5°. Hence,

$$\theta = 26.4° + 0.0375° = 26.4375°$$

Again it becomes necessary to round off the answer in order to prevent a false impression of accuracy. Hence, we write

$$26.44° = \arcsin 0.4452$$

EXAMPLE 11   Find θ if $\cos \theta = 0.3732$.

SOLUTION
$$\begin{array}{r} 0.3746 = \cos 68.0° \\ 0.3730 = \cos 68.1° \\ \text{Difference} = \overline{0.0016} \text{ for} \quad 0.1° \end{array}$$

Since the value of the cosine decreases 0.0016 as the angle increases 0.1° from 68.0°, a subtraction must be made in interpolating. The given cosine value is 0.0002 larger than the smallest value taken from the table:

$$0.3732 − 0.3730 = 0.0002$$

Then the given cosine value is $0.0002/0.0016 = \frac{1}{8}$ of the way from 0.3730 to 0.3746. Therefore, we assume that θ is $\frac{1}{8}$, or 0.125, of the way from 68.1° to 68.0°. Hence, $\theta = 68.1° − 0.0125° = 68.0875°$, which, when rounded off, gives

$$68.09° = \arccos 0.3732$$

EXAMPLE 12   Find θ if $\theta = \arctan 0.5920$.

SOLUTION
$$\begin{array}{r} 0.5938 = \tan 30.7° \\ 0.5914 = \tan 30.6° \\ \text{Difference} = \overline{0.0024} \text{ for} \quad 0.1° \end{array}$$

For an increase of 0.1° the tangent increases 0.0024. The given tangent value is 0.0006 larger than the tangent of the smaller angle taken from the table (0.5920 − 0.5914 = 0.0006). Then the given tangent value is 0.0006/0.0024 = ¼, or 0.25, of the way from 0.5914 to 0.5938. Therefore, we assume that θ is ¼, or 0.25, of the way from 30.6° to 30.7°. Hence,

$$\theta = 30.6° + 0.025° = 30.625°$$

which, when rounded off, gives

$$30.62° = \text{arctan } 0.5920$$

28 – 4   Accuracy

The methods of interpolation illustrated here are for the use of those who require a greater degree of accuracy than that given by working with angles to the nearest tenth of a degree. In our considerations of a-c circuits, we shall confine our accuracy to three significant figures and angles to the nearest tenth of a degree. This, except for isolated cases, will more than meet all practical requirements. Also, it reduces interpolation to an inspection of the values of the tabulated functions in order to determine which tenth of a degree to choose.

Inside the front cover of this book is a three-place table of sines, cosines, and tangents for each degree from 0 to 90°. With the confidence gained from working with the components that form all but the most precise circuits, you will find that this table will serve most of your needs.

The use of a slide rule obviates the necessity of using a table of trigonometric functions except for cases where an extremely high degree of accuracy is desired. Finding an angle corresponding to a given function or finding a function corresponding to a given angle is accomplished by one setting of the indicator. It is in working with trigonometric functions that the use of the modern slide rule really begins to be rewarding in saving time and labor.

PROBLEMS 28 – 2

1 Find the angles having the following as sines: (*a*) 0.3955, (*b*) 0.1167, (*c*) 0.8406, (*d*) 0.0122, (*e*) 0.9991.
2 Find the angles having the following as cosines: (*a*) 0.9979, (*b*) 0.0157, (*c*) 0.5721, (*d*) 0.3173, (*e*) 0.9796.
3 Find the angles having the following as tangents: (*a*) 0.0087, (*b*) 1.7532, (*c*) 573.0 (*d*) 0.3522, (*e*) 4.5864.

4   (a) $\theta = $ arctan 10.78. $\theta = $? (b) $\theta = $ arccos 0.7944. $\theta = $? (c) $\theta = $ arcsin 0.9553. $\theta = $? (d) $\theta = $ arccos 0.9992. $\theta = $? (e) $\theta = $ arcsin 0.8980. $\theta = $?

5   (a) $\theta = $ arccos 0.6727. $\theta = $? (b) $\theta = $ arctan 0.4823. $\theta = $? (c) $\theta = $ arcsin 0.0373. $\theta = $? (d) $\theta = $ arctan 0.1315. $\theta = $? (e) $\theta = $ arcsin 0.9581. $\theta = $?

8 – 5   Functions of angles greater than 90°

You have noted that the trigonometric functions have been tabulated only for angles of 0 to 90°. The signs and magnitudes for angles in all quadrants were considered in the preceding chapter, and it is evident that a table of functions for all angles will be needed. Because the existing tables are for angles in the first quadrant, there must be methods of expressing any angle in terms of an angle of the first quadrant in order to make use of the table of functions.

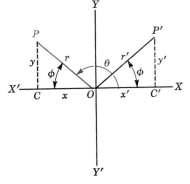

8 – 6   To find the functions of an angle in the second quadrant

In Fig. 28–1, let θ represent any angle in the second quadrant. From any point P on the radius vector r, draw the perpendicular y to the horizontal axis.

FIG. 28–1 θ and ϕ are supplementary angles; $\theta + \phi = 180°$.

The acute angle that r makes with the horizontal axis is designated by ϕ. Then, since $\theta + \phi = 180°$, θ and ϕ are supplementary angles. Hence,

$$\phi = 180° - \theta$$

Now construct the angle XOP' in the first quadrant equal to ϕ, make r' equal to r, and draw y' perpendicular to OX. Since the right triangles OPC and $OP'C'$ are equal, $x = -x'$ and $y = y'$. Then

$$\sin (180° - \theta) = \frac{y}{r} = \frac{y'}{r'} = \sin \phi$$

$$\cos (180° - \theta) = \frac{x}{r} = \frac{-x'}{r'} = -\cos \phi$$

$$\tan (180° - \theta) = \frac{y}{x} = \frac{y'}{-x'} = -\tan \phi$$

These relations show that the function of an angle has the same absolute value as the same function of its supplement. That is, if two angles are supplementary, their sines are equal and their cosines and tangents are of equal magnitude but opposite in sign.

EXAMPLE 13 $\sin 140° = \sin (180° - 140°) = \sin 40° = 0.6428$
$\cos 100° = -\cos (180° - 100°) = -\cos 80° = -0.1736$
$\tan 175° = -\tan (180° - 175°) = -\tan 5° = -0.0875$

28 – 7   To find the function of an angle in the third quadrant

In Fig. 28–2, let θ represent any angle in the third quadrant, and let ϕ

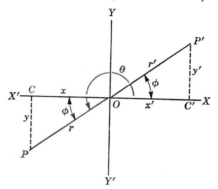

FIG. 28–2 θ is in the third quadrant.
$\phi = \theta - 180°$.

be the acute angle that the radius vector r makes with the horizontal axis. Then

$$\phi = \theta - 180°$$

Now construct the angle XOP' in the first quadrant equal to ϕ, make r' equal to r, and draw y and y' perpendicular to the horizontal axis. Since the right triangles OPC and $OP'C'$ are equal, $x = -x'$ and $y = -y'$. Then

$$\sin (\theta - 180°) = \frac{y}{r} = \frac{-y'}{r'} = -\sin \phi$$

$$\cos (\theta - 180°) = \frac{x}{r} = \frac{-x'}{r'} = -\cos \phi$$

$$\tan (\theta - 180°) = \frac{y}{x} = \frac{-y'}{-x'} = \tan \phi$$

These relations show that the function of an angle in the third quadrant has the same absolute value as the same function of the acute angle between the radius vector and the horizontal axis. The signs of the functions are the same as for any angle in the third quadrant, as discussed in Sec. 27–6.

EXAMPLE 14 $\sin 200° = -\sin (200° - 180°) = -\sin 20° = -0.3420$
$\cos 260° = -\cos (260° - 180°) = -\cos 80° = -0.1736$
$\tan 234° = \tan (234° - 180°) = \tan 54° = 1.3764$

28 – 8 To find the functions of an angle in the fourth quadrant

In Fig. 28–3, let θ represent any angle in the fourth quadrant, and let ϕ be the acute angle that the radius vector r makes with the horizontal axis. Then

$$\phi = 360° - \theta$$

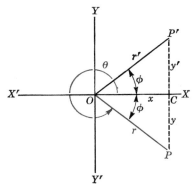

FIG. 28–3 θ is in the fourth quadrant. $\phi = 360° - \theta$.

Now construct the angle XOP' in the first quadrant equal to ϕ, make r' equal to r, and draw y and y' perpendicular to the horizontal axis. Since the right triangles OPC and $OP'C$ are equal, $y = -y'$. Then

$$\sin (360° - \theta) = \frac{y}{r} = \frac{-y'}{r'} = -\sin \phi$$

$$\cos (360° - \theta) = \frac{x}{r} = \frac{x}{r'} = \cos \phi$$

$$\tan (360° - \theta) = \frac{y}{x} = \frac{-y'}{x} = -\tan \phi$$

These relations show that the functions of an angle in the fourth quadrant have the same absolute value as the same functions of an acute angle in the first quadrant equal to $360° - \theta$. The signs of the functions, however, are those for an angle in the fourth quadrant, as discussed in Sec. 27–6.

EXAMPLE 15 $\sin 300° = -\sin (360° - 300°) = -\sin 60° = -0.8660$
$\cos 285° = \cos (360° - 285°) = \cos 75° = 0.2588$
$\tan 316° = -\tan (360° - 316°) = -\tan 44° = -0.9657$

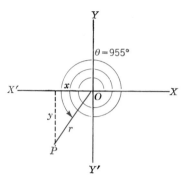

FIG. 28–4 $\theta = 955°$.

28 – 9   To find the function of an angle greater than 360°

Any angle θ greater than 360° has the same trigonometric functions as θ minus an integral multiple of 360°. That is, a function of an angle larger than 360° is found by dividing the angle by 360° and finding the required function of the remainder. Thus θ, in Fig. 28–4, is a positive angle of 955°. To find any function of 955°, divide 955° by 360°, which gives 2 with a remainder of 235°. Hence,

$$\sin 955° = \sin 235° = -\sin (235° - 180°)$$
$$= -\sin 55° = -0.8192$$
$$\cos 955° = \cos 235° = -\cos (235° - 180°)$$
$$= -\cos 55° = -0.5736$$
$$\tan 955° = \tan 235° = \tan (235° - 180°)$$
$$= \tan 55° = 1.4281$$

28 – 10   To find the function of a negative angle

In Fig. 28–5, let $-\theta$ represent a negative angle in the fourth quadrant made by the radius vector r and the horizontal axis. Construct the angle θ in the first quadrant equal to $-\theta$, make r' equal to r, and draw y and y' perpendicular to the horizontal axis. Since the right triangles OPC and $OP'C$ are equal, $y = -y'$. Then

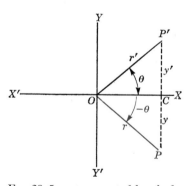

FIG. 28–5 $-\theta$ generated by clockwise rotation.

$$\sin (-\theta) = \frac{y}{r} = \frac{-y'}{r'} = -\sin \theta$$

$$\cos (-\theta) = \frac{x}{r} = \frac{x}{r'} = \cos \theta$$

$$\tan (-\theta) = \frac{y}{x} = \frac{-y'}{x'} = -\tan \theta$$

These relations are true for any values of $-\theta$, regardless of the quadrant or the magnitude of the angle.

EXAMPLE 16 $\sin(-65°) = -\sin 65° = -0.9063$
$\cos(-150°) = \cos 150° = -\cos(180° - 150°) = -\cos 30° = -0.8660$
$\tan(-287°) = -\tan 287° = -\tan(360° - 287°) = -(-\tan 73°)$
$$= 3.2709$$

28 — 11   To reduce the functions of any angle to the functions of an acute angle

It has been shown in the preceding sections that all angles can be reduced to terms of $(180° - \theta)$, $(\theta - 180°)$, $(360° - \theta)$, or θ. These results can be summarized as follows:

RULE   To find any function of any angle θ, take the same function of the acute angle formed by the terminal side (radius vector) and the horizontal axis and prefix the proper algebraic sign for that quadrant.

When finding the functions of angles, you should make a sketch showing the approximate location of the angle. This procedure will clarify the trigonometric relationships, and in addition, many errors will be avoided.

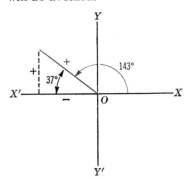

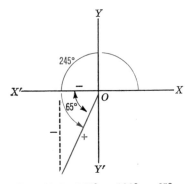

Fig. 28–6 $180° - 143° = 37°$.   Fig. 28–7 $245° - 180° = 65°$.

EXAMPLE 17   Find the functions of 143°.
SOLUTION   Construct the angle 143°, and mark the signs of the radius vector, abscissa, and ordinate, as shown in Fig. 28–6. (The radius vector is always positive.) Since $180° - 143° = 37°$, the acute angle for the functions is 37°. Hence,

$$\sin 143° = \sin 37° = 0.6018$$
$$\cos 143° = -\cos 37° = -0.7986$$
$$\tan 143° = -\tan 37° = -0.7536$$

EXAMPLE 18   Find the functions of 245°.
SOLUTION   Construct the angle 245° as shown in Fig. 28–7. Since

$$245° - 180° = 65°$$

the acute angle for the functions is 65°. Hence,

$$\sin 245° = -\sin 65° = -0.9063$$
$$\cos 245° = -\cos 65° = -0.4226$$
$$\tan 245° = \tan 65° = 2.1445$$

EXAMPLE 19   Find the functions of 312°.

SOLUTION   Construct the angle 312° as shown in Fig. 28–8. Since

$$360° - 312° = 48°$$

the acute angle for the functions is 48°. Hence,

$$\sin 312° = -\sin 48° = -0.7431$$
$$\cos 312° = \cos 48° = 0.6691$$
$$\tan 312° = -\tan 48° = -1.1106$$

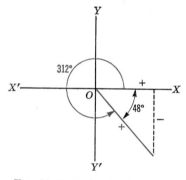

FIG. 28–8   360° − 312° = 48°.

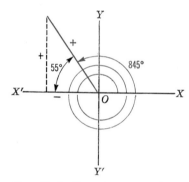

FIG. 28–9   Functions of 845° are same as for 125°.

EXAMPLE 20   Find the functions of 845°.

SOLUTION   845°/360° = 2 + 125°. Therefore, the functions of 125° will be identical with those of 845°. The construction is shown in Fig. 28–9. Since 180° − 125° = 55°, the acute angle for the functions is 55°. Hence,

$$\sin 845° = \sin 55° = 0.8192$$
$$\cos 845° = -\cos 55° = -0.5736$$
$$\tan 845° = -\tan 55° = -1.4281$$

EXAMPLE 21   Find the functions of −511°.

SOLUTION   −511°/360° = −(1 + 151°). Therefore, the functions of −151° will be identical with those of −511°. The construction is shown in Fig. 28–10. Since 180° − 151° = 29°, the acute angle for the functions is 29°. Hence,

$$\sin\ (-151°) = -\sin 29° = -0.4848$$
$$\cos\ (-151°) = -\cos 29° = -0.8746$$
$$\tan\ (-151°) = \tan 29° = 0.5543$$

– 12 Angles corresponding to inverse functions

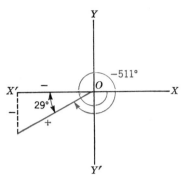

Fig. 28–10   Functions for −511° are same as for −151°.

Now that we are able to express all angles as acute angles in order to use the table of functions from 0 to 90°, it has probably occurred to you that an important distinction exists between the direct trigonometric functions and the inverse trigonometric functions.   The trigonometric functions of any given angle have only one value, whereas a given function corresponds to an infinite number of angles.   For example, an angle of 30° has but one sine value, which is 0.5000, but an angle whose sine is 0.5000 (arcsin 0.5000) may be taken as 30°, 150°, 390°, 480°, 510°, etc.

To avoid confusion, it has been agreed that the values of arcsin θ and arctan θ which lie between $+90°$ and $-90°$, in the first and fourth quadrants, are to be known as the *principal values* of arcsin θ and arctan θ.   The principal value is often denoted by using a capital letter, as Arcsin θ.   Thus, Arcsin 0.5750 = 35.1°, and Arcsin (−0.9980) = −86.4°.   Also, Arctan 1.4826 = 56°, and Arctan (−0.0699) = −4°.

The principal values of arccos θ are taken as the values between 0 and 180° and are denoted by Arccos θ.   Thus, Arccos 0.1736 = 80°, and Arccos (−0.9816) = 169°.

PROBLEMS 28 – 3

1   Find the sine, cosine, and tangent of (*a*) 101°, (*b*) 150°, (*c*) 120.5°, (*d*) 163.2°, (*e*) 179.3°.

2   Find the sine, cosine, and tangent of (*a*) 185°, (*b*) 267°, (*c*) 220.7°, (*d*) 180.2°, (*e*) 229.6°.

3   Find the sine, cosine, and tangent of (*a*) 285°, (*b*) 319°, (*c*) 357.4°, (*d*) 302.6°, (*e*) 342.9°.

4   Find the sine, cosine, and tangent of (*a*) 500°, (*b*) 683°, (*c*) −147.3°, (*d*) 936.4°, (*e*) −333.7°.

5   Find the sine, cosine, and tangent of (*a*) 1,153.2°, (*b*) −15.5°, (*c*) 729°, (*d*) −470.1°, (*e*) 895.6°.

6 Find θ if (a) $\theta =$ Arccos 0.9888, (b) $\theta =$ Arcsin 0.4586, (c) $\theta =$ Arccos 0.1650, (d) $\theta =$ Arctan (-26.03), (e) $\theta =$ Arcsin (-0.6569).

7 Find ϕ if (a) $\phi =$ Arctan 1.455, (b) $\phi =$ Arccos (-0.0122), (c) $\phi =$ Arcsin 0.8358, (d) $\phi =$ Arccos (-0.0366), (e) $\phi =$ Arctan (-3.952).

8 The illumination on a surface that is not perpendicular to the rays of light from a source of light is given by the formula

$$E = \frac{I \cos \theta}{d^2}$$

where E = illumination at point on surface, ft-c
     I = luminous intensity of source, cp
     d = distance from source of light, ft
     θ = angle between incident ray and a line perpendicular to surface

Solve for d, I, and θ.

9 In the formula of Prob. 8, find the value of d if $I = 265$ cp, $\theta = 65°$, and $E = 12$ ft-c.

10 A certain 100-watt lamp has a luminous intensity of 108 cp. Disregarding reflection, compute the illumination at a point on a surface 10 ft from the lamp if the plane of the surface is at an angle of 20° from the incident rays.

11 In the formula of Prob. 8, at what angle to the incident ray will the plane of the surface be for the greatest amount of light?

12 The illumination on a horizontal surface from a source of light at a given vertical distance from the surface is given by the formula

$$E_h = \frac{I}{h^2} \cos^3 \theta$$

where E_h = illumination at a point on horizontal surface, ft-c
     I = luminous intensity of source, cp
     h = vertical distance from horizontal surface to source of light, ft

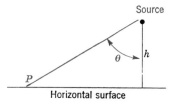

FIG. 28–11 Illumination at P from source.

     θ = angle between incident ray and a vertical line, as shown in Fig. 28–11.

NOTE $\cos^3 \theta$ means cos θ raised to the third power. Thus, $\cos^3 \theta = (\cos \theta)^3$.

Solve for h, I, and θ.

13 Using the formula of Prob. 12, solve for E_h if $I = 225$ ft-c, $h = 15$ ft, and $\theta = 35°$.

14 Using the formula of Prob. 12, find the value of I if $h = 10$ ft, $E_h = 25$ ft-c, and $\theta = 70°$.

15 According to present standards, 8 to 12 ft-c of illumination on the printed page should be used for ordinary reading purposes. A 50-watt 45-cp lamp is suspended 6 ft above a reading table. The reflector used with the lamp projects 70 per cent of the light downward. Does this produce enough illumination for reading a book directly under the lamp?

16 To produce 10 ft-c on the book in the above problem, what candlepower lamp would be required?

CHAPTER 29
SOLUTION OF RIGHT TRIANGLES

One of the most important applications of trigonometry is the solution of triangles, both right and oblique. This chapter is concerned with the former. The right triangle is probably the most universally used geometric figure; with the aid of trigonometry, it is applied to numerous problems in measurement that otherwise might be impossible to solve.

A large percentage of the problems relating to the analysis of a-c circuits and networks involves the solution of the right triangle in one form or another.

29 – 1   Facts concerning right triangles

Before proceeding with the actual solutions of right triangles, the following useful facts regarding the properties of the right triangle should be reviewed:

1   The square of the hypotenuse is equal to the sum of the squares of the other two sides ($c^2 = a^2 + b^2$).
2   The acute angles are complements of each other; that is, the sum of the two acute angles is 90° ($A + B = 90°$).
3   The hypotenuse is greater than either of the other sides and is less than their sum.

4   The greater angle is opposite the greater side, and the greater side is opposite the greater angle.

These facts will often serve as a material aid in checking computations made by trigonometric methods.

29 – 2   Procedure for solution of right triangles

Every triangle has three sides and three angles, and these are called the six *elements* of the triangle.   To *solve* a triangle is to find the values of the unknown elements.

A triangle can be solved by two methods:

1   By constructing the triangle accurately from known elements with scale, protractor, and compasses.   The unknown elements can then be measured with the scale and the protractor.

2   By computing the unknown elements from those that are known.

The first method has been used to some extent in preceding chapters.   However, as previously discussed, the graphical method is cumbersome and has a limited degree of accuracy.

Trigonometry, combined with simple algebraic processes, furnishes a powerful tool for solving triangles by the second method listed above.   Moreover, the degree of accuracy is limited only by the number of significant figures to which the elements have been measured and the number of significant figures in the table of functions used for the solution.

As pointed out in earlier chapters, every type of problem should be approached and solved in a planned and systematic manner.   Only in this way are the habits of clear and ordered thinking developed, the principles of the problem understood, and the possibility of errors reduced to a minimum.   With the foregoing in mind, the following suggestions for solving right triangles are listed as a guide:

1. Make an accurate drawing to scale of the triangle, and mark the known (given) elements.   This shows the relation of the elements, helps in choosing the functions needed, and will serve as a check for the solution.   List what is to be found.

2. To find an unknown element, select a formula that contains two known elements and the required unknown element.   Substitute the known elements in the formula, and solve for the unknown.

3. As a rough check on the solution, compare the results with the drawing.   To check the values accurately, note whether they satisfy

relations different from those already employed for the solution of the values being checked. A convenient check for the sides of a right triangle is the relation

$$a^2 = c^2 - b^2 = (c + b)(c - b)$$

4. In the computations, round off the numbers representing the lengths of sides to three significant figures and all angles to the nearest tenth of a degree. This means that the values of the functions employed in computations are to be used to only three significant figures. As previously stated, such accuracy is sufficient for ordinary practical circuit computations.

Heretofore, the right triangles used in figures for illustrative examples have been lettered in the conventional manner, as shown in Figs. 27–1, 27–2, etc. At this point the notation for the various elements will be changed to that of Fig. 29–1. This change of lettering in no way has any effect on the fundamental relations existing among the elements of a right triangle, nor are any new ideas involved in connection with the trigonometric functions. Because certain a-c problems will employ this form of notation, this is a convenient place to introduce it in order that we may become accustomed to solving right triangles lettered in this manner.

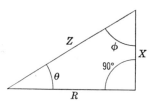

Fig. 29–1 Lettering of right triangle.

The following articles illustrate all the possible conditions encountered in the solution of right triangles.

29 – 3 Given an acute angle and a side not the hypotenuse

EXAMPLE 1   Given $R = 30.0$ and $\theta = 25.0°$. Solve for Z, X, and ϕ.

SOLUTION   The construction is shown in Fig. 29–2.

$$\phi = 90° - \theta = 90° - 25° = 65°$$

An equation containing the two known elements and one unknown is

$$\tan \theta = \frac{X}{R}$$

Solving for X, $X = R \tan \theta$

Substituting the values of R and $\tan \theta$,

$$X = 30 \times 0.466 = 14.0$$

Also, since $\sin \theta = \frac{X}{Z}$

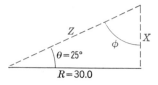

Fig. 29–2 Construction for solution of Example 1.

solving for Z,
$$Z = \frac{X}{\sin \theta}$$

Substituting the values of X and $\sin \theta$,
$$Z = \frac{14.0}{0.423} = 33.1$$

This solution can be checked by using some relation other than the ones used in solving. Thus, substituting values in

$$X^2 = (Z + R)(Z - R)$$

results in
$$14.0^2 = (33.1 + 30.0)(33.1 - 30.0)$$
$$196 = 63.1 \times 3.10 = 196$$

Since all results were rounded off to three significant figures, the check shows the solution to be correct for this degree of accuracy.

The value of Z can be checked by employing a function not used in the solution. Thus, since
$$R = Z \cos \theta$$
by substituting the values, $30 = 33.1 \times 0.906$

Still another check could be made by use of an inverse function employing two of the elements found in the solution. For example,

$$\phi = \arccos \frac{X}{Z} = \frac{14.0}{33.1} = 0.423 = \cos 65°$$

EXAMPLE 2   Given $X = 106$ and $\theta = 36.4°$. Solve for Z, R, and ϕ.

SOLUTION   The construction is shown in Fig. 29–3.

$$\phi = 90° - \theta = 90° - 36.4° = 53.6°$$

An equation containing two known elements and one unknown is

$$\sin \theta = \frac{X}{Z}$$

Solving for Z,
$$Z = \frac{X}{\sin \theta}$$

Substituting the values of X and $\sin \theta$,

$$Z = \frac{106}{0.593} = 179$$

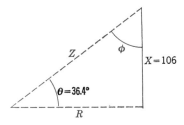

Also, since
$$\cos \theta = \frac{R}{Z}$$

FIG. 29–3 Triangle of Example 2.

solving for R, $\quad R = Z \cos \theta$

Substituting the values of Z and $\cos \theta$,
$$R = 179 \times 0.805 = 144$$

Check the solution by one of the methods previously explained.

EXAMPLE 3   Given $R = 8.35$ and $\phi = 62.7°$. Find Z, X, and θ.
SOLUTION   The construction is shown in Fig. 29–4.

$$\theta = 90° - \phi = 90° - 62.7° = 27.3°$$

When θ is found, the methods to be used in the solution of this example become identical with those of Example 1. Hence,

$$X = R \tan \theta = 8.35 \tan 27.3° = 8.35 \times 0.516 = 4.31$$
$$Z = \frac{X}{\sin \theta} = \frac{4.31}{\sin 27.3°} = \frac{4.31}{0.459} = 9.39$$

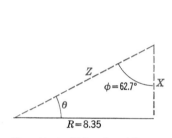

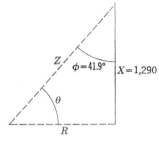

FIG. 29–4 Triangle of Exam-   FIG. 29–5 $2X = 1,290$, $\phi = $
ple 3. $41.9°$.

Check the solution by a method considered most convenient.

EXAMPLE 4   Given $X = 1,290$ and $\phi = 41.9°$. Find Z, R, and θ.
SOLUTION   The construction is shown in Fig. 29–5.

$$\theta = 90° - \phi = 90° - 41.9° = 48.1°$$

When θ is found, the methods to be used in the solution of this example become identical with those of Example 2. Hence,

$$Z = \frac{X}{\sin \theta} = \frac{1,290}{\sin 48.1°} = \frac{1,290}{0.744} = 1,730$$
$$R = Z \cos \theta = 1,730 \cos 48.1° = 1,730 \times 0.688 = 1,160$$

Check the solution by a method considered most convenient.

With the exception of finding the unknown acute angle, which involves subtraction, any of the foregoing examples and the following problems can be solved with two movements on many types of slide rules.

PROBLEMS 29 – 1

Solve the following right triangles for the unknown elements. Check each by making a construction and by substituting into a formula not used in the solution:

1   $R = 73.6, \theta = 15.0°$ 2 $R = 425, \theta = 23.6°$
3   $R = 17.0, \theta = 69.1°$ 4 $X = 38.0, \theta = 73.3°$
5   $X = 109, \theta = 10.3°$ 6 $X = 5.30, \theta = 47.9°$
7   $R = 76.3, \phi = 15.4°$ 8 $R = 3,060, \phi = 80.5°$
9   $R = 3.12, \phi = 37.7°$ 10 $X = 200, \phi = 29.1°$
11 $X = 20.3, \phi = 87.3°$ 12 $X = 1,800, \phi = 33.7°$
13 $R = 0.327, \theta = 16.8°$ 14 $X = \frac{3}{8}, \phi = 7.6°$
15 $R = \frac{2}{3}, \phi = 38.1°$

9–4   Given an acute angle and the hypotenuse

EXAMPLE 5   Given $Z = 45.3$ and $\theta = 20.3°$. Find R, X, and ϕ.
SOLUTION   The construction is shown in Fig. 29–6.

$$\phi = 90° - \theta = 90° - 20.3° = 69.7°$$

An equation containing two known elements and one unknown is

$$\cos \theta = \frac{R}{Z}$$

Solving for R, $R = Z \cos \theta$
Substituting the values of Z and $\cos \theta$,
$$R = 45.3 \times 0.938 = 42.5$$

Another convenient equation is

$$\sin \theta = \frac{X}{Z}$$

Solving for X, $X = Z \sin \theta$
Substituting the values of Z and $\sin \theta$,
$$X = 45.3 \times 0.347 = 15.7$$

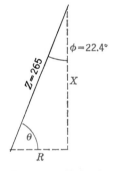

FIG. 29–7 $Z = 265$,
$\phi = 22.4°$.

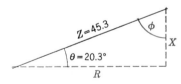

FIG. 29–6 $Z = 45.3$, $\theta = 20.3°$.

The solution can be checked by any of the usual methods.

EXAMPLE 6   Given $Z = 265$ and $\phi = 22.4°$. Find R, X, and θ.
SOLUTION   The construction is shown in Fig. 29–7.

$$\theta = 90° - \phi = 90° - 22.4° = 67.6°$$

When θ is found, this triangle is solved by the methods used in Example 1.
Hence,
$$R = Z \cos \theta = 265 \cos 67.6° = 265 \times 0.381 = 101$$
$$X = Z \sin \theta = 265 \sin 67.6° = 265 \times 0.924 = 245$$

Check the solution by one of the several methods.

PROBLEMS 29 – 2

Solve the following right triangles for the unknown elements. Check each by construction and by substituting in an equation not used in the solution.

1   $Z = 26.8,\ \theta = 34.7°$ 2 $Z = 72.0,\ \theta = 3.5°$
3   $Z = 600,\ \theta = 45°$ 4 $Z = 36.0,\ \phi = 80.1°$
5   $Z = 500,\ \phi = 26.3°$ 6 $Z = 13.4,\ \phi = 58.8°$
7   $Z = 0.742,\ \theta = 8.6°$ 8 $Z = 10^6,\ \phi = 62.3°$
9   $Z = \frac{5}{6},\ \theta = 6.4°$ 10 $Z = \sqrt{2},\ \phi = 30°$

29 – 5   Given the hypotenuse and one other side

EXAMPLE 7   Given $Z = 38.3$ and $R = 23.1$. Find X, θ, and ϕ.

SOLUTION   The construction is shown in Fig. 29–8.

An equation containing two known elements and one unknown is

$$\cos \theta = \frac{R}{Z}$$

Substituting the values of R and Z,

$$\cos \theta = \frac{23.1}{38.3} = 0.603$$

$$\therefore \theta = 52.9°$$

$$\phi = 90° - \theta = 90° - 52.9° = 37.1°$$

Then, since $\sin \theta = \dfrac{X}{Z}$

solving for X, $X = Z \sin \theta$

Substituting the values of Z and $\sin \theta$,

$$X = 38.3 \times 0.798 = 30.6$$

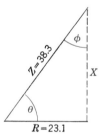

FIG. 29–8   Triangle of Example 7.

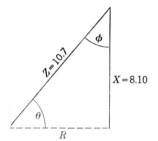

FIG. 29–9   Triangle of Example 8.

EXAMPLE 8   Given $Z = 10.7$ and $X = 8.10$. Find R, θ, and ϕ.

SOLUTION   The construction is shown in Fig. 29–9.

An equation containing two known elements and one unknown is

$$\sin \theta = \frac{X}{Z}$$

Substituting the values of X and Z,

$$\sin \theta = \frac{8.10}{10.7} = 0.757$$

$$\therefore \theta = 49.2°$$

$$\phi = 90° - \theta = 90° - 49.2° = 40.8°$$

Then, since $\qquad \cos \theta = \dfrac{R}{Z}$

solving for R, $\qquad R = Z \cos \theta$

Substituting the values of Z and $\cos \theta$,

$$R = 10.7 \times 0.653 = 6.99$$

PROBLEMS 29 – 3

Solve the following right triangles, and check each as in the preceding problems:

1 $Z = 70.0, R = 63.5$ 2 $Z = 51.7, R = 10.3$
3 $Z = 179, R = 175$ 4 $Z = 48.7, X = 48.4$
5 $Z = 0.403, X = 0.290$ 6 $Z = 1,030, X = 867$
7 $Z = 0.238, R = 0.105$ 8 $Z = 10^4, X = 6.21 \times 10^3$
9 $Z = 1.02, R = 0.230$ 10 $Z = 1, X = \frac{1}{2}$

9 – 6 Given two sides not the hypotenuse

EXAMPLE 9   Given $R = 76.0$ and $X = 37.4$. Find Z, θ, and ϕ.

SOLUTION   The construction is shown in Fig. 29–10.

An equation containing two known elements and one unknown is

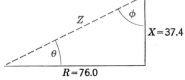

$$\tan \theta = \frac{X}{R}$$

Substituting the values of X and R,

$$\tan \theta = \frac{37.4}{76.0} = 0.492$$

$$\therefore \theta = 26.2°$$

$$\phi = 90° \times \theta = 90° - 26.2° = 63.8°$$

FIG. 29–10. Triangle of Example 9.

$Z = 84.7$ can be found by one of the methods explained in the preceding articles.

PROBLEMS 29 – 4

Solve the following right triangles, and check each as in the preceding problems:

1 $R = 8.10, X = 21.1$ 2 $X = 57.0, R = 403$
3 $X = 44.7, R = 40.0$ 4 $R = 454, X = 1,530$

5 $R = 525, X = 401$ 6 $R = 249, X = 408$

7 $X = 6{,}210, R = 7{,}840$ 8 $R = 0.932, X = 0.171$

9 $X = 124, R = 100$ 10 $X = R = \dfrac{\sqrt{2}}{2}$

29 – 7   Terms relating to miscellaneous trigonometric problems

If an object is higher than an observer's eye, the *angle of elevation* of the object is the angle between the horizontal and the line of sight to the object. This is illustrated in Fig. 29–11.

If an object is lower than an observer's eye, the *angle of depression* of the object is the angle between the horizontal and the line of sight to the object. This is illustrated in Fig. 29–12.

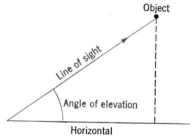

FIG. 29–11 Angle of elevation.   FIG. 29–12   Angle of depression.

The *horizontal distance* between two points is the distance from one of the two points to a vertical line drawn through the other. Thus, in Fig. 29–13, the line AC is a vertical line through the point A, and CB is a horizontal line through the point B. Then the horizontal distance from A to B is the distance between C and B.

FIG. 29–13 Vertical and horizontal distances.

The *vertical distance* between two points is the distance from one of the two points to the horizontal line drawn through the other. Thus, the vertical distance from A to B, in Fig. 29–13, is the distance between A and C.

Calculations of distance in the vertical plane are made by means of right triangles having horizontal and vertical sides. The horizontal side is usually called the *run*, and the vertical side is called the *rise* or *fall*, as the case may be.

The *slope* or *grade* of a line is the rise or fall divided by the run. Thus if a road rises 5 ft in a run of 100 ft, the grade of the road is $\frac{5}{100} = 0.05 = 5$ per cent.

PROBLEMS 29 – 5

1 What is the angle of inclination of a stairway with the floor if the steps have a tread of 11 in. and a rise of 6 in.?

2 What angle does a rafter make with the horizontal if it has a rise of 4 ft in a run of 6 ft?

3 A road rises 350 ft in a run of 2,500 ft. What is the percentage of grade? What is the angle of inclination of the roadbed with the horizontal?

4 A radio tower cast a shadow 473 ft long. At the same time the angle of elevation of the sun was observed to be 32.4°. What is the height of the tower?

5 A radio tower 600 ft high cast a shadow 262 ft long. What was the angle of elevation of the sun at this time?

6 At a horizontal distance of 125 ft from the foot of a radio tower, the angle of elevation to the top is found to be 62°. How high is the tower?

7 A telephone pole 40 ft high is to be guyed from its middle, and the guy is to make an angle of 45° with the ground. Allowing 2 ft extra for splicing, how long must the guy wire be?

8 A ladder 35 ft in length rests against a vertical wall. The foot of the ladder is 10 ft from the wall. How far up the wall does the ladder reach? What angle does the ladder make with the ground?

9 A ladder 50 ft long can be placed so that it will reach a point on a wall 42 ft above the ground. By tipping the ladder back without moving its foot, it will reach a point on another wall 32 ft above the ground. What is the horizontal distance between the walls?

10 From the top of a cliff 426 ft high the angle of depression of a ship is observed to be 18.2°. How far out is the ship?

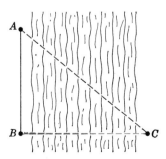

Fig. 29–14 Measuring across a river.

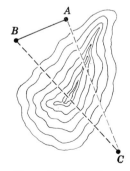

Fig. 29–15 Measuring across a pond.

11   In order to find the width BC of a river, a distance AB was laid off
     along the bank, the point B being directly opposite a tree C on the
     opposite side, as shown in Fig. 29–14. If the angle BAC was observed to
     be 51.6° and AB was 325 ft, find the width of the river.

12   In order to measure the distance AC across a pond, a surveyor lays off
     a line AB such that the angle $BAC = 90°$, as shown in Fig. 29–15. At
     point B, 500 ft from A, he observes that angle $ABC = 68.2°$. Find the
     distance AC.

CHAPTER 30

PERIODIC FUNCTIONS

In Sec. 27–11, it was shown that the trigonometric functions could be represented by the ratios of lengths of certain lines to the unit radius vector. Also, in Sec. 27–12, the variation of the functions was represented by lines.

The complete variation of the functions is more clearly illustrated and better understood by plotting their continuous values on rectangular coordinates.

30 – 1   The graph of the sine curve $y = \sin x$

The equation $y = \sin x$ can be plotted just as the graphs of algebraic equations are plotted, that is, by assigning values to the angle x (the independent variable), computing the corresponding value of y (the dependent variable), plotting the points whose coordinates are thus obtained, and drawing a smooth curve through the points. This is the same procedure used for plotting linear equations in Chap. 21 and for plotting quadratic equations in Chap. 29.

The first questions that come to mind in preparing to graph this equation are, "What values shall be assigned to x? Shall they be in radians or degrees?" Either might be used, but it is more reasonable to use radians. In Sec. 26–5, it was shown that an angle measured in radians can be represented by the arc intercepted by this angle on the circumference of a circle of unit radius. Since, as previously mentioned, the functions of an angle can be represented by suitable lengths of lines, it follows that if an angle is expressed in radian measure both the angle and its functions can be expressed in terms of a common unit of length. Therefore, we shall select a suitable unit of length and plot both x and y values in terms of this unit. Then to graph the equation $y = \sin x$, the procedure is as follows:

1. Assign values to x.

2. From the slide rule or the tables, determine the corresponding values of y (Table 30–1).

3. Take each pair of values of x and y as coordinates of a point, and plot the point.

4. Draw a smooth curve through the points.

TABLE 30 – 1

x, degrees	x, radians (π measure)	x, radians (unit measure)	y ($\sin x$)	Point
0	0	0	0	$P_0 = (0,0)$
30	$\dfrac{\pi}{6}$	0.52	0.50	$P_1 = (0.52, 0.50)$
60	$\dfrac{\pi}{3}$	1.05	0.87	$P_2 = (1.05, 0.87)$
90	$\dfrac{\pi}{2}$	1.57	1.00	$P_3 = (1.57, 1.00)$
120	$\dfrac{2\pi}{3}$	2.09	0.87	$P_4 = (2.09, 0.87)$
150	$\dfrac{5\pi}{6}$	2.62	0.50	$P_5 = (2.62, 0.50)$
180	π	3.14	0	$P_6 = (3.14, 0)$

It is not necessary to tabulate values of $\sin x$ between π and 2π radians (180 to 360°), for these values are negative but equal in magnitude to the sines of the angles between 0 and π radians (0 to 180°). The curve should be plotted with the angle and the function having the same unit or scale; that is, one unit on the Y axis should be the same length as that representing 1 radian on the X axis. When the curve is so plotted, it is called a *proper sine curve*, as shown in Fig. 30–1. This wave-shaped curve is called the *sine curve* or *sinusoid*.

If additional values of x are chosen, both positive and negative, the curve continues indefinitely in both directions, repeating in value. Notice that, as x increases from 0 to $\pi/2$, sin x increases from 0 to 1; as x increases from $\pi/2$ to π, sin x decreases from 1 to 0; as x increases from π to $3\pi/2$, sin x decreases from 0 to -1; and as x increases from

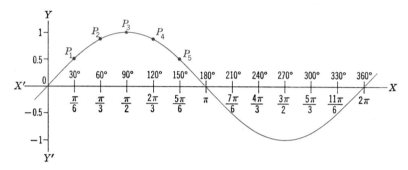

Fig. 30–1 Graph of the equation $y = \sin x$.

$3\pi/2$ to 2π, sin x increases from -1 to 0. Thus the curve repeats itself for every multiple of 2π radians.

30 – 2 The graph of the cosine curve $y = \cos x$

By following the procedure for plotting the sine curve, it is easily shown that the graph of $y = \cos x$ appears as shown in Fig. 30–2.

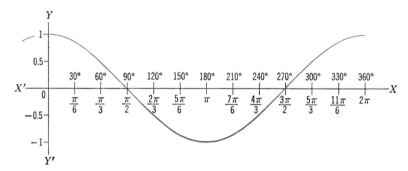

Fig. 30–2 Graph of the equation $y = \cos x$.

Note that, as x increases from 0 to $\pi/2$, cos x decreases from 1 to 0; as x increases from $\pi/2$ to π, cos x decreases from 0 to -1; as x increases from π to $3\pi/2$, cos x increases from -1 to 0; and as x increases from $3\pi/2$ to 2π, cos x increases from 0 to 1. If additional values of x are chosen, both positive and negative, the curve will repeat itself indefinitely in both directions. The cosine curve is identical in shape with the sine curve except that there is a difference of 90° between corresponding points on the two curves. Another similarity between these curves is that both curves repeat their values for every multiple of 2π radians.

30 – 3 The graph of the tangent curve y = tan x

The graph of the equation $y = \tan x$, shown in Fig. 30–3, has different characteristics from the sine or cosine curves. The curve slopes

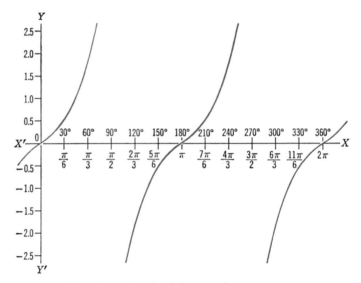

FIG. 30–3 Graph of the equation $y = \tan x$.

upward and to the right. At points where x is an odd multiple of $\pi/2$, the curve is discontinuous. This is to be expected from the discussion of the tangent function in Sec. 27–12.

The tangent curve repeats itself at intervals of π radians and is thus seen to be a series of separate curves, or branches, rather than a continuous curve.

PROBLEMS 30 – 1

1   Plot the equation $y = \sin x$ from -2π to 2π radians.
2   Plot the equation $y = \cos x$ from -2π to 2π radians.
3   Plot the equation $y = \cot x$ from 0 to 2π radians.
4   Plot the equation $y = \sec x$ from 0 to 2π radians.
5   Plot the equation $y = \csc x$ from 0 to 2π radians.

6   Plot the equation $y = \sin^2 x$ and $y = \cos^2 x$ on the same coordinates and
to the same scale.   In computing points, remember that when a negative
number is squared, the result is positive.   Add the respective ordinates
of the curves for several different values of angle, and plot the results.
What conclusion do you draw from these results?

0 – 4   Periodicity

From the graphs plotted in the preceding figures and from earlier
considerations of the trigonometric functions, it is evident that each
trigonometric function repeats itself exactly in the same order and at
regular intervals.   A function that repeats itself periodically is called
a *periodic function*.   From this definition, it is apparent that the
trigonometric functions are periodic functions.

Owing to the fact that many natural phenomena are periodic in
character, the sine and cosine curves lend themselves ideally to
graphical representation and mathematical analysis of these recurrent
motions.   For example, the rise and fall of tides, motions of certain
machines, the vibrations of a pendulum, the rhythm of our bodily
life, sound waves, and water waves are all familiar happenings that
can be represented and analyzed by the use of these curves.   An
alternating current follows these variations, as will be shown in
Chap. 32, and it is because of this fact that you must have a good
grounding in trigonometry.   It is essential that you understand the
mathematical expressions for various periodic functions and especially
their applications to a-c circuits.

The tangent, cotangent, secant, and cosecant curves are not used to
represent recurrent happenings, for although these curves are periodic, they are discontinuous for certain values of angles.

0 – 5   Angular motion

The *linear velocity* of a point or object moving in a particular direction
is the rate at which distance is traveled by the point or object.   The
unit of velocity is the distance traveled in unit time when the motion
of the point or object is uniform, such as miles per hour, feet per
second, and centimeters per second.

The same concept is used to measure and define *angular velocity*.
In Fig. 30–4 the radius vector r is turning about the origin in a
counterclockwise direction to generate the angle θ.   The *angular
velocity* of such a rotating line is the rate at which an angle is generated
by rotation.   When the rotation is uniform, the unit of angular

velocity is the angle generated per unit of time. Thus, angular velocity is measured in degrees per second or radians per second, the latter being the more widely used.

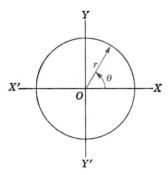

FIG. 30–4   Radius vector *r* generates angle *θ*.

Angular velocity may be expressed in terms of revolutions per minute (rpm) or revolutions per second (rps). For example, if *f* is the number of revolutions per second of the vector of Fig. 30–4, then $2\pi f$ is the number of radians generated per second. The angular velocity in radians per second is denoted by *ω* (Greek letter omega). Thus, if the radius vector is rotating *f* revolutions per second,

$$\omega = 2\pi f \qquad \textbf{radians/sec}$$

If the armature of a generator is rotating at 1,800 rpm, which is 30 rps, it has an angular velocity of

$$\omega = 2\pi f = 2\pi \times 30 = 188.4 \text{ radians/sec}$$

The total angle *θ* generated by a rotating line in *t* sec at an angular velocity of *ω* radians/sec is

$$\theta = \omega t \qquad \textbf{radians}$$

Thus the angle generated by the armature in 0.01 sec is

$$\theta = \omega t = 188.4 \times 0.01 = 1.884 \text{ radians}$$
or
$$\theta = 1.884 \times 57.3° = 108°$$

EXAMPLE 1   A flywheel has a velocity of 300 rpm.   (*a*) What is the angular velocity?   (*b*) What angle will be generated in 0.2 sec?   (*c*) How much time is required for the wheel to generate 628 radians?

SOLUTION   (*a*) $f = \dfrac{300 \text{ rpm}}{60} = 5 \text{ rps}$

Then, $\omega = 2\pi f = 2\pi \times 5 = 10\pi$ or 31.4 radians/sec

(*b*) $\theta = \omega t = 10\pi \times 0.2 = 2\pi$ radians

                              $\theta = 360°$

(*c*) Since $\theta = \omega t$

then $t = \dfrac{\theta}{\omega} = \dfrac{628}{10\pi} = 20 \text{ sec}$

PROBLEMS 30 – 2

1 What is the angular velocity in terms of π radians/sec of (a) the hour hand of a clock, (b) the minute hand of a clock, (c) the second hand of a clock?

2 Express the angular velocity of 6 rps in (a) radians per second, (b) degrees per second.

3 If a satellite circles the earth in 100 min, what is its average angular velocity in (a) degrees per minute, (b) radians per minute?

4 A revolution counter on an armature shaft recorded 375 revolutions in 15 sec. What is the angular velocity of the armature in (a) radians per second, (b) degrees per second?

5 The radius vector r of Fig. 30–4 is rotating at the rate of 3,600 rpm. What is the value of θ in radians at the end of (a) 0.001 sec, (b) 0.005 sec, (c) 0.3 sec?

6 If the radius vector r of Fig. 30–4 is rotating at the rate of 1 rps, what is the value of sin ωt at the end of (a) 0.10 sec, (b) 0.30 sec, (c) 0.65 sec, (d) 0.80 sec?

30 – 6 Projection of a point having uniform circular motion

In Fig. 30–5 the radius vector r rotates about a point in a counterclockwise direction with a uniform angular velocity of 1 rps. Then every point on the radius vector, such as the end point P, rotates with uniform angular velocity. If the radius vector starts from 0°, at

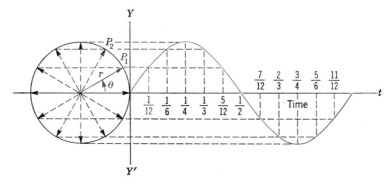

Fig. 30–5   Radius vector r generating sine curve.

the end of $\frac{1}{12}$ sec it will have rotated 30°, or 0.5236 radian, to P_1; at the end of $\frac{1}{6}$ sec, it will have rotated to P_2 and generated an angle of 60°, or 1.047 radians, etc.

The projection of the end point of the radius vector, that is, its ordinate value at any time, can be plotted as a curve. This is accomplished by extending the horizontal diameter of the circle to the right for use as an X axis along which time is to be plotted. Choosing a convenient length along the X axis, divide it into as many intervals as there are angle values to be plotted. In Fig. 30–5, projections have been made every 30°, starting from 0°. Therefore the X axis is divided into 12 divisions, and since one complete revolution takes place in 1 sec, each division on the time axis will represent $\frac{1}{12}$ sec, or 30° rotation.

Through the points of division on the time axis (X axis), construct vertical lines, and through the corresponding points, made by the end point of the radius vector at that particular time, draw lines parallel to the time axis. Draw a smooth curve through the points of intersection. Thus the resulting sine curve traces the ordinate of the end point of the radius vector for any time t, and from it we could obtain the sine value for any angle generated by the radius vector.

As the vector continues to rotate, successive revolutions will generate repeating, or periodic, curves.

Since the y value of the curve is proportional to the sine of the generated angle and the length of the radius vector, we have

$$y = r \sin \theta$$

Then, since the radius vector rotates through 2π radians in 1 sec, the y value at any time t is

$$y = r \sin 2\pi t$$
or
$$y = r \sin 6.28t$$

which is the equation of the sine curve of Fig. 30–5.

From the foregoing considerations, it is apparent that if a straight line of length r rotates about a point with a uniform angular velocity of ω radians per unit time, starting from a horizontal position when the time $t = 0$, the projection y of the end point upon a vertical straight line will have a motion that can be represented by the relation

$$y = r \sin \omega t \qquad [1]$$

This equation is of fundamental importance in describing the motion of any object or quantity that varies periodically, or with simple harmonic motion. Thus the value of an alternating emf at any instant can be completely described in terms of such an equation as will be shown in Chap. 32. Any motion that can be described by this equation, that is, if the motion or variation can be represented by a sine curve, is said to be *sinusoidal* or to vary *sinusoidally*.

EXAMPLE 2   A crank 6 in. long, starting from 0°, turns in a counter-clockwise direction at the rate of 1 revolution in 10 sec. (a) What is the equation for the projection of the crank handle upon a vertical line at any instant? That is, what is the vertical distance from the crankshaft at any time? (b) What is the vertical distance from the handle to the shaft at the end of 3 sec? (c) At the end of 8 sec?

SOLUTION   (a) The general equation for the projection of the end point on a vertical line is

$$y = r \sin \omega t \qquad (1)$$

where r = length of rotating object
     ω = angular velocity, radians/sec
     t = time at any instant, sec

Then, since the crank makes 1 revolution, or 2π radians, in 10 sec, the angular velocity is

$$\omega = \frac{2\pi}{10} = \frac{\pi}{5}, \text{ or } 0.628, \text{ radian/sec}$$

Substituting the values of r and ω in Eq. [1],

$$y = 6 \sin 0.628t \qquad \text{in.}$$

(b) At the end of 3 sec the crank will have turned through

$$0.628 \times 3 = 1.88 \text{ radians}$$

which is $1.88 \times 57.3° = 108°$. Substituting this value for $0.628t$ in Eq. [1] results in

$$y = 6 \sin 108° = 6 \times 0.951 = 5.71 \text{ in.}$$

which is the vertical distance of the handle from the shaft at the end of 3 sec.

(c) At the end of 8 sec the crank will have turned through

$$0.628 \times 8 = 5.02 \text{ radians}$$

which is $5.02 \times 57.3° = 288°$. Substituting this value for $0.628t$ in the above equation results in

$$y = 6 \sin 288° = 6 \times (-0.951) = -5.71 \text{ in.}$$

which is the vertical distance of the handle from the shaft at the end of 8 sec. The negative sign denotes that the handle is *below* the shaft, that is, the distance is measured downward, whereas the distance in (b) above was taken as positive, or *above* the shaft.

If it is desired to express the projection of the end point of the radius vector upon the horizontal, the relation is

$$y = r \cos \omega t \qquad\qquad [2]$$

which, when plotted, results in a cosine curve. Thus, in the foregoing example, the horizontal distance (Sec. 29–7) between the handle and shaft at the end of 8 sec will be

$$y = 6 \cos 288° = 6 \times 0.309 = 1.85 \text{ in.}$$

30 – 7   Amplitude

The graphs of Figs. 30–1, 30–2, and 30–5 have an equal amplitude of 1, that is, an equal vertical displacement from the horizontal axis. The value of the radius vector r determines the amplitude of a general curve, and for this reason the factor r in the general equation

$$y = r \sin \omega t$$

is called the *amplitude factor*. Thus the amplitude of a periodic curve is taken as the maximum displacement, or value, of the curve. It is apparent that, if the length of the radius vector which generates

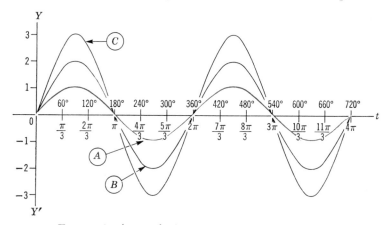

FIG. 30–6 $A{:}y = \sin \theta$, $B{:}y = 2 \sin \theta$, $C{:}y = 3 \sin \theta$.

a sine wave is varied, the amplitude of the sine wave will be varied accordingly. This is illustrated in Fig. 30–6.

30 – 8   Frequency

When the radius vector makes one complete revolution, regardless of its starting point, it has generated one complete sine wave; hence, we say the sine wave has gone through one complete *cycle*. Thus the number of cycles occurring in a periodic curve in a unit of time is called the *frequency* of the curve. For example, if the radius vector rotated 5 rps, the curve describing its motion would go through 5 cycles in 1 sec of time. The frequency f in cycles per second is obtained by dividing the angular velocity ω by 360° when the latter is measured in degrees or by 2π when measured in radians. That is,

$$f = \frac{\omega}{2\pi} \qquad \text{cps} \qquad\qquad [\,3\,]$$

Curves for different frequencies are shown in Fig. 30-7.

In the equation $y = r \sin \frac{1}{2}t$, since $\omega t = \frac{1}{2}t$, the angular velocity ω is $\frac{1}{2}$ radian/sec. That is, at the end of 2π, or 6.28, sec the curve has gone through one-half cycle, or 3.14 radians of angle, as shown in Fig. 30-7.

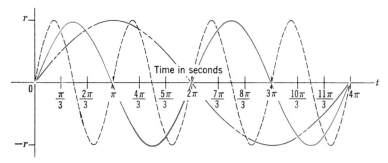

FIG. 30-7 $y = r \sin t$—, $y = r \sin 2t$ - - - -, $y = r \sin \frac{1}{2}t$ — - — - —.

In the equation $y = r \sin t$, since $\omega t = t$, the angular velocity ω is 1 radian/sec. Thus at the end of 2π sec the curve has gone through one complete cycle, or 2π radians of angle.

Similarly, in the equation $y = r \sin 2t$, the angular velocity ω is 2 radians/sec. Then at the end of 2π sec the curve has completed two cycles, or 4π radians of angle.

30 – 9   Period

The time T required for a periodic function, or curve, to complete one cycle is called the *period*. Hence if the frequency f is given by

$$f = \frac{\omega}{2\pi} \qquad \text{cps}$$

it follows that

$$T = \frac{2\pi}{\omega} = \frac{1}{f} \quad \text{sec} \qquad\qquad [4]$$

For example, if a curve repeats itself 60 times in 1 sec, it has a frequency of 60 cps and a period of

$$T = \frac{1}{60} = 0.0167 \text{ sec}$$

Similarly, in Fig. 30–7, the curve represented by $y = r \sin \frac{1}{2}t$ has a frequency of $\omega/2\pi = 0.5/2\pi = 0.0796$ cps and a period of 12.6 sec. The curve of $y = r \sin t$ has a frequency of $\omega/2\pi = 1/2\pi = 0.159$ cps and a period of 6.28 sec. The curve of $y = r \sin 2t$ has a frequency of 0.318 cps and a period of 3.14 sec.

30 – 10   Phase

In Fig. 30–8, two radius vectors are rotating about a point with equal angular velocities of ω and separated by the constant angle θ. That is, if r starts from the horizontal axis, then r_1 starts ahead of r by the angle θ and maintains this angular difference.

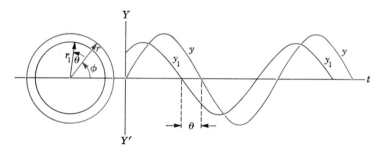

Fig. 30–8 $y = r \sin \omega t, y_1 = r_1 \sin (\omega t + \theta).$

When $t = 0$, r starts from the horizontal axis to generate the curve $y = r \sin \omega t$. At the same time, r_1 is ahead of r by an angle θ; hence, r_1 generates the curve $y_1 = r_1 \sin (\omega t + \theta)$. It will be noted that this *displaces* the y_1 curve along the horizontal by an angle θ as shown in the figure.

The angular difference θ between the two curves is called the *phase angle*, and since y_1 is *ahead* of y, we say that y_1 leads y. Thus, in the equation $y_1 = r_1 \sin (\omega t + \theta)$, θ is called the *angle of lead*. In Fig. 30–8, y_1 leads y by 30°; therefore the equation for y_1 becomes

$$y_1 = r_1 \sin (\omega t + 30°)$$

In Fig. 30–9, the radius vectors r and r_1 are rotating about a point with equal angular velocities of ω, except that now r_1 is *behind* r by a constant angle θ. The phase angle between the two curves is θ, but in this case, y_1 lags y. Hence the equation for the curve generated by r_1 is

$$y_1 = r_1 \sin (\omega l - \theta)$$

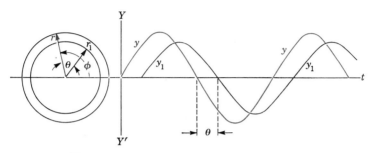

FIG. 30–9 $y = r \sin \omega t$, $y_1 = r_1 \sin (\omega l - \theta)$.

In Fig. 30–9, the *angle of lag* is $\theta = 60°$; therefore, the equation for y_1 becomes

$$y_1 = r_1 \sin (\omega l - 60°)$$

0 – 11   Summary

The general equation

$$y = r \sin (\omega t \pm \theta) \qquad\qquad [\,5\,]$$

describes a periodic event, and its graph results in a periodic curve. By choosing the proper values for the three arbitrary constants r, ω, and θ you can describe or plot any periodic sequence of events because a change in any one of these will change the curve accordingly. Hence,

1. If r is changed, the *amplitude* of the curve will be changed proportionally. For this reason, r is called the *amplitude factor*.

2. If ω is changed, the *frequency*, or period, of the curve will be changed. Thus, ω is called the *frequency factor*.

3. If θ is changed, the curve is moved along the time axis with no other change. Thus, if θ is made larger, the curve is displaced to the left and results in a leading phase angle. If θ is made smaller, the curve is moved to the right and results in a lagging phase angle. Hence the angle θ in the general equation is called the *phase angle* or the *angle of lead or lag*.

EXAMPLE 3   Discuss the equation $y = 147 \sin (377t + 30°)$.

SOLUTION   Given $y = 147 \sin (377t + 30°)$.

Comparing the given equation with the general equation, it is seen that $r = 147$, $\omega = 377$ radians/sec, and $\theta = 30°$. Therefore the curve represented by this equation is a sine curve with an amplitude of 147. The angular velocity is 377 radians/sec; hence the frequency is

$$f = \frac{\omega}{2\pi} = \frac{377}{2\pi} = 60 \text{ cps}$$

The period is
$$T = \frac{1}{f} = \frac{1}{60} = 0.0167 \text{ sec}$$

The curve has been displaced to the left 30°; that is, it leads the curve $y = r \sin 377t$ by a phase angle of 30°. Therefore, when $t = 0$, the curve begins at an angle of 30° with a value of

$$y = 147 \sin (\omega t + 30°) = 147 \sin (0° + 30°) = 147 \times 0.5 = 73.5$$

PROBLEMS 30 – 3

In the following equations of periodic curves, specify (a) amplitude, (b) angular velocity, (c) frequency, (d) period, (e) angle of lead or lag with respect to a curve of the same frequency but having no displacement angle.

1 $y = 25 \sin (2\pi t + 30°)$ 2 $y = 32 \sin (37.7t - 10°)$
3 $e = 325 \sin (314t - 18°)$ 4 $e = E_m \sin (157t + 17°)$
5 $i = I_m \sin (6.28 \times 10^3 - 90°)$

Plot the curves that represent the following motions:

6 $y = \sin 2\pi t$ 7 $y = 5 \sin 15t$
8 $y = 16 \sin 120t$ 9 $y = 8 \sin (120t + 30°)$
10 $y = 32 \sin (120t - 30°)$

11 A crank 10 in. long starts from a horizontal position (0°) and turns in a counterclockwise (positive) direction in a vertical plane at the rate of 6 rps.
   (a) Plot the curve that shows the projection of the handle upon a vertical line at any time.
   (b) Write the equation of the curve.
   (c) What is the distance of the handle from the horizontal at the end of 0.1 sec?
   (d) What is the horizontal distance from the handle to the shaft at the end of 0.06 sec?
   (e) Through how many radians will the crank turn in 0.45 sec?

12 A crank 12 in. long starts from a position of 23° with the horizontal and turns in a positive direction at the rate of 14 rps.

(a) Plot the curve that shows the projection of the handle upon a vertical line at any time.

(b) Write the equation of the curve.

(c) What is the height of the handle above the horizontal at the end of 0.714 sec?

(d) What is the horizontal distance from the handle to the shaft at the end of 0.5 sec?

(e) Through how many radians will the crank turn in 3 sec?

CHAPTER 31
ELEMENTARY PLANE VECTORS

Many physical quantities can be expressed by specifying a certain number of units. For example, the volume of a tank may be expressed as so many cubic feet, the temperature of a room is expressed as a certain number of degrees, the speed of a moving object can be expressed by a number of linear units per unit of time such as miles per hour and feet per second. Such quantities are *scalar quantities*, and the numbers that represent them are called *scalars*. A scalar quantity is one having only magnitude; that is, it is a quantity fully described by a number, but it does not involve any concept of direction.

31 – 1 Vectors

Many other types of physical quantities need to be expressed more definitely than is possible by specifying magnitude alone. For example, the velocity of a moving object has a direction as well as a magnitude. Also, a force due to a push or a pull is not completely described unless the direction as well as the magnitude of the force is given. In addition, electric-circuit analysis is built up around the idea of expressing the directions and magnitudes of voltages and currents. Those quantities which have both magnitude and direction are called *vector quantities*. A vector quantity is conveniently represented by a directed straight-line segment called a *vector*, whose length is proportional to the magnitude and whose head points in the direction of the vector quantity.

EXAMPLE 1   If a vessel steams northeast at a speed of 15 knots, its speed can be represented by a line whose length represents 15 knots, to some

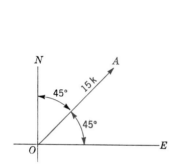

FIG. 31–1   Vector *OA* of Example 1.

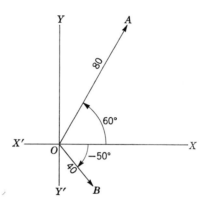

FIG. 31–2   Vector diagram of Example 2.

convenient scale, as shown in Fig. 31–1. The direction of the line represents the direction in which the vessel is traveling. Thus the line *OA* is a vector that completely describes the velocity of the vessel.

EXAMPLE 2   In Fig. 31–2, the vector *OA* represents a force of 80 lb pulling on a body at *O* in a direction of 60°. The vector *OB* represents a force of 40 lb acting on the same body in a direction of 310° or −50°.

Two vectors are equal if they have the same magnitude and direction. Thus, in Fig. 31–3, vectors *A*, *B*, and *C* are equal.

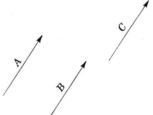

FIG. 31–3   Vectors *A*, *B*, and *C* are equal.

1 – 2   Notation

As you progress in the study of vectors, you will find that vectors and scalars satisfy different algebraic laws. For example, a scalar when reduced to its simplest terms is simply a number and as such obeys all the laws of ordinary algebraic operations. Since a vector involves direction, in addition to magnitude, it does not obey the usual algebraic laws and therefore has an analysis peculiar to itself.

From the foregoing, it is apparent that it is desirable to have a notation that indicates clearly which quantities are scalars and which are vectors. Several methods of notation are used, but you will find little cause for confusion, for most authors specify and explain their particular system of notation.

A vector can be denoted by two letters, the first indicating the origin, or initial point, and the second indicating the head, or terminal point. This form of notation was used in Examples 1 and 2 of the preceding section. Sometimes a small arrow is placed over these letters to emphasize that the quantity considered is a vector. Thus, $\overrightarrow{OA}$ could be used to represent the vector from O to A as in Fig. 31–2. In most texts, vectors are indicated by boldface type; thus, **A** denotes the vector A. Other common forms of specifying a vector quantity, as, for example, the vector A, are $\bar{A}$, $\dot{A}$, and $\underset{\cdot}{A}$.

31 – 3　Addition of vectors

Scalar quantities are added algebraically.

Thus　　　　　　　　　20 cents $+$ 8 cents $=$ 28 cents

and　　　　　　　16 insulators $-$ 7 insulators $=$　9 insulators

Since vector quantities involve direction as well as magnitude, they cannot be added algebraically unless their directions are parallel. Figure 31–4 illustrates vectors OA and AB. Vector OA can be considered as a motion from O to A, and vector AB as a motion from A to B. Then the sum of the vectors represents the sum of the motions from O to A and from A to B, which is the motion from O to B. This sum is the vector OB; that is, the *vector sum* of OA and AB is OB. Therefore, the sum of two vectors is the vector joining the initial point of the first to the terminal point of the second if the initial point of the second vector is joined to the terminal point of the first vector as shown in Fig. 31–4.

In Fig. 31 – 5, vectors OC and OD are equal to vectors OA and AB, respectively, of Fig. 31–4. In Fig. 31–5, however, the vectors start from the same origin. That their sum can be represented by the diagonal of a parallelogram of which the vectors are adjacent sides is evident by comparing Figs. 31–4 and 31–5. This is known as the *parallelogram law* for the composition of forces and holds for the composition or addition of all vector quantities.

The addition of vectors that are not at right angles to each other will be considered from a mathematical viewpoint in a later chapter.

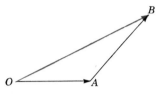

Fig. 31–4   Vector *OB* is the sum of *OA* and *AB*.

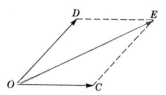

Fig. 31–5   Resultant vector *OE* is the sum of *OC* and *OD*.

At this time, it is sufficient to know that two forces acting simultaneously on a point, or an object, can be replaced by a single force called the *resultant*. That is, the resultant force will produce the same effect on the object as the joint action of the two forces. Thus, in Fig. 31–4 the vector *OB* is the resultant of vectors *OA* and *AB*. Similarly, in Fig. 31–5, the vector *OE* is the resultant of the vectors *OC* and *OD*. Note that *OB* = *OE*.

EXAMPLE 3   Three forces *A*, *B*, and *C* are acting on point *O* as shown in Fig. 31–6. Force *A* exerts 150 lb at an angle of 60°, *B* exerts 100 lb at an angle of 135°, and *C* exerts 150 lb at an angle of 260°. What is the resultant force on point *O*?

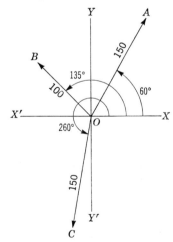

Fig. 31–6   Vector diagram of Example 3.

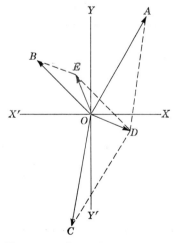

Fig. 31–7   *OE* is the vector sum of vectors *A*, *B*, and *C*.

SOLUTION   The resultant of vectors A, B, and C can be found graphically by two methods.

(*a*) First draw the vectors to scale. Find the resultant of any two vectors, such as OA and OC, by constructing a parallelogram with OA and OC as adjacent sides. Then the resultant of OA and OC will be the diagonal OD of the parallelogram $OADC$ as shown in Fig. 31–7. In effect, there are now but two forces, OB and OD, acting on point O. The resultant of these two forces is found as before by constructing a parallelogram with OB and OD as adjacent sides. The resultant force on point O is then the diagonal OE of the parallelogram $OBED$. Upon measuring with scale and protractor, OE is found to be 57 lb acting at an angle of 112°.

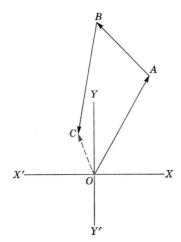

(*b*) Draw the vectors to scale as shown in Fig. 31–8, joining the initial point of B to the terminal point of A and then joining the initial point of C to the terminal point of B. The vector drawn from the point O to the terminal point of C is the resultant force, and measurements show it to be the same as that found by the method illustrated in Fig. 31–7.

FIG. 31–8 OC is the vector sum of vectors A, B, and C.

A figure such as $OABCO$, in Fig. 31–8, is called a *polygon of forces*. The vectors can be joined in any order as long as the initial point of one vector joins the terminal point of another vector and the vectors are drawn with the proper magnitude and direction. The length and direction of the line that is necessary to close the polygon, that is, the line from the original initial point to the terminal point of the last vector drawn, constitute a vector that represents the magnitude and the direction of the resultant.

PROBLEMS 31 – 1

1,2,3,4   Find the magnitude and direction, with respect to the positive X axis, of the vectors shown in Figs. 31–9 to 31–12.

31 – 4   Components of a vector

From what has been considered regarding combining or adding vectors, it follows that a vector can be resolved into components along any two specified directions. For example, in Fig. 31–4, the vectors OA and AB are components of the vector OB. If the directions of the components are chosen so that they are at right angles to each other, the components are called *rectangular components*.

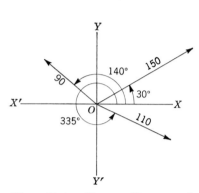

Fig. 31-9   Vector diagram of Prob. 1.

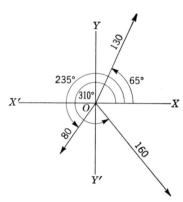

Fig. 31-10   Vector diagram of Prob. 2.

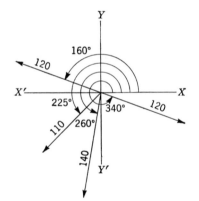

Fig. 31-11   Vector diagram of Prob. 3.

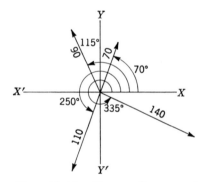

Fig. 31-12   Vector diagram of Prob. 4.

By placing the initial point of a vector at the origin of the X and Y axes, the rectangular components are readily obtained either graphically or mathematically.

EXAMPLE 4   A vector with a magnitude of 10 makes an angle of 53.1° with the horizontal. What are the vertical and horizontal components?

SOLUTION   The vector is illustrated in Fig. 31-13 as the directed line segment OA, whose length drawn to scale represents the magnitude of 10, and making an angle of 53.1° with the X axis.

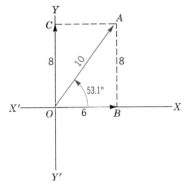

FIG. 31–13 Vertical and horizontal components of vector.

The *horizontal component* of OA is the horizontal distance (Sec. 29–7) from O to A and is found graphically by projecting the vector OA upon the X axis. Thus the vector OB is the horizontal component of OA.

The *vertical component* of OA is the vertical distance from O to A and is found graphically by projecting the vector OA upon the Y axis. Similarly, the vector OC is the vertical component of OA.

Finding the horizontal and vertical components of OA by mathematical methods is simply a problem in solving a right triangle as outlined in Sec. 29–4. Hence,

$$OB = 10 \cos 53.1° = 6$$
and
$$OC = BA = 10 \sin 53.1° = 8$$
CHECK
$$\theta = \arctan \tfrac{8}{6} = \arctan 1.33 = \tan 53.1°$$
or
$$10^2 = 6^2 + 8^2 = 36 + 64 = 100$$

The foregoing can be summarized as follows:

RULE

1   The horizontal component of a vector is the projection of the vector upon a horizontal line and equals the magnitude of the vector multiplied by the cosine of the angle made by the vector with the horizontal.

2   The vertical component of a vector is the projection of the vector upon a vertical line and equals the magnitude of the vector multiplied by the sine of the angle made by the vector with the horizontal.

EXAMPLE 5   An airplane is flying on a course of 40° at a speed of 250 mph. How many miles per hour is the plane advancing in a due eastward direction? In a direction due north?

SOLUTION   Draw the vector diagram as shown in Fig. 31–14. (Courses are measured from the north.) The vector OB, which is the horizontal component of OA, represents the velocity of the airplane in an eastward direction. The vector OC, which is the vertical component of OA, represents the velocity of the airplane in a northward direction.

Again, the process of finding the magnitude of OB and OC resolves into a problem in solving the right triangle OBA. Hence,

$$OB = 250 \cos 50° = 161 \text{ mph eastward}$$
and $\qquad OC = BA = 250 \sin 50° = 192 \text{ mph northward}$

If the vector diagram has been drawn to scale, an approximate check can be made by measuring the lengths of OB and OC. Such a check will disclose any large errors in the mathematical solution.

EXAMPLE 6   A radius vector of unit length is rotating about a point with a velocity of 2π radians/sec. What are its horizontal and vertical components

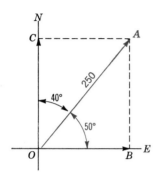

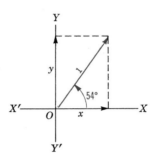

FIG. 31–14 Vector diagram of Example 5.

FIG. 31–15 When $t = 0.15$ sec, $\theta = 54°$.

(a) at the end of 0.15 sec, (b) at the end of 0.35 sec, (c) at the end of 0.75 sec?

SOLUTION   (a) At the end of 0.15 sec the rotating vector will have generated $2\pi \times 0.15 = 0.942$ radian, or $0.942 \times 57.3° = 54°$ as shown in Fig. 31–15. The horizontal component, measured along the X axis, is

$$x = 1 \cos 54° = 0.588$$

The vertical component, measured along the Y axis, is

$$y = 1 \sin 54° = 0.809$$

Check the solution by measurement or any other method considered convenient.

(b) At the end of 0.35 sec the rotating vector will have generated an angle of $2\pi \times 0.35 = 2.20$ radians, or $2.20 \times 57.3° = 126°$ as shown in Fig. 31–16. The horizontal component, measured along the X axis, is

$$x = 1 \cos 126° = 1(-\cos 54°) = -0.588 \qquad \text{(Sec. 28–11)}$$

The vertical component, measured along the Y axis, is

$$y = 1 \sin 126° = 1 \sin 54° = 0.809 \qquad \text{(Sec. 28–11)}$$

Check by some convenient method.

(c) At the end of 0.75 sec the rotating vector will have generated $2\pi \times 0.75 = 4.71$ radians, or $4.71 \times 57.3° = 270°$ as shown in Fig. 31–17. The horizontal component is

$$x = 1 \cos 270° = 0$$

The vertical component is

$$y = 1 \sin 270° = -1$$

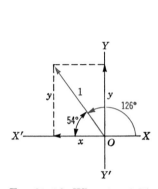

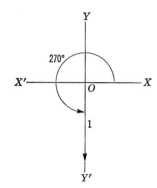

Fig. 31–16 When $t = 0.35$ sec, $\theta = 126°$.

Fig. 31–17 When $t = 0.75$ sec, $\theta = 270°$.

PROBLEMS 31 – 2

Find the horizontal and vertical components, denoted by x and y, respectively, of the following vectors. Check the mathematical solution of each by drawing a vector diagram to scale.

1 42.0 at 81.2°

2 108 at 10.9°

3 1.92 at 40.0°

4 1,600 at 106.5°

5 72 at 180°

6 364 at 285.1°

7 500 at 270°

8 61.2 at 221.4°

9 36 at 90°

10 40.9 at 116.5°

11 The resultant of two forces acting at right angles is a force of 350 lb that makes an angle of 66.7° with one of the forces. Find the two component forces.

12 A missile is fired at an angle of 85° from the horizontal. At one point its speed was 1,000 mph. Find its horizontal velocity in miles per minute.

13 A vessel sails 41 miles southeast. How far south has it sailed?

14 Resolve a force of 500 lb into two rectangular components, one of which is 43.3 lb.

15 The resultant of two forces acting at right angles is 523 lb. One of the forces is 106 lb. What is the other?

1 – 5   Vector addition of rectangular components

If two forces that are at right angles to each other are acting on a body, their resultant can be found by the usual methods of vector addition as outlined in Sec. 31–3. However, the resultant can be obtained by geometric or trigonometric methods, for the problem is that of solving for the hypotenuse of a right triangle when the other two sides are given, as outlined in Sec. 29–6.

EXAMPLE 7   Two vectors are acting on a point. One with a magnitude of 6 is directed along the horizontal to the right of the point, and the other with a magnitude of 8 is directed vertically above the point. Find the resultant.

SOLUTION 1   In Fig. 31–18 the horizontal vector, with a magnitude of 6, is shown as OB. The vertical vector, with a magnitude of 8, is shown as OC. The resultant of these two vectors can be obtained graphically by completing the parallelogram of forces $OCAB$, as outlined in Sec. 31–3. Thus, the

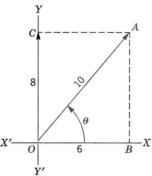

FIG. 31–18   Addition of rectangular components.

magnitude of the resultant will be represented by the length of OA in Fig. 31–18. The angle, or direction of the resultant, can be measured with the protractor.

Graphical methods have a limited degree of accuracy, as pointed out in earlier sections. They should be used as an approximate check for more precise mathematical methods.

SOLUTION 2   Since $BA = OC$ in Fig. 31–18, then OBA is a right triangle the hypotenuse of which is the resultant OA. Therefore the magnitude of the resultant is

$$OA = \sqrt{\overline{OB}^2 + \overline{BA}^2} = \sqrt{6^2 + 8^2} = 10$$

The angle, or direction of the resultant, is

$$\theta = \arctan \frac{BA}{OB} = \frac{8}{6} = 1.33 = \arctan 53.1°$$

Although the method of Solution 2 is accurate and mathematically correct, there are several operations involved. For example, in finding the magnitude, 6 and 8 must be squared, these squares must be added, and then the square root of this sum must be extracted. This involves four operations.

SOLUTION 3   Since OBA is a right triangle for which OB and BA are given, the hypotenuse (resultant) can be computed as explained in Sec. 29–6. Hence,

$$\tan \theta = \frac{BA}{OB} = 1.33$$

$$\therefore \theta = 53.1°$$

Then

$$OA = \frac{OB}{\cos 53.1°} = \frac{6}{0.6} = 10$$

or

$$OA = \frac{BA}{\sin 53.1°} = \frac{8}{0.8} = 10$$

The method of Solution 3 is to be preferred, owing to the minimum number of operations involved; in addition, this is the method used when the slide rule is used for solving the resultant. It is worthy of note that this solution can be completed with a total of three movements on many types of slide rules and without referring to a table of trigonometric functions.

It should be noted that Example 4 of Sec. 31–4 involves the same quantities as those used in the example of this section and that Figs. 31–13 and 31–18 are alike. In the earlier example a vector is given that is resolved into its rectangular components. In the example of this section, the same components are given as vectors which are added vectorially to obtain the vector of the first example. From this it is apparent that resolving a vector into its rectangular components and adding vectors that are separated by 90° are inverse operations. Basically, either problem resolves itself into the solution of a right triangle.

PROBLEMS 31 – 3

Find the resultant forces of the following vectors:
1   527 at 0° and 600 at 90°
2   195 at 90° and 95.9 at 0°
3   32.3 at 0° and 32.3 at 90°
4   5.8 at 90° and 9 at 0°
5   234 at 90° and 730 at 0°
6   29.3 at 0° and 16.8 at 0°
7   40.6 at 0° and 63.9 at 180°
8   117 at 180° and 201 at 90°

 9 108 at 270° and 92.6 at 90°

10 42.1 at 270° and 50 at 0°

11 37.4 at 90° and 76.0 at 0°

12 71.4 at 90°, 38.0 at 0°, and 46.2 at 0°

13 19.7 at 270°, 49.0 at 90°, 46.0 at 0°, and 78.0 at 180°

14 201 at 270°, 239 at 0°, 56.0 at 180°, and 89.0 at 90°

15 15.0 at 0°, 69.2 at 270°, 25.0 at 90°, 4.80 at 270°, 21.0 at 90°, and 13.0 at 0°

CHAPTER 32

ALTERNATING CURRENTS

FUNDAMENTAL IDEAS

Thus far, we have considered direct voltages and direct currents, that is, voltages that do not change in polarity and currents that do not change in their directions of flow.

In this chapter, you will begin the study of mathematics as applied to alternating currents. An *alternating current* is one that alternates, or changes its direction, periodically.

The fact that over 90 per cent of the electric energy produced is generated in the form of alternating current makes this subject very important, for the operation of all radio and communication circuits is based on a-c phenomena. The first requisite in the study of electronics engineering is a solid foundation in the principles of alternating currents.

32 – 1   Generation of an alternating electromotive force

A coil of wire, with its ends connected to slip rings, rotating in a counterclockwise direction in a uniform magnetic field, is illustrated in Fig. 32–1. That an alternating emf will be generated in the coil is apparent from a consideration of generated currents. For example, when the side of the coil ab moves from its present position away from the S pole, the emf generated in it will be directed from b to a; that is, a will be positive with respect to b. At the same time, the side of the coil cd is moving away from the N pole, thus cutting magnetic lines of force with a motion opposite to that

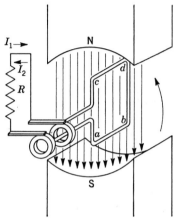

of ab. Then the emf generated in cd will be directed from c to d and will add to the emf from b to a to send a current I_1 through the resistance R.

When the coil has rotated 90° from the position shown in 32–1, the plane of the coil is perpendicular to the magnetic field, and at this instant the sides of the coil are moving parallel to the magnetic field, thus cutting no lines of force. There is no emf generated at this instant.

Fig. 32–1   Representation of elementary alternator.

As the side of the coil ab begins to move up toward the N pole, the emf generated in it will now be directed from a to b. Similarly, because the side of the coil cd is now moving down toward the S pole, the emf in cd will be directed from d to c. This reversal of the direction of generated emf is due to a change of direction of motion with respect to the direction of the lines of force. Therefore, the flow of current I_2 through R will be in the direction indicated by the arrow.

When the coil rotates so that the plane of the coil is again perpendicular to the lines of force (270° from the position shown in Fig. 32–1), no emf will be generated at that instant. Rotation beyond this position, however, causes an emf to be generated such that current flows in the original direction I_1. Such an emf, which periodically reverses its direction, is known as an *alternating electromotive force*, and the resulting current is known as an *alternating current*.

In some engineering textbooks the generation of an emf is explained as due to the change of magnetic flux through the rotating coil. In the final analysis, the results are the same. Here we are interested mainly in the behavior of the circuits connected to sources of alternating currents.

32 – 2 Variation of an alternating electromotive force

The first questions that come to mind are, "In what manner does an alternating emf vary? How can we represent that variation graphically?"

Figure 32–2 shows a cross section of the elementary alternator of

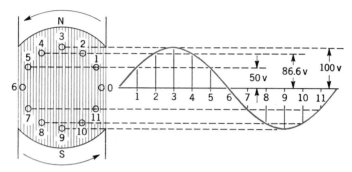

Fɪɢ. 32–2   Generation of voltage sine wave.

Fig. 32–1. The circles represent either side of the rotating coil at successive instants during the rotation.

When a conductor passes through a magnetic field, there must be a component of its velocity at right angles to the lines of force in order to generate an emf. For example, a conductor must actually *cut* lines in order to develop an emf the amount of which will be proportional to the number of lines cut and the rate of cutting.

From studies of rotation and a consideration of Fig. 32–2, it is evident that the component of horizontal velocity of the rotating conductor is proportional to the sine of the angle of rotation. Because the horizontal velocity is perpendicular to the magnetic field, it is this component that develops an emf. For example, at position 0, where the angle of rotation is zero, the conductor is moving parallel to the field; hence, no voltage is generated. As the conductor rotates toward 90°, the component of horizontal velocity becomes greater, thus generating a higher voltage. Therefore, the sine curve of Fig. 32–2 is a graphical representation of the induced emf in a conductor rotating in a uniform magnetic field. The voltage starts from zero, increases in a positive direction to a maximum value (100 volts in the figure) at 90°, decreases to zero at 180°, increases in the opposite or negative direction until it attains maximum negative value at 270°, and finally decreases to zero value again at 360°.

It follows, then, that the induced emf can be completely described by the relation

$$e = E_m \sin \theta \qquad \text{volts} \qquad [1]$$

where e = instantaneous value of emf at any angle θ
E_m = maximum value of emf
θ = angular position of coil

2–3   Vector representation

Since the sine wave of emf is a periodic function, a simpler method of representing the relation of the emf induced in a coil to the angle of rotation is available. The rotating conductor can be replaced by a rotating radius vector whose length represents the magnitude of the maximum generated voltage E_m. Then the instantaneous value for any position of the conductor can be represented by the vertical component of the vector (Sec. 31–4).

In Fig. 32–3, which is the vector diagram for the conductor at position 0 in Fig. 32–2, the vector E_m is at 0° position and therefore has no vertical component. Thus the value of the emf in this position is zero. Or, since

$$e = E_m \sin \theta$$

by substituting the values of E_m and θ,

$$e = 100 \sin 0° = 0$$

In Fig. 32–4, which is the vector diagram for the conductor at position 2 in Fig. 32–2, the coil has moved 60° from the zero position. The vector E_m is therefore at an angle of 60° from the reference axis,

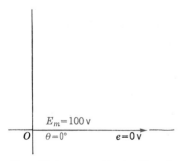

Fig. 32–3 $e = 100 \sin 0° = 0$ volts.

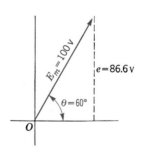

Fig. 32–4 $e = 100 \sin 60° = 86.6$ volts.

and the instantaneous value of the induced emf is represented by the vertical component of E_m. Then, since

$$e = E_m \sin \theta$$

by substituting the values of E_m and θ,

$$e = 100 \sin 60° = 86.6 \text{ volts}$$

EXAMPLE 1   What is the instantaneous value of an alternating emf when it has reached 58° of its cycle? The maximum value is 500 volts.

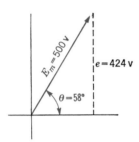

SOLUTION   Draw the vector diagram to scale as shown in Fig. 32–5. The instantaneous value is the vertical component of the vector E_m. Then, since

$$e = E_m \sin \theta$$

by substituting the values of E_m and θ,

$$e = 500 \sin 58° = 424 \text{ volts}$$

FIG. 32–5 $e = 500$ $\sin 58° = 424$ volts.

EXAMPLE 2   What is the instantaneous value of an alternating emf when it has reached 216° of its cycle? The maximum value is 163 volts.

SOLUTION   Draw the vector diagram to scale as shown in Fig. 32–6. The instantaneous value is the vertical component of the vector E_m. Then, since

$$e = E_m \sin \theta$$

by substituting the values of E_m and θ,

$$e = 163 \sin 216° = 163[-\sin (216° - 180°)] = 163(-\sin 36°)$$

$$= -95.8 \text{ volts}$$

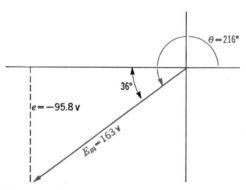

FIG. 32–6 $e = 163(-\sin 36°) = -95.8$ volts.

A vector diagram drawn to scale should be made for every a-c problem. This gives you a better insight into the functioning of alternating currents and at the same time serves as a good check on the mathematical solution.

Since the current in a circuit is proportional to the applied voltage, it follows that an alternating emf which varies periodically will produce a current of similar variation. Hence the instantaneous current of a sine wave of alternating current is given by

$$i = I_m \sin \theta \qquad \text{amp} \qquad [\,2\,]$$

where i = instantaneous value of current
   I_m = maximum value of current
   θ = angular position of coil

PROBLEMS 32 – 1

1   An alternating emf has a maximum value of 165 volts. What are the instantaneous values of this emf at the following points in its cycle: (a) 24°, (b) 76°, (c) 122°, (d) 216°, (e) 342°?

2   The instantaneous value of an alternating emf is 48.6 volts at 25°. What is its maximum value?

3   The instantaneous value of an alternating emf is −203 volts at 218°. What is its maximum value?

4   An alternating current has a maximum value of 65 amp. What are the instantaneous values of this current at the following points in its cycle: (a) 11°, (b) 201°, (c) 101°, (d) 303°, (e) 3.0°?

5   The instantaneous value of an alternating emf is 115 volts at 48°. What will be its value at 254°?

6   The instantaneous value of an alternating emf is −117 volts at 229°. What will be its value at 103°?

7   The instantaneous value of an alternating current is 3.40 amp at 166.6°. What will be its value at 215°?

8   An alternating current has a maximum value of 14.1 amp. At what angles will it be 86.6 per cent of its positive maximum value?

9   At what angles are the instantaneous values of an alternating current equal to 50 per cent of the maximum negative value?

10   What is the instantaneous value of an alternating current 170° after its maximum positive value of 12.5 amp?

32 – 4   Cycles, frequency, and poles

Each revolution of the coil in Fig. 32–1 results in one complete *cycle* which consists of one positive and one negative loop of the sine wave

(Sec. 30–8). The number of cycles generated in 1 sec is called the *frequency* of the alternating emf, and the *period* is the time required to complete one cycle. One-half cycle is called an *alternation*. Thus, by a 60-cycle alternating current is meant that the current passes through 60 cycles per second, which results in a period of 0.0167 sec. Also, a 60-cycle current completes 120 alternations per second.

Figure 32–7 represents a coil rotating in a four-pole machine.

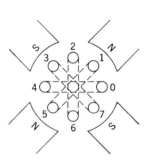

Fig. 32–7 Elementary four-pole alternator.

When one side of the coil has rotated from position 0 to position 4, it has passed under the influence of an *N* and an *S* pole, thus generating one complete sine wave, or electrical cycle. This corresponds to 2π electrical radians, or 360 electrical degrees, although the coil has rotated only 180 space-degrees. Therefore, in one complete revolution the coil will generate two complete cycles, or 720 electrical degrees, so that for every *space-degree* there result two *electrical time-degrees*.

In any alternator the armature, or field, must move an angular distance equal to the angle formed by two consecutive like poles in order to complete one cycle. It is evident, then, that a two-pole machine must rotate at twice the speed of a four-pole machine to produce the same frequency. Therefore, to find the frequency of an alternator in cycles per second, *the number of pairs of poles is multiplied by the speed of the armature in revolutions per second*. That is,

$$f = \frac{PS}{60} \quad \textbf{cps} \qquad [3]$$

where f = frequency, cps

P = number of pairs of poles

S = rpm of armature, or field

EXAMPLE 3   What is the frequency of an alternator having four poles with a speed of 1,800 rpm?

SOLUTION $f = \dfrac{2 \times 1,800}{60} = 60$ cps

32 – 5   Equations of voltages and currents

Since each cycle consists of 360 electrical degrees, or 2π electrical radians, the variation of an alternating emf can be expressed in terms of time. Thus, a frequency of f cps results in $2\pi f$ radians/sec, which is denoted by ω (Sec. 30–5). Hence, the instantaneous emf at any time t is given by the relation

$$e = E_m \sin \omega t \qquad \text{volts} \qquad [4]$$

The instantaneous current is

$$i = I_m \sin \omega t \qquad \text{amp} \qquad [5]$$

You should review Secs. 30–6 to 30–10 to ensure a complete understanding of the relations between the general equation for a periodic function and Eqs. [4] and [5] above. Thus, E_m and I_m are the amplitude factors of their respective equations, and ω is the frequency factor.

EXAMPLE 4   Write the equation of a 60-cycle alternating voltage that has a maximum value of 156 volts.

SOLUTION   The angular velocity ω is 2π times the frequency or

$$2\pi \times 60 = 377 \text{ radians/sec}$$

Substituting 156 volts for E_m and 377 for ω in Eq. [4],

$$e = 156 \sin 377t \qquad \text{volts}$$

EXAMPLE 5   Write the equation of an r-f current of 700 kc that has a maximum value of 21.2 amp.

SOLUTION $I_m = 21.2$ amp and $f = 700$ kc $= 7 \times 10^5$ cycles. Then $\omega = 2\pi f = 2\pi \times 7 \times 10^5 = 4.4 \times 10^6$. Substituting these values in Eq. [5],

$$i = 21.2 \sin (4.4 \times 10^6)t \qquad \text{amp}$$

EXAMPLE 6   If the time $t = 0$ when the voltage of Example 4 is zero and increasing in a positive direction, what is the instantaneous value of the voltage at the end of 0.002 sec?

SOLUTION   Substituting 0.002 for t in the equation for the voltage,

$$e = 156 \sin (377 \times 0.002) = 156 \sin 0.754 \qquad \text{volts}$$

where 0.754 is the time angle in *radians*. Then, since 1 radian $= 57.3°$,

$$e = 156 \sin (0.754 \times 57.3°) = 156 \sin 43.2°$$

Hence, $e = 107$ volts

PROBLEMS 32 – 2

1   An alternator with 36 poles has a speed of 3,000 rpm and develops a maximum voltage of 324 volts.

   (*a*) What is the frequency of the alternating current?
   (*b*) What is the period of the alternating current?
   (*c*) Write the equation for the instantaneous voltage at any time *t*.

2   An alternator with four poles has a speed of 1,800 rpm and develops a maximum voltage of 70.5 volts.
   (*a*) What is the frequency?
   (*b*) Write the equation for the instantaneous voltage at any time *t*.

3   A 400-cycle generator that develops a maximum voltage of 155 volts has a speed of 2,000 rpm.
   (*a*) How many poles has it?
   (*b*) Write the equation for the voltage.
   (*c*) What is the instantaneous voltage when the time *t* is equal to 0.5 msec?

4   An 800-cycle alternator generates a maximum voltage of 170 volts at 4,000 rpm.
   (*a*) How many poles has it?
   (*b*) Write the equation for the voltage.
   (*c*) What is the value of the voltage when time *t* is equal to 796 μsec?

5   At what speed must a 12-pole 60-cycle generator be driven in order to develop its rated frequency?

6   The equation for a certain alternating current is $i = 84.6 \sin 377t$. What is its frequency?

7   The equation for an alternating voltage is $e = 0.05 \sin (3.14 \times 10^9)t$. What is its frequency?

8   The equation for an alternating current is $i = (1.5 \times 10^{-4}) \sin (2.02 \times 10^8)t$.
   (*a*) What is the maximum instantaneous current?
   (*b*) What is the frequency?

9   A 145-Mc current has a maximum instantaneous value of 125 μamp. Write the equation of the current.

10   A broadcasting station operating on 710 kc develops a maximum potential of 0.155 mv across a listener's antenna. Write the equation for this voltage.

32 – 6   Average value of current or voltage

Since an alternating current or voltage is of sine-wave form, it follows that the average current or voltage of one cycle is zero owing to the reversal of direction each half cycle. The term *average value* is usually understood to mean the average value of one alternation without regard to positive or negative values. The average value of a sine wave, such as that shown in Fig. 32–2, can be computed to a fair degree of accuracy by taking the average of many instantaneous values between two consecutive zero points of the curve, the values chosen being separated by equal values of angle. Thus, the average value is equal to the average height of any voltage or current loop. The exact average value is $2/\pi \cong 0.637$ times the maximum value. Thus, if I_{av} and E_{av} denote the average values of alternating current and voltage, respectively, we obtain

$$I_{av} = \frac{2}{\pi} I_m \cong 0.637 I_m \qquad \text{amp} \qquad [6]$$

and

$$E_{av} = \frac{2}{\pi} E_m \cong 0.637 E_m \qquad \text{volts} \qquad [7]$$

EXAMPLE 7   The maximum value of an alternating voltage is 622 volts. What is its average value?

SOLUTION $E_{av} = 0.637 E_m = 0.637 \times 622 = 396$ volts

32 – 7   Effective value of current or voltage

If a direct current of I amp is caused to flow through a resistance of R Ω, the resulting energy converted into heat equals I^2R watts. We should not expect an alternating current with a maximum value of 1 amp to produce as much heat as a direct current of 1 amp, for the former does not maintain a constant value. Thus, the above a-c ampere is not so effective as the d-c ampere. The *effective value* of an alternating current is rated in terms of direct current; that is, an alternating current has an effective value of 1 amp if, flowing through a given resistance, it will produce heat at the same rate as a d-c ampere.

The effective value of a sine wave of current can be computed to a fair degree of accuracy by taking equally spaced instantaneous values and extracting the square root of their average, or mean, squared values. For this reason, the effective value is often called the *root-mean-square* (rms) value. The exact effective value of an alternating current or voltage is $1/\sqrt{2} \cong 0.707$ times the maximum value. Thus, if I and E denote the effective values of current and voltage, respectively, we obtain

$$I = \frac{I_m}{\sqrt{2}} \cong 0.707 I_m \qquad \text{amp} \qquad [8]$$

and

$$E = \frac{E_m}{\sqrt{2}} \cong 0.707 E_m \qquad \text{volts} \qquad [9]$$

It should be noted that all meters, unless marked to the contrary, read effective values of current and voltage.

EXAMPLE 8   The maximum value of an alternating voltage is 311 volts. What is the effective value?

SOLUTION $E = 0.707E_m = 0.707 \times 311 = 220$ volts

EXAMPLE 9   An a-c ammeter reads 15 amp. What is the maximum value of the current?

SOLUTION   Since $I = 0.707I_m$

then $I_m = \dfrac{I}{0.707}$

Substituting 15 amp for I,

$$I_m = \frac{15}{0.707} = 21.2 \text{ amp}$$

ALTERNATE SOLUTION   Since

$$I = \frac{I_m}{\sqrt{2}}$$

then $I_m = I\sqrt{2} = 1.41I$

Substituting for I, $I_m = 1.41 \times 15 = 21.2$ amp

Hence the maximum value of an alternating current or voltage is equal to 1.41 times the effective value.

PROBLEMS 32 – 3

1   What is the average value of an alternating voltage whose maximum value is 165 volts?

2   An alternating voltage has an average value of 200 volts. What is the maximum value?

3   The average value of an alternating current is 46.0 amp. What is its maximum value?

4   The maximum value of an alternating voltage is 65.0 μv. What is the average value?

5   The maximum value of an alternating voltage is 165 volts. What is the effective value?

6   A voltmeter indicates 230 volts of alternating voltage. What is the maximum value of the voltage?

7   What is the effective value of an alternating current that has a maximum value of 39.6 amp?

8   What is the effective value of an alternating voltage that has an average value of 34.7 volts?

9   What is the average value of an alternating voltage that has an effective value of 161 volts?

10 An ammeter indicates 12.5 amp. What is the average value of the current?

32 – 8 Phase relations—phase angles

Nearly all a-c circuits contain circuit elements, or components, that cause the voltage and current to pass through their corresponding zero values at different times. The effects of such conditions are given detailed consideration in the next chapter.

An alternating voltage and the resulting alternating current of the same frequency passing through corresponding zero values at the same instant are said to be *in phase.*

If the current passes through a zero value before the corresponding zero value of the voltage, the current and voltage are *out of phase* and the current is said to *lead* the voltage.

Figure 32–8 illustrates a vector diagram and the corresponding

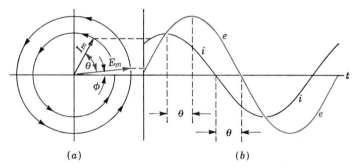

(a)   (b)

Fig. 32–8 Current i leads voltage e by phase angle of θ.

sine waves for a current of i amp leading a voltage of e volts by a *phase angle* of θ (Sec. 30–10). Hence, if the voltage is taken as reference, the general equation of the voltage is

$$e = E_m \sin \omega t \qquad \text{volts} \qquad\qquad [10]$$

and the current is given by

$$i = I_m \sin (\omega t + \theta) \qquad \text{amp} \qquad\qquad [11]$$

The instantaneous values of the voltage and current for any angle ϕ of the voltage are

$$e = E_m \sin \phi \qquad \text{volts} \qquad\qquad [12]$$

and $\qquad\qquad i = I_m \sin (\phi + \theta) \qquad \text{amp} \qquad\qquad [13]$

EXAMPLE 10   In Fig. 32–8, the maximum values of the voltage and the current are 156 volts and 113 amp, respectively. The frequency is 60 cps, and the current leads the voltage by 40°. (a) Write the equation for the voltage at any time t. (b) Write the equation for the current at any time t. (c) What is the instantaneous value of the current when the voltage has reached 10° of its cycle?

SOLUTION   Given

$$\text{Maximum voltage} = E_m = 156 \text{ volts}$$
$$\text{Maximum current} = I_m = 113 \text{ amp}$$
$$\text{Frequency} = f = 60 \text{ cps}$$
$$\text{Phase angle} = \theta = 40° \text{ lead}$$
$$\text{Voltage angle} = \phi = 10°$$

Draw a vector diagram as shown in Fig. 32–8a. (The circles are not necessary; they simply denote rotation of the vectors.)

(a) Substituting given values in Eq. [10],

$$e = 156 \sin 2\pi \times 60t$$

or

$$e = 156 \sin 377t \qquad \text{volts}$$

(b) Substituting given values in Eq. [11],

$$i = 113 \sin (377t + 40°) \qquad \text{amp}$$

NOTE   The quantity $377t$ is in *radians*.

(c) Substituting given values in Eq. [13],

$$i = 113 \sin (10° + 40°)$$

or

$$i = 113 \sin 50° = 86.6 \text{ amp}$$

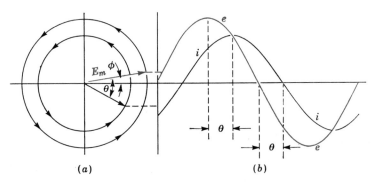

(a)   (b)

FIG. 32–9   Current i lags voltage e by phase angle θ.

Figure 32–9 illustrates a vector diagram and the corresponding sine waves for a current of i amp lagging a voltage of e volts by a *phase angle* of θ. Therefore, if the voltage is taken as reference, the general equation of the voltage will be as given by Eq. [10] and the current will be

$$i = I_m \sin (\omega t - \theta) \qquad \text{amp} \qquad [14]$$

The instantaneous value of the current for any angle ϕ of the voltage is

$$i = I_m \sin (\phi - \theta) \qquad \text{amp} \qquad [15]$$

EXAMPLE 11   In Fig. 32–9, the maximum values of the voltage and the current are 170 volts and 14.1 amp, respectively. The frequency is 800 cps, and the current lags the voltage by 40°. (a) Write the equation for the voltage at any time t. (b) Write the equation for the current at any time t. (c) What is the instantaneous value of the current when the voltage has reached 10° of its cycle?

SOLUTION   Given

$$\text{Maximum voltage} = E_m = 170 \text{ volts}$$
$$\text{Maximum current} = I_m = 14.1 \text{ amp}$$
$$\text{Frequency} = f = 800 \text{ cps}$$
$$\text{Phase angle} = \theta = 40° \text{ lag}$$
$$\text{Voltage angle} = \phi = 10°$$

Draw a vector diagram as shown in Fig. 32–9a.

(a) Substituting given values in Eq. [10],

$$e = 170 \sin 2\pi \times 800t$$
or
$$e = 170 \sin 5030t \qquad \text{volts}$$

(b) Substituting given values in Eq. [14],

$$i = 14.1 \sin (5030t - 40°) \qquad \text{amp}$$

(c) Substituting given values in Eq. [15],

$$i = 14.1 \sin (10° - 40°)$$
or
$$i = 14.1 \sin (-30°) = -7.05 \text{ amp}$$

EXAMPLE 12   In a certain a-c circuit a current of 14 amp lags a voltage of 220 volts by an angle of 60°. What is the instantaneous value of the voltage when the current has completed 245° of its cycle?

NOTE   Unless otherwise specified, all voltages and currents are to be considered *effective* values.

SOLUTION   Draw the vector diagram as shown in Fig. 32–10.

$$E_m = \sqrt{2}E = \sqrt{2} \times 220 = 311 \text{ volts}$$
$$\phi = 245° + \theta = 245° + 60° = 305° = -55°$$

Then, substituting the values of E_m and θ in Eq. [12],

$$e = 311 \sin (-55°) = -255 \text{ volts}$$

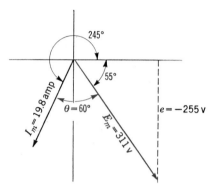

Fig. 32–10   Vector diagram of Example 12.

PROBLEMS 32 – 4

1   A 60-cycle alternator generates a maximum voltage of 9,330 volts and a maximum current of 1,410 amp. The current leads the voltage by an angle of 30°.

    (a) Write the equation for the current at any time t.

    (b) What is the instantaneous value of the current when the voltage has completed 20° of the cycle?

2   A 25-cycle alternator is generating 6,600 volts at 700 amp. The current lags the voltage by an angle of 22°.

    (a) Write the equation for the current at any time t.

    (b) What is the instantaneous value of the current when the voltage has completed 50° of its cycle?

3   In the alternator of Prob. 1, what will be the instantaneous value of the current when the voltage has completed 190° of its cycle?

4   In the alternator of Prob. 2, what will be the instantaneous value of the current when the voltage has completed 184° of its cycle?

5   A 50-cycle alternator generates 2,300 volts with a current of 200 amp. The phase angle is 25° lagging.

    (a) Write the equation for the current at any time t.

    (b) What is the instantaneous value of the current when the voltage has completed 70° of its cycle?

6   In the alternator of Prob. 5, what is the instantaneous value of the voltage when the current has completed 230° of its cycle?

7   An alternating voltage has a maximum value of 170 volts and a maximum current of 42.4 amp. If the instantaneous value of the voltage is

66.4 volts when the instantaneous value of the current is 30 amp, what is the phase angle between current and voltage?

8   In Prob. 7, what will be the instantaneous value of the current when the voltage has reached its maximum negative value?

9   A 60-cycle current has a value of 30 amp at 230 volts. If the instantaneous value of the voltage is −67.6 volts when the instantaneous value of the current is 26.1 amp, what is the phase angle between current and voltage?

10   (a) Write the equation for the current in Prob. 9.

    (b) In Prob. 9, what will be the instantaneous value of the voltage when the current has reached its maximum positive value?

CHAPTER 33
ALTERNATING CURRENTS
SERIES CIRCUITS

The phenomena occurring in a-c circuits make them a very interesting subject for study. Unlike circuits carrying direct currents, in a-c circuits the product of the voltage and current is seldom equal to the reading of a wattmeter connected in the circuit; the current may lag or lead the voltage; or the potential difference across an inductance or capacitance may be several times the supply voltage. This chapter deals with the computation of such effects in series circuits.

In the application of Ohm's law to a-c circuits, there is always the possibility of confusion until you clearly understand that Ohm's law applies with respect to the relations existing among *voltage*, *current*, and *resistance* only. These relations as stated in Sec. 13–2 always hold true, either with direct currents or with alternating currents, as long as the relative values of these three are concerned. However, counter emfs resulting from the presence of inductances or capacitors, or a combination of both, introduce voltage reactions that must be taken into account in the analysis of a-c circuits. Ohm's law does not concern itself with these effects.

33 – 1   The resistive circuit

Figure 33–1 represents a 60-cycle alternator supplying 220 volts to two resistances connected in series.

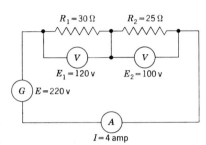

This circuit contains resistance only; therefore, Ohm's law applies in every respect. The internal resistance of the alternator and the resistance of the connecting wires being neglected, the current

FIG. 33–1 Alternator supplying resistive circuit.

through the circuit is given by the familiar relation

$$I = \frac{E}{R_t} = \frac{E}{R_1 + R_2} = \frac{220}{30 + 25} = \frac{220}{55} = 4 \text{ amp}$$

Again, as with direct currents, the voltage drops, or potential differences, across the resistances are

$$E_1 = IR_1 = 4 \times 30 = 120 \text{ volts}$$

and
$$E_2 = IR_2 = 4 \times 25 = \underline{100 \text{ volts}}$$
$$\text{Applied voltage} = \overline{220 \text{ volts}}$$

In an a-c circuit containing only resistance, the voltage and current are in phase. That is, the voltage and current pass through corresponding parts of their cycles at the same instant.

From the above it follows that if

$$e = E_m \sin \omega t = 311 \sin 377t \qquad \text{volts}$$

is the equation for the alternator voltage of Fig. 33–1, then the current through the circuit is

$$i = I_m \sin(\omega t + \theta) = I_m \sin(\omega t + 0°) = 5.66 \sin 377t \qquad \text{amp}$$

Figure 33–2 is the vector diagram for the circuit of Fig. 33–1. It will be noted that the voltage vector and the current vector coincide. This is as anticipated from the equations for the voltage and current, for they differ only in amplitude factors; the frequency factors are equal, and the phase angle is 0° (Secs. 30–7 to 30–9).

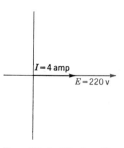

It is evident that Ohm's law says nothing about maximum, average, or effective values of current and voltage. Any of these values can be used; that is, maximum voltage can be used to find maximum current, or average voltage to find average current, etc. Naturally, maximum voltage is not used to find effective current unless the proper conversion constant is introduced into the equation. As previously stated, all voltage and current values here are to be considered as effective values unless otherwise specified (Sec. 32–7).

Fig. 33–2 Vector diagram for circuit of Fig. 33–1.

33 – 2   Power in the resistive circuit

In d-c circuits the power is equal to the product of the voltage and the current (Sec. 13–5). This is true for a-c circuits for *instantaneous values* of voltage and current. That is, the *instantaneous power* is

$$p = ei \qquad \text{va} \qquad\qquad [1]$$

and is measured in *volt-amperes* or *kilovolt-amperes*, abbreviated va and kva, respectively.

When a sine wave of voltage is impressed across a resistance, the relations among voltage, current, and power are as shown in Fig. 33–3. The voltage existing across the resistance is in phase with the current flowing through it. The power delivered to the resistance at any instant is represented by the height of the power curve which is the product of the instantaneous values of voltage and current at that instant. The shaded area under the power curve represents the total power delivered to the circuit during one

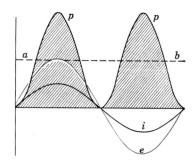

Fig. 33–3 Power curves for circuit containing only resistance.

complete cycle of voltage. It will be noted that the power curve is of sine-wave form, having a frequency twice that of the voltage.

Also, the power curve lies entirely above the X axis, there being no negative values of power.

The maximum height of the power curve is the product of the maximum values of voltage and current. Stated as an equation,

$$P_m = E_m I_m \qquad [2]$$

The average power delivered to a resistance load is represented by the height of the line ab in Fig. 33-3, which is half the maximum height of the power curve, or its average height. Then, since

$$\text{Average power} = P = \frac{P_m}{2}$$

by dividing both members of Eq. [2] by 2 we obtain

$$\frac{P_m}{2} = \frac{E_m I_m}{2}$$

Substituting for the value of $P_m/2$ and factoring the denominator of the right member,

$$P = \frac{E_m I_m}{\sqrt{2}\sqrt{2}}$$

Substituting for the values in the right member (Sec. 32-7),

$$P = EI \qquad \text{watts} \qquad [3]$$

Hence, the alternating power consumed by a resistance load is equal to the product of the effective values of voltage and current. As in d-c circuits, alternating power is measured in watts and kilowatts.

EXAMPLE 1   What is the power expended in the resistances of Fig. 33-1?

SOLUTION
$$\text{Voltage across } R_1 = E_1 = 120 \text{ volts}$$
$$\text{Voltage across } R_2 = E_2 = 100 \text{ volts}$$
$$\text{Current through circuit} = I = 4 \text{ amp}$$
$$\text{Power expended in } R_1 = P_1 = E_1 I = 120 \times 4 = 480 \text{ watts}$$
$$\text{Power expended in } R_2 = P_2 = E_2 I = 100 \times 4 = \underline{400 \text{ watts}}$$
$$\text{Total} = 880 \text{ watts}$$

Also, the total power is $P_t = EI = 220 \times 4 = 880$ watts.

Because $P = EI$, the usual Ohm's law relations hold for resistances in a-c circuits. Hence,

$$P = I^2R \qquad \text{watts} \qquad\qquad [4]$$

and
$$P = \frac{E^2}{R} \qquad \text{watts} \qquad\qquad [5]$$

Thus, the power consumed by R_1 of Fig. 33–1 can be computed by using Eq. [4] or [5]. Hence,

$$P_1 = I^2R_1 = 4^2 \times 30 = 480 \text{ watts}$$

or
$$P_1 = \frac{E_1^2}{R_1} = \frac{120^2}{30} = 480 \text{ watts}$$

PROBLEMS 33 – 1

1   A 400-cycle alternator supplies 220 volts across a combination of three series resistors of 20, 50, and 18 Ω.

(a) How much current flows in the circuit?

(b) Write the equations for the alternator voltage and the circuit current.

(c) How much power is dissipated in the 20-Ω resistor?

(d) What is the voltage across the 18-Ω resistor?

(e) What is the instantaneous value of the current when the instantaneous voltage is 146 volts?

2   Given the circuit of Fig. 33–4.

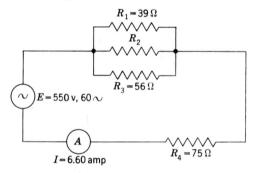

Fig. 33–4   Circuit of Probs. 2 and 3.

(a) Write the equation for the emf of the alternator.

(b) Write the equation for the total current of the circuit.

(c) What is the voltage across R_3?

(d) How much power is dissipated in R_2?

(e) How much current flows through R_1?

(f) What is the instantaneous value of the total current when the instantaneous value of the alternator voltage is 36.5 volts?

3   In the circuit of Fig. 33–4, what is the instantaneous value of the voltage across R_2 when the instantaneous value of the current through R_4 is 7.50 amp?

4 An 800-cycle alternator is connected to a 200-Ω resistor. A wattmeter indicates that the resistor is dissipating 25 watts. What is the maximum instantaneous voltage developed across the resistor?

5 What is the maximum instantaneous value of the current of Prob. 4?

33–3 The inductive circuit

A circuit, or an inductance coil, has the property of inductance when there is an emf set up in it due to a *change* of current through it. Thus, a circuit has an inductance of 1 henry when a change of current of 1 amp/sec induces an emf of 1 volt (Sec. 11–6). Expressed as an equation,

$$E_{av} = L\frac{I}{t} \quad \text{volts} \qquad [6]$$

where E_{av} is the average voltage induced in a circuit of L henrys by a *change* of current of I amp in t sec.

An alternating current of I_m amp makes *four changes* during each cycle. These are

1. From zero to maximum positive value
2. From maximum positive value to zero
3. From zero to maximum negative value
4. From maximum negative value to zero

The time required for one complete cycle of alternating current is $T = 1/f$ sec (Sec. 30–9), and each of the above changes occurs in ¼ of the time required for the completion of each cycle. Then the time for each change is $\frac{1}{4f}$ sec. Substituting this value of t, and I_m for I, in Eq. [6],

$$E_{av} = L\frac{I_m}{\dfrac{1}{4f}} = 4fLI_m \quad \text{volts} \qquad [7]$$

Equation [7] is cumbersome if used in its present form, for it contains an average voltage term and a maximum current term. The equation can be expressed in terms of the relation between average and maximum values as given in Sec. 32–6:

$$E_{av} = \frac{2}{\pi}E_m$$

Substituting in Eq. [7] for this value of E_{av},

$$\frac{2}{\pi}E_m = 4fLI_m$$

which becomes $$E_m = 2\pi fLI_m \qquad\qquad [8]$$

Because both voltage and current in Eq. [8] are now in terms of maximum values, effective values can be used. Thus,

$$E = 2\pi fLI \qquad \text{volts} \qquad\qquad [9]$$

The factors $2\pi fL$ in Eqs. [8] and [9] represent a reaction due to the frequency of the alternating current and the amount of inductance contained in the circuit. Hence the alternating voltage E required to cause a current of I amp with a frequency of f cps to flow through an inductance of L henrys is given by Eq. [9]. That is, the voltage must overcome the reaction $2\pi fL$, which is called the *inductive reactance*. From Eq. [9] the inductive reactance, which is denoted by X_L and expressed in ohms, is given by

$$\frac{E}{I} = 2\pi fL$$

or $$X_L = 2\pi fL = \omega L \qquad \Omega \qquad\qquad [10]$$

where f = frequency, cps
L = inductance, henrys

Note the similarity of the relations between voltage and current for inductive reactance and resistance. Both inductive reactance and resistance offer an opposition to a flow of alternating current, both are expressed in ohms, and both are equal to the voltage divided by the current. Here the similarity ends; there is no inductive reactance to steady-state direct currents because there is no *change* in current, and, as explained later, inductive reactances consume no alternating power.

Figure 33–5 represents a 60-cycle alternator delivering 220 volts to a coil having an inductance of 0.165 henry. The opposition, or inductive reactance, to the flow of current is

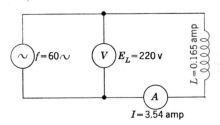

FIG. 33–5 $E_L = 220$ volts, $L = 0.165$ henry.

$$X_L = 2\pi fL = 2\pi \times 60 \times 0.165 = 62.2 \ \Omega$$

Although it is impossible to construct an inductance containing no resistance, to simplify basic considerations we shall consider the coil of Fig. 33-5 as being an inductance with negligible resistance. (The effects of inductance and resistance acting together are discussed in Sec. 33-7.)   The current in the circuit due to the action of voltage and inductive reactance is

$$I = \frac{E_L}{X_L} = \frac{220}{62.2} = 3.54 \ \text{amp}$$

EXAMPLE 2   What is the inductive reactance of an inductance of 17 μh at a frequency of 2,500 kc?

SOLUTION $f = 2,500 \ \text{kc} = 2.5 \times 10^6 \ \text{cps}$
$L = 17 \ \mu\text{h} = 1.7 \times 10^{-5} \ \text{henry}$
$X_L = 2\pi fL = 2\pi \times 2.5 \times 10^6 \times 1.7 \times 10^{-5}$
$ = 2\pi \times 1.7 \times 2.5 \times 10 = 267 \ \Omega$

EXAMPLE 3   An inductor is connected to 115 volts, 60 cycles. An ammeter connected in series with the coil reads 0.714 amp. On the assumption that the coil contains negligible resistance, what is its inductance?

SOLUTION $E_L = 115 \ \text{volts}$
$f = 60 \ \text{cps}$
$I = 0.714 \ \text{amp}$

$$X_L = \frac{E_L}{I} = \frac{115}{0.714} = 161 \ \Omega$$

Since $X_L = 2\pi fL$

then $L = \frac{X_L}{2\pi f} = \frac{161}{2\pi \times 60} = 0.427 \ \text{henry}$

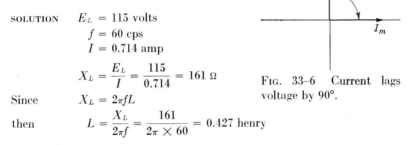

FIG. 33-6   Current lags voltage by 90°.

In a circuit containing inductance, a change of current induces an emf of such polarity that it always opposes the change of current. Because an alternating current is constantly changing, in an inductive circuit there is always present a reaction that opposes this change.   The net effect of this, in a *purely inductive circuit*, is to cause the *current to lag the voltage by* 90°.   This is illustrated by the vector diagram of Fig. 33-6 which shows the voltage of the circuit of Fig. 33-5 to be at maximum positive value when the current is passing through zero.

The instantaneous voltage across the inductance is given by

$$e = E_m \sin \omega t$$

or
$$e = 311 \sin 377t$$

Since the current lags the voltage by a phase angle θ of 90°, the equation for the current through the inductance is

$$i = I_m \sin (\omega t - \theta) \qquad [11]$$

or
$$i = 5 \sin (377t - 90°) \qquad [12]$$

If the voltage has completed ϕ degrees of its cycle, the instantaneous current is

$$i = 5 \sin (\phi - 90°) \qquad [13]$$

EXAMPLE 4   What is the instantaneous value of the current in Fig. 33–5 when the voltage has completed 120° of its cycle?

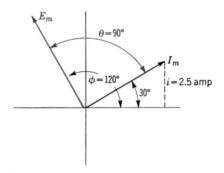

FIG. 33–7   Vector diagram of Example 4.

SOLUTION   Draw a vector diagram of the current and voltage relations as shown in Fig. 33–7. The instantaneous value of the current is found from Eq. [13] and is

$$i = I_m \sin (\phi - 90°) = 5 \sin (120° - 90°) = 5 \sin 30° = 2.5 \text{ amp}$$

PROBLEMS 33 – 2

1   What is the reactance of a coil of 0.260 henry at a frequency of 60 cps?

2   What is the reactance of a 0.3-henry inductor at a frequency of 400 cps?

3   A tuning coil in a radio transmitter has an inductance of 300 μh. What is its reactance at a frequency of 1,500 kc?

4   A coil in a television receiver has an inductance of 3.25 μh. What is its reactance at 183 Mc?

5   Assuming negligible resistance, what current would flow through an inductance of 0.0250 henry at a voltage of 220 volts, 400 cps?

6 A current of 379 μamp at 2.5 volts flows through an inductor at a frequency of 200 Mc. Assuming negligible resistance, what is the inductance?

7 A current of 425 ma, 50 cps, flows through an inductor of 1.65 henrys. Assuming negligible resistance, what is the voltage across the inductor?

8 What is the instantaneous value of the current in Prob. 6 when the voltage has completed 50° of its cycle?

9 What is the instantaneous value of the voltage in Prob. 7 when the current has completed 120° of its cycle?

10 What happens to the inductive reactance of a circuit when (a) the inductance is held constant and the frequency is varied, (b) the frequency is held constant and the inductance is varied?

3 – 4 The capacitive circuit

A capacitance is formed between two conductors when there is an insulating material between them. A circuit, or a capacitor, is said to have a capacitance of 1 farad when a *change* of 1 volt per second produces a current of 1 ampere (Sec. 11–7). Expressed as an equation,

$$I_{av} = C \frac{E}{t} \qquad amp \qquad [\,14\,]$$

where I_{av} is the average current in amperes that is caused to flow through a capacitance of C farads by a *change* of E volts in t sec.

In all probability the above definition does not clearly indicate to you *how much* electricity, or charge, a given capacitor will contain. Perhaps a more understandable definition is that a circuit, or a capacitor, has a capacitance of 1 farad when a difference of potential of 1 volt will produce on it 1 coulomb of charge. Expressed as an equation,

$$Q = CE \qquad \textbf{coulombs} \qquad [\,15\,]$$

where Q is the charge in coulombs placed on a capacitor of C farads by a difference of potential of E volts across the capacitor.

It was shown in Sec. 33–3 that the time t required for one change of an alternating emf was $\frac{1}{4f}$ sec. Thus, if an alternating emf of E_m volts at a frequency of f cps is impressed across a capacitor of C farads, by substituting the above value of t, and E_m for E, in Eq. [14],

$$I_{av} = C\frac{E_m}{\dfrac{1}{4f}} = 4fCE_m \qquad amp \qquad [\,16\,]$$

Again, as in Eq. [7], the above equation contains an average term and a maximum term. As given in Sec. 32–6,

$$I_{av} = \frac{2}{\pi} I_m$$

Substituting in Eq. [16] for this value of I_{av},

$$\frac{2}{\pi} I_m = 4fCE_m$$

which becomes $I_m = 2\pi fCE_m$ [17]

Because both voltage and current in Eq. [17] are now in terms of maximum values, effective values can be used. Thus,

$$I = 2\pi fCE \qquad\qquad [18]$$

The factors $2\pi fC$ represent a reaction due to the frequency of the alternating emf and the amount of capacitance; hence, it is evident that the amount of current in a purely capacitive circuit depends upon these factors. As in the case of resistive circuits and inductive circuits, the opposition to the flow of current is obtained by dividing the voltage by the current. Then, from Eq. [18],

$$\frac{E}{I} = \frac{1}{2\pi fC} \quad \Omega \qquad\qquad [19]$$

The right member of Eq. [19], which represents the opposition to a flow of alternating current in a purely capacitive circuit, is called the *capacitive reactance*. It is denoted by X_C and expressed in ohms. Thus,

$$X_C = \frac{1}{2\pi fC} = \frac{1}{\omega C} \quad \Omega \qquad\qquad [20]$$

where f = frequency, cps
       C = capacitance, farads

Figure 33–8 represents a 60-cycle alternator delivering 220 volts to a capacitor having a capacitance of 14.5 μf. The opposition, or capacitive reactance, to the flow of current is

$$X_C = \frac{1}{2\pi fC} = \frac{1}{2\pi \times 60 \times 14.5 \times 10^{-6}} = \frac{10^4}{2\pi \times 6 \times 1.45} = 183 \ \Omega$$

Neglecting the resistance of the connecting leads and the extremely small losses at low frequencies in a well-constructed capacitor, the current in the circuit due to the action of the voltage and capacitive reactance is

$$I = \frac{E_C}{X_C} = \frac{220}{183} = 1.20 \text{ amp}$$

Fig. 33–8 $E_C = 220$ volts, $C = 14.5 \ \mu f$.

EXAMPLE 5   What is the capacitive reactance of a 350-$\mu\mu f$ capacitor at a frequency of 1,200 kc?

SOLUTION
$$f = 1,200 \text{ kc} = 1.2 \times 10^6 \text{ cps}$$
$$C = 350 \ \mu\mu f = 3.5 \times 10^{-10} \text{ farads}$$
$$X_C = \frac{1}{2\pi f C} = \frac{1}{2\pi \times 1.2 \times 10^6 \times 3.5 \times 10^{-10}}$$
$$= \frac{10^4}{2\pi \times 1.2 \times 3.5} = 379 \ \Omega$$

EXAMPLE 6   A capacitor is connected across 110 volts, 60 cycles. A milliammeter connected in series with the capacitor reads 350 ma. What is the capacitance of the capacitor?

SOLUTION
$$E_C = 110 \text{ volts}$$
$$f = 60 \text{ cps}$$
$$I = 350 \text{ ma} = 0.350 \text{ amp}$$
$$X_C = \frac{E_C}{I} = \frac{110}{0.35} = 314 \ \Omega$$

Since
$$X_C = \frac{1}{2\pi f C}$$

then
$$C = \frac{1}{2\pi f X_C} = \frac{1}{2\pi \times 60 \times 314} = \frac{10^{-3}}{2\pi \times 6 \times 3.14}$$
$$= 8.44 \times 10^{-6} \text{ farad} = 8.44 \ \mu f$$

Because current flows in a capacitor only when the voltage across it is changing, it is evident that, when an alternating voltage is impressed, current is flowing at all times because the potential difference across the capacitor is constantly changing. Furthermore, the greatest amount of current will flow when the voltage is changing most rapidly, this occurring when the voltage passes through zero value. This property, in conjunction with the effects of the counter emf, *causes the current to lead the voltage by 90° in a purely capacitive circuit.* This is illustrated by the vector diagram of Fig. 33–9 which shows the current through the circuit of Fig. 33–8 to be at maximum positive value when the voltage is passing through zero.

The instantaneous voltage across the capacitor is given by

$$e = E_m \sin \omega t \qquad [\,21\,]$$

or
$$e = 311 \sin 377t \qquad [\,22\,]$$

Therefore, the equation for the current is

$$i = I_m \sin (377t + \theta) \qquad [\,23\,]$$

or

$$i = 1.70 \sin (377t + 90°) \qquad [\,24\,]$$

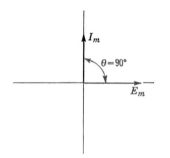

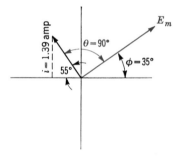

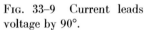

FIG. 33–9   Current leads voltage by 90°.

FIG. 33–10   Vector diagram for Example 7.

If the voltage has completed ϕ degrees of its cycle, the instantaneous current is

$$i = I_m \sin (\phi + 90°) \qquad \textbf{volts} \qquad [\,25\,]$$

EXAMPLE 7   What is the instantaneous value of the current in Fig. 33–8 when the voltage has completed 35° of its cycle?

SOLUTION   Draw a vector diagram of the current and voltage relations as shown in Fig. 33–10. The instantaneous value of the current is found from Eq. [25] and is

$$i = I_m \sin (\phi + 90°) = 1.70 \sin (35° + 90°) = 1.70 \sin 125° = 1.39 \text{ amp}$$

3 – 5   **Capacitors in parallel and in series**

Figure 33–11 represents two capacitors C_1 and C_2 connected across a
voltage E. The quantity of charge in capacitor C_1 will be

$$Q_1 = C_1E \qquad\qquad [\,26\,]$$

and that in capacitor C_2 will be

$$Q_2 = C_2E \qquad\qquad [\,27\,]$$

Since the total quantity in both capacitors is $Q_1 + Q_2$, then

$$Q_1 + Q_2 = C_tE \qquad\qquad [\,28\,]$$

where C_t is the total capacitance of the combination.   Adding Eq.
[26] and Eq. [27],

$$Q_1 + Q_2 = C_1E + C_2E$$

or $\qquad\qquad\qquad Q_1 + Q_2 = (C_1 + C_2)E$

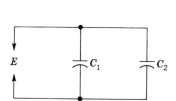

Fig. 33–11   Capacitors C_1 and
C_2 connected in parallel.

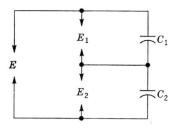

Fig. 33–12   Capacitors C_1 and
C_2 connected in series.

Substituting the value of $(Q_1 + Q_2)$ from Eq. [28],

$$C_tE = (C_1 + C_2)E$$
$$C_t = C_1 + C_2$$

which results in $\qquad\qquad\qquad\qquad\qquad\qquad\qquad\qquad$ [29]

From the foregoing, it is apparent that capacitors in parallel
combine like resistances in series; that is, the capacitance of paralleled
capacitors is equal to the sum of the individual capacitances.

Figure 33–12 represents two capacitors C_1 and C_2 connected in
series with a voltage E across the combination.   Because the
capacitors are in series, the same quantity of electricity must be sent
into each of them.   Then, if E_1 and E_2 represent the potential
differences across C_1 and C_2, respectively, Q represents the quantity
of electricity in each capacitor and C_t is the capacitance of the
combination.   Hence,

$$E = \frac{Q}{C_t}$$

$$E_1 = \frac{Q}{C_1}$$

and
$$E_2 = \frac{Q}{C_2}$$

Since
$$E = E_1 + E_2 \qquad\qquad [30]$$

by substituting the values for all voltages into Eq. [30],

$$\frac{Q}{C_t} = \frac{Q}{C_1} + \frac{Q}{C_2}$$

or
$$\frac{1}{C_t} = \frac{1}{C_1} + \frac{1}{C_2} \qquad\qquad [31]$$

Equation [31] resolves into

$$C_t = \frac{C_1 C_2}{C_1 + C_2} \qquad\qquad [32]$$

The above illustrates the fact that capacitors in series combine like resistances in parallel; that is, the reciprocal of the combined capacitance of capacitors in series is equal to the sum of the reciprocals of the capacitances of the individual capacitors.

EXAMPLE 8   (a) What is the capacitance of a 6-μf capacitor in parallel with a capacitor of 4 μf?

(b) What is the capacitance of these capacitors when connected in series?

SOLUTION   (a) $C_t = 6 + 4 = 10 \ \mu$f

(b) $C_t = \dfrac{6 \times 4}{6 + 4} = 2.4 \ \mu$f

PROBLEMS 33 – 3

1   What is the capacitive reactance of a capacitor of 5 μf at a frequency of 400 cps?

2   What is the capacitive reactance of a capacitor of 10 μf at a frequency of 400 cps?

3   What is the reactance of a capacitor of 50 $\mu\mu$f at a frequency of 400 Mc?

4   A filter capacitor in a radio transmitter has a capacitance of 0.0025 μf. What is its reactance at a frequency of 980 kc?

5   What will be the reactance of the capacitor in Prob. 4 if the frequency is increased to 1,450 kc?

6   How much current will flow in a capacitor of 4 μf when 120 volts, 800 cps is impressed across it?

7   When 240 volts, 60 cps is connected across a capacitor, 452 ma flows. What is the capacitance?

8 A current of 2.21 amp, 400 cps flows through a 2-μf capacitor. What is the voltage across the capacitor?

9 What is the instantaneous value of the current of Prob. 8 when the voltage has completed 125° of its cycle?

10 What is the instantaneous value of the voltage of Prob. 8 when the current has completed 16° of its cycle?

11 (a) What is the resulting capacitance when a 350-$\mu\mu$f capacitor is connected in parallel with a 500-$\mu\mu$f capacitor?

(b) What is the resulting capacitance when these capacitors are connected in series?

12 Two capacitors, 8 and 4 μf, are connected in series across 180 volts, 120 cps.

(a) How much current flows through the capacitors?

(b) Which capacitor has the greater voltage across it?

13 Two capacitors, 50 and 200 $\mu\mu$f, are connected in parallel. A current of 500 ma, 3,500 kc flows through the 200-$\mu\mu$f capacitor. How much current flows through the other capacitor?

14 What happens to the capacitive reactance of a circuit when (a) the capacitance is held constant and the frequency is varied, (b) the frequency is held constant and the capacitance is varied?

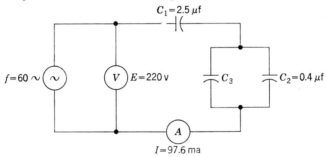

FIG. 33-13 Circuit of Prob. 15.

15 Neglecting the resistance of the connecting wires in Fig. 33-13, (a) write the equation for the emf of the alternator, (b) write the equation for the circuit current.

(c) What is the voltage across C_1?

(d) What is the capacitance of C_3?

(e) How much current flows through C_2?

3-6 Power in circuits containing only inductance or capacitance

Figure 33-14 illustrates the voltage, current, and power relations when a sine wave of emf is impressed across an inductor whose resistance is negligible.

When the current is increasing from zero to maximum positive value, during the time interval from 1 to 2, power is being taken from the source of emf and is being stored in the magnetic field about the coil. As the current through the inductor decreases from maximum positive value to zero, during the time from 2 to 3, the magnetic field is collapsing, thus returning its power to the circuit. Thus, during the intervals from 1 to 2 and from 3 to 4, the inductor is taking power from the source that is represented by the *positive*

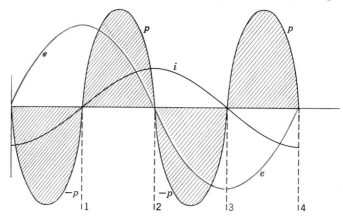

Fig. 33–14   Voltage, current, and power in an inductive circuit.

power in the figure. During the intervals from 0 to 1 and 2 to 3, the inductor is returning power to the source that is represented by the *negative* power in the figure. As previously stated, the instantaneous power is equal to the product of the voltage and current, being positive when the voltage and current are of like sign and negative when of unlike sign. Note that between points 3 and 4, although the voltage and current are both negative, the power is positive.

When an alternating emf is impressed across a capacitor, power is taken from the source and stored in the capacitor as the voltage increases from zero to maximum positive value. As the voltage decreases from maximum positive value to zero, the capacitor discharges and returns power to the source. As in the case of the inductor, half of the power loops are positive and half are negative; therefore, no power is expended in either circuit, for the power alternately flows to and from the source. This power is called *reactive* or *apparent power* and is given by the relation

$$P = EI \qquad \text{va}$$

33–7 Resistance and inductance in series

It has been explained that in a circuit containing only resistance the voltage applied across the resistance and the current through the resistance are in phase and that in a circuit containing only reactance the voltage and current are 90° out of phase. However, circuits encountered in practice contain both resistance and reactance. Such a condition is shown in Fig. 33–15, where an alternating emf of 100 volts is impressed across a combination of 6 Ω resistance in series with 8 Ω inductive reactance.

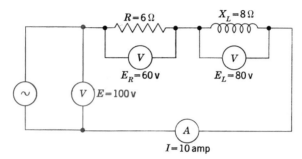

FIG. 33–15 Series circuit containing resistance and inductance.

As with d-c circuits, the sum of the voltage drops around the circuit comprising the load must equal the applied emf. In the consideration of resistance and reactance, however, we are dealing with voltages that can no longer be added or subtracted arithmetically. This is because the voltage drop across the resistance is in phase with the current and the voltage drop across the inductive reactance is 90° ahead of the current.

Because the current is the same in all parts of a series circuit, we can use it as a reference and plot the voltage across the resistance and that across the inductive reactance as shown in Fig. 33–16. The resultant of these two voltages, which can be treated as rectangular components (Sec. 31–4), must be equal to the applied emf. Hence, if IR

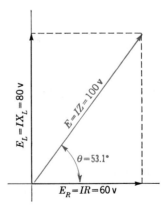

FIG. 33–16 Vector diagram for circuit of Fig. 33–15.

and IX_L are the potential differences across the resistance and inductive reactance, respectively,

$$E = \sqrt{(IR)^2 + (IX_L)^2} \qquad [\,33\,]$$

or
$$E = \sqrt{60^2 + 80^2} = 100 \text{ volts}$$

The phase angle θ between voltage and current can be found by using any of the trigonometric functions. For example,

$$\tan \theta = \frac{IX_L}{IR} = \frac{80}{60} = 1.33$$

$$\therefore \ \theta = 53.1°$$

and it is apparent from the vector diagram that the current through the circuit lags the applied voltage by this amount.

Although the foregoing demonstrates that the *vector sum* of the voltage across the resistance and the voltage across the reactance is equal to the applied emf, no relation between applied voltage and circuit current has been given as yet.

Since $E = \sqrt{(IR)^2 + (IX_L)^2}$

then $E = \sqrt{I^2R^2 + I^2X_L^2}$

Factoring, $E = \sqrt{I^2(R^2 + X_L^2)}$

Hence, $E = I\sqrt{R^2 + X_L^2} \qquad \Omega \qquad [\,34\,]$

As previously stated, the applied voltage divided by the current results in a quotient that represents the opposition offered to the flow of current. Hence, from Eq. [34],

$$\frac{E}{I} = \sqrt{R^2 + X_L^2} \qquad [\,35\,]$$

The expression $\sqrt{R^2 + X_L^2}$ is called the *impedance* of the circuit. It is denoted by Z and measured in ohms. Therefore

$$Z = \sqrt{R^2 + X_L^2} \qquad \Omega \qquad [\,36\,]$$

Applying Eq. [36] to the circuit of Fig. 33–15,

$$Z = \sqrt{6^2 + 8^2} = 10 \ \Omega$$

and
$$I = \frac{E}{Z} = 10 \text{ amp}$$

From Eq. [35], Eq. [36] can be written

$$E = IZ = I\sqrt{R^2 + X_L^2}$$

The foregoing illustrates that the factor I is common to all expressions, which is the same as saying that the current is the same in all parts of the circuit. Because this condition exists, it is permissible to plot the resistance and reactance as rectangular components as shown in Fig. 33–17. Hence the impedance of a series circuit is simply the vector sum of the resistance and reactance. The various methods used in solving for the impedance are the same as those given for vector addition of rectangular components in Example 4 of Sec. 31–4. Note that the values are identical.

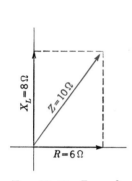

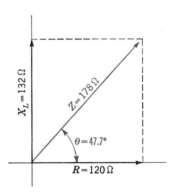

FIG. 33–17 Z can be plotted as vector sum of R and X_L.

FIG. 33–18 Vector diagram for circuit of Example 9.

EXAMPLE 9   A circuit consisting of 120 Ω resistance in series with an inductance of 0.35 henry is connected across a 440-volt 60-cycle alternator. Determine (a) the phase angle between voltage and current, (b) the impedance of the circuit, (c) the current through the circuit.

SOLUTION   (a) Drawing and labeling the circuit is left to you. The inductive reactance is

$$X_L = 2\pi f L = 2\pi \times 60 \times 0.35 = 132 \ \Omega$$

Draw the vector diagram as shown in Fig. 33–18. Then, since

$$\tan \theta = \frac{X_L}{R} = \frac{132}{120} = 1.10$$

$$\therefore \theta = 47.7°$$

Note that the phase angle denotes the position of the applied voltage with respect to the current which is taken as a reference. Thus an inductive series circuit always has a "lagging" phase angle which is a *positive angle* when resistance, reactance, and impedance are plotted vectorially.

(b) $$Z = \frac{R}{\cos \theta} = \frac{120}{\cos 47.7°} = 178 \ \Omega$$

or
$$Z = \frac{X_L}{\sin \theta} = \frac{132}{\sin 47.7°} = 178 \text{ } \Omega$$

(c)
$$I = \frac{E}{Z} = \frac{440}{178} = 2.47 \text{ amp}$$

33 – 8   Resistance and capacitance in series

Figure 33–19 represents a circuit in which an alternating emf of 100 volts is applied across a combination of 6 Ω resistance in series with 8 Ω capacitive reactance. Note the similarity between the circuits of Figs. 33–15 and 33–19. Both have the same values of

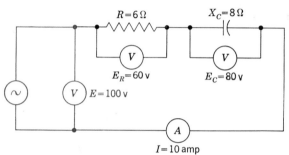

Fig. 33–19   Series circuit consisting of resistance and capacitance.

resistance and absolute values of reactance. However, in the circuit of Fig. 33–19 the voltage drop across the capacitive reactance is 90° behind the current. Again using the current as a reference, because it is the same in all parts of the circuit, the voltage across the resistance and the voltage across the capacitive reactance are plotted as shown in Fig. 33–20 and treated as rectangular components of the applied emf. The impedance of the circuit is found in the same manner as that of the inductive circuit, that is, by vector addition of the rectangular components. The phase angle is found by the same method.

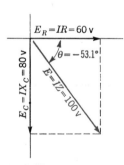

Fig. 33–20   Vector diagram for circuit of Fig. 33–19.

$$\tan \theta = \frac{X_C}{R} = \frac{8}{6} = 1.33$$
$$\therefore \theta = -53.1°$$

In the capacitive circuit the current leads the voltage, and we prefix the phase angle with a minus sign because of its position (Sec. 26–2).

EXAMPLE 10   A circuit consisting of 175 Ω resistance in series with a capacitor of 5.0 μf is connected across a source of 150 volts, 120 cycles. Determine (a) the phase angle between voltage and current, (b) the impedance of the circuit, (c) the current through the circuit.

SOLUTION   (a) Drawing and labeling the circuit is left to you.   The capacitive reactance is

$$X_C = \frac{1}{2\pi f C} = \frac{1}{2\pi \times 120 \times 5 \times 10^{-6}} = \frac{10^4}{2\pi \times 1.2 \times 5} = 265 \ \Omega$$

Draw the vector diagram as shown in Fig. 33-21.   Then, since

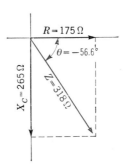

$$\tan \theta = \frac{X_C}{R} = \frac{265}{175} = 1.51$$

$$\therefore \theta = -56.6°$$

Thus the current is leading the voltage by 56.6°, as shown by the vector diagram.

(b) $$Z = \frac{R}{\cos \theta} = \frac{175}{\cos 56.6°} = 318 \ \Omega$$

or $$Z = \frac{X_C}{\sin \theta} = \frac{265}{\sin 56.6°} = 318 \ \Omega$$

(c) $$I = \frac{E}{Z} = \frac{150}{318} = 0.472 \text{ amp}$$

FIG. 33-21   Vector diagram for Example 10.

PROBLEMS 33-4

1   A series circuit consists of a 200-Ω resistor and a 0.75-henry inductor. The circuit is supplied by 230 volts, 60 cps. Find (a) the impedance of the circuit, (b) the current flowing through the circuit, (c) the voltage across the resistor, (d) the voltage across the inductor.

2   A 2,000-volt, 1,000-kc source is connected across a series circuit consisting of an 800-Ω resistor and a 360-μh inductor of negligible resistance. Find (a) the impedance of the circuit, (b) the current flowing through the circuit, (c) the voltage across the resistor, (d) the voltage across the inductor.

3   In the circuit of Prob. 2, the applied voltage is held constant while the frequency is decreased until the current is twice the value found in Prob. 2. Under this condition, find (a) the impedance, (b) the frequency.

4   A 0.025-henry choke has an effective resistance of 25.0 Ω at 400 cps. If this choke is connected across 28 volts, 400 cps, find (a) the impedance of the choke, (b) the current.

5   A 117-volt, 60-cps source is connected across a series circuit consisting of a 27-Ω resistor and a 50-μf capacitor. Find (a) the impedance of the

circuit, (b) the current flowing through the circuit, (c) the voltage across
the resistor, (d) the voltage across the capacitor.

6   A series circuit consists of a 25-Ω resistor and a 75-μμf capacitor. What
is its impedance at 21 Mc?

7   What will be the impedance of the circuit of Prob. 6 if an additional
capacitor of 75 μμf is connected in parallel with the original capacitor?

8   What will be the impedance of the circuit of Prob. 6 if an additional
resistor of 50 Ω is connected in series with the original circuit?

9   A series circuit consisting of a 100-Ω resistor and a 250-μμf capacitor is
connected to 500 volts, 1,500 kc. Find (a) the impedance of the circuit,
(b) the current flowing through the circuit, (c) the voltage across the
resistor, (d) the voltage across the capacitor.

10   In the circuit of Prob. 9, what capacitor must be connected in parallel
with the original capacitor in order to obtain three times the current
found in Prob. 9?

33 – 9   Resistance, inductance, and capacitance in series

It has been shown that inductive reactance causes the current to
lag the voltage and that capacitive reactance causes the current to
lead the voltage; hence, these two reactions are exactly opposite in
effect. Figure 33–22 represents a series circuit consisting of re-

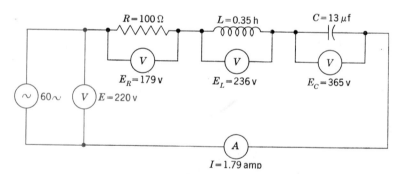

FIG. 33–22   Series circuit consisting of R, L, and C.

sistance, inductance, and capacitance connected across an alternator
that supplies 220 volts, 60 cycles.

Now
$$\omega = 2\pi f = 2\pi \times 60 = 377$$
$$\therefore X_L = \omega L = 377 \times 0.35 = 132 \ \Omega$$

and
$$X_C = \frac{1}{\omega C} = \frac{1}{377 \times 13 \times 10^{-6}} = \frac{10^3}{3.77 \times 1.3} = 204 \ \Omega$$

Figure 33–23 is a vector diagram of the conditions existing in the circuit. Since X_L and X_C are oppositely directed vectors, it is evident that the resultant reactance will have a magnitude equal to their algebraic sum and with the direction of the greater. Therefore, the net reactance of the circuit is a capacitive reactance of 72 Ω as illustrated in Fig. 33–23. Thus the entire circuit could be replaced by an equivalent series circuit consisting of 100 Ω resistance and 72 Ω capacitive reactance, provided that the frequency of the alternator remains constant.

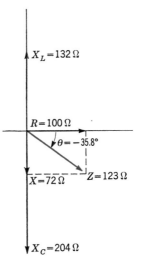

The impedance, current, and potential differences are found by the usual methods.

$$\tan \theta = \frac{X_C}{R} = \frac{72}{100} = 0.72$$

$$\therefore \theta = -35.8°$$

$$Z = \frac{X}{\sin \theta} = \frac{72}{\sin 35.8°} = 123 \ \Omega$$

$$I = \frac{E}{Z} = \frac{220}{123} = 1.79 \text{ amp}$$

$$E_R = IR = 1.79 \times 100 = 179 \text{ volts}$$
$$E_L = IX_L = 1.79 \times 132 = 236 \text{ volts}$$
$$E_C = IX_C = 1.79 \times 204 = 365 \text{ volts}$$

Fig. 33–23 Vector diagram for circuit of Fig. 33–22.

Note that the potential difference across the reactances is greater than the voltage impressed across the entire circuit. This is reasonable, for the applied voltage is across the impedance of the circuit, which is a smaller value, in ohms, than the reactances. Because the current is common to all circuit components, it follows that the greatest potential difference will exist across the component offering the greatest opposition.

– 10   Power in a series circuit of resistance and reactance

It has been shown that, in a circuit consisting of resistance only, no power is returned to the source of voltage. Also, it has been shown that a circuit containing reactance alone consumes no power; that is, a reactance alternately receives and returns all power to the source. It is evident, therefore, that in a circuit containing both resistance and reactance there must be some power expended in the resistance and also some returned to the source by the reactance. Figure 33–24 represents the relation among voltage, current, and power in the circuit of Fig. 33–22.

As previously stated, the instantaneous power in the circuit is equal to the product of the applied voltage and the current through

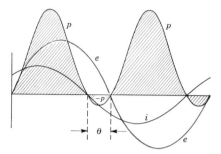

FIG. 33–24 Voltage, current, and power
relations for circuit of Fig. 33–22.

the circuit. When the voltage and current are of the same sign, they are acting together and taking power from the source. When their signs are unlike, they are operating in opposite directions and power is returned to the source. The *apparent power* is

$$P_a = EI \qquad \text{va} \qquad\qquad [\,37\,]$$

and the actual power taken by the circuit, which is called the *true power* or *active power*, is

$$P = I^2R \qquad \text{watts} \qquad\qquad [\,38\,]$$

or $$P = E_RI \qquad \text{watts} \qquad\qquad [\,39\,]$$

where E_R is the potential difference across the resistance of the circuit.

The *power factor* of a circuit is the ratio of the true power to the apparent power. That is,

$$\mathrm{pf} = \frac{P}{P_a} \qquad\qquad [\,40\,]$$

Substituting the value of P from Eq. [\,38\,] and that of P_a in Eq. [\,37\,],

$$\mathrm{pf} = \frac{I^2R}{EI} = \frac{IR}{E}$$

Then, since $$E = IZ$$

$$\mathrm{pf} = \frac{IR}{IZ}$$

or $$\mathrm{pf} = \frac{R}{Z} \qquad\qquad [\,41\,]$$

Hence, the power factor of a series circuit can be obtained by dividing the resistance of a circuit by its impedance. The power factor is often expressed in terms of the angle of lead or lag. From preceding vector diagrams, it is evident that

$$\frac{R}{Z} = \cos \theta$$

$$\therefore \text{pf} = \cos \theta \qquad [42]$$

From Eq. [40], $P = P_a \text{ pf}$

Substituting for P_a, $P = EI \text{ pf}$

Substituting for the pf, $P = EI \cos \theta \qquad [43]$

From the foregoing, it is seen that the power expended in a circuit can be obtained by utilizing different relations. For example, in the circuit of Fig. 33–22,

$$P = I^2 R = 1.79^2 \times 100 = 320 \text{ watts}$$
$$P = E_R I = 179 \times 1.79 = 320 \text{ watts}$$

and $P = EI \cos \theta = 220 \times 1.79 \times \cos 35.8° = 320 \text{ watts}$

The power factor of a circuit can be expressed as a decimal or as a percentage. Thus the power factor of this circuit is

$$\cos \theta = \cos 35.8° = 0.812$$

Expressed as percentage,

$$\text{pf} = 100 \cos 35.8° = 81.2 \text{ per cent}$$

–11   **Solution of series circuits by employing the tangent of the phase angle**

A method of computing the impedance of series circuits that is convenient for slide-rule operators confines itself to the use of the tangent of the phase angle. The derivation of this method is based upon the relation

$$Z = \sqrt{R^2 + X^2}$$

Multiplying and dividing by R^2,

$$Z = \frac{R^2 \sqrt{R^2 + X^2}}{R^2}$$

Then $Z = R\sqrt{\dfrac{R^2}{R^2} + \dfrac{X^2}{R^2}} = R\sqrt{1 + \left(\dfrac{X}{R}\right)^2} = R\sqrt{1 + \tan^2 \theta}$

The impedance is found on the slide rule as follows: Divide the reactance by the resistance, using scales C and D, so that the quotient, which is tan θ, appears on scale D opposite the index of C. Now tan$^2 \theta$ is on scale A opposite the index of B. Add 1 to the value of tan$^2 \theta$, and set the index of B to $(1 + \tan^2 \theta)$ on A.

Now $\sqrt{1 + \tan^2 \theta}$ is on scale D opposite the index of C, ready to be multiplied by the resistance.

33 – 12 **Notation for series circuits**

In Sec. 8–5, it was shown that positive and negative "real" numbers could be represented graphically by plotting them along a horizontal line. The positive numbers were plotted to the right of zero, and the negative numbers were plotted to the left. This idea was expanded in Sec. 21–2 where the original horizontal line was made the X axis for a system of rectangular coordinates.

In Sec. 23–13 the system of representation was extended to include the "imaginary" numbers by agreeing to plot them along the Y axis, the letter j being used as a symbol of operation. Thus, when some number is prefixed with j, it means that the vector which the number represents is to be rotated through an angle of 90°. The rotation is positive, or in a counterclockwise direction, when the sign of j is positive, and negative, or in a clockwise direction, when the sign of j is negative.

From the foregoing, it is evident that resistance, when plotted on a vector diagram, is considered as a "real" number because it is plotted along the X axis. In this instance the term *real* may well define resistance, for it is the only opposition to the flow of current that consumes power.

Since reactances are displaced 90° from resistance in a vector diagram, it follows that inductive reactance can be prefixed with a plus j and capacitive reactance by a minus j. Thus, an inductive reactance of 75 Ω would be written $j75$ Ω and plotted on the positive Y axis; a capacitive reactance of 86 Ω would be written $-j86$ Ω and plotted on the negative Y axis.

It has been shown that a vector can be completely described in terms of its rectangular components. For example, the circuit of Fig. 33–15 can be described as consisting of an impedance of 10 Ω at an angle of 53.1°, which would be written

$$Z = 10\underline{/53.1°}\ \Omega$$

where the angle sign is included for emphasis and the number of degrees denotes the angle that the vector makes with the positive

X axis. This is known as *polar form*. Since this impedance is made up of 6 Ω of resistance and 8 Ω of inductive reactance, we can write

$$Z = R + jX_L = 6 + j8 \ \Omega$$

This is known as *rectangular form*.

The rectangular form is a very convenient method of notation. For example, instead of writing "A series circuit of 4 Ω resistance and 3 Ω capacitive reactance," we can write "A series circuit of

Circuit	Vector	Z Rectangular form	Z Polar form
 $R=10\,\Omega$	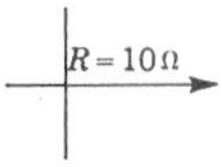 $R=10\,\Omega$	$Z=10+j0\ \Omega$	$Z=10\underline{/0^\circ}\ \Omega$
 $X_L=7\,\Omega$	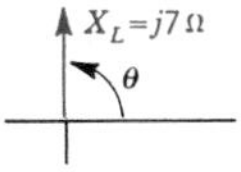 $X_L=j7\,\Omega$ θ	$Z=0+j7\ \Omega$	$Z=7\underline{/90^\circ}\ \Omega$
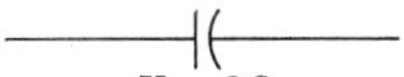 $X_C=6\,\Omega$	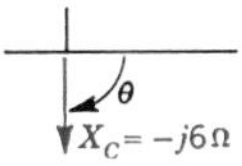 θ $X_C=-j6\,\Omega$	$Z=0-j6\ \Omega$	$Z=6\underline{/-90^\circ}\ \Omega$
$R=4\,\Omega$ 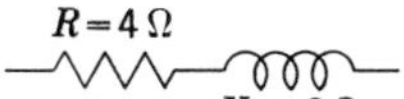 $X_L=3\,\Omega$	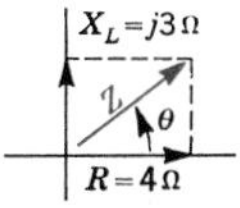 $X_L=j3\,\Omega$ θ $R=4\,\Omega$	$Z=4+j3\ \Omega$	$Z=5\underline{/36.9^\circ}\ \Omega$
$R=6\,\Omega$ 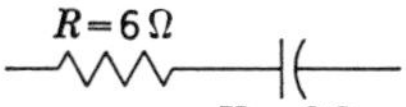 $X_C=8\,\Omega$	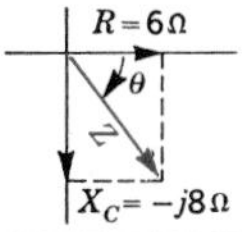 $R=6\,\Omega$ θ $X_C=-j8\,\Omega$	$Z=6-j8\ \Omega$	$Z=10\underline{/-53.1^\circ}\ \Omega$
$R=7\,\Omega$ $X_C=40\,\Omega$ 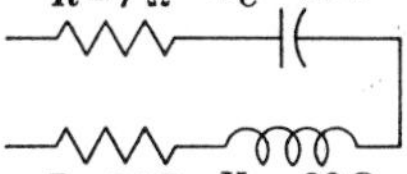 $R=13\,\Omega$ $X_L=20\,\Omega$	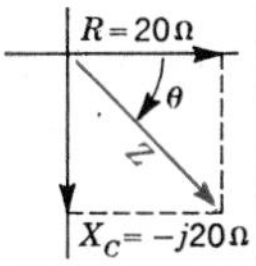 $R=20\,\Omega$ θ $X_C=-j20\,\Omega$	$Z=20-j20\ \Omega$	$Z=28.2\underline{/-45^\circ}\ \Omega$

Fig. 33-25   Vector notation for series circuits.

$4 - j3 \ \Omega$." Figure 33-25 shows the various types of series circuits with their proper vector diagram and corresponding notation.

Note that the sign of the phase angle is the same as that of j in the rectangular form.

It must be understood that neither the rectangular form nor the polar form is a method for solving series circuits. These forms are simply convenient forms of notation that completely describe circuit conditions from both electrical and mathematical viewpoints.

33 – 13   Conversion from rectangular to polar form and vice versa

In converting from rectangular to polar form, the usual methods of solution are used.

EXAMPLE 11   Find the vector impedance of a series circuit of $250 - j100\ \Omega$.

SOLUTION   Given $Z = R - jX = 250 - j100\ \Omega$

$$\tan\theta = \frac{X}{R} = \frac{100}{250} = 0.400$$

$$\therefore\ \theta = -21.8°$$

$$Z = \frac{X}{\sin\theta} = \frac{100}{\sin 21.8°} = 269\ \Omega$$

or

$$Z = \frac{R}{\cos\theta} = \frac{250}{\cos 21.8°} = 269\ \Omega$$

Hence $Z = 269\ \underline{/-21.8°}\ \Omega$

Converting from rectangular form to polar form, which is simply vector addition of rectangular components, can be completed with a total of three movements on many types of slide rule.

Converting from polar form, in which the magnitude and angle are given, to rectangular form is simplified by making use of the trigonometric functions. Since

$$R = Z\cos\theta$$
$$X = Z\sin\theta$$

and $Z = R \pm jX$ [44]

by substitution, $Z = Z\cos\theta + jZ\sin\theta$ [45]

Factoring, $Z = Z\ (\cos\theta + j\sin\theta)$ Ω [46]

The $\pm$ sign is omitted in Eqs. [45] and [46] because, if the proper angles are used (positive or negative), the respective sine values will determine the proper sign of the reactance component.

EXAMPLE 12   A series circuit has an impedance of $269\ \Omega$ with a leading power factor of 0.928. What are the reactance and resistance of the circuit?
SOLUTION   Given $Z = 269\ \Omega$ and $pf = 0.928$. The power factor, when expressed as a decimal, is equal to the cosine of the phase angle. Hence,

if $0.928 = \cos \theta$

then $\theta = -21.8°$

The angle was given the minus sign because a "leading power factor" means the current leads the voltage. Therefore,

$$Z = 269 \underline{/-21.8°}\ \Omega$$

Substituting these values in Eq. [45],

$$Z = 269 \cos 21.8° - j269 \sin 21.8° = 250 - j100\ \Omega$$

– 14   The general series circuit

In a series circuit consisting of several resistances and reactances, the total resistance of the circuit is the sum of all the series resistances and the total reactance is the algebraic sum of the series reactances. That is, the total resistance is

$$R_t = R_1 + R_2 + R_3 + \cdots$$

and the reactance of the circuit is

$$X = j(\omega L_1 + \omega L_2 + \omega L_3 + \cdots) - j\left(\frac{1}{\omega C_1} + \frac{1}{\omega C_2} + \frac{1}{\omega C_3} + \cdots\right)$$

Hence, the impedance is

$$\boldsymbol{Z} = \boldsymbol{R_t \pm jX} \qquad \Omega$$

As an alternate method, such a circuit can always be reduced to an equivalent series circuit by combining inductances and capacitances before computing reactances. Thus, the total inductance is

$$L_t = L_1 + L_2 + L_3 + \cdots$$

and the capacitance of the circuit is

$$\frac{1}{C_t} = \frac{1}{C_1} + \frac{1}{C_2} + \frac{1}{C_3} + \cdots$$

However, when voltage drops across individual reactances are desired, it is best to find the equivalent circuit by combining reactances.

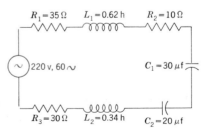

FIG. 33–26   Series circuit of Example 13.

EXAMPLE 13   Given the circuit of Fig. 33–26, which is supplied by 220 volts, 60 cycles. Find (a) the equivalent series circuit, (b) the impedance of the circuit, (c) current, (d) power factor, (e) power expended in the circuit, (f) apparent power, (g) voltage drop across C_1, (h) power expended in R_2.

SOLUTION   (a) $R_t = R_1 + R_2 + R_3 = 35 + 10 + 30 = 75 \; \Omega$

$$\omega = 2\pi f = 2\pi \times 60 = 377$$

$$L_t = L_1 + L_2 = 0.62 + 0.34 = 0.96 \text{ henry}$$

$$X_L = \omega L = 377 \times 0.96 = 362 \; \Omega$$

$$X_{C_1} = \frac{1}{\omega C_1} = \frac{1}{377 \times 30 \times 10^{-6}} = \frac{10^3}{3.77 \times 3} = 88.4 \; \Omega$$

$$X_{C_2} = \frac{1}{\omega C_2} = \frac{1}{377 \times 20 \times 10^{-6}} = \frac{10^3}{3.77 \times 2} = 132.6 \; \Omega$$

$$X_C = 88.4 + 132.6 = 221 \; \Omega$$

$$X = X_L - X_C = 362 - 221 = 141 \; \Omega$$

The equivalent series circuit consists of a resistance of 75 Ω and an inductive reactance of 141 Ω. That is,

$$Z = 75 + j141 \; \Omega$$

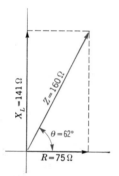

FIG. 33–27 Vector diagram for circuit of Fig. 33–26.

The vector diagram for the equivalent circuit is shown in Fig. 33–27.

(b) $\tan \theta = \dfrac{X}{R_t} = \dfrac{141}{75} = 1.88$

$$\therefore \; \theta = 62°$$

$$Z = \frac{R}{\cos \theta} = \frac{75}{\cos 62°} = 160 \; \Omega$$

Hence, $Z = 160 \; \underline{/62°} \; \Omega$

(c) $I = \dfrac{E}{Z} = \dfrac{220}{160} = 1.38 \text{ amp}$

(d) $\text{pf} = \cos \theta = \cos 62° = 0.470$

Expressed as a percentage,

pf = 47.0 per cent

(e) $P = EI \cos \theta = 220 \times 1.38 \times \cos 62° = 143 \text{ watts}$

or $P = I^2 R = 1.38^2 \times 75 = 143 \text{ watts}$

(f) $P_a = EI = 220 \times 1.38 = 304 \text{ va}$

(g) $E_{C_1} = IX_{C_1} = 1.38 \times 88.4 = 122 \text{ volts}$

(h) $P_{R_2} = I^2 R_2 = 1.38^2 \times 10 = 19 \text{ watts}$

You will find it convenient to compute the value of the angular velocity $\omega = 2\pi f$ for all a-c problems, for this factor is common to all reactance equations.

As with all electric-circuit problems, a neat diagram of the circuit should be made, with all known circuit components, voltages, and currents clearly marked. In addition, a vector diagram should be drawn to scale in order to check the mathematical solution.

PROBLEMS 33 – 5

Given the circuit of Fig. 33–28, with values as listed in Table 33–1. Draw a vector diagram for each circuit, and find (a) the impedance of the circuit,

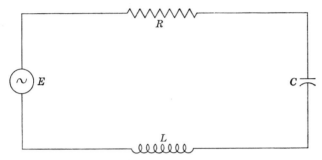

FIG. 33–28   Circuit for Probs. 1 to 10.

(b) the current flowing through the circuit, (c) the equation of the current, (d) the pf of the circuit, (e) the power expended in the circuit.

TABLE 33–1   PROBLEMS 1 to 10

Problem	E, volts	f	R	L	C
1	440	60 cps	500 Ω	3.5 henrys	12 µf
2	660	25 cps	600 Ω	8.0 henrys	50 µf
3	110	50 cps	1,000 Ω	5.1 henrys	8.5 µf
4	110	800 cps	50 Ω	4.8 mh	25 µf
5	1,250	100 kc	250 Ω	800 µh	0.015 µf
6	1	1,000 kc	20 Ω	90 µh	250 µµf
7	500	355 kc	15 Ω	375 µh	500 µµf
8	50	28 Mc	4.5 Ω	1.2 µh	25 µµf
9	100	7,200 kc	10 Ω	12.5 µh	45 µµf
10	220	60 cps	200 Ω	1.5 henrys	5 µf

11 A certain choke coil, when connected across 110 volts direct current, draws 2 amp from the line. When connected across 110 volts, 60 cps, the current is 0.25 amp.

(a) What is the resistance of the coil?
(b) What is its inductive reactance?
(c) What is the inductance?

12 On the assumption that the effective resistance of the coil of Prob. 11 remains constant, how much power would it consume when connected across 120 volts, 800 cps?

13 The following 60-cycle impedances are connected in series: $Z_1 = 3 - j6\ \Omega; Z_2 = 10 + j19\ \Omega; Z_3 = 2 - j7\ \Omega; Z_4 = 5 + j14\ \Omega$.

(*a*) What is the vector impedance of the circuit?

(*b*) What value of capacitance must be added in series to make the pf of the circuit 70.7 per cent leading?

14 The meters represented in Fig. 33–29 are connected such a short distance

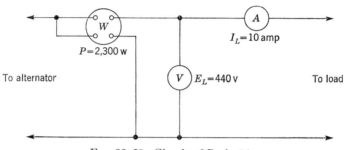

$P = 2,300$ w

To alternator

$I_L = 10$ amp

V $E_L = 440$ v

To load

FIG. 33–29   Circuit of Prob. 14.

from an inductive load that line drop from meters to load is negligible. What is the equivalent series circuit of the load?

15 A single-phase induction motor, with 440 volts across its input terminals, delivers 10.8 mechanical horsepower at an efficiency of 90 per cent and a pf of 86.6 per cent.

(*a*) What is the line current?

(*b*) How much power is taken by the motor?

16 Given any series circuit, for example, 110 volts at 60 cps applied across $3 + j4\ \Omega$. On the same set of axes and to the same scale, plot instantaneous values of the applied voltage e, the potential difference across the resistance R, and the potential difference across the reactance X. What is your conclusion?

33 – 15   Series resonance

It has been shown that the inductive reactance of a circuit varies directly as the frequency and that the capacitive reactance varies inversely as the frequency. That is, the inductive reactance will increase and the capacitive reactance will decrease as the frequency is increased and vice versa. Then, for any value of inductance and capacitance in a circuit, there is a frequency at which the inductive reactance and the capacitive reactance are equal. This is called the *resonant frequency* of the circuit. Since, in a series circuit,

$$Z = R + j\left(\omega L - \frac{1}{\omega C}\right)$$

at resonance, $\omega L = \dfrac{1}{\omega C}$ [47]

Hence, $Z = R$

Therefore, at the resonant frequency of a series circuit, the resistance is the only circuit component that limits the flow of current, for the net reactance of the circuit is zero. Thus the current is in phase with the applied voltage which results in a circuit power factor of 100 per cent.

EXAMPLE 14   There is impressed 10 volts at a frequency of 1,000 kc across a circuit consisting of a coil of 92.2 μh in series with a capacitance of 275 $\mu\mu$f. The effective resistance of the coil at this frequency is 10 Ω, and the resistance of the connecting wires and capacitance are negligible. (*a*) What is the impedance of the circuit? (*b*) How much current flows through the circuit? (*c*) What are the voltages across the reactances?

SOLUTION   The resistance of the coil is treated as being in series with the inductive reactance.

(*a*) $\omega = 2\pi f = 6.28 \times 10^6$
           $X_L = \omega L = 6.28 \times 10^6 \times 92.2 \times 10^{-6} = 6.28 \times 92.2 = 579\ \Omega$

           $X_C = \dfrac{1}{\omega C} = \dfrac{1}{6.28 \times 10^6 \times 275 \times 10^{-12}} = \dfrac{10^4}{6.28 \times 2.75} = 579\ \Omega$

Since $X_L = X_C$

then $Z = R = 10\ \Omega$

(*b*) $I = \dfrac{E}{Z} = \dfrac{10}{10} = 1\ \text{amp}$

(*c*) $E_C = IX_C = 1 \times 579 = 579\ \text{volts}$
                                 $E_L = IX_L = 1 \times 579 = 579\ \text{volts}$

Note that the voltages across the inductance and capacitance are much greater than the applied voltage.

The *merit* of an inductance, denoted by Q, is defined as the ratio of its inductive reactance to its resistance. Thus,

$$Q = \frac{\omega L}{R}$$ [48]

Then, at resonance, $E_C = E_L = I\omega L$

Substituting for I, $E_C = E_L = \dfrac{E\omega L}{R}$

Substituting for $\omega L/R$,

$$E_C = E_L = EQ \qquad \text{volts} \qquad\qquad [49]$$

Because the average radio circuit has purposely been designed for high Q values, it is seen that very high voltages can be developed in resonant series circuits.

33 – 16   Resonant frequency

The resonant frequency of a circuit can be determined by rewriting Eq. [47]. Thus,

$$2\pi f L = \frac{1}{2\pi f C}$$

$$\therefore f = \frac{1}{2\pi \sqrt{LC}} \qquad \text{cps} \qquad\qquad [50]$$

where f, L, and C are in the usual units, cycles per second, henrys, and farads, respectively.

EXAMPLE 15   A series circuit consists of an inductance of 500 μh and a capacitor of 400 $\mu\mu$f. What is the resonant frequency of the circuit?

SOLUTION $L = 500\ \mu\text{h} = 5 \times 10^{-4}\ \text{henry}$
                  $C = 400\ \mu\mu\text{f} = 4 \times 10^{-10}\ \text{farad}$

$$f = \frac{1}{2\pi\sqrt{LC}} = \frac{1}{2\pi\sqrt{5 \times 10^{-4} \times 4 \times 10^{-10}}} = \frac{10^7}{2\pi\sqrt{20}} = 356{,}000\ \text{cps}$$

or $f = 356\ \text{kc}$

From Eq. [50] it is evident that the resonant frequency of a series circuit depends *only* upon the LC product. This means there is an infinite number of combinations of L and C that will resonate to a particular frequency.

EXAMPLE 16   How much capacitance is required to obtain resonance at 1,500 kc with an inductance of 45 μh?

SOLUTION $f = 1{,}500\ \text{kc} = 1.5 \times 10^6\ \text{cps}$
                  $L = 45\ \mu\text{h} = 4.5 \times 10^{-5}\ \text{henry}$
                  $\omega = 2\pi f = 2\pi \times 1.5 \times 10^6 = 9.42 \times 10^6$

From Eq. [50], $C = \dfrac{1}{(2\pi f)^2 L} = \dfrac{1}{\omega^2 L}$

$$\therefore C = \frac{1}{(9.42 \times 10^6)^2 \times 4.5 \times 10^{-5}} = 250\ \mu\mu\text{f}$$

PROBLEMS 33 – 6

1 Twenty-five volts, 600 kc, is impressed across a series circuit consisting of 350 $\mu\mu$f and 201 μh. At this frequency the effective resistance of the inductance is 13 Ω.

(a) How much current flows through the circuit?

(b) How much power is expended in the circuit?

(c) What are the voltages existing across the inductive and capacitive reactances?

2 What is the Q of the coil in Prob. 1?

3 A tuning capacitor has a maximum capacitance of 100 $\mu\mu f$ and a minimum capacitance of 10 $\mu\mu f$. What inductance must be used with the capacitor if the lowest resonant frequency is to be 3,750 kc? What is the highest resonant frequency?

4 A series circuit consists of an inductance of 8 μh, with an effective resistance of 5 Ω, and a capacitor. A current of 0.5 amp flows through the circuit at its resonant frequency of 7,500 kc.

(a) What is the Q of the coil?

(b) What is the capacitance of the capacitor?

(c) What is the impressed voltage across the circuit?

(d) What is the voltage across the capacitor?

5 What is the equivalent circuit of a series circuit when operating at

(a) resonant frequency, (b) at a frequency less than resonant frequency,

(c) at a frequency greater than resonant frequency?

CHAPTER 34
ALTERNATING CURRENTS
PARALLEL CIRCUITS

Parallel circuits are the most commonly encountered circuits in use. The average distribution circuit has many types of loads all connected in parallel with each other, lighting circuits, motors, transformers for various uses, etc. The same is true for electronic circuits, which range from the most simple parallel circuits to complex networks.

This chapter deals with the solutions of parallel circuits. These solutions consist in reducing a parallel circuit to an equivalent series circuit that, when connected to the same source of emf as the given parallel circuit, would result in the same line current and phase angle.

34 – 1   Resistances in parallel

It was explained in Secs. 33–1 and 33–2 that, in an a-c circuit containing resistance only, the voltage, current, and power relations were the same as in d-c circuits. However, in order to build a foundation from which all parallel circuits can be analyzed, the case of

518

paralleled resistances must be considered from a vector viewpoint.

Figure 34–1 represents a 60-cycle 220-volt alternator connected to three resistances in parallel.

Neglecting the internal resistance of the alternator and the resistance of the connecting wires, the emf of the alternator is impressed

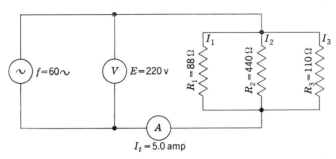

FIG. 34–1   Alternator connected to three resistors in parallel.

across each of the three resistances.   Then, if I_1, I_2, and I_3 represent the currents flowing through R_1, R_2, and R_3, respectively, by Ohm's law,

$$I_1 = 2.5 \text{ amp}$$
$$I_2 = 0.5 \text{ amp}$$
and $$I_3 = 2.0 \text{ amp}$$

Since all currents are in phase, the total current flowing in the line, or external circuit, will be equal to the sum of the branch currents, or 5.0 amp.   The vector diagram for the three currents is shown in Fig. 34–2.   All currents are plotted in phase with the applied emf, which is used as a reference vector because the voltage is common to all resistances.   Then, using vector notation,

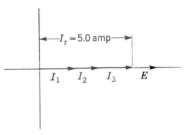

FIG. 34–2   Vector diagram for the circuit of Fig. 34–1.

$$I_1 = 2.5 + j0 \text{ amp}$$
$$I_2 = 0.5 + j0 \text{ amp}$$
$$\overline{I_3 = 2.0 + j0 \text{ amp}}$$
$$I_t = 5.0 + j0 \text{ amp}$$
or $$I_t = 5.0 \underline{/0°} \text{ amp}$$

As with all other circuits, the equivalent series impedance, which in this case is a pure resistance, is found by dividing the voltage across the circuit by the total current. That is,

$$Z = \frac{E}{I_t} = \frac{220}{5} = 44 \ \Omega$$

or
$$Z = 44 \ \underline{/0^\circ} \ \Omega$$

34 – 2   Inductance and capacitance in parallel

When a purely inductive reactance and a capacitive reactance are connected in parallel, as shown in Fig. 34–3, the currents flowing

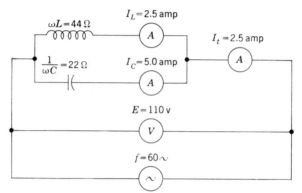

Fig. 34-3 X_L and X_C connected in parallel.

through these reactances differ in phase by 180°.

The current flowing through the inductor is

$$I_L = \frac{E}{X_L} = \frac{E}{\omega L} = \frac{110}{44} = 2.5 \text{ amp}$$

and that through the capacitor is

$$I_C = \frac{E}{X_C} = \omega C E = \frac{110}{22} = 5.0 \text{ amp}$$

In series circuits, the current is used as the reference vector because the current is the same in all parts of the circuit. In parallel circuits there are different values of currents in various parts of a circuit; therefore, the current cannot be used as the reference vector.

Since the same voltage exists across two or more parallel branches, the applied voltage can be used as the reference vector as shown in Fig. 34–4.

Note that the current I_L through the inductor is plotted as *lagging* the alternator voltage by 90° and the current I_C through the capacitor is *leading* the voltage by 90°. The total line current I_t, which is the vector sum of the branch currents, is leading the applied voltage by 90°. That is, using vector notation,

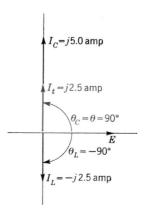

$$I_L = 0 - j2.5 \text{ amp}$$
$$I_C = 0 + j5.0 \text{ amp}$$
$$\overline{I_t = 0 + j2.5 \text{ amp}}$$

or $\quad\quad I_t = 2.5\ \underline{/90°}\ \text{amp}$

Since the line current leads the alternator voltage by 90°, the equivalent series circuit consists of a capacitive reactance of

Fig. 34–4 Vector diagram for circuit of Fig. 34–3.

$$\frac{E}{I_t} = \frac{110}{2.5} = 44\ \Omega$$

That is, the parallel circuit could be replaced with a 60.3-μf capacitor which would result in a current of 2.5 amp leading the voltage by 90°; in other words, the alternator would not sense the difference.

Note the difference between reactances in series and reactances in parallel. In a series circuit the *greatest* reactance of the circuit results in the equivalent series circuit containing the same kind of reactance. For this reason, it is said that reactances, or voltages across reactances, are the controlling factors of series circuits. In a parallel circuit the *least* reactance of the circuit, which passes the greatest current, results in the equivalent series circuit containing the same kind of reactance. For this reason, it is said that currents are the controlling factors of parallel circuits.

34 – 3 Assumed voltages

The solutions of the great majority of parallel circuits are facilitated by assuming a voltage to exist across a parallel combination. The current through each branch, due to the assumed voltage, is then added vectorially to obtain the total current. The assumed voltage is then divided by the total current, the quotient being the joint impedance of the parallel branches.

The assumed voltage should always be some power of 10 in order that you can make full use of the reciprocal scales and reciprocal relations on your slide rule.

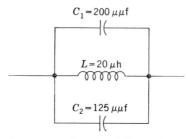

$C_1 = 200 \, \mu\mu f$

$L = 20 \, \mu h$

$C_2 = 125 \, \mu\mu f$

FIG. 34–5   Circuit of Example 1.

In order to avoid small decimal quantities the assumed voltage should be greater than the largest impedance of any parallel branch.

EXAMPLE 1   Given the circuit of Fig. 34–5. What are the impedance and the power factor of the circuit at a frequency of 2,500 kc?

SOLUTION C_1 and C_2 are in parallel; hence, the total capacitance is

$$C_t = C_1 + C_2 = 200 + 125 = 325 \, \mu\mu f$$

This simplifies the circuit to a capacitor C of 325 $\mu\mu f$ in parallel with an inductance L of 20 μh.

$$\omega = 2\pi f = 2\pi \times 2.5 \times 10^6 = 1.57 \times 10^7$$
$$X_L = \omega L = 1.57 \times 10^7 \times 2 \times 10^{-5} = 314 \, \Omega$$
$$X_C = \frac{1}{\omega C} = \frac{1}{1.57 \times 10^7 \times 325 \times 10^{-12}} = \frac{10^3}{1.57 \times 3.25} = 196 \, \Omega$$

Assume 1,000 volts across the parallel branch. Then the current through the capacitors is

$$I_C = \frac{E_a}{X_C} = \frac{1,000}{196} = 5.10 \, \text{amp}$$

and the current through the inductance is

$$I_L = \frac{E_a}{X_L} = \frac{1,000}{314} = 3.18 \, \text{amp}$$

Since I_C leads the assumed voltage by 90° and I_L lags the assumed voltage by 90°, they are plotted with the assumed voltage as reference vector as shown in Fig. 34–6. Then the total current I_t that would flow because of assumed voltage would be the vector sum of I_C and I_L. Adding vectorially,

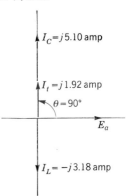

FIG. 34–6   Vector diagram for circuit of Example 1.

$$I_C = 0 + j5.10 \, \text{amp}$$
$$I_L = 0 - j3.18 \, \text{amp}$$
$$I_t = 0 + j1.92 \, \text{amp}$$

or

$$I_t = 1.92 \, \underline{/90°} \, \text{amp}$$

Again, since the total current leads the voltage by 90°, the equivalent series circuit consists of a capacitor whose capacitive reactance is

$$\frac{E_a}{I_t} = \frac{1,000}{1.92} = 521 \ \Omega$$

Since $\theta = 90°$, $\mathrm{pf} = \cos\theta = 0$

You should solve the circuit of Fig. 34-5, using different values of assumed voltages.

34-4 Resistance and inductance in parallel

When a resistance and an inductive reactance are connected in parallel, as represented in Fig. 34-7, currents flow that differ in phase by 90°.

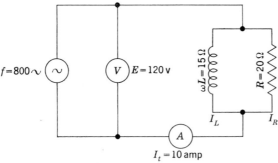

Fig. 34-7 R and X_L in parallel.

The current flowing through the resistance is

$$I_R = \frac{E}{R} = \frac{120}{20} = 6.0 \ \mathrm{amp}$$

and that through the inductance is

$$I_L = \frac{E}{\omega L} = \frac{120}{15} = 8.0 \ \mathrm{amp}$$

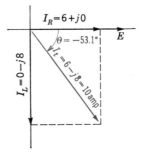

Fig. 34-8   Vector diagram for circuit of Fig. 34-7.

Since the current through the resistance is in phase with the applied voltage and the current through the inductance lags the applied voltage by 90°, I_R and I_L are plotted with the applied voltage as reference vector as shown in Fig. 34-8. Then the total current I_t, or line current, is the vector sum of I_R and I_L. Adding these vectorially,

$$I_R = 6.0 + j0 \quad \text{amp}$$
$$I_L = 0 \quad - j8.0 \text{ amp}$$
$$\overline{I_t = 6.0 - j8.0 \text{ amp}}$$

Hence, the total current, which consists of an inphase component of 6.0 amp and a 90° lagging component of 8.0 amp, is expressed in terms of its rectangular components. The magnitude and phase angle are then found by the usual trigonometric methods. Thus,

$$I_t = 10 \,\underline{/-53.1°} \text{ amp}$$

The power factor of the circuit is

$$\text{pf} = \cos \theta = \cos (-53.1°) = 0.60 \text{ lagging}$$

The power expended in the circuit is

$$P = EI \cos \theta = 120 \times 10 \times 0.60 = 720 \text{ watts}$$
or $$\qquad P = I_R{}^2 R = 6^2 \times 20 = 720 \text{ watts}$$

The joint impedance, or total impedance, of the circuit is

$$Z_t = \frac{E}{I_t} = \frac{120}{10} = 12 \ \Omega$$

Since the entire circuit has a lagging pf of 0.60, it follows that the equivalent series circuit consists of a resistance and an inductive reactance in series, the vector sum of which is 12 Ω at a phase angle θ such that cos θ = 0.60. Therefore, θ = 53.1°, and

$$Z_t = 12\underline{/53.1°} \ \Omega = 12 \ (\cos 53.1° + j \sin 53.1°) = 7.2 + j9.6 \ \Omega$$

From the foregoing, it is evident that the parallel circuit of Fig. 34–7 could be replaced by a series circuit of 7.2 Ω resistance and 9.6 Ω inductive reactance and that the alternator would be working under exactly the same load conditions as before.

In order to justify such solutions, solve for the joint impedance of the circuit of Fig. 34–7 by using an assumed voltage and then using the *actual* voltage to obtain the power.

34 – 5   Resistance and capacitance in parallel

When resistance and capacitive reactance are connected in parallel, as represented in Fig. 34–9, the current through the resistance is in phase with the voltage across the parallel combination, and the current through the capacitive reactance leads this voltage by 90°.

The circuit of Fig. 34–9 is similar to that of Fig. 34–7 except that Fig. 34–9 contains a capacitive reactance of 15 Ω in place of the

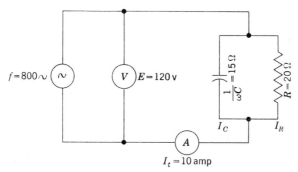

FIG. 34–9 R and X_C in parallel.

inductive reactance of 15 Ω. The vector diagram of currents is shown in Fig. 34–10, and it is evident that the total current is

$$I_t = 6.0 + j8.0 \text{ amp} = 10 \,/\underline{53.1°} \text{ amp}$$

The power factor of the circuit is

$$\text{pf} = \cos \theta = \cos 53.1° = 0.60 \text{ leading}$$

Similarly, the total impedance of the circuit is 12 Ω; and since the circuit has a leading pf of 0.60, it follows that the equivalent series circuit consists of resistance and capacitive reactance in series the vector sum of which is 12 Ω at a phase angle θ such that $\cos \theta = 0.60$. Therefore,

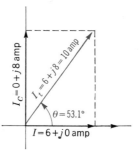

FIG. 34–10   Vector diagram for circuit of Fig. 34–9.

$$\theta = -53.1°$$
and $$Z_t = 12 \,/\underline{-53.1°} \text{ Ω} = 7.2 - j9.6 \text{ Ω}$$

If the parallel circuit of Fig. 34–9 was replaced by a series circuit of 7.2 Ω resistance and 9.6 Ω capacitive reactance, the alternator would be working under exactly the same load conditions as before.

34 – 6   Resistance, inductance, and capacitance in parallel

When resistance, inductive reactance, and capacitive reactance are connected in parallel, as represented in Fig. 34–11, the line current is the vector sum of the several currents.

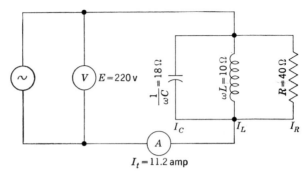

FIG. 34–11   *L, C,* and *R* in parallel.

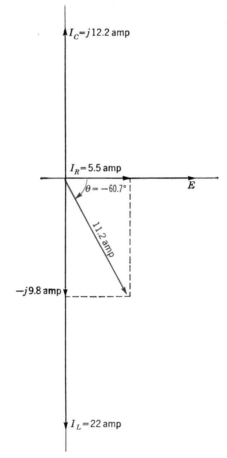

FIG. 34–12   Vector diagram for circuit of Fig. 34–11.

The currents through the branches are

$$I_R = {}^{220}\!/_{40} = 5.5 \text{ amp}$$
$$I_L = {}^{220}\!/_{10} = 22 \text{ amp}$$
and
$$I_C = {}^{220}\!/_{18} = 12.2 \text{ amp}$$

Adding these currents vectorially as shown in Fig. 34–12,

$$I_R = 5.5 + j0 \quad \text{amp}$$
$$I_L = 0 \quad - j22 \quad \text{amp}$$
$$I_C = 0 \quad + j12.2 \text{ amp}$$
$$\overline{I_t = 5.5 - j9.8 \text{ amp}} = 11.2 \,\underline{/-60.7°}\, \text{amp}$$
$$\text{pf} = \cos(-60.7°) = 0.489 \text{ lagging}$$

The total impedance is

$$Z_t = \frac{E}{I_t} = \frac{220}{11.2} = 19.6 \,\Omega$$

Since the circuit has a lagging pf of 0.489, the equivalent series circuit consists of a resistance and an inductive reactance. The vector sum of these must be 19.6 Ω at a phase angle θ such that $\cos\theta = 0.489$. Therefore, $\theta = 60.7°$ and

$$Z_t = 19.6 \,\underline{/60.7°}\, \Omega = 9.59 + j17.1 \,\Omega$$

which are the values comprising the equivalent series circuit.

EXAMPLE 2   Given the circuit represented in Fig. 34–13. Solve for the equivalent series circuit at a frequency of 5,000 kc.

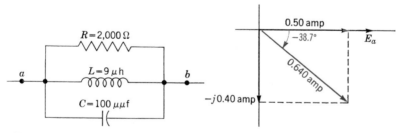

FIG. 34–13 Circuit of Example 2.   FIG. 34–14 Vector diagram of circuit of Fig. 34–13.

SOLUTION
$$f = 5{,}000 \text{ kc} = 5 \times 10^6 \text{ cps}$$
$$L = 9 \,\mu\text{h} = 9 \times 10^{-6} \text{ henry}$$
$$C = 100 \,\mu\mu\text{f} = 10^{-10} \text{ farad}$$
$$\omega = 2\pi f = 2\pi \times 5 \times 10^6 = 3.14 \times 10^7$$
$$X_L = \omega L = 3.14 \times 10^7 \times 9 \times 10^{-6} = 283 \,\Omega$$
$$X_C = \frac{1}{\omega C} = \frac{1}{3.14 \times 10^7 \times 10^{-10}} = \frac{10^3}{3.14} = 318 \,\Omega$$

Assume $E_a = 1,000$ volts applied between a and b.

$$I_R = \frac{E_a}{R} = \frac{1,000}{2,000} = 0.50 \text{ amp}$$

$$I_L = \frac{E_a}{X_L} = \frac{1,000}{283} = 3.54 \text{ amp}$$

$$I_C = \frac{E_a}{X_C} = \frac{1,000}{318} = 3.14 \text{ amp}$$

The total current I_t is the vector sum of the three branch currents as represented in the vector diagram of Fig. 34–14. Adding vectorially,

$$
\begin{aligned}
I_R &= 0.50 + j0 \quad \text{amp} \\
I_L &= 0 \quad - j3.54 \text{ amp} \\
I_C &= 0 \quad + j3.14 \text{ amp} \\
\hline
I_t &= 0.50 - j0.40 \text{ amp} = 0.640 \underline{/-38.7°} \text{ amp} \\
\text{pf} &= \cos(-38.7°) = 0.78 \text{ lagging}
\end{aligned}
$$

The total impedance Z_t, which is the impedance between points a and b, is

$$Z_t = Z_{ab} = \frac{E_a}{I_t} = \frac{1,000}{0.64} = 1,560 \ \Omega$$

Since the current is lagging the voltage, the equivalent series circuit consists of a resistance and an inductive reactance. The vector sum of these is $1,560 \ \Omega$ at a phase angle θ such that $\cos\theta = 0.78$. Therefore, $\theta = 38.7°$ and

$$Z_t = 1,560 \underline{/38.7°} \ \Omega = 1,220 + j976 \ \Omega$$

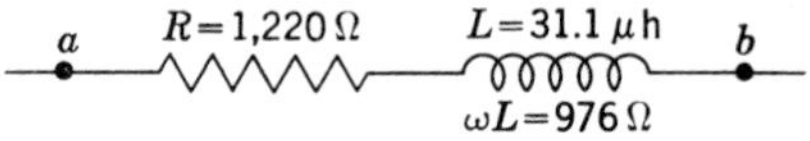

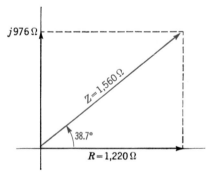

Fig. 34–15 Equivalent series circuit.

Fig. 34–16 Vector diagram for equivalent series circuit.

That is, the equivalent series circuit is a resistance of $R = 1,220$ Ω and an inductive reactance of $\omega L = 976$ Ω. Since

$$\omega L = 976 \ \Omega$$

then
$$L = \frac{976}{\omega} = \frac{976}{3.14 \times 10^7} = 31.1 \ \mu\text{h}$$

which results in the equivalent circuit as represented in Fig. 34–15 with the vector diagram of Fig. 34–16.

PROBLEMS 34 – 1

1 In Fig. 34–17, $R = 250$ Ω, $L = 0.5$ henry, $C = 4$ μf, $f = 60$ cps, and $E = 440$ volts.
  (a) What is the reading of the ammeter?
  (b) How much power is expended in the circuit?
  (c) What is the equivalent series circuit?
2 In Fig. 34–17, $R = 8,000$ Ω, $L = 120$ μh, $C = 350$ μμf, $f = 750$ kc, and $E = 1,000$ volts.
  (a) What is the reading of the ammeter?
  (b) What is the pf of the circuit?
  (c) What is the equivalent series circuit?

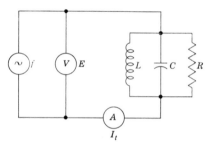

3 Using the values of Prob. 2, what capacitance must be connected in parallel with C in order to obtain a circuit pf of 1.0?

FIG. 34–17   Circuit for Probs. 1 to 5.

4 Using the values of Prob. 2, (a) at what frequency would the circuit have a pf of 1.0, (b) what is the impedance of the circuit at this frequency?
5 In Fig. 34–17, $R = 600$ Ω, $L = 0.03$ henry, $C = 1$ μf, $f = 800$ cps, and $E = 120$ volts.
  (a) What is the reading of the ammeter?
  (b) What capacitance must be connected in parallel with C in order to obtain a circuit pf of 1.0?

34 – 7   Vector impedances in parallel

Figure 34–18 represents an alternator supplying 220 volts across two paralleled impedances.
   The impedance of branch a is

$$Z_a = R_a + jX_L = 35 + j50 = 61 \ \underline{/55°} \ \Omega$$

and the current through this branch is

$$I_a = \frac{E}{Z_a} = \frac{220}{61} = 3.61 \text{ amp}$$

Similarly, $Z_b = R_b - jX_C = 75 - j30 = 80.8 \;\underline{/-21.8°}\; \Omega$

and $I_b = \dfrac{E}{Z_b} = \dfrac{220}{80.8} = 2.72 \text{ amp}$

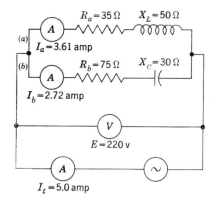

FIG. 34–18   Vector impedances in parallel.

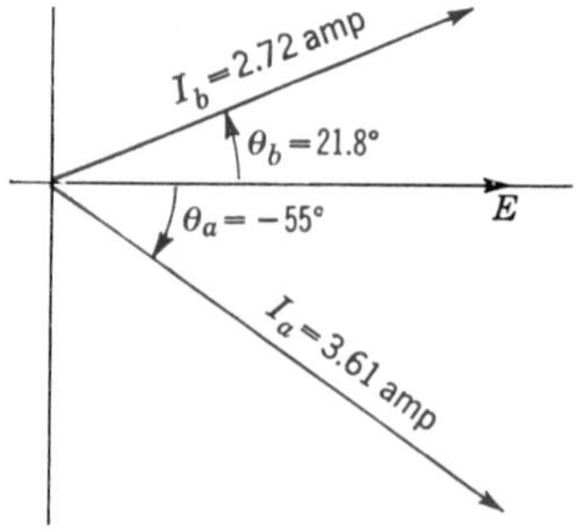

FIG. 34–19   Vector diagram for circuit of Fig. 34–18.

Figure 34–19 is the vector diagram of the branch currents I_a and I_b. The applied voltage E is used as reference vector because it is common to both impedances, or branches.   Note that the angles of the current vectors are opposite in sign to those of their respective impedances.   That is, I_a lags the applied voltage, whereas I_b leads the voltage.

The applied voltage E must be divided by the current I_t in order to obtain the total impedance of the circuit Z_t.   The total current, or line current, is the vector sum of the branch currents I_a and I_b and can be found by graphical methods, as explained in Sec. 31–3. However, the vector sum of two or more vectors is found readily and accurately by the addition of their respective rectangular components.   Hence, the resistive, or *inphase*, component of I_a is

$$I_a \cos \theta_a = 3.61 \cos (-55°) = 2.07 \text{ amp}$$

and the reactive component is

$$I_a \sin \theta_a = 3.61 \sin (-55°) = -2.96 \text{ amp}$$

Similarly, the resistive component of I_b is

$$I_b \cos \theta_b = 2.72 \cos 21.8° = 2.53 \text{ amp}$$

and the reactive component is

$$I_b \sin \theta_b = 2.72 \sin 21.8° = 1.01 \text{ amp}$$

The above process of determining the rectangular components of the vectors is simply a matter of converting the vectors from polar form to rectangular form, as explained in Sec. 33–13. This conversion is more compactly written

$$I_a = 3.61[\cos(-55°) + j\sin(-55°)] = 2.07 - j2.96 \text{ amp}$$
$$I_b = 2.72(\cos 21.8° + j\sin 21.8°) \quad\;\; = \underline{2.53 + j1.01} \text{ amp}$$
$$I_t = 4.60 - j1.95 \text{ amp}$$

The total current I_t is now expressed in terms of its rectangular components, which consist of a resistive component of 4.60 amp and a lagging component of 1.95 amp. The magnitude of I_t and the phase angle are found by the usual methods of vector addition. Thus,

$$I_t = 4.60 - j1.95 = 5.00 \; \underline{/-23°} \text{ amp}$$

As with all a-c problems, vector diagrams should be drawn in order to clarify the various relations and to serve as an approximate check on the results obtained by computations. Thus, the magnitude and direction of I_t can be checked by graphical vector addition by either of the methods explained in Sec. 31–3. The first method is utilized in Fig. 34–20, and the second method in Fig. 34–21.

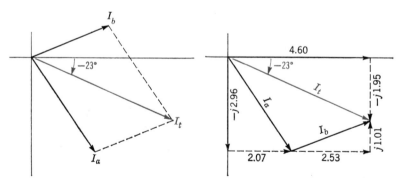

FIG. 34–20 I_t is the vector sum of I_a and I_b.

FIG. 34–21   Second method of obtaining I_t graphically.

Since the current is lagging the voltage by 23° in the external circuit, the equivalent series circuit must be a resistance and an inductive reactance. Hence,

$$Z_t = \frac{E}{I_t} = \frac{220}{5} = 44 \underline{/23°}\ \Omega$$
$$= 44(\cos 23° + j\sin 23°) = 40.5 + j17.2\ \Omega$$
$$\text{pf} = \cos 23° = 0.920 \text{ lagging}$$
$$P = EI \cos \theta = 220 \times 5 \times \cos 23° = 1{,}010 \text{ watts}$$
or
$$P = I^2R = 5^2 \times 40.5 = 1{,}010 \text{ watts}$$

EXAMPLE 3   A 60-cycle alternator delivers 110 volts to a load that consists of seventy-five 100-watt lamps and a 15-hp induction motor that operates at 90 per cent efficiency with a pf of 0.80 lagging. How much current is supplied by the alternator, and what is the pf?

SOLUTION   The current taken by the lamps, which can be considered as a resistive load, is

$$I_L = \frac{75 \times 100}{110} = 68.2 \text{ amp}$$

The power delivered to the motor is

$$P = \frac{746 \times 15}{0.90} = 12.4 \text{ kw}$$

Then, since $P = EI$ pf

the current taken by the motor is

$$I_M = \frac{P}{E \text{ pf}} = \frac{12{,}400}{110 \times 0.80} = 141 \text{ amp}$$

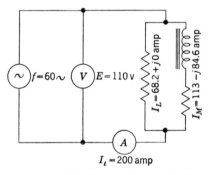

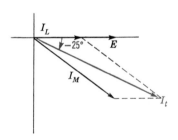

FIG. 34–22   Circuit of Example 3.   FIG. 34–23   Vector diagram for circuit of Example 3.

which consists of a resistive component and a lagging reactive component. The phase angle θ is 36.9° (pf $= \cos \theta = 0.8$). That is,

$$I_M = 141 \underline{/-36.9°} \text{ amp} = 141[\cos(-36.9°) + j\sin(-36.9°)]$$
$$= 113 - j84.6 \text{ amp}$$

The circuit is represented in Fig. 34–22 and the vector diagram of the currents in Fig. 34–23.

The current I_t supplied by the alternator is the vector sum of the load currents I_L and I_M. Hence,

$$
\begin{aligned}
I_L &= 68.2 + j0 \quad \text{amp} \\
I_M &= 113 - j84.6 \text{ amp} \\
\hline
I_t &= 181.2 - j84.6 \text{ amp} \\
&= 200 \;/\!-25° \text{ amp} \\
\text{pf} &= \cos\,(-25°) = 0.906 \text{ lagging}
\end{aligned}
$$

or
$$
\text{pf} = \frac{181.2}{200} = 0.906 \text{ lagging}
$$

34 – 8 Summarized procedure for solving parallel circuits by the total current method

1. Draw a neat, simplified diagram of the circuit.

2. Label, on the diagram, all the known values such as voltages, currents, resistances, reactances, and impedances.

3. Carefully study the circuit so that all relations are understood.

4. Find the vector impedance (polar form) of each parallel branch.

5. If the voltage across a parallel branch is not known, assume a voltage to be across it.

6. Divide the voltage of step 5, either actual or assumed, by the vector impedance of each parallel branch. The quotient is the vector current through the branch and must be assigned an angle equal in magnitude but opposite in sign to the respective impedance.

7. Resolve the currents through the parallel branches into their rectangular components, and add them. This sum represents the rectangular components of the total current through the parallel combination.

8. Find the vector current (polar form) of the total current found in step 7.

9. Divide the voltage of step 5 by the vector current found in step 8. The quotient is the joint vector impedance of the parallel combination and must be assigned an angle equal in magnitude but opposite in sign to the total current found in step 8.

10. Resolve the joint impedance found in step 9 into an equivalent series circuit.

11. The equivalent series circuit found in step 10 can be combined with other series resistances and reactances in order to find the total impedance of the circuit.

12. Draw vector diagrams throughout the solution. These will help in understanding circuit conditions and will serve as a valuable check to computations.

EXAMPLE 4   Given the circuit of Fig. 34–24. Solve for the equivalent series circuit Z_t, the total current I_t, the power expended in the circuit, and the power factor.

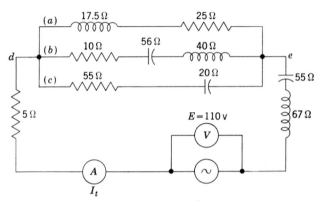

FIG. 34–24 Circuit of Example 4.

SOLUTION   Although you are familiar with the mathematical methods involved in this solution, all steps will be shown because everything learned regarding series and parallel circuits must be utilized.

The numbered parts of the solution correspond to those in the summary above. The three parallel branches are marked (a), (b), and (c). These letters will be used as subscripts to represent quantities involved in the respective branches. Thus, Z_a is the impedance of branch (a), I_b is the current through branch (b), etc.

Step 4 $Z_a = R + jX_L = 25 + j17.5$ Ω

$$\theta_a = \arctan \frac{X_L}{R_a} = \frac{17.5}{25} = 0.700$$

$\therefore \theta_a = 35°$

$$Z_a = \frac{X_L}{\sin \theta_a} = \frac{17.5}{\sin 35°} = \frac{17.5}{0.574} = 30.5 \ \Omega = 30.5 \ \underline{/35°} \ \Omega$$

$Z_b = R + j(X_L - X_C) = 10 - j16$ Ω

$$\theta_b = \arctan \frac{X_C}{R_b} = \frac{16}{10} = 1.6$$

$\therefore \theta_b = -58°$

$$Z_b = \frac{X_C}{\sin \theta_b} = \frac{16}{\sin 58°} = \frac{16}{0.848} = 18.9 \ \Omega$$

$$\therefore Z_b = 18.9 \;\underline{/-58°}\; \Omega$$
$$Z_c = R - jX_C = 55 - j20 \; \Omega$$
$$\theta_c = \arctan \frac{X_C}{R_c} = \frac{20}{55} = 0.364$$

$$\therefore \theta_c = -20°$$
$$Z_c = \frac{X_C}{\sin \theta_c} = \frac{20}{\sin 20°} = \frac{20}{0.342} = 58.5 \; \Omega$$
$$\therefore Z_c = 58.5 \;\underline{/-20°}\; \Omega$$

Step 5. Because the actual voltage across the parallel combination is not known, a voltage must be assumed. Therefore, assume that 100 volts exists across d and e.

Step 6 $\quad I_a = \dfrac{E_{de}}{Z_a} = \dfrac{100}{30.5} = 3.28 \;\underline{/-35°}\; \text{amp}$

$\qquad\quad I_b = \dfrac{E_{de}}{Z_b} = \dfrac{100}{18.9} = 5.30 \;\underline{/58°}\; \text{amp}$

$\qquad\quad I_c = \dfrac{E_{de}}{Z_c} = \dfrac{100}{58.5} = 1.71 \;\underline{/20°}\; \text{amp}$

Step 7 $\quad I_a = I_a(\cos \theta_a + j \sin \theta_a) = 3.28[\cos (-35°) + j \sin (-35°)]$
$\qquad\qquad = 2.69 - j1.88 \; \text{amp}$
$\qquad\quad I_b = I_b(\cos \theta_b + j \sin \theta_b) = 5.30(\cos 58° + j \sin 58°)$
$\qquad\qquad = 2.81 + j4.50 \; \text{amp}$
$\qquad\quad I_c = I_c(\cos \theta_c + j \sin \theta_c) = 1.71(\cos 20° + j \sin 20°)$
$\qquad\qquad = 1.61 + j0.585 \; \text{amp}$

The total current I_t in rectangular form is the sum of I_a, I_b, and I_c.

$$I_a = 2.69 - j1.88 \; \text{amp}$$
$$I_b = 2.81 + j4.50 \; \text{amp}$$
$$I_c = 1.61 + j0.585 \; \text{amp}$$
$$\overline{I_t = 7.11 + j3.205 \; \text{amp}}$$

Step 8 $\quad \theta_{de} = \arctan \dfrac{\text{reactive component of } I_t}{\text{resistive component of } I_t} = \dfrac{3.20}{7.11} = 0.450$

$\qquad\qquad = \underline{/24.2°}$

$\qquad\quad I_{de} = \dfrac{\text{reactive component of } I_{de}}{\sin \theta_{de}} = \dfrac{3.20}{\sin 24.2°} = 7.80 \; \text{amp}$

or $\qquad I_{de} = \dfrac{\text{resistive component of } I_{de}}{\cos \theta_{de}} = \dfrac{7.11}{\cos 24.2°} = 7.80 \; \text{amp}$

$\qquad\qquad = 7.80 \;\underline{/24.2°}\; \text{amp}$

Step 9

$$Z_{de} = \frac{E_{de}}{I_{de}} = \frac{100}{7.80} = 12.8 \;\underline{/-24.2°}\; \Omega$$

Step 10
$$Z_{de} = Z_{de}(\cos \theta + j \sin \theta) = 12.8[\cos (-24.2°) + j \sin (-24.2°)]$$
$$= 11.7 - j5.26 \ \Omega$$

Step 11.   The resistance and reactance in series with the parallel combination make up a series impedance Z_s that is in series with the equivalent series impedance Z_{de} of the paralleled branches.   Therefore, the vector sum of Z_s and Z_{de} is the equivalent series impedance of the entire circuit.   Thus,

$$
\begin{array}{l}
Z_{de} = 11.7 - j5.26 \ \Omega \\
\underline{Z_s = \ \ 5 \ \ + j12 \ \Omega} \\
Z_t = 16.7 + j6.74 \ \Omega
\end{array}
$$

$$\theta_t = \arctan \frac{X_t}{R_t} = \frac{6.74}{16.7} = 0.404$$

$$\therefore \theta_t = 22°$$

$$Z_t = \frac{X_t}{\sin \theta_t} = \frac{6.74}{\sin 22°} = 18.0 \ \underline{/22°} \ \Omega$$

$$I_t = \frac{E}{Z_t} = \frac{110}{18.0} = 6.11 \ \text{amp}$$

$$P = EI_t \cos \theta_t = 110 \times 6.11 \times \cos 22° = 623 \ \text{watts}$$

or
$$P = I_t^2 R_t = 6.11^2 \times 16.7 = 623 \ \text{watts}$$

$$\text{pf} = \cos \theta_t = \cos 22° = 0.927 \ \text{lagging}$$

Figure 34–25 is the vector diagram for the current relations in the parallel branches, and the impedance diagram for the entire circuit is shown in Fig. 34–26.

Although the solutions of such circuits involve a large number of computations, time and labor are saved in working all problems

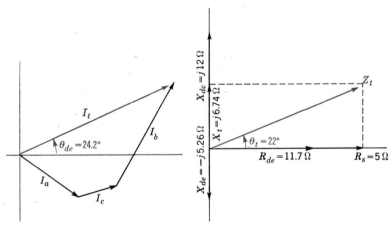

FIG. 34–25   Vector diagram for currents.

FIG. 34–26   Impedance vector diagram.

by careful planning. In addition, the student who does not use a slide rule should endeavor to become proficient in the use of the tables.

Proficiency in the operation of a slide rule will enable you to solve such circuits in a fraction of the time required for solutions made by ordinary computations.

PROBLEMS 34 – 2

1   Impedances $Z_a = 30 + j36$ and $Z_b = 76 - j50$ are connected in parallel. If a potential difference of 440 volts is impressed across them, determine (a) the equivalent series impedance of the circuit, (b) the power expended in the circuit.

2   An alternator supplies 220 volts across a load consisting of impedances $Z_a = 55 \underline{/40°}\ \Omega$ and $Z_b = 71 \underline{/-36°}\ \Omega$ in parallel. Find (a) the pf of the load, (b) the power expended in Z_b.

3   An induction motor, which takes 85 amp at a lagging pf of 80 per cent from a 440-volt line, is operating in parallel with a synchronous motor that draws 50 amp at a pf of 60 per cent leading.

    (a) What is the line current?

    (b) What is the pf of the combination?

    (c) What is the power taken from the line?

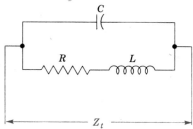

4   In Fig. 34–27, $R = 50\ \Omega$, $L = 0.705$ henry, and $C = 10\ \mu f$. At a frequency of 50 cycles, find (a) total impedance Z_t, (b) equivalent series circuit, (c) pf.

Fig. 34–27   Circuit for Probs. 4 to 9.

5   Work Prob. 4, using a frequency of 60 cycles.

6   Work Prob. 4, using a frequency of 70 cycles.

7   In Fig. 34–27, $R = 17\ \Omega$, $L = 180\ \mu h$, and $C = 250\ \mu\mu f$. At a frequency of 730 kc, find (a) total impedance Z_t, (b) equivalent series circuit, (c) pf.

8   Work Prob. 7, using a frequency of 750 kc.

9   Work Prob. 7, using a frequency of 770 kc.

10 An 800-cycle alternator supplies 120 volts to an impedance of $9.16\underline{/40.2°}\ \Omega$.

    (a) How much current is supplied by the alternator?

    (b) What sized capacitor must be connected in parallel with the impedance in order to make the combination a load of unity pf?

(c) How much current will be taken from the alternator after the capacitor is connected across the impedance?

11 A 16-μf capacitor must be connected in parallel with a load Z_R in order to obtain unity pf. This results in a current of 10 amp at 120 volts from an 800-cycle alternator.

(a) How much current did the alternator supply to the load before connecting the capacitor?

(b) What was the pf of the load before connecting the capacitor?

(c) What is the equivalent series impedance of Z_R?

(d) How much power is expended in the load?

12 A 60-cycle alternator supplies 440 volts, 6.64 amp to a coil. When a 20-μf capacitor is connected in parallel with the coil, the line pf becomes unity.

(a) What is the effective resistance of the coil?

(b) What is the inductance of the coil?

13 Two separate shops are supplied with a-c power from the same alternator. The load taken by one shop is 64 kw at a pf of 0.80 lagging. The total load on the alternator is 130 kw at a pf of 0.65 lagging. What is the pf of the other shop?

14 A load consisting of impedances $Z_a = 25 - j18.5$, $Z_b = 75 + j30$, and $Z_c = 10 - j15$ is connected in parallel across an alternator with an internal impedance of $Z_s = 1.5 + j2.6$. If the emf of the alternator is 260 volts, find (a) current taken by the load, (b) power taken by the load.

15 The load on a 230-volt 60-cycle alternator consists of a 50-hp motor with a pf of 87 per cent lagging and an efficiency of 85 per cent, a lighting load of 10 kw with unity pf, and a synchronous motor that takes 100 amp with a pf of 55 per cent leading.

(a) How much power is taken by the entire load?

(b) How much current is taken by the 50-hp motor?

16 An induction motor (lagging pf) draws 37.1 amp from a 440-volt 60-cycle line. A resistance across the line draws 19 amp. An ammeter connected in the line reads a total of 53.6 amp.

(a) What is the pf of the motor?

(b) How much power is taken by the motor?

(c) What sized capacitor must be connected across the line in order to reduce the line current to unity pf?

17 In Fig. 34–28, let $R_1 = 50$ Ω, $R_2 = 100$ Ω, $R_3 = 100$ Ω, $L = 10$ μh, $C = 100$ μμf, and $f = 5,000$ kc.

(a) What is the impedance Z_t across the alternator?

(b) If a current of 287 ma flows through R_3, what is the alternator voltage E?

18 In Fig. 34–28, let $R_1 = 10\ \Omega$, $R_2 = 250\ \Omega$, $R_3 = 200\ \Omega$, $L = 120\ \mu h$, $C = 150\ \mu\mu f$, and $f = 1,200$ kc.

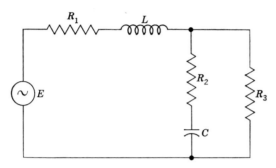

FIG. 34–28   Circuit for Probs. 17, 18, and 19.

(a) What is the impedance across the alternator?
(b) If a potential difference of 11.3 volts exists across R_1, what is the alternator voltage E?

19 In Fig. 34–28, let $R_1 = 40\ \Omega$, $R_2 = 500\ \Omega$, $R_3 = 1,000\ \Omega$, $L = 0.15$ henry, $C = 2\ \mu f$, and $f = 1,000$ cycles.
(a) What is the impedance of the circuit?
(b) What is the pf of the circuit?
(c) If a potential difference of 2.84 volts exists across R_2, what is the alternator voltage E?

20 In Fig. 34–29, let $R_1 = 200\ \Omega$, $R_2 = 100\ \Omega$, $R_3 = 150\ \Omega$, $R_4 = 5\ \Omega$, $\omega L_1 = 39.6\ \Omega$, $X_C = 53.2\ \Omega$, $\omega L_2 = 450\ \Omega$, $\omega L_3 = 3\ \Omega$, and $E = 220$ volts. Find (a) line current I_t, (b) circuit pf, (c) potential difference between points a and b, (d) current through R_3.

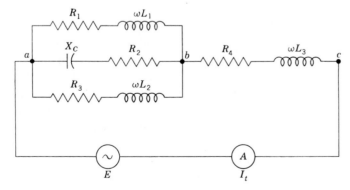

FIG. 34–29   Circuit for Probs. 20 to 24.

21 In Fig. 34–29, let $R_1 = 5\,\Omega$, $R_2 = 15\,\Omega$, $R_3 = 10\,\Omega$, $R_4 = 1.5\,\Omega$, $\omega L_1 = 22\,\Omega$, $X_C = 8\,\Omega$, $\omega L_2 = 31\,\Omega$, $\omega L_3 = 2.1\,\Omega$, and $E = 100$ volts. Find (*a*) line current I_t, (*b*) circuit pf, (*c*) potential difference across capacitor, (*d*) current through R_1.

22 In Prob. 21, if the frequency is 800 cycles, what sized capacitor must be connected across points *a* and *c* in order to reduce the line current to unity pf?

23 In Fig. 34–29, let $R_1 = 3\,\Omega$, $R_2 = 5\,\Omega$, $R_3 = 12\,\Omega$, $R_4 = 4\,\Omega$, $\omega L_1 = 4.8\,\Omega$, $X_C = 4.66\,\Omega$, $\omega L_2 = 7.5\,\Omega$, and $\omega L_3 = 6\,\Omega$. If the potential difference across the capacitor is 26.4 volts, find (*a*) line current I_t, (*b*) alternator voltage E, (*c*) circuit pf, (*d*) difference of potential across points *b* and *c*.

24 In Prob. 23, how much current will flow through R_3 if points *b* and *c* are short-circuited?

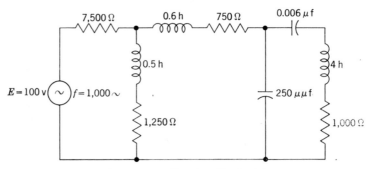

FIG. 34–30   Circuit of Prob. 25.

25 Given the circuit of Fig. 34–30, (*a*) what is the impedance of the circuit, (*b*) how much current is taken from the alternator, (*c*) would the removal of the 250-μμf capacitor cause an appreciable change in the total current?

34 – 9 Parallel resonance

Communication circuits and electronic networks contain resonant parallel circuits. Figure 34–31 represents a typical parallel circuit consisting of an inductor and capacitor in parallel. The resistance of the capacitor, which is very small, can be neglected, and the resistance *R* represents the effective resistance of the inductor.

At low frequencies the inductive reactance is a low value whereas the capacitive reactance is high. Hence, a large current flows through the inductive branch, and a small current flows through the capacitive branch. The vector sum of these currents causes a large lagging line current which, in effect, results in an equivalent series

circuit of low impedance consisting of resistance and inductive reactance. At high frequencies the inductive reactance is large and the
capacitive reactance is small. This results in a large leading line
current with an attendant equivalent series circuit of low impedance
consisting of resistance and capac-
itive reactance.

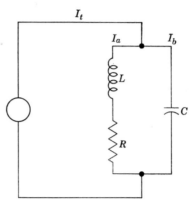

There is one frequency, between
those mentioned above, at which
the lagging component of current
through the inductive branch is
equal to the leading current
through the capacitive branch.
This condition results in a small
line current that is in phase with
the voltage across the parallel circuit and therefore an impedance
that is equivalent to a very high
resistance.

FIG. 34–31   Parallel LC circuit. R
represents effective resistance of L.

The resonant frequency of a
parallel circuit is often a source of confusion to the student studying
parallel resonance for the first time. The reason for this is that different definitions for the resonant frequency are encountered in various
texts. Thus, the resonant frequency of a parallel circuit can be
defined by any one of the following as:

1. The frequency at which the parallel circuit acts as a pure
resistance.

2. The frequency at which the line current becomes minimum.

3. The frequency at which the inductive reactance equals the
capacitive reactance. This is the same definition as that for the
resonant frequency of a series circuit. That is,

$$\omega L = \frac{1}{\omega C}$$

or
$$f = \frac{1}{2\pi\sqrt{LC}}$$ [1]

A little consideration of these definitions will convince you that,
in high Q circuits, the three resonant frequencies differ by an amount
so small as to be negligible.

In the circuit of Fig. 34–31,

$$I_b = \frac{E}{1/\omega C} = \omega CE$$

Also, $$I_a = \frac{E}{R + j\omega L}$$

Rationalizing (Sec. 23–17),

$$I_a = \frac{E}{R + j\omega L} \cdot \frac{R - j\omega L}{R - j\omega L} = \frac{E(R - j\omega L)}{R^2 + (\omega L)^2}$$

$$= \frac{ER}{R^2 + (\omega L)^2} - j\,\frac{\omega LE}{R^2 + (\omega L)^2}$$

In order to satisfy the first definition for resonant frequency, the line current must be in phase with the applied voltage; that is, the out-of-phase, or quadrature, component of the current through the inductive branch must be equal to the current through the capacitive branch. Thus,

$$\frac{\omega LE}{R^2 + (\omega L)^2} = \omega CE$$

D:ωE, $$\frac{L}{R^2 + (\omega L)^2} = C$$

M:$[R^2 + (\omega L)^2]$, $$L = [R^2 + (\omega L)^2]C \qquad [\,2\,]$$

or $$\frac{L}{C} - R^2 = (\omega L)^2$$

Hence, $$\omega = \frac{\sqrt{L/C - R^2}}{L} = \sqrt{\frac{1}{LC} - \frac{R^2}{L^2}}$$

Substituting $2\pi f$ for ω, $$2\pi f = \sqrt{\frac{1}{LC} - \frac{R^2}{L^2}}$$

Thus, the resonant frequency is

$$f = \frac{1}{2\pi}\sqrt{\frac{1}{LC} - \frac{R^2}{L^2}} \qquad [\,3\,]$$

If the Q of the inductance is at all large, then $\omega L \gg R$, which, for all practical purposes, makes the term R^2/L^2 in Eq. [3] of such low value that it can be neglected, Eq. [3] being thus reduced to Eq. [1].

Similarly, it can be shown that the condition of maximum impedance, as given in the second definition of parallel resonance, will be obtained when

$$f = \frac{1}{2\pi}\sqrt{\frac{1}{LC} - \frac{R^4 C}{2L^3}} \qquad [\,4\,]$$

Equation [4] is similar to Eq. [3] in that both will reduce to Eq. [1] for nearly all radio circuits. Work out several examples, using different circuit values, and compare the resonant frequencies obtained from the formulas. In this connection, it is left as an exercise to show that in a parallel-resonant circuit, as represented in Fig. 34-31, the line current and applied voltage will be in phase (unity power factor) when

$$R^2 = X_L(X_C - X_L)$$ [5]

— 10 Impedance of parallel-resonant circuits

When a parallel circuit is operating at the frequency at which the circuit acts as a pure resistance, the circuit has unity pf and the line current I_t (Fig. 34-31) consists of the inphase component of I_a. That is,

$$I_t = \frac{ER}{R^2 + (\omega L)^2}$$ [6]

Then, since $$Z_t = \frac{E}{I_t}$$

substituting in Eq. [6] for I_t,

$$\frac{E}{Z_t} = \frac{ER}{R^2 + (\omega L)^2}$$

Hence, $$Z_t = \frac{R^2 + (\omega L)^2}{R}$$ [7]

From Eq. [2], $$R^2 + (\omega L)^2 = \frac{L}{C}$$

Substituting this value in Eq. [7],

$$Z_t = \frac{L}{CR}$$ [8]

EXAMPLE 5   In the circuit of Fig. 34-31, let $L = 203$ μh, $C = 500$ $\mu\mu$f, and $R = 6.7\,\Omega$. (a) What is the resonant frequency of the circuit? (b) What is the impedance of the circuit at resonance?

SOLUTION

(a) $$f = \frac{1}{2\pi\sqrt{LC}} = \frac{1}{2\pi\sqrt{2.03 \times 10^{-4} \times 5 \times 10^{-10}}} = 500\,\text{kc}$$

(b) $$Z_t = \frac{L}{CR} = \frac{203 \times 10^{-6}}{500 \times 10^{-12} \times 6.7} = \frac{203}{5 \times 6.7} \times 10^4 = 60,600\,\Omega$$

If the value of C is unknown, Eq. [8] can be used in different form. Thus, by multiplying both numerator and denominator by ω,

$$Z_t = \frac{\omega L}{\omega C R} = \frac{1}{\omega C}\frac{\omega L}{R}$$

Since at resonance, $$\omega L = \frac{1}{\omega C}$$

then $$Z_t = \frac{(\omega L)^2}{R} \qquad [9]$$

Moreover, since $$Q = \frac{\omega L}{R}$$

substituting in Eq. [9], $$Z_t = \omega L Q \qquad [10]$$

EXAMPLE 6   In the circuit of Fig. 34–31, let $L = 70.4 \; \mu h$ and $R = 5.31 \; \Omega$. If the resonant frequency of the circuit is 1,200 kc, determine (a) impedance of the circuit at resonance, (b) the capacitance of the capacitor.

SOLUTION $f = 1{,}200 \text{ kc} = 1.2 \times 10^6 \text{ cycles}$

$\omega = 2\pi f = 2\pi \times 1.2 \times 10^6 = 7.54 \times 10^6$

(a) $$Z_t = \frac{(\omega L)^2}{R} = \frac{(7.54 \times 10^6 \times 70.4 \times 10^{-6})^2}{5.31} = 53{,}100 \; \Omega$$

(b) Since, at resonance, $\omega L = 1/\omega C$ and $\omega L = 531 \; \Omega$,

then $$\frac{1}{\omega C} = 531 \; \Omega$$

Hence, $$C = \frac{1}{531\omega} = 250 \; \mu\mu f$$

What is the Q of this circuit?

PROBLEMS 34 – 3

1 An inductor of 24 μh and a capacitor of 75 $\mu\mu f$ are connected in parallel as shown in Fig. 34–31. If the effective resistance of the coil is 113 Ω, find (a) resonant frequency of circuit according to Definition 1 (Sec. 34–9), (b) resonant frequency of circuit according to Definition 2 (Sec. 34–9), (c) resonant frequency of circuit according to Definition 3 (Sec. 34–9), (d) Q of the inductance.

2 Repeat Prob. 1, but with the inductance having an effective resistance of 56.5 Ω.

3 An inductor of 14 μh with a Q of 100 is connected in parallel with a capacitor of 32.2 $\mu\mu f$.
    (a) What is the resonant frequency of the circuit?
    (b) What is the impedance of the circuit at resonance?
    (c) What is the effective resistance of the inductor?

4 How much power will be expended in the circuit of Prob. 3 if the impressed voltage across the parallel combination is 1,000 volts at the resonant frequency?

5   An inductor of 100 μh with a Q of 90 is connected in parallel with a capacitor of 254 $\mu\mu$f.
    (a) What is the resonant frequency of the circuit?
    (b) What is the impedance of the circuit at resonance?
    (c) What is the effective resistance of the inductor?

6   How much power will be expended in the circuit of Prob. 5 if the impressed voltage across the parallel combination is 100 volts at the resonant frequency?

7   A capacitor of 500 $\mu\mu$f is connected in parallel with an inductor. The resonant frequency was found by measurement to be 356 kc. The impedance of the circuit was measured at the resonant frequency and found to be 64,000 Ω. What is the Q of the inductor?

8   An inductor was measured with a Q meter and found to have a Q of 120. When a capacitor was connected in parallel with the inductor, the resulting parallel circuit was resonant at 450 kc with an impedance of 84,000 Ω. What is the value of the inductor?

9   What is the capacitance of the capacitor in Prob. 8?

10 A capacitor of 200 $\mu\mu$f is connected across an inductance. When 1,000 volts, at the resonant frequency of 1,500 kc, is applied across this parallel circuit, the resulting line current is 18.9 ma. What is the Q of the inductance?

CHAPTER 35

VECTOR ALGEBRA

In the analysis of a-c circuits, it is often desirable to treat voltages, currents, and impedances algebraically in order to deal with circuit equations in general terms and simplify solutions. Moreover, many a-c problems are difficult to solve by the total-current method of solution described in Chap. 34.

Because alternating currents and voltages are vector rather than scalar quantities, a form of vector algebra is introduced in this chapter to facilitate a-c circuit analysis.

35 – 1   Addition and subtraction of vectors in rectangular form

Complex numbers were introduced in Sec. 23–14, and it was shown in Sec. 33–12 that a vector can be completely described in terms of its rectangular components by expressing it as a complex number. For example, a vector 10 units in length and operating at an angle of 36.9° can be expressed in *polar form* by writing $10/\underline{36.9°}$. The same vector, expressed in terms of its *rectangular components*, is written as the complex number $8 + j6$.

As stated in Sec. 23–15, complex numbers, or vectors in rectangular form, can be added or subtracted by treating them as ordinary binomials.

EXAMPLE 1   Add $4.60 + j2.82$ and $2.11 - j8.10$.

SOLUTION
$$4.60 + j2.82$$
$$\underline{2.11 - j8.10}$$
$$6.71 - j5.28$$

Expressing the sum in polar form,
$$6.71 - j5.28 = 8.54 \;\underline{/-38.2°}$$

EXAMPLE 2   Subtract $3.7 + j4.62$ from $14.6 - j8.84$.

SOLUTION
$$14.6 - j8.84$$
$$\underline{3.7 + j4.62}$$
$$10.9 - j13.46$$

Expressing the result in polar form,
$$10.9 - j13.46 = 17.3 \;\underline{/-51°}$$

PROBLEMS 35 – 1

Express the indicated sums in polar form. Check results by graphical methods.

1	$6.4 - j\,8.5$	2	$28.5 + j\,30.0$	3	$600 - j425$
	$10.3 + j19.8$		$71.1 - j115$		$500 + j825$
4	$-5.43 - j16.8$	5	$126 + j843$	6	$-439 + j143$
	$11.05 - j23.2$		$-568 - j102$		$123 - j578$

Perform the following indicated subtractions, expressing the results in polar form. Check results by graphical methods.

7	$25.9 - j46.8$	8	$6.73 - j\,1.20$	9	$600 - j\,800$
	$14.7 - j10.4$		$-8.17 + j12.4$		$900 - j1,200$
10	$80.9 - j45.2$				
	$143 + j40.6$				

35 – 2   Multiplication of vectors in rectangular form

Multiplication of complex numbers was explained in Sec. 23–16 where it was shown that vectors expressed in terms of their rectangular components are multiplied by treating them as ordinary binomials.

EXAMPLE 3   Multiply $8 + j5$ by $10 + j9$.

SOLUTION
$$8 + j5$$
$$\underline{10 + j9}$$
$$80 + j50$$
$$\underline{\quad\;\; + j72 + j^2 45}$$
$$80 + j122 + j^2 45$$

Since $j^2 = -1$, the product is

$$80 + j122 + (-1)45 = 80 + j122 - 45 = 35 + j122$$

Expressing the product in polar form,

$$35 + j122 = 127 \underline{/74°}$$

EXAMPLE 4   Multiply $80 + j39$ by $35 - j50$.

SOLUTION

$$80 + j39$$
$$35 - j50$$
$$\overline{2,800 + j1,365}$$
$$\quad\quad - j4,000 - j^21,950$$
$$\overline{2,800 - j2,635 - j^21,950}$$

Since $j^2 = -1$, the product is

$$2,800 - j2,635 - (-1)1,950 = 2,800 - j2,635 + 1,950 = 4,750 - j2,635$$

Expressing the product in polar form,

$$4,750 - j2,635 = 5,430 \underline{/-29°}$$

35 – 3   Division of vectors in rectangular form

As explained in Sec. 23–17, division of complex numbers, or vectors in rectangular form, is accomplished by rationalizing the denominator in order to obtain a "real" number for a divisor. Multiplying a complex number by its conjugate always results in a product that is a real number, that is, a number not affected by the operator j.

EXAMPLE 5   Find the quotient of $\dfrac{50 + j35}{8 + j5}$.

SOLUTION   Multiply both dividend and divisor (numerator and denominator) by the conjugate of the divisor, which is $8 - j5$.

Thus, $$\dfrac{50 + j35}{8 + j5} \cdot \dfrac{8 - j5}{8 - j5} = \dfrac{400 + j30 - j^2175}{64 - j^225} = \dfrac{575 + j30}{89}$$

That is, $$\dfrac{575 + j30}{89} = \dfrac{575}{89} + j\dfrac{30}{89} = 6.46 + j0.337$$

Expressing the quotient in polar form,

$$6.46 + j0.337 \cong 6.46 \underline{/3.0°}$$

EXAMPLE 6   Simplify $\dfrac{10}{3 + j4}$.

SOLUTION   Multiply both numerator and denominator by the conjugate of the denominator, which is $3 - j4$.

Thus, $$\dfrac{10}{3 + j4} \cdot \dfrac{3 - j4}{3 - j4} = \dfrac{10(3 - j4)}{9 - j^216} = \dfrac{30 - j40}{25} = 1.2 - j1.6$$

Expressing the quotient in polar form,

$$1.2 - j1.6 = 2.0/\underline{-53.1°}$$

PROBLEMS 35 – 2

Express the indicated products in polar form:

1   $(3 + j4)(3 - j6)$ 2 $(13 + j17)(23 + j11)$
3   $(3.4 + j9.3)(1.2 + j8.7)$ 4 $(180 - j35.0)(3.20 + j0.621)$
5   $(6.8 - j4.6)(5.5 - j7.2)$ 6 $(3 - j9)(2 - j8)$

Express the indicated quotients in polar form:

7   $\dfrac{6 + j8}{4 + j3}$ 8 $\dfrac{90 - j20}{35 - j73}$

9   $\dfrac{7 - j38}{5 + j13}$ 10 $\dfrac{1}{16 - j12}$

5 – 4   Addition and subtraction of polar vectors

As explained in previous sections, vectors expressed in polar form can be added or subtracted by graphical methods only unless their directions are parallel. In order to add or subtract them algebraically, they must be expressed in terms of their rectangular components.

EXAMPLE 7   Add $5.40\ /\underline{31.5°}$ and $8.37\ /\underline{-75.4°}$.

SOLUTION   Converting the vectors into their rectangular components,

$$5.40\ /\underline{31.5°} = 5.40(\cos 31.5° + j \sin 31.5°) = 4.60 + j2.82$$
$$8.37\ /\underline{-75.4°} = 8.37(\cos 75.4° - j \sin 75.4°) = 2.11 - j8.10$$

Adding,   Sum $= 6.71 - j5.28$

Expressing the sum in polar form,

$$6.71 - j5.28 = 8.54\ /\underline{-38.2°}$$

Note that the vectors of this example are the same as those of Example 1 of Sec. 35–1.

EXAMPLE 8   Subtract $5.92\ /\underline{51.3°}$ from $17.1\ /\underline{-31.2°}$.

SOLUTION   Converting the vectors into their rectangular components,

$$17.1\ /\underline{-31.2°} = 17.1(\cos 31.2° - j \sin 31.2°) = 14.6 - j8.86$$
$$5.92\ /\underline{51.3°} = 5.92(\cos 51.3° + j \sin 51.3°) = \underline{3.7 + j4.62}$$

Subtracting,   Result $= 10.9 - j13.48$

Expressing the result in polar form,

$$10.9 - j13.48 = 17.3\ /\underline{-51°}$$

Note that the vectors of this example are the same as those of Example 2 of Sec. 35–1.

PROBLEMS 35 – 3

Perform the indicated operations, expressing the results in polar form. Check results by graphical methods.

1   $10.6 \, \underline{/-53°} + 22.3 \, \underline{/62.5°}$ 2 $41.4 \, \underline{/46.5°} + 135 \, \underline{/-58.2°}$
3   $735 \, \underline{/-35.3°} + 965 \, \underline{/58.8°}$ 4 $17.7 \, \underline{/-107.9°} + 25.7 \, \underline{/-64.5°}$
5   $852 \, \underline{/81.5°} + 577 \, \underline{/-169.8°}$ 6 $462 \, \underline{/162°} + 591 \, \underline{/-78°}$
7   $53.5 \, \underline{/-61°} - 18.0 \, \underline{/-35.3°}$ 8 $6.84 \, \underline{/-10.1°} - 14.8 \, \underline{/123.4°}$
9   $1,000 \, \underline{/-53.1°} - 1,500 \, \underline{/-36.9°}$ 10 $92.7 \, \underline{/-29.2°} - 149 \, \underline{/15.9°}$

35 – 5 Multiplication of polar vectors

In Example 3 of Sec. 35–2, it was shown that

$$(8 + j5)(10 + j9) = 127 \, \underline{/74°}$$

Now $8 + j5 = 9.44 \, \underline{/32°}$

and $10 + j9 = 13.45 \, \underline{/42°}$

Multiplying the magnitudes and adding the angles,

$$(9.44 \times 13.45) \, \underline{/32° + 42°} = 127 \, \underline{/74°}$$

which is the same product as that obtained by multiplying the vectors when expressed in terms of their rectangular components.

Similarly, in Example 4 of Sec. 35–2, it was shown that

$$(80 + j39)(35 - j50) = 5{,}430 \, \underline{/-29°}$$

Now $80 + j39 = 89.0 \, \underline{/26°}$

and $35 - j50 = 61.0 \, \underline{/-55°}$

Multiplying the magnitudes and adding the angles,

$$(89 \times 61.0) \, \underline{/26° + (-55°)} = 5{,}430 \, \underline{/-29°}$$

which is the same product as that obtained by multiplying the vectors when expressed in terms of their rectangular components.

From the foregoing, it is evident that the product of two polar vectors is found by multiplying their magnitudes and adding their angles algebraically.

35 – 6 Division of polar vectors

In Example 5 of Sec. 35–3, it was shown that

$$\frac{50 + j35}{8 + j5} = 6.46 \, \underline{/3.0°}$$

Now $50 + j35 = 61.0 \, \underline{/35°}$

and $8 + j5 = 9.44 \, \underline{/32°}$

Dividing the magnitudes and subtracting the angle of the divisor from the angle of the dividend,

$$\frac{61.0\ /35°}{9.44\ /32°} = \frac{61.0}{9.44}\ /35° - 32° = 6.46\ /3.0°$$

which is the same quotient as that obtained by dividing the vectors when expressed in terms of their rectangular components.

Similarly, in Example 6 of Sec. 35–3, it was shown that

$$\frac{10}{3 + j4} = 2.0\ /-53.1°$$

Since 10 is a positive number, it is plotted on the 0° axis (Sec. 8–5) and expressed as

$$10\ /0°$$

Now $$3 + j4 = 5\ /53.1°$$

Dividing the magnitudes and subtracting the angle of the divisor from the angle of the dividend,

$$\frac{10\ /0°}{5\ /53.1°} = \frac{10}{5}\ /0° - 53.1° = 2.0\ /-53.1°$$

which is the same quotient as that obtained by dividing the vectors when expressed in terms of their rectangular components.

From the foregoing, it is evident that the quotient of two polar vectors is found by dividing their magnitudes and subtracting the angle of the divisor from the angle of the dividend.

5–7   Exponential form

In the preceding two sections it has been demonstrated that angles are added when vectors are multiplied and that angles are subtracted when one vector is divided by another. These operations can be further justified from a consideration of the sine and cosine when expanded in series form.

By Maclaurin's theorem, a treatment of which is beyond the scope of this book, $\cos\theta$ and $\sin\theta$ can be expanded into series form as follows:

$$\cos\theta = 1 - \frac{\theta^2}{2!} + \frac{\theta^4}{4!} - \frac{\theta^6}{6!} + \cdots \qquad [1]$$

$$\sin\theta = \theta - \frac{\theta^3}{3!} + \frac{\theta^5}{5!} - \frac{\theta^7}{7!} + \cdots \qquad [2]$$

The symbol $n!$ denotes the product of 1, 2, 3, 4, . . . , n, and is read "factorial n." Thus, 5! (factorial five) is $1 \times 2 \times 3 \times 4 \times 5$. Similarly, it can be shown that

$$\epsilon^{j\theta} = 1 + j\theta - \frac{\theta^2}{2!} - j\frac{\theta^3}{3!} + \frac{\theta^4}{4!} + j\frac{\theta^5}{5!} - \frac{\theta^6}{6!} - j\frac{\theta^7}{7!} + \cdots \quad [3]$$

where ϵ is the base of the natural system of logarithms $\cong 2.718$. By collecting and factoring j terms, Eq. [3] can be written

$$\epsilon^{j\theta} = \left(1 - \frac{\theta^2}{2!} + \frac{\theta^4}{4!} - \frac{\theta^6}{6!} + \cdots\right)$$
$$+ j\left(\theta - \frac{\theta^3}{3!} + \frac{\theta^5}{5!} - \frac{\theta^7}{7!} + \cdots\right) \quad [4]$$

Note that the first term of the right member of Eq. [4] is $\cos \theta$ as given in Eq. [1] and that the second term in the right member of Eq. [4] is $j \sin \theta$. Therefore,

$$\epsilon^{j\theta} = \cos \theta + j \sin \theta \quad [5]$$

Since a vector, such as $Z \underline{/\theta}$, can be expressed in terms of its rectangular components by the relation

$$Z \underline{/\theta} = Z(\cos \theta + j \sin \theta) \quad [6]$$

it follows from Eqs. [5] and [6] that

$$Z \underline{/\theta} = Z\epsilon^{j\theta} \quad [7]$$

Similarly, it can be shown that

$$Z \underline{/-\theta} = Z\epsilon^{-j\theta} \quad [8]$$

Equations [7] and [8] show that the angles of vectors can be treated as exponents.

Two vectors $Z_1 \underline{/\theta}$ and $Z_2 \underline{/\phi}$ are multiplied by multiplying the magnitudes of the vectors and adding their angles algebraically. That is,

$$(Z_1 \underline{/\theta})(Z_2 \underline{/\phi}) = Z_1 Z_2 \underline{/\theta + \phi}$$

Also,

$$\frac{Z_1 \underline{/\theta}}{Z_2 \underline{/\phi}} = \frac{Z_1}{Z_2} \underline{/\theta - \phi}$$

and

$$\frac{Z_a \underline{/\theta}}{Z_b \underline{/-\phi}} = \frac{Z_a}{Z_b} \underline{/\theta + \phi}$$

EXAMPLE 9   Multiply $Z_1 = 8.4 \,\underline{/15°}$ by $Z_2 = 10.5 \,\underline{/20°}$.

SOLUTION $Z_1 Z_2 = 8.4 \times 10.5 \,\underline{/15° + 20°} = 88.2 \,\underline{/35°}$

EXAMPLE 10   Multiply $Z_a = 164 \,\underline{/-39°}$ by $Z_b = 2.2 \,\underline{/-26°}$.

SOLUTION $Z_a Z_b = 164 \times 2.2 \,\underline{/-39° + (-26°)} = 361 \,\underline{/-65°}$

EXAMPLE 11   Divide $Z_1 = 54.2 \,\underline{/47°}$ by $Z_2 = 18 \,\underline{/16°}$.

SOLUTION $\dfrac{Z_1}{Z_2} = \dfrac{54.2}{18} \,\underline{/47° - 16°} = 3.01 \,\underline{/31°}$

EXAMPLE 12   Divide $Z_a = 886 \,\underline{/18°}$ by $Z_b = 31.2 \,\underline{/-50°}$.

SOLUTION $\dfrac{Z_a}{Z_b} = \dfrac{886}{31.2} \,\underline{/18° - (-50°)} = 28.4 \,\underline{/68°}$

5-8   Powers and roots of polar vectors

In addition to following the laws of exponents for multiplication and division, vectorial angles can be used as any other exponents when powers or roots of vectors are desired. For example, to square a vector, the magnitude is squared and the angle is multiplied by 2. Similarly, the root of a vector is found by extracting the root of the magnitude and dividing the angle by the index of the root.

EXAMPLE 13   Find the square of $Z_1 = 14 \,\underline{/18°}$.

SOLUTION $Z_1{}^2 = (14 \,\underline{/18°})^2 = 14^2 \,\underline{/18° \times 2} = 196 \,\underline{/36°}$

EXAMPLE 14   Find the square root of $Z_a = 625 \,\underline{/60°}$.

SOLUTION $\sqrt{Z_a} = \sqrt{625 \,\underline{/60°}} = \sqrt{625} \,\underline{/60° \div 2} = 25 \,\underline{/30°}$

PROBLEMS 35-4

Multiply:

1   $5 \,\underline{/53.1°}$ by $16 \,\underline{/10.9°}$ 2 $66.8 \,\underline{/13°}$ by $4.73 \,\underline{/24°}$

3   $1.07 \,\underline{/-37.3°}$ by $52.6 \,\underline{/31°}$ 4 $319 \,\underline{/-60°}$ by $0.242 \,\underline{/-97.3°}$

5   $0.0924 \,\underline{/47°}$ by $185 \,\underline{/-73°}$ 6 $1.87 \,\underline{/-180°}$ by $3.54 \,\underline{/-180°}$

Divide:

7   $77.8 \,\underline{/42°}$ by $2.87 \,\underline{/19°}$ 8 $610 \,\underline{/17°}$ by $33.5 \,\underline{/7°}$

9   $146 \,\underline{/75°}$ by $256 \,\underline{/-12°}$ 10 $6.56 \,\underline{/-43°}$ by $3.57 \,\underline{/17°}$

11   $45.4 \,\underline{/11°}$ by $6.74 \,\underline{/39°}$ 12 $0.297 \,\underline{/-78°}$ by $0.626 \,\underline{/-81°}$

Perform the indicated operations:

13   $\sqrt{169 \,\underline{/16°}}$ 14 $\sqrt{576 \,\underline{/-23°}}$

15   $(28 \,\underline{/40°})^2$ 16 $(1.7 \,\underline{/-70°})^2$

17   $\sqrt[3]{8 \,\underline{/120°}}$ 18 $\sqrt[3]{343 \,\underline{/-18.6°}}$

19   $(2 \,\underline{/17°})^3$ 20 $(3 \,\underline{/-18°})^4$

35 – 9   Parallel circuits

It was shown in Sec. 18–2 that the reciprocal of the joint resistance R_t of several resistances in parallel is expressed by the relation

$$\frac{1}{R_t} = \frac{1}{R_1} + \frac{1}{R_2} + \frac{1}{R_3} + \frac{1}{R_4} + \cdots$$

and that when two resistances R_1 and R_2 are connected in parallel, the joint resistance is

$$R_t = \frac{R_1 R_2}{R_1 + R_2}$$

An analogous condition exists when two or more impedances are connected in parallel. By following the line of reasoning used for resistances in parallel, the reciprocal of the joint impedance of several impedances in parallel is found to be

$$\frac{1}{Z_t} = \frac{1}{Z_1} + \frac{1}{Z_2} + \frac{1}{Z_3} + \frac{1}{Z_4} + \cdots \qquad [\,9\,]$$

Similarly, the joint impedance Z_t of two impedances Z_1 and Z_2 connected in parallel is

$$Z_t = \frac{Z_1 Z_2}{Z_1 + Z_2} \qquad [\,10\,]$$

Note that the impedances of Eqs. [9] and [10] are in polar form.

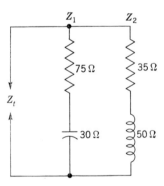

Z_1 Z_2

$75\,\Omega$ $35\,\Omega$

Z_t

$30\,\Omega$ $50\,\Omega$

FIG. 35–1   Circuit of Example 15.

EXAMPLE 15   Find the joint impedance of the circuit of Fig. 35–1.

SOLUTION   First express the given impedances in terms of both rectangular and polar forms.

$$Z_1 = 75 - j30 = 80.8 \,\underline{/-21.8°}\, \Omega$$
$$Z_2 = 35 + j50 = 61.0 \,\underline{/55°}\, \Omega$$

As pointed out in Sec. 35–4, vectors in polar form cannot be added algebraically; they must be added in terms of their rectangular components. Therefore, in substituting the given impedance values in Eq. [10], the impedances in the denominator must be in rectangular form in order to carry out the indicated addition. Substituting,

$$Z_t = \frac{(80.8\,\underline{/-21.8°})(61.0\,\underline{/55°})}{(75 - j30) + (35 + j50)} = \frac{4{,}930\,\underline{/33.2°}}{110 + j20}$$

Because the denominator is in rectangular form and the numerator is in polar form, the denominator must be converted to polar form in order to complete the indicated division. Thus, by adding the terms of the denominator vectorially,

$$Z_t = \frac{4{,}930\ /33.2°}{112\ /10.3°} = \frac{4{,}930}{112}\ /33.2° - 10.3° = 44\ /22.9°\ \Omega$$

Note that the circuit values of Fig. 35-1 are identical with those of Fig. 34-18.

EXAMPLE 16   Find the joint impedance of the circuit of Fig. 35-2.

SOLUTION   Expressing the impedance in rectangular and polar form,

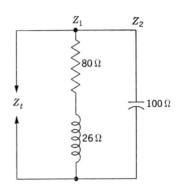

$$Z_1 = 80 + j26 = 84.1\ /18°\ \Omega$$
$$Z_2 = 0 - j100 = 100\ /-90°\ \Omega$$

Substituting these values in Eq. [10],

$$Z_t = \frac{(84.1\ /18°)(100\ /-90°)}{(80 + j26) + (0 - j100)}$$
$$= \frac{8{,}410\ /-72°}{80 - j74}$$

FIG. 35-2   Circuit of Example 16.

Performing the vector addition in the denominator,

$$Z_t = \frac{8{,}410\ /-72°}{109\ /-42.8°}$$
$$\therefore Z_t = 77.2\ /-29.2°\ \Omega$$

The equivalent series circuit is found by the usual method of converting from rectangular form to polar form, namely,

$$77.2\ /-29.2° = 77.2(\cos 29.2° - j\sin 29.2°)$$
$$= 77.2\cos 29.2° - j77.2\sin 29.2° = 67.4 - j37.7\ \Omega$$

5 – 10   Series-parallel circuits

An equation for the joint impedance of a series-parallel circuit is obtained in the same manner as the equation for the joint resistance of a combination of resistances in series and parallel as outlined in Sec. 18-3. For example, in the circuit represented in Fig. 35-3, the total impedance is

$$Z_t = Z_s + \frac{Z_1 Z_2}{Z_1 + Z_2} \qquad\qquad [11]$$

EXAMPLE 17   In the circuit of Fig. 35–3, $Z_s = 12.4 + j25.6$ Ω, $Z_1 = 45 + j12.9$ Ω, and $Z_2 = 35 - j75$ Ω. Determine the equivalent impedance of the circuit.

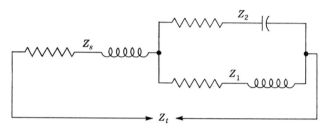

FIG. 35–3   Series-parallel circuit of Example 17.

SOLUTION   Since Z_1 and Z_2 must be multiplied, it is necessary to express them in polar form.

$$Z_1 = 45 + j12.9 = 46.8 \,\underline{/16°} \,\text{Ω}$$
and
$$Z_2 = 35 - j75 = 82.8 \,\underline{/-65°} \,\text{Ω}$$

Substituting the values in Eq. [11],

$$Z_t = (12.4 + j25.6) + \frac{(46.8 \,\underline{/16°})(82.8 \,\underline{/-65°})}{(45 + j12.9) + (35 - j75)}$$

The solution is completed in the usual manner and results in

$$Z_t = 53.2 \,\underline{/20°}$$

From the foregoing examples, it is evident that an equation for the impedance of a network is expressed exactly as in direct-current problems, impedances in polar form being substituted for the resistances.

PROBLEMS 35 – 5

1   What is the joint impedance of two impedances $Z_1 = 58.6 \,\underline{/55°}$ Ω and $Z_2 = 86 \,\underline{/-24°}$ Ω connected in parallel?

2   What is the joint impedance of two impedances $Z_a = 168 \,\underline{/27°}$ Ω and $Z_b = 57.2 \,\underline{/-61°}$ Ω connected in parallel?

3   What is the joint impedance of two impedances $Z_1 = 100 - j27$ Ω and $Z_2 = 24.3 + j125$ Ω connected in parallel?

4   What is the joint impedance of two impedances $Z_a = 250 + j30.7$ Ω and $Z_b = 500 - j61.6$ Ω connected in parallel?

5   What is the joint impedance of an impedance of $79.3 \,\underline{/35°}$ Ω connected in parallel with a resistance of 100 Ω?

6   What is the joint impedance of an impedance of 609 $\underline{/-9°}$ Ω connected in parallel with a capacitor having a capacitive reactance of 100 Ω?

7   What is the joint impedance of an impedance of 201 $\underline{/6°}$ Ω connected in parallel with an inductor that has an inductive reactance of 50 Ω?

8   The joint impedance of two parallel impedances is 82 $\underline{/-44°}$ Ω. One of the impedances $Z_1 = 155$ $\underline{/36°}$ Ω. What is the value of the other impedance? HINT: Solve Eq. [10] for Z_2.

9   What value of impedance must be connected in parallel with an impedance of $250 + j67$ Ω in order to result in a joint impedance of $146 + j27.2$ Ω?

10 In the circuit of Fig. 35–4, $Z_s = 2.0 + j4.25$ Ω, $Z_1 = 32.4 - j40$ Ω, and $Z_2 = 35 + j18.6$ Ω. Find the joint impedance Z_t.

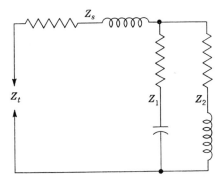

FIG. 35–4   Circuit for Probs. 10, 11, and 12.

11 In the circuit of Fig. 35–4, $Z_s = 3.0$ $\underline{/12°}$ Ω, $Z_1 = 15 - j7$ Ω, and $Z_2 = 6 + j5$ Ω. Find the joint impedance Z_t.

12 In the circuit of Fig. 35–4, $Z_s = 3.93 + j0.992$ Ω, $Z_1 = 9.22$ $\underline{/-49.4°}$ Ω, and $Z_2 = 9.44$ $\underline{/32°}$ Ω. Find the joint impedance Z_t.

13 The primary current I_p of a coupled circuit is expressed by the equation

$$I_p = \frac{E}{Z_p + (\omega M)^2/Z_s}$$

Compute the value of the primary current if the applied voltage E is $10\underline{/0°}$ volts, the primary impedance Z_p is $16 - j36$ Ω, the secondary impedance Z_s is $20 - j45$ Ω, and ωM ($2\pi f$ times the mutual inductance between primary and secondary) is 18.

14 The secondary current I_s of a coupled circuit is expressed by the equation

$$I_s = \frac{-j\omega ME}{Z_p Z_s + (\omega M)^2}$$

Compute the value of the secondary current if $\omega M = 12$, $E = 10$ volts, $Z_p = 25 + j40$ Ω, and $Z_s = 40 + j13$ Ω.

35 – 11   Equivalent Y and Δ circuits

When networks contain complex impedances, the equations for converting from a Δ network to an equivalent Y network, or vice versa, are derived by methods identical with those of Sec. 25–8. Thus, in Fig. 35–5, each equivalent Y impedance is equal to the product of the two *adjacent* Δ impedances divided by the summation of the Δ impedances, or

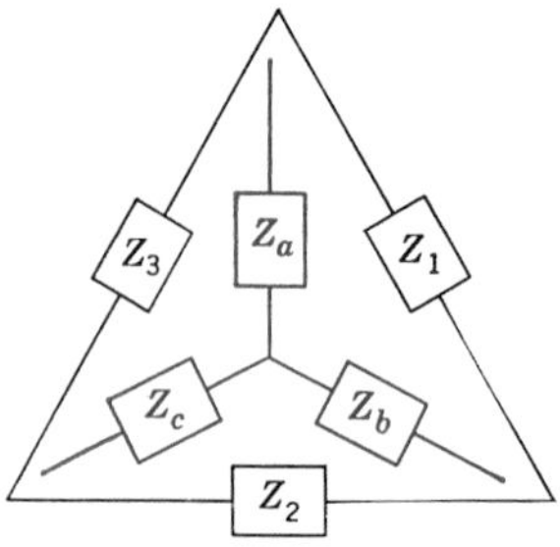

$$Z_a = \frac{Z_1 Z_3}{\Sigma Z_\Delta} \qquad [\,12\,]$$

$$Z_b = \frac{Z_1 Z_2}{\Sigma Z_\Delta} \qquad [\,13\,]$$

and $\qquad Z_c = \frac{Z_2 Z_3}{\Sigma Z_\Delta} \qquad [\,14\,]$

where $\quad \Sigma Z_\Delta = Z_1 + Z_2 + Z_3$

Fig. 35–5   Equivalent Y and Δ impedances.

and all impedances are expressed in polar form.

Similarly, each equivalent Δ impedance is equal to the summation of the Y impedances divided by the *opposite* Y impedance. Thus,

$$Z_1 = \frac{\Sigma Z_Y}{Z_c} \qquad [\,15\,]$$

$$Z_2 = \frac{\Sigma Z_Y}{Z_a} \qquad [\,16\,]$$

and $\qquad Z_3 = \frac{\Sigma Z_Y}{Z_b} \qquad [\,17\,]$

where $\qquad \Sigma Z_Y = Z_a Z_b + Z_b Z_c + Z_a Z_c$

and all impedances are expressed in polar form.

EXAMPLE 18   In Fig. 35–5, $Z_1 = 7.07 + j7.07$ Ω, $Z_2 = 4 + j3$ Ω, and $Z_3 = 6 - j8$ Ω. What are the values of the equivalent Y circuit?

SOLUTION   Express all impedances in both rectangular and polar forms.

$$Z_1 = 7.07 + j7.07 = 10 \,\underline{/45°}\ \Omega$$
$$Z_2 = 4 + j3 = 5 \,\underline{/36.9°}\ \Omega$$
and $\qquad Z_3 = 6 - j8 = 10 \,\underline{/-53.1°}\ \Omega$
$$\Sigma Z_\Delta = (7.07 + j7.07) + (4 + j3) + (6 - j8) = 17.2 \,\underline{/6.91°}\ \Omega$$

Substituting in Eq. [12],

$$Z_a = \frac{(10\ \underline{/45°})(10\ \underline{/-53.1°})}{17.2\ \underline{/6.91°}} = 5.62 - j1.51\ \Omega$$

Substituting in Eq. [13],

$$Z_b = \frac{(10\ \underline{/45°})(5\ \underline{/36.9°})}{17.2\ \underline{/6.91°}} = 0.752 + j2.81\ \Omega$$

Substituting in Eq. [14],

$$Z_c = \frac{(5\ \underline{/36.9°})(10\ \underline{/-53.1°})}{17.2\ \underline{/6.91°}} = 2.67 - j1.14\ \Omega$$

The solution can be checked by converting the above Y network equivalents back to the original Δ by using Eqs. [15], [16], and [17].

EXAMPLE 19   Determine the equivalent impedance between points a and c in Fig. 35–6.

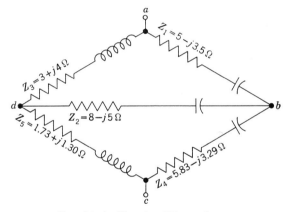

FIG. 35–6 Circuit of Example 19.

SOLUTION   Convert one of the Δ circuits of Fig. 35–6 to its equivalent Y circuit. Thus, for the delta abd,

$$Z_1 = 5 - j3.5 = 6.1\ \underline{/-35°}\ \Omega$$
$$Z_2 = 8 - j5 = 9.44\ \underline{/-32°}\ \Omega$$
$$Z_3 = 3 + j4 = 5\ \underline{/53.1°}\ \Omega$$
$$\Sigma Z_\Delta = (5 - j3.5) + (8 - j5) + (3 + j4) = 16.6\ \underline{/-15.7°}\ \Omega$$

Substituting in Eq. [12],

$$Z_a = \frac{(6.1\ \underline{/-35°})(5\ \underline{/53.1°})}{16.6\ \underline{/-15.7°}} = 1.84\ \underline{/33.8°} = 1.53 + j1.02\ \Omega$$

Substituting in Eq. [13],

$$Z_b = \frac{(6.1 \ / -35°)(9.44 \ / -32°)}{16.6 \ / -15.7°} = 3.47 \ / -51.3° = -217 - j2.71 \ \Omega$$

Substituting in Eq. [14],

$$Z_c = \frac{(9.44 \ / -32°)(5 \ / 53.1°)}{16.6 \ / -15.7°} = 2.84 \ / 36.8° = 2.27 + j1.70 \ \Omega$$

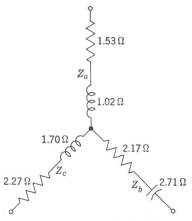

FIG. 35–7 Equivalent Y impedances for circuit of Fig. 35–6.

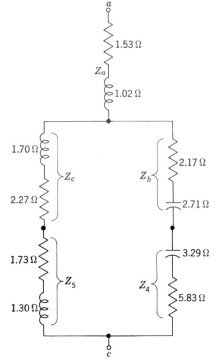

FIG. 35–8 Equivalent Y impedances connected to remainder of circuit of Fig. 35–6.

The equivalent Y impedances are shown in Fig. 35–7.

The equivalent Y impedances are connected to the remainder of the circuit as shown in Fig. 35–8 and solved as an ordinary series-parallel circuit. Thus,

$$Z_{ac} = Z_a + \frac{(Z_c + Z_5)(Z_b + Z_4)}{Z_c + Z_5 + Z_b + Z_4}$$

$$= 1.53 + j1.02$$

$$+ \frac{[(2.27 + j1.70) + (1.73 + j1.30)][(2.17 - j2.71) + (5.83 - j3.29)]}{(2.27 + j1.70) + (1.73 + j1.30) + (2.17 - j2.71) + (5.83 - j3.29)}$$

$$= 5.45 + j2.0 \ \Omega$$

PROBLEMS 35 – 6

1 In the circuit of Fig. 35–5, $Z_1 = 56 + j47$ Ω, $Z_2 = 26 - j85$ Ω, and $Z_3 = 63 + j70$ Ω. Determine the impedances of the equivalent Y circuit.

2 In the circuit of Fig. 35–5, $Z_1 = 100 + j90$ Ω, $Z_2 = 95 - j69$ Ω, and $Z_3 = 31 + j90$ Ω. Determine the impedances of the equivalent Y circuit.

3 In the circuit of Fig. 35–5, $Z_1 = 605 /\underline{7.5°}$ Ω, $Z_2 = 505 /\underline{-8.2°}$ Ω, and $Z_3 = 458 /\underline{10.7°}$ Ω. Determine the impedances of the equivalent Y circuit.

4 In the circuit of Fig. 35–5, $Z_1 = 5 - j4.2$ Ω, $Z_2 = 6.53 + j0$ Ω, and $Z_3 = 5 + j4.2$ Ω. Determine the impedances of the equivalent Y circuit.

5 In the circuit of Fig. 35–9, $Z_1 = 100 /\underline{-36.9°}$ Ω, $Z_2 = 50 /\underline{53.1°}$ Ω, $Z_3 = 100 /\underline{45°}$ Ω, $Z_4 = 63.6 /\underline{-42°}$ Ω, and $Z_5 = 27.7 /\underline{17°}$ Ω. What is the equivalent impedance between points a and b?

6 In Prob. 5, if $E = 100$ volts, how much current flows through Z_4?

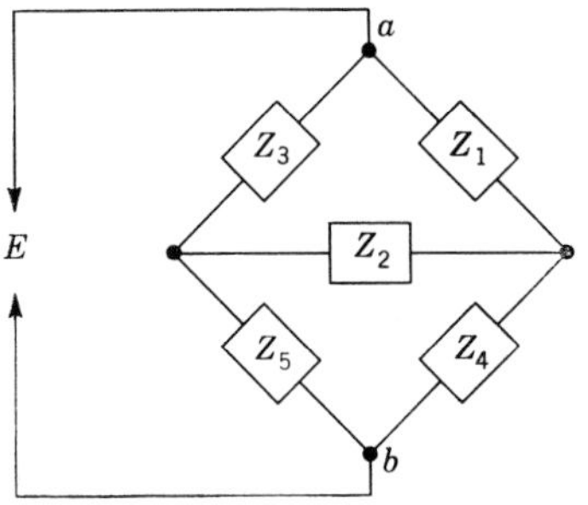

7 In the circuit of Fig. 35–9, $Z_1 = 217 /\underline{61.1°}$ Ω, $Z_2 = 145 /\underline{-12.7°}$ Ω,

FIG. 35–9 Circuit for Probs. 5 to 13.

$Z_3 = 434 /\underline{-28.9°}$ Ω, $Z_4 = 50 /\underline{-53.1°}$ Ω, and $Z_5 = 100 /\underline{-36.9°}$ Ω. Determine the equivalent impedance between points a and b.

8 In Prob. 7, if $E = 500$ volts, how much current flows through Z_5?

9 In Prob. 7, if $E = 100$ volts, how much power is expended in Z_4?

10 In Prob. 7, if $E = 250$ volts, how much current flows through Z_3?

11 In the circuit of Fig. 35–9, $Z_1 = 151 /\underline{-54°}$ Ω, $Z_2 = 119 /\underline{-9°}$ Ω, $Z_3 = 177 /\underline{-19°}$ Ω, $Z_4 = 50 /\underline{0°}$ Ω, and $Z_5 = 24.5 /\underline{90°}$ Ω. Determine the equivalent impedance between points a and b.

12 In Prob. 11, if $E = 100$ volts, how much current flows through Z_5?

13 In Prob. 11, if $E = 150$ volts, how much power is expended in Z_1?

14 In the circuit of Fig. 35–10, $Z_1 = 5 /\underline{36.9°}$ Ω, $Z_2 = 8.04 + j35.8$ Ω, $Z_3 = 7.13 - j40$ Ω, $Z_4 = 81.4 /\underline{-37°}$ Ω, $Z_5 = 86.4 /\underline{80°}$ Ω, $Z_6 = 53.8 /\underline{-42°}$ Ω, $Z_7 = 8 - j6$ Ω, and $E = 100$ volts. How much current flows through Z_1?

15 In the circuit of Fig. 35–11, $Z_1 = 548 /\underline{35.4°}$ Ω, $Z_2 = 769 /\underline{28.4°}$ Ω, $Z_3 = 992 /\underline{25.4°}$ Ω, $Z_4 = 992 /\underline{-25.4°}$ Ω, $Z_5 = 769 /\underline{-28.4°}$ Ω, $Z_6 = 548 /\underline{-35.4°}$ Ω, and $Z_L = 200 /\underline{0°}$ Ω. Determine the equivalent impedance between points a and b.

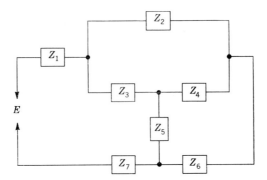

FIG. 35–10   Circuit for Prob. 14.

16   In Prob. 15, if $E = 15$ volts, how much current flows through the load impedance Z_L?

17   In the circuit of Fig. 35–11, $Z_1 = 295 \; \underline{/40.6°} \; \Omega$, $Z_2 = 1,140 \; \underline{/37.6°} \; \Omega$,

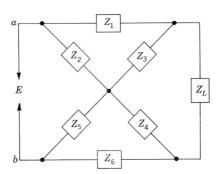

FIG. 35–11   Circuit for Probs. 15 to 18.

$Z_3 = 1,000 \; \underline{/28.6°} \; \Omega$, $Z_4 = 295 \; \underline{/-40.6°} \; \Omega$, $Z_5 = 1,140 \; \underline{/-37.6°} \; \Omega$, $Z_6 = 1,000 \; \underline{/-28.6°} \; \Omega$, and $Z_L = 600 \; \underline{/0°} \; \Omega$. Determine the equivalent impedance between points a and b.

18   In Prob. 17, if $E = 45$ volts, how much power is dissipated in the load impedance Z_L?

CHAPTER 36
LOGARITHMS

In problems pertaining to engineering, there often occurs the need for numerical computations involving multiplication, division, powers, or roots. Some of these problems can be solved more readily by the use of logarithms than by ordinary arithmetical processes.

The credit for the invention of logarithms is chiefly due to John Napier, whose tables appeared in 1614. This was an extremely important event in the development of mathematics; for, by the use of logarithms,

1. Multiplication is reduced to addition.
2. Division is reduced to subtraction.
3. Raising to a power is reduced to one multiplication.
4. Extracting a root is reduced to one division.

In some phases of engineering, computation by logarithms is utilized to a great extent because of the high degree of accuracy desired and the amount of labor saved by their use. Because the slide rule is convenient and because slide-rule results meet the ordinary demands for accuracy in problems relating to electricity and radio, it is not necessary to make wide use of logarithms for computations in the general field. However, it is essential that

563

the electrical engineer and, more particularly, the electronics engineer have a thorough understanding of logarithmic processes.

36 – 1 Definition

The *logarithm* of a quantity is the exponent of the power to which a given number, called the *base*, must be raised in order to equal the quantity.

EXAMPLE 1   Since $10^3 = 1,000$, then $3 =$ logarithm of 1,000 to the base 10.

EXAMPLE 2   Since $2^3 = 8$, then $3 =$ logarithm of 8 to the base 2.

EXAMPLE 3   Since $a^x = b$, then $x =$ logarithm of b to the base a.

36 – 2 Notation

If
$$b^x = N \qquad [1]$$

then x is the logarithm of N to the base b. This statement is abbreviated by writing

$$x = \log_b N \qquad [2]$$

It is evident that Eqs. [1] and [2] mean the same thing and are simply different methods of expressing the same relation among b, x, and N. Equation [1] is called the *exponential form*, and Eq. [2] is called the *logarithmic form*.

As an aid in remembering that *a logarithm is an exponent*, Eq. [1] can be written in the form

$$(\textbf{Base})^{\log} = \textbf{number}$$

The following example illustrates relations between exponential and logarithmic forms.

EXAMPLE 4

Exponential notation	*Logarithmic notation*
$2^4 = 16$	$4 = \log_2 16$
$3^5 = 243$	$5 = \log_3 243$
$25^{0.5} = 5$	$0.5 = \log_{25} 5$
$10^2 = 100$	$2 = \log_{10} 100$
$10^4 = 10,000$	$4 = \log_{10} 10,000$
$a^b = c$	$b = \log_a c$
$\epsilon^x = y$	$x = \log_\epsilon y$

From the foregoing examples, it is apparent that any positive number, other than 1, can be selected as a base for a system of logarithms. Because 1 raised to any power is 1, it cannot be used as a base.

PROBLEMS 36 – 1
Express the following equations in logarithmic form:

1	$10^3 = 1,000$	2	$10^5 = 100,000$
3	$5^2 = 25$	4	$4^3 = 64$
5	$6^0 = 1$	6	$a^0 = 1$
7	$5^4 = 625$	8	$9^{0.5} = 3$
9	$r^s = t$	10	$3^{2x} = M$

Express the following equations in exponential form:

11	$2 = \log_{10} 100$	12	$\log_{10} 1,000 = 3$
13	$\log_7 49 = 2$	14	$\log_4 64 = 3$
15	$\log_4 2 = 0.5$	16	$\log_\epsilon \epsilon = 1$
17	$\log_a a = 1$	18	$\log_{10} 10 = 1$
19	$\log_a 1 = 0$	20	$\log_{10} 1 = 0$

Find the value of x:

21	$2^x = 4$	22	$3^x = 81$
23	$10^x = 100,000$	24	$x = \log_3 27$
25	$3^x = \sqrt{3}$	26	$\log_5 x = 3$

27 Show that $\log_{10} 100 = \log_{10} 100,000 - \log_{10} 1,000$.
28 Show that $\log_b b = 1$.
29 What are the logarithms of 2, 4, 8, 16, 32, 64, 128, 256, and 512 to the base 2?
30 What are the logarithms of 3, 9, 27, 81, 243, and 729 to the base 3?

36 – 3 The logarithm of a product

The logarithm of a product is equal to the sum of the logarithms of the factors.

Consider the two factors M and N, and let x and y be their respective logarithms to the base a; then,

$$x = \log_a M \qquad\qquad [3]$$
and
$$y = \log_a N \qquad\qquad [4]$$

Writing Eq. [3] in exponential form,

$$a^x = M \qquad\qquad [5]$$

Writing Eq. [4] in exponential form,

$$a^y = N \qquad\qquad [6]$$

Then
$$M \cdot N = a^x \cdot a^y = a^{x+y}$$
$$\therefore \log_a (M \cdot N) = x + y = \log_a M + \log_a N$$

EXAMPLE 5 $2 = \log_{10} 100$ or $10^2 = 100$
             $4 = \log_{10} 10{,}000$ or $10^4 = 10{,}000$

Then $100 \times 10{,}000 = 10^2 \cdot 10^4 = 10^{2+4} = 10^6$
$$\therefore \log_{10}(100 \times 10{,}000) = 2 + 4 = \log_{10} 100 + \log_{10} 10{,}000$$

The above proposition is also true for the product of more than two factors. Thus, by successive applications of the proof, it can be shown that

$$\log_a (A \cdot B \cdot C \cdot D) = \log_a A + \log_a B + \log_a C + \log_a D$$

36 – 4   The logarithm of a quotient

The logarithm of the quotient of two numbers is equal to the logarithm of the dividend minus the logarithm of the divisor.

As in Sec. 36–3,

let $x = \log_a M$ [3]
and $y = \log_a N$ [4]

Writing Eq. [3] in exponential form,
$$a^x = M \qquad\qquad [5]$$

Writing Eq. [4] in exponential form,
$$a^y = N \qquad\qquad [6]$$

Dividing Eq. [5] by Eq. [6],
$$\frac{a^x}{a^y} = \frac{M}{N}$$

That is, $a^{x-y} = \dfrac{M}{N}$ [7]

Writing Eq. [7] in logarithmic form,

$$x - y = \log_a \frac{M}{N} \qquad\qquad [8]$$

Substituting in Eq. [8] for the values of x and y,

$$\log_a M - \log_a N = \log_a \frac{M}{N}$$

EXAMPLE 6 $2 = \log_{10} 100$ or $10^2 = 100$
             $4 = \log_{10} 10{,}000$ or $10^4 = 10{,}000$

Then
$$\frac{10,000}{100} = \frac{10^4}{10^2} = 10^{4-2} = 10^2$$

$$\therefore \log_{10} \frac{10,000}{100} = 4 - 2 = \log_{10} 10,000 - \log_{10} 100$$

36–5 The logarithm of a power

The logarithm of a power of a number equals the logarithm of the number multiplied by the exponent of the power.

Again, let $\qquad\qquad x = \log_a M \qquad\qquad$ [3]

Then $\qquad\qquad\qquad M = a^x \qquad\qquad\qquad$ [9]

Raising both sides of Eq. [9] to the nth power,

$$M^n = a^{nx} \qquad\qquad [10]$$

Writing Eq. [10] in logarithmic form,

$$\log_a M^n = nx \qquad\qquad [11]$$

Substituting in Eq. [11] for the value of x,

$$\log_a M^n = n \log_a M$$

EXAMPLE 7 $\qquad 2 = \log_{10} 100 \qquad$ or $\qquad 100 = 10^2$

Since $\qquad\qquad (10^2)^2 = 10^{2 \cdot 2} = 10^4 = 10,000$

then $\qquad\qquad \log_{10} 10,000 = 4$

$$\therefore \log_{10} 100^2 = 2 \log_{10} 100 = 2 \cdot 2 = 4$$

36–6 The logarithm of a root

The logarithm of a root of a number is equal to the logarithm of the number divided by the index of the root.

Again, let $\qquad\qquad x = \log_a M \qquad\qquad$ [3]

Then $\qquad\qquad\qquad M = a^x \qquad\qquad\qquad$ [9]

Extracting the nth root of both sides of Eq. [9],

$$M^{1/n} = a^{x/n} \qquad\qquad [12]$$

Writing Eq. [12] in logarithmic form,

$$\log_a M^{1/n} = \frac{x}{n} \qquad\qquad [13]$$

Substituting in Eq. [13] for the value of x,

$$\log_a M^{1/n} = \frac{\log_a M}{n}$$

EXAMPLE 8 $4 = \log_{10} 10,000$ or $10,000 = 10^4$

Since $\sqrt{10,000} = \sqrt{10^4} = 10^{4/2} = 10^2 = 100$

then $\log_{10}\sqrt{10,000} = \dfrac{\log_{10} 10,000}{2} = \dfrac{4}{2} = 2$

36 – 7   Summary

It is evident that if the logarithms of numbers are used for computations instead of the numbers themselves, then *multiplication, division, raising to powers*, and *extracting roots* are replaced by *addition, subtraction, multiplication*, and *division*, respectively. Because you are familiar with the laws of exponents, especially as applied to the powers of 10, the foregoing operations with logarithms involve no new ideas. The sole idea behind logarithms is that every positive number can be expressed as a power of some base. That is,

$$\textbf{Any positive number} = \textbf{(base)}^{\log}$$

36 – 8   The common system

Since 10 is the base of our number systems, both integral and decimal, the base 10 has been chosen for a system of logarithms. This system is called the *common system* or *Briggs's system*. The natural system, of which the base to five decimal places is 2.71828, will be discussed later.

Hereafter, when no other base is stated, the base will be 10. For example, $\log_{10} 625$ will be written $\log 625$, the base 10 being understood.

36 – 9   Characteristics

Table 36–1 illustrates the connection between the power of 10 and the logarithms of certain numbers.

TABLE 36 – 1

Exponential form	Logarithmic form
$10^4 = 10,000$	$\log 10,000 = 4$
$10^3 = 1,000$	$\log 1,000 = 3$
$10^2 = 100$	$\log 100 = 2$
$10^1 = 10$	$\log 10 = 1$
$10^0 = 1$	$\log 1 = 0$
$10^{-1} = 0.1$	$\log 0.1 = -1$
$10^{-2} = 0.01$	$\log 0.01 = -2$
$10^{-3} = 0.001$	$\log 0.001 = -3$
$10^{-4} = 0.0001$	$\log 0.0001 = -4$

Inspection of the table shows that only powers of 10 have integers for logarithms. Also, it is evident that the logarithm of any number between 10 and 100, for example, is between 1 and 2; that is, it is 1 plus a decimal. Similarly the logarithm of any number between 100 and 1,000 is between 2 and 3, and so on. Therefore, to represent all numbers, it is necessary to utilize fractional powers. For example,

$$\log 37 = 1.5682$$
That is, $$37 = 10^{1.5682}$$
Also, $$\log 461 = 2.6637$$
That is, $$461 = 10^{2.6637}$$

In the same manner, it follows that the logarithm of a number between 0.01 and 0.001 is -3 plus a decimal or -2 minus a decimal.

In order that the decimal part of a logarithm can always be positive, it has been agreed that the logarithm of a number less than 1 is to be taken so that the integral part only is negative.

From the foregoing, it follows that every logarithm has two parts, an integer and a decimal fraction.

The *integral* part is called the *characteristic* and may be positive or negative.

The *fractional part* is called the *mantissa* and is *always positive.*

– 10   Rules for determining the characteristic

The use of the base 10 makes it possible to simplify computation by logarithms and to express them in a compact tabulated form. For example, determining the characteristic becomes a matter of inspection, as is evident from the following:

RULE
1   The characteristic of a number greater than 1 is positive and is one less than the number of digits to the left of the decimal point.
2   The characteristic of a positive number less than 1 is negative and is one more than the number of zeros immediately to the right of the decimal point.

If the characteristic is negative, it is customary to write the negative sign *above* the characteristic to emphasize that the characteristic alone is negative. For example, in

$$\log 0.000647 = \bar{4}.8109$$

the $\overline{4}.8109$ means $-4 + 0.8109$. To write it -4.8109 would indicate that both characteristic and mantissa were negative. This would be incorrect, for it has been agreed that the mantissa shall always be considered positive.

To avoid the use of a negative characteristic, it is convenient to add 10 to the characteristic and subtract 10 at the right of the mantissa. Thus log $0.000647 = \overline{4}.8109$ would be written $6.8109 - 10$.

The application of the rules for determining the characteristic becomes a simple matter if all numbers are expressed as a number between 1 and 10 times the proper power of 10.

By so doing, the power of 10 is always the characteristic of the logarithm of the number so expressed.

The foregoing is illustrated in Table 36–2.

TABLE 36 – 2

Number	Standard notation	Characteristic	Refer to rule
682	6.82×10^2	2	1
3,765	3.765×10^3	3	1
14	1.4×10^1	1	1
1	1×10^0	0	
0.00425	4.25×10^{-3}	-3 or $7 - 10$	2
0.1	1×10^{-1}	-1 or $9 - 10$	2
0.000072	7.2×10^{-5}	-5 or $5 - 10$	2

36 – 11   The mantissa

Note that all numbers whose logarithms are given below have the same significant figures. These logarithms were obtained by first finding log 2.207 from a table, as will be discussed later. The remaining logarithms were then obtained by applying the properties of logarithms as stated in Secs. 36–3 and 36–4.

$$\log 2207 = \log 1000(2.207) = \log 1000 + \log 2.207 = 3 + 0.3438$$
$$\log 220.7 = \log 100(2.207) = \log 100 + \log 2.207 = 2 + 0.3438$$
$$\log 22.07 = \log 10(2.207) = \log 10 + \log 2.207 = 1 + 0.3438$$
$$\log 2.207 = \log 1(2.207) = \log 1 + \log 2.207 = 0 + 0.3438$$

$$\log 0.2207 = \log \frac{2.207}{10} = \log 2.207 - \log 10 = -1 + 0.3438$$

$$\log 0.02207 = \log \frac{2.207}{100} = \log 2.207 - \log 100 = -2 + 0.3438$$

From the above examples, it is apparent that the mantissa is not affected by a shift of the decimal point. That is, *the mantissa of the logarithm of a number depends only on the sequence of the significant figures in the number.* Because of this, 10 is ideally suited as a base for a system of logarithms to be used for computation.

PROBLEMS 36 – 2

Write the characteristics of the logarithms of the following numbers:

1	63	2	106	3	784	4	43.2
5	432	6	4,320	7	0.432	8	4.32
9	8,425	10	0.08425	11	8.425	12	84.25
13	5,060	14	0.5060	15	5.060	16	506,000
17	0.0004	18	0.00723	19	8.642	20	0.9463

Find the value of each of the following expressions:

21   $\log 100 + \log 0.001$ 22 $\log \sqrt{100}$

23   $\log \sqrt{\dfrac{1,000}{10}}$ 24 $\log \sqrt{1,000} - \log 100$

25   $\log \sqrt{0.001}$

Write the following expressions in expanded form:

26   $\log \dfrac{642 \times 8.63}{37.2}$

SOLUTION $\log \dfrac{642 \times 8.63}{37.2} = \log 642 + \log 8.63 - \log 37.2$

27   $\log \dfrac{3,793 \times 70.2}{264}$ 28 $\log \dfrac{9.30 \times 479}{3.42 \times 4,869}$

29   $\log \sqrt{\dfrac{893 \times 0.642}{2.376 \times 20.4}}$ 30 $\log \sqrt[4]{7,182 \times 17.53 \times 69.3}$

31   $\log \dfrac{abc}{de}$ 32 $\log \dfrac{x^3 y^4}{a \sqrt[3]{b}}$

Given $\log 48.54 = 1.6861$, find the logarithms of the following numbers:

33	4.854	34	4,854	35	0.04854
36	0.0004854	37	48,540	38	$4,854 \times 10^{-4}$
39	48.54×10^6	40	0.004854×10^{-3}		

Given $\log 8.162 = 0.9118$, find the numbers that correspond to the following logarithms:

41	1.9118	42	3.9118	43	6.9118 − 10
44	6.9118	45	9.9118 − 10	46	1.9118 − 10
47	2.9118	48	7.9118 − 10	49	10.9118
50	2.9118 − 10				

36 – 12 Tables of logarithms

Because the characteristic of the logarithm of any number is obtainable by inspection, it is necessary to tabulate only the mantissas of the logarithms of numbers. Though mantissas can be computed by use of advanced mathematics, for convenience the mantissas of the logarithms to a number of significant figures have been computed and arranged in tables. Table 6 in the Appendix is a four-place table of logarithms. That is, the mantissas therein have been computed and rounded off to four decimal places.

In order for you to learn how to use tables of logarithms, Table 6 is used in the following sections and examples. In addition, inside the front cover of this book is a three-place table of mantissas. You will find that this table will serve most of your needs when working with logarithms related to electronic applications.

36 – 13 To find the logarithm of a given number

Table 36–3 is a portion of Table 6 in the Appendix.

TABLE 36 – 3

N	0	1	2	3	4	5	6	7	8	9
40	6021	6031	6042	6053	6064	6075	6085	6096	6107	6117
41	6128	6138	6149	6160	6170	6180	6191	6201	6212	6222
42	6232	6243	6253	6263	6274	6284	6294	6304	6314	6325
43	6335	6345	6355	6365	6375	6385	6395	6405	6415	6425

Examination of the table shows that the first column has **N** at top and bottom. **N** is an abbreviation for "number." The other columns are labeled **0, 1, 2, 3, 4, . . . , 9**. Therefore, any number consisting of three significant figures has its first two figures in the **N** column and its third figure in another column. This will be illustrated in the following examples.

When finding the logarithm of a number, always write the characteristic at once, before looking for the mantissa.

EXAMPLE 9   Find the log 40.
SOLUTION $40 = 4 \times 10^1$; therefore the characteristic is 1.

Since 40 has no third significant figure other than zero, the mantissa of 40 is found at the right of 40 in the N column, in the column headed zero. It is 0.6021.

$$\therefore \log 40 = 1.6021$$

EXAMPLE 10   Find log 416.
SOLUTION $416 = 4.16 \times 10^2$; therefore the characteristic is 2.

The first two digits of 416 are found in the N column and the third digit in the column headed 6. Then the mantissa is read in the row containing 41 and in the column headed 6. It is 0.6191.

$$\therefore \log 416 = 2.6191$$
Similarly, $$\log 4.16 = 0.6191$$
$$\log 41.6 = 1.6191$$
$$\log 4{,}160 = 3.6191$$
$$\log 0.00416 = 7.6191 - 10, \text{ etc.}$$

That is, the mantissa of any number having 416 as significant figures is 0.6191.

EXAMPLE 11   Find log 4,347.
SOLUTION $4{,}347 = 4.347 \times 10^3$; therefore the characteristic is 3.

Since 4,347 is between 4,340 and 4,350, its mantissa must be between the mantissas of 4,340 and 4,350.

$$\text{Mantissa of } 4{,}350 = 0.6385$$
$$\text{Mantissa of } 4{,}340 = \underline{0.6375}$$
$$\text{Difference} = 0.0010$$

The *tabular difference* between these mantissas is 0.0010, and it is apparent that an *increase* of 10 in the number causes the mantissa to *increase* by 0.0010. Therefore an increase of 7 in the number will increase the mantissa 0.7 as much. Hence the increase in the mantissa will be $0.0010 \times 0.7 = 0.0007$, and the mantissa of 4,347 will be

$$0.6375 + 0.0007 = 0.6382$$
$$\therefore \log 4{,}347 = 3.6382$$
Similarly, $$\log 43.47 = 1.6382$$
$$\log 4.347 = 0.6382$$
$$\log 434{,}700 = 5.6382$$
$$\log 0.0004347 = 6.6382 - 10, \text{ etc.}$$

That is, the mantissa of any number having 4,347 as significant figures is 0.6382.

The foregoing process of finding the mantissa is called *interpolation* and is based on the assumption that the increase in the logarithm is proportional to the increase in the number.

EXAMPLE 12   Find log 0.000042735.
SOLUTION $0.000042735 = 4.2735 \times 10^{-5}$; therefore the characteristic is -5, or $5 - 10$.

Since 42,735 is between 42,700 and 42,800, its mantissa must be between the mantissas of 42,700 and 42,800.

$$\begin{aligned} \text{Mantissa of } 42,800 &= 0.6314 \\ \text{Mantissa of } 42,700 &= \underline{0.6304} \\ \text{Tabular difference} &= 0.0010 \end{aligned}$$

Since an increase of 100 in the number causes the mantissa to increase 0.0010, an increase of 35 in the number would cause an increase in the mantissa of $0.0010 \times 0.35 = 0.000350$. Then the mantissa of 42,735 will be

$$0.6304 + 0.000350 = 0.630750$$

This mantissa, as written above, is another example of how the retention of decimals might easily give a false impression of accuracy. The table from which the mantissa is taken is correct to four significant figures. Therefore, any mantissa found by interpolation from such a table cannot be correct beyond four significant figures. Hence, it is correct to write

$$\log 0.000042735 = 5.6308 - 10$$

Summarizing, we have the following:

RULE   To find the logarithm of a number containing three significant figures,
1   Determine the characteristic.
2   Locate the first two significant figures in the column headed N.
3   In the same row and in the column headed by the third significant figure, find the required mantissa.

RULE   To find the logarithm of a number containing more than three significant figures,
1   Determine the characteristic.

2 Find the mantissa for the first three significant figures of a number.

3 Find the next higher mantissa, and take the tabular difference of the two mantissas.

4 Add to the lesser mantissa the product of the tabular difference and the remaining figures of the number considered as a decimal.

PROBLEMS 36 – 3

Find the logarithms of the following:

1	3	2	300	3	30
4	356	5	642	6	747
7	101	8	500	9	242,000
10	0.0000499	11	8,425	12	4,672,000
13	0.9792	14	141,700	15	342.56
16	246,300	17	1.493×10^{-5}	18	703.3×10^{7}
19	6.28	20	3.1416	21	2.7183
22	376.92	23	0.000982	24	746,000
25	79,990	26	5,645,000	27	5.645×10^{6}
28	0.00006	29	8×10^{-12}	30	34.63×10^{-5}

– 14 **To find the number corresponding to a given logarithm**

The number corresponding to a given logarithm is called the *antilogarithm* and is written "antilog." For example, if log 692 = 2.8401, then the number corresponding to the logarithm 2.8401 is 692. That is,

$$\text{antilog } 2.8401 = 692$$

To find the antilog of a given logarithm, we reverse the process of finding the logarithm when the number is given.

EXAMPLE 13   Find the number whose logarithm is 3.9101.

SOLUTION   The characteristic tells only the position of the decimal point. Therefore, to find the significant figures of the number (antilog), the mantissa must be found in Table 6 in the Appendix. To the left of the mantissa 0.9101 in column **N**, find the first two significant figures of the number, which are 81, and at the head of the column of the mantissa, find the third significant figure, which is 3. Hence the number has the significant figures 813. The position of the decimal point is fixed by the characteristic, and because the characteristic is 3, there must be four figures to the left of the decimal point.

Thus,

$$\text{antilog } 3.9101 = 8{,}130$$

Similarly,
$$\text{antilog } 0.9101 = 8.13$$
$$\text{antilog } 7.9101 - 10 = 0.00813$$
$$\text{antilog } 6.9101 = 8{,}130{,}000, \text{ etc.}$$

A change in the characteristic changes only the position of the decimal point.

EXAMPLE 14   Find the number whose logarithm is 2.3680.

SOLUTION   Examination of Table 6 shows that there the mantissa of the logarithm is not given exactly.

Find the two consecutive mantissas between which the given mantissa lies. These are 0.3674 and 0.3692. Then, considering only significant figures,

$$0.3692 \quad = \text{mantissa of log } 234$$
$$\underline{0.3674} \quad = \text{mantissa of log } \underline{233}$$
$$\text{Tabular difference} = 0.0018, \text{ number difference} = \quad 1$$

Hence a difference of 0.0018 in the mantissa makes a difference of 1 in the number. Now the given mantissa is 0.0006 larger than the smaller one (0.3680 − 0.3674 = 0.0006). Then the required number is

$$\frac{0.0006}{0.0018} \times 1 = 0.33$$

larger than 233. The sequence of significant figures is 233.33 or 233.3, for results were computed from a four-place table.

$$\therefore \text{ antilog } 2.3680 = 233.3$$
or
$$2.3680 = \log 233.3$$

EXAMPLE 15   Find the number whose logarithm is 6.9793 − 10.

SOLUTION $0.9795 \quad = \text{mantissa of log } 954$
$$\underline{0.9791} \quad = \text{mantissa of log } \underline{953}$$
$$\text{Tabular difference} = 0.0004, \text{ number difference} = \quad 1$$
$$\text{Given mantissa} = 0.9793$$
$$\text{Next lower mantissa} = \underline{0.9791}$$
$$\text{Difference} = 0.0002$$

Since the difference between numbers is proportional to the difference of the corresponding mantissas, the fourth significant figure to be added to 953 is

$$\frac{0.0002}{0.0004} \times 1 = 0.5$$

The required significant figures are 953.5.

$$\therefore \text{antilog } 6.9793 - 10 = 0.0009535$$
$$= 9.535 \times 10^{-4}$$

or
$$6.9793 - 10 = \log 9.535 \times 10^{-4}$$

PROBLEMS 36 – 4

Find the antilogarithm of each of the following logarithms:

1	0.8785	2	3.8785	3	8.8785 − 10
4	2.9948	5	1.5911	6	4.1335
7	6.1335 − 10	8	5.8686	9	8.9440
10	3.9440 − 10	11	0.00000	12	0.3010
13	0.4969	14	0.7980	15	3.7067 − 10
16	0.8952	17	1.8515	18	4.8295
19	7.4138 − 10	20	2.5061	21	9.5904 − 10
22	3.7707	23	9.9918 − 10	24	0.4627
25	5.9636	26	2.5412	27	8.4300 − 10
28	8.9600 − 20	29	3.1245	30	9.8560 − 20

36 – 15   Addition and subtraction of logarithms

Since the mantissa of a logarithm is always positive, care must be exercised in adding or subtracting logarithms.

Adding logarithms with positive characteristics is the same as adding arithmetical numbers.

EXAMPLE 16   Add the logarithms 2.7642 and 4.3046.

SOLUTION   2.7642
4.3046
7.0688

When adding logarithms with negative characteristics, you must bear in mind that the mantissas are always positive.

EXAMPLE 17   Add the logarithms $\overline{4}.3265$ and 6.2843.

SOLUTION   The mantissas are added as positive numbers, and the characteristics added algebraically:

$$\overline{4}.3265$$
$$6.2843$$
$$\text{Sum} = \overline{2}.6108$$

EXAMPLE 18   Add the logarithms $\overline{4}.3283$, $\overline{3}.7642$, and $\overline{1}.1048$.

SOLUTION $\overline{4}.3283$
$\overline{3}.7642$
$\overline{1}.1048$
$$\text{Sum} = \overline{7}.1973$$

In this example the sum of the mantissas is 1.1973 and the 1 must be carried over for addition with the characteristics. Since the 1 from the mantissa sum is positive and the characteristics are negative, they are added algebraically to obtain −7.

EXAMPLE 19   Subtract the logarithm 6.9860 from the logarithm 4.1073.

SOLUTION   4.1073
                               6.9860
               Remainder = $\overline{3}$.1213

EXAMPLE 20   Subtract the logarithm $\overline{5}$.7856 from the logarithm $\overline{2}$.6725.

SOLUTION $\overline{2}$.6725
                            $\overline{5}$.7856
               Remainder = 2.8869

In this example, in order to subtract the mantissas, it was necessary to add 1 to the mantissa minuend to make it 1.6725. This 1, which had to be positive, was taken from the characteristic −2, the subtraction resulting in −3. Therefore when the characteristic subtrahend −5 was subtracted algebraically, the remainder characteristic resulted in 2.

Another method of handling logarithms whose characteristics are negative is to express them as logarithms with a positive characteristic, writing the proper multiple of negative 10 after the mantissa.

EXAMPLE 21   Add the logarithms $\overline{4}$.3265 and 6.2843.

SOLUTION $\overline{4}$.3265 = 6.3265 − 10

                        6.3265 − 10
                        6.2843
               Sum = 12.6108 − 10 = 2.6108

Note that this is the same as Example 17.

If, in the sum, −10, −20, −30, −40, etc., appear after the mantissa and the characteristic is greater than 9, subtract from both characteristic and mantissa a multiple of 10 that will make the characteristic less than 10.

EXAMPLE 22   Add the logarithms $\overline{4}$.3283, $\overline{3}$.7642, and $\overline{1}$.1048.

SOLUTION
$$
\begin{array}{r}
6.3283 - 10 \\
7.7642 - 10 \\
\underline{9.1048 - 10} \\
23.1973 - 30 \\
\text{Sum} = \quad 3.1973 - 10
\end{array}
$$

Note that this is the same as Example 18.

When a larger logarithm is subtracted from a smaller, the characteristic of the smaller should be increased by 10 and −10 written after the mantissa to preserve equality.

EXAMPLE 23   Subtract the logarithm 6.9860 from the logarithm 4.1073.

SOLUTION
$$
\begin{array}{r}
4.1073 = 14.1073 - 10 \\
6.9860 \\
\hline
\text{Remainder} = \quad 7.1213 - 10
\end{array}
$$

Also, when a negative logarithm is subtracted from a positive logarithm, the characteristic of the minuend should be made positive by adding to it the proper multiple of 10 and writing that multiple negative after the mantissa in order to preserve equality.

EXAMPLE 24   Subtract the logarithm 5.7856 − 10 from the logarithm 1.6725.

SOLUTION   Adding 10 to the characteristic,

$$
\begin{array}{r}
1.6725 = 11.6725 - 10 \\
5.7856 - 10 \\
\hline
\text{Remainder} = \quad 5.8869
\end{array}
$$

EXAMPLE 25   Subtract the logarithm 8.6754 − 20 from the logarithm 2.4625.

SOLUTION   Adding 20 to the characteristic,

$$
\begin{array}{r}
2.4625 = 22.4625 - 20 \\
8.6754 - 20 \\
\hline
\text{Remainder} = 13.7871
\end{array}
$$

PROBLEMS 36−5

Add the following logarithms:

1	$3.6874 + 2.3265$	2	$8.7263 + 1.1289$
3	$\bar{6}.2642 + 3.7655$	4	$\bar{3}.7827 + \bar{4}.4683$
5	$8.7112 + \bar{6}.8683$	6	$\bar{7}.2863 + 3.4433$

Perform the indicated subtractions:

7	$0.3680 - \bar{2}.2562$	8	$0.1400 - \bar{4}.5611$
9	$\bar{3}.1875 - 0.2178$	10	$\bar{1}.6532 - \bar{2}.1227$
11	$8.9316 - \bar{4}.4208$	12	$\bar{6}.3217 - 4.6483$

36 – 16   **Multiplication by logarithms**

It was shown in Sec. 36–3 that the logarithm of a product is equal to the sum of the logarithms of the factors. This property, with the aid of the tables, is of value in multiplication.

EXAMPLE 26   Find the product of 2.79×684.

SOLUTION   Let p = the desired product.

Then $$p = 2.79 \times 684 \qquad\qquad [\,14\,]$$

Taking the logarithms of both members of Eq. [14],

$$\log p = \log 2.79 + \log 684$$

Looking up the logarithms and tabulating them,

$$\log 2.79 = 0.4456$$
$$\log 684 = \underline{2.8351}$$

Adding logarithms, $\log p = 3.2807$

Interpolating to find the value of p,

$\log 1{,}910 = 3.2810$	$\log p$	$= 3.2807$
$\log 1{,}900 = 3.2788$	$\log 1{,}900$	$= \underline{3.2788}$
Tabular difference $= 0.0022$	Difference	$= 0.0019$

Then the value of p is $(0.0019/0.0022) \times 10 = 8 +$ larger than 1,900. There is no need to express the result of the above division beyond one significant figure, for interpolation in a four-place table is not correct beyond four significant figures. Thus,

$$p = 1{,}900 + 8 = 1{,}908$$

The above quotient to three significant figures is 8.64. Adding this to 1,900 would have resulted in a product of 1,908.64, whereas the product obtained by actual multiplication is 1,908.36.

EXAMPLE 27   Given $X_L = 2\pi f L$. Find the value of X_L when $f = 10{,}600{,}000$ and $L = 0.0000251$. Use $2\pi = 6.28$.

SOLUTION $X_L = 6.28 \times 10{,}600{,}000 \times 0.0000251$

Taking logarithms,

$$\log X_L = \log 6.28 + \log 10{,}600{,}000 + \log 0.0000251$$

Tabulating,   log 6.28 =   0.7980
                        log 10,600,000 =   7.0253
                        log 0.0000251 =   5.3997 − 10
                              log X_L = 13.2230 − 10 = 3.2230
By interpolation, X_L = 1,671

In using logarithms, a form should be written out for all the work before beginning any computations. The form should provide places for all logarithms as taken from Table 6 and for other work necessary to complete the problem.

36 – 17   Computation with negative numbers

Because a negative number has an imaginary logarithm, the logarithms of negative numbers cannot be used in computation. However, the numerical results of multiplications and divisions are the same regardless of the algebraic signs of the factors. Therefore, to make computations involving negative numbers, first determine whether the final result will be positive or negative. Then find the numerical value of the expression by logarithms, considering all numbers as positive, and affix the proper sign to the result.

PROBLEMS 36 – 6

Compute by logarithms:

1	16×6	2	84×3
3	2×50	4	4×250
5	$2 \times 25 \times 0.02$	6	$38 \times (-42)$
7	$(-76) \times 3.4$	8	$0.0025 \times (-45)$
9	682×4.03	10	$0.906 \times (-0.0024)$
11	81.2×542	12	$2,046 \times (-1.052)$
13	$6.282 \times (-0.1592)$	14	$5 \times 8 \times 42$
15	$7.24 \times 38.6 \times 462$	16	$5.96 \times 888 \times 0.00604$
17	$(-0.00253) \times 700 \times 985$	18	$17.62 \times (-8.772) \times 0.2275$
19	$846.4 \times 405 \times 1,922$	20	$(-2,846) \times 9,438 \times (-6,848)$

36 – 18   Division by logarithms

It was shown in Sec. 36–4 that the logarithm of the quotient of two numbers is equal to the logarithm of the dividend minus the logarithm of the divisor. This property allows division by the use of logarithms.

EXAMPLE 28   Find the value of $948 \tfrac{8}{2}37$, using logarithms.
SOLUTION   Let q = quotient.

Then $q = {}^{948}\!/_{237}$
Taking logarithms, $\log q = \log 948 - \log 237$
Tabulating, $\log 948 = 2.9768$
                                      $\log 237 = \underline{2.3747}$
Subtracting, $\log q = 0.6021$
Taking antilogs, $q = 4$

EXAMPLE 29   Find the value of $-24.68/682{,}700$, using logarithms.
SOLUTION   By inspection the quotient will be negative. Let

$$q = \text{quotient}$$

Then $$q = \frac{-24.68}{682{,}700}$$

Taking logarithms, $\log q = \log 24.68 - \log 682{,}700$
Interpolating and tabulating, $\log 24.68 = 11.3923 - 10$
                                   $\log 682{,}700 = \underline{5.8342}$
Subtracting, $\log q = 5.5581 - 10$
Taking antilogs, $q = -3.615 \times 10^{-5}$

NOTE $\log 24.68 = 1.3923$, but 10 was added to the characteristic and subtracted after the mantissa in order to facilitate the subtraction of a larger logarithm, as explained in Sec. 36–15.

PROBLEMS 36 – 7
Compute by logarithms:

1 $1^{9}\!/_{5}$ 2 ${}^{60}\!/_{12}$ 3 ${}^{288}\!/_{36}$

4 $\dfrac{2{,}450}{-3.5}$ 5 $\dfrac{0.423}{0.0047}$ 6 $\dfrac{786}{-943}$

7 $\dfrac{-1{,}397}{8.742}$ 8 $\dfrac{0.0006043}{-5.763}$ 9 $\dfrac{2{,}804}{0.0009006}$

10 $\dfrac{-74.23}{-0.008040}$

36 – 19   Cologarithms

The logarithm of the reciprocal of a number is called the *cologarithm* of that number. It is abbreviated *colog*. Hence, to express the cologarithm of the number N, we write colog N. Because, by definition,

$$\text{colog } N = \log \frac{1}{N}$$

then $$\text{colog } N = \log 1 - \log N$$

Since log 1 = 0, by substituting in the above equation,

$$\log \frac{1}{N} = 0 - \log N$$

$$\therefore \log \frac{1}{N} = -\log N$$

The foregoing illustrates that the cologarithm of a number equals *minus* the logarithm of the number. The minus sign affects the entire logarithm; that is, both characteristic and mantissa of a cologarithm are negative. However, to avoid a negative mantissa in the cologarithm, we agree to subtract the logarithm of the number from 10.0000 − 10. Note that this is the same as subtracting from zero, except for the resulting sign of the mantissa.

EXAMPLE 30   Find colog 40.

SOLUTION   colog 40 = log ¼₀ = log 1 − log 40
Now   log 1 = 0

or   log 1 = 10.0000 − 10
Also,   log 40 = 1.6021
Subtracting,   colog 40 = 8.3979 − 10

EXAMPLE 31   Find colog 0.00075.

SOLUTION   log 1 = 10.0000 − 10
                 log 0.00075 = 6.8751 − 10
Subtracting,   colog 0.00075 = 3.1249

To divide by any number is the same as multiplying by the reciprocal of that number. That is,

$$^{873}\!/_{432} \text{ is the same as } 873 \times {}^{1}\!/_{432}$$

or, in general, $\dfrac{A}{N} = A \dfrac{1}{N}$

Therefore, *in computing a quotient, add the cologarithm of each factor of the denominator to the logarithm of the numerator.*

EXAMPLE 32   Evaluate $\alpha = 14.63/(0.00362 \times 8,767)$.
SOLUTION   The above could be expressed as

$$\alpha = 14.63 \cdot \frac{1}{0.00362} \cdot \frac{1}{8,767}$$

That is, $\log \alpha = \log 14.63 + \text{colog } 0.00362 + \text{colog } 8,767$

Tabulating, $\log 14.63 = 1.1652$
$\log 0.00362 = 7.5587 - 10$; hence, $\text{colog } 0.00362 = 2.4413$
$\log 8{,}767 = 3.9428$; hence, $\text{colog } 8{,}767 = \underline{6.0572 - 10}$
Adding, $\log \alpha = 9.6637 - 10$
Taking antilogs, $\alpha = 0.461$

EXAMPLE 33   Evaluate

$$\phi = (64.28 \times 0.00973)/(4{,}006 \times 0.05134 \times 0.002085).$$

SOLUTION   Always make up a skeleton form before looking up the logarithms in the tables, thus:

$$\log 64.28 =$$
$$\log 0.00973 =$$
$\log 4{,}006 \quad =$ $\text{colog } 4{,}006 =$
$\log 0.05134 \quad =$ $\text{colog } 0.05134 =$
$\log 0.002085 =$ $\text{colog } 0.002085 = \underline{\hspace{2cm}}$

$$\log \phi =$$
$$\phi =$$

Tabulating, $\log 64.28 = 1.8080$
$$\log 0.00973 = 7.9881 - 10$$
$\log 4{,}006 = 3.6027$ $\text{colog } 4{,}006 = 6.3973 - 10$
$\log 0.05134 = 8.7105 - 10$ $\text{colog } 0.05134 = 1.2895$
$\log 0.002085 = 7.3191 - 10$ $\text{colog } 0.002085 = \underline{2.6809}$
$$\log \phi = 0.1638$$
$$\therefore \phi = 1.458$$

PROBLEMS 36 – 8

Using logarithms, compute the results of the following:

1. $\dfrac{3.8 \times 2.6}{4.3}$ 2. $\dfrac{7.3 \times 9.8}{6.3 \times 8.5}$

3. $\dfrac{44.1 \times 1.82}{10.27 \times 0.32}$ 4. $\dfrac{57.4 \times 0.0347}{0.6258}$

5. $\dfrac{0.335}{326.1 \times 0.00276}$ 6. $\dfrac{1.001}{3.141 \times 0.703}$

7. $\dfrac{0.000008604}{5.28 \times 0.000000117}$ 8. $\dfrac{1}{27.98 \times 0.395 \times 0.00148}$

9. $\dfrac{1}{8.96 \times 7{,}333 \times 0.000801}$ 10. $\dfrac{6.28 \times 0.159 \times 10^{-3}}{0.00425 \times 235 \times 10^{2}}$

36 – 20 Raising to a power by logarithms

It was shown in Sec. 36–5 that the logarithm of a power of a number is equal to the logarithm of the number multiplied by the exponent of the power.

EXAMPLE 34   Find by logarithms the value of 12^3.
SOLUTION $\log 12^3 = 3 \log 12$
                           $\log 12 = 1.0792$

Multiplying by 3, $\dfrac{3}{3.2376} = \log 1{,}728$

                           $\therefore \ 12^3 = 1{,}728$

EXAMPLE 35   Find by logarithms the value of $(0.0563)^5$.
SOLUTION $\log (0.0563)^5 = 5 \log 0.0563$
                           $\log 0.0563 = 8.7505 - 10$

Multiplying by 5, $\dfrac{5}{5 \log 0.0563 = 43.7525 - 50}$

                           $= 3.7525 - 10$

                 antilog $3.7525 - 10 = 5.656 \times 10^{-7}$
                 $\therefore \ (0.0563)^5 = 5.656 \times 10^{-7}$

EXAMPLE 36   Find by logarithms the value of 5^{-3}.
SOLUTION   By the laws of exponents,

$$5^{-3} = \frac{1}{5^3}$$

Then $\log 5^{-3} = \log 1 - \log 5^3$
                           $= \log 1 - 3 \log 5$

$\log 5 = 0.6990$ $\log 1 = 10.0000 - 10$
Multiplying, $\dfrac{3}{3 \log 5 = 2.0970}$ $\dfrac{3 \log 5 = \ \ 2.0970}{\log 5^{-3} = \ \ 7.9030 - 10}$

                         antilog $7.9030 - 10 = \ \ 0.008$
                         $\therefore \ 5^{-3} = \ \ 0.008$

36 – 21   Extracting roots by logarithms

It was shown in Sec. 36–6 that the logarithm of a root of a number is equal to the logarithm of the number divided by the index of the root.

EXAMPLE 37   Find by logarithms the value of $\sqrt[3]{815}$.
SOLUTION   By the laws of exponents,

                 $\sqrt[3]{815} = (815)^{1/3}$
Then $\log (815)^{1/3} = \frac{1}{3} \log 815$
                 $\log 815 = 2.9112$

$$\frac{1}{3} \log 815 = \frac{2.9112}{3} = 0.9704$$

                 antilog $0.9704 = 9.34$
                 $\therefore \ \sqrt[3]{815} = 9.34$ to three significant figures.

EXAMPLE 38   Find by logarithms the value of $\sqrt[4]{0.00955}$.

SOLUTION $\sqrt[4]{0.00955} = (0.00955)^{1/4}$

Then $\log (0.00955)^{1/4} = \frac{1}{4} \log 0.00955$

$\log 0.00955 = 7.9800 - 10$

$\frac{1}{4} \log 0.00955 = 1.9950 - 2.5$

This result, though correct, is not in the standard form for a negative characteristic. This inconvenience can be obviated by writing the logarithm in such a manner that the negative part when divided results in a quotient of -10. Thus,

$\log 0.00955 = 7.9800 - 10$

would be written $\log 0.00955 = 37.9800 - 40.$

Since it is necessary to divide the logarithm by 4 in order to obtain the fourth root, 30 was subtracted from the negative part to make it exactly divisible by 4. Therefore, to preserve equality, it was necessary to add 30 to the positive part. Then

$$\log \sqrt[4]{0.00955} = \frac{37.9800 - 40}{4} = 9.4950 - 10$$

$$\text{antilog } 9.4950 - 10 = 0.3126$$

$$\therefore \sqrt[4]{0.00955} = 0.3126$$

36 – 22   Fractional exponents

Computations involving fractional exponents are made by combining the operations of raising to powers and extracting roots.

EXAMPLE 39   Find by logarithms the value of $\sqrt[4]{(0.0542)^3}$.

SOLUTION $\sqrt[4]{(0.0542)^3} = (0.0542)^{3/4}$

Then $\log (0.0542)^{3/4} = \frac{3}{4} \log 0.0542$

$\log 0.0542 = 8.7340 - 10$

$3 \log 0.0542 = 26.2020 - 30$

Adding 10 to the characteristic and subtracting 10 from the negative part in order to make it evenly divisible by 4,

$$3 \log 0.0542 = 36.2020 - 40$$

$$\frac{3}{4} \log 0.0542 = \frac{36.2020 - 40}{4} = 9.0505 - 10$$

$$\text{antilog } 9.0505 - 10 = 0.112$$

$$\therefore \sqrt[4]{(0.0542)^3} = 0.112$$

Instead of adding 10 to the characteristic, as above, it would also have been correct to subtract 10 from the characteristic and add 10 to the mantissa, thus obtaining $16.2020 - 20$. It is immaterial what numbers are added and subtracted as long as the resulting negative part of the logarithm will result in an integral quotient.

PROBLEMS 36–9

Using logarithms, compute the results of the following:

1	$(18.7)^3$	2	$(63.9)^6$	3	$(0.0293)^4$
4	$(0.761)^4$	5	$\sqrt[3]{987}$	6	$\sqrt[4]{815}$
7	$(0.00563)^{1/3}$	8	$(0.715)^{1/5}$	9	$(0.850)^{1/2}$
10	$\sqrt[4]{928}$	11	$(143)^{2/3}$	12	$\sqrt[3]{(8.91)^4}$
13	$(25.7)^{3/2}$		14	$(0.00314)^3$	

15 $\sqrt{\dfrac{163 \times 0.977}{14.4}}$ 16 $\sqrt[3]{\dfrac{0.541 \times 47.3}{0.0157}}$

17 $(198\!\!\not{5}\!\!\not{2}76)^{3/2}$ 18 $(534\!\!\not{5}\!\!175)^{3/2}$

19 $\sqrt[5]{0.000230} \times \sqrt[4]{387}$ 20 $\left[\dfrac{10^7 \times 0.000000683}{10^8 \times (0.00000343)^3}\right]^{3/2}$

36–23 Change of base

The natural system of logarithms has for its base the number $\epsilon = 2.71828 \ldots$. There are many formulas in the various branches of science where this base is used. A table of natural logarithms has not been included in this book because, for purposes of computation, all that is necessary is to remember that the natural logarithm of a number is approximately 2.3026 times the common logarithm of the same number. The common logarithm of a number is 0.4343 times the natural logarithm of the same number. These relations can be written

$$\log_\epsilon N = 2.3026 \log_{10} N \qquad\qquad [\,15\,]$$
$$\log_{10} N = 0.4343 \log_\epsilon N \qquad\qquad [\,16\,]$$

EXAMPLE 40 $\log_\epsilon 1{,}000 = 2.3026 \log_{10} 1{,}000 = 2.3026 \times 3 = 6.9078$

EXAMPLE 41 $\log_{10} 100 = 0.4343 \log_\epsilon 100 = 0.4343 \times 4.6052 = 2.0000$

EXAMPLE 42   Given $x = \log_\epsilon 48$. Solve for x.

SOLUTION $\log_\epsilon 48 = 2.3026 \log_{10} 48 = 2.3026 \times 1.6812$
$x = 3.871$

36–24 Graph of $y = \log_{10} x$

The graph of $y = \log_{10} x$ is shown in Fig. 36–1. A study of this graph shows the following:

1. A negative number has no real logarithm.

2. The logarithm of a positive number less than 1 (a decimal between 0 and 1) is negative.

3. The logarithm of 1 is zero.

4. The logarithm of a positive number greater than 1 is positive.

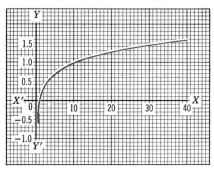

Fig. 36–1   Graph of the equation $y = \log_{10} x$.

5. As the number approaches zero, its logarithm decreases without limit.

6. As the number increases indefinitely, its logarithm increases without limit.

Is the method of interpolation that treats a short distance on the logarithmic curve as a straight line sufficiently accurate for computation?

36 – 25   Logarithmic equations

An equation in which there appears the logarithm of some expression involving the unknown quantity is called a *logarithmic equation*.

Logarithmic equations have wide application in electric-circuit analysis. In addition, the communication engineer uses them in computations involving decibels and transmission-line characteristics.

EXAMPLE 43   Solve the equation $4 \log x + 3.7960 = 4.6990 + \log x$.

SOLUTION   Given $4 \log x + 3.7960 = 4.6990 + \log x$

Transposing, $4 \log x - \log x = 4.6990 - 3.7960$

Collecting terms, $3 \log x = 0.9030$

D:3, $\log x = 0.3010$

From tables or slide rule, $x = 2$

In solving logarithmic equations, the logarithm of the unknown, as $\log x$ in Example 43, is considered as any other literal coefficient.

That is, in general, the rules for solving ordinary algebraic equations apply to logarithmic equations.

A common error made by students in solving logarithmic equations is confusing coefficients of logarithms with coefficients of the unknown. For example,

$$3 \log x \neq \log 3x$$

because the left member denotes the product of 3 times the logarithm of x, whereas the right member denotes the logarithm of the quantity 3 times x, that is, $\log (3x)$.

EXAMPLE 44   Given $500 = 276 \log (d/0.05)$. Solve for d.

SOLUTION   Given $500 = 276 \log \dfrac{d}{0.05}$

Then $500 = 276 \,(\log d - \log 0.05)$

D:276, $1.81 = \log d - \log 0.05$

Transposing, $\log d = 1.81 + \log 0.05$

Substituting $8.6990 - 10$ for $\log 0.05$, $\log d = 1.81 + 8.6990 - 10$

Collecting terms, $\log d = 0.5090$

From tables or slide rule, $d = 3.23$

ALTERNATE SOLUTION   Given $500 = 276 \log \dfrac{d}{0.05}$

D:276, $1.81 = \log \dfrac{d}{0.05}$

Taking antilogs of both members, $64.6 = \dfrac{d}{0.05}$

Solving for d, $d = 3.23$

36 – 26   Exponential equations

An equation in which the unknown appears in an exponent is called an *exponential equation*. In the equation

$$x^3 = 125$$

it is necessary to find some value of x that, when cubed, will equal 125. In this equation *the exponent is a constant.*

In the *exponential equation*

$$5^x = 125$$

the situation is different. *The unknown appears as an exponent,* and it is now necessary to find to what power 5 must be raised to obtain 125.

Some exponential equations can be solved by inspection. For example, the value of x in the foregoing equation is 3. In general, taking the logarithms of both sides of an exponential equation will result in a logarithmic equation that can be solved by the usual methods.

EXAMPLE 45   Given $4^x = 256$. Solve for x.

SOLUTION   Given $4^x = 256$

Taking the logarithms of both members, $\log 4^x = \log 256$

or $x \log 4 = \log 256$

D:$\log 4$, $x = \dfrac{\log 256}{\log 4}$

From tables or slide rule, $x = \dfrac{2.408}{0.602} = 4$

CHECK $4^4 = 256$

EXAMPLE 46   Given $5^{x-3} = 52$. Solve for x.

SOLUTION   Given $5^{x-3} = 52$

Taking the logarithms of both members, $\log 5^{x-3} = \log 52$

or $(x - 3) \log 5 = \log 52$

D:$\log 5$, $x - 3 = \dfrac{\log 52}{\log 5}$

From tables or slide rule, $x - 3 = \dfrac{1.716}{0.699}$

A:3, $x = \dfrac{1.716}{0.699} + 3$

or $x = 5.46$

How is this solution checked?

PROBLEMS 36 – 10

Solve the following equations:

1 $x = \log_e 508$

2 $x = \log_e 1.25$

3 $\log x + 2 \log x = 3$

4 $\log x + \log 10x = 101$
   (HINT: $\log 10x = \log 10 + \log x$.)

5 $\log 3x + 3 \log x = 20$

6 $\log \dfrac{P}{4} = 16$ $P = 4 \times 10^{16}$

7 $\log \dfrac{P_1}{6} = 1.3$

8 $\log \dfrac{6}{E} = 0.1$

9 $\log x^2 - \log x = 0.3$

10 $x^3 = 216$

11 $2^x = 16$

12 $3^x = 81$

13 $2^x = 10$

14 $3^{x-2} = 10$ $x = 4.096$

15 $4^{2x} = 100$

16 $x^{2.3} = 14$

17 In an inductive circuit, the equation for the growth of current is given by

$$i = \frac{E}{R}(1 - \epsilon^{-\frac{Rt}{L}}) \qquad \textbf{amp} \qquad [\,17\,]$$

where i = current, amp

　　　t = any elapsed time after switch is closed, sec

　　　E = constant impressed voltage, volts

　　　L = inductance of the circuit, henrys

　　　R = circuit resistance, Ω

　　　ϵ = base of natural system of logarithms

A circuit of 0.75-henry inductance and 15-Ω resistance is connected across a 12-volt battery. What is the value of the current at the end of 0.06 sec after the circuit is closed?

SOLUTION　　　The circuit is shown in Fig. 36–2.

Given　　　　　　$$i = \frac{E}{R}(1 - \epsilon^{-\frac{Rt}{L}})$$

Substituting the known values,

$$i = {}^{12}\!\!/_{15}(1 - \epsilon^{-\frac{15 \times 0.06}{0.75}})$$
$$= 0.8(1 - \epsilon^{-1.2})$$

Multiplying,　　　　$i = 0.8 - 0.8\epsilon^{-1.2}$

or　　　　　　　　$$i = 0.8 - \frac{0.8}{\epsilon^{1.2}} \qquad\qquad [\,18\,]$$

Now　　　　　$\log_{10}\epsilon^{1.2} = 1.2\log_{10}\epsilon = 1.2 \times 0.4343$
$$= 0.5212$$

Taking antilogs,　　$\epsilon^{1.2} = 3.32$

Substituting the value of $\epsilon^{1.2}$ in Eq. [18],

$$i = 0.8 - \frac{0.8}{3.32} = 0.559\ \text{amp}$$

The growth of the current in the circuit of Fig. 36–2 is shown graphically in Fig. 36–3.

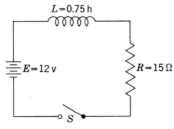

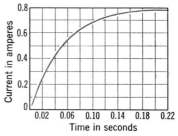

FIG. 36–2   Circuit for Probs. 17 to 20.

FIG. 36–3   Graph of current in RL circuit.

18   The inductance of the circuit of Fig. 36–2 is doubled, and the resistance is thus increased 1.4 times its original value.   Other circuit values remaining the same, what will be the value of the current 0.06 sec after the switch is closed?

19   Using the circuit values of Fig. 36–2, what will be the value of the current (*a*) 1 sec after the switch is closed, (*b*) 2 sec after the switch is closed?

20   In the circuit of Fig. 36–2, after the switch is closed, how long will it take the current to reach 50 per cent of its maximum value?

21   If $\dfrac{L}{R}$ is substituted for t in the equation $i = \dfrac{E}{R} (1 - \epsilon^{-\frac{Rt}{L}})$, show that the value of the current i will be 63.2 per cent of its steady-state value.   The numerical value of $\dfrac{L}{R}$ in seconds is known as the circuit *time constant*.   It is useful in determining the rapidity with which current rises or falls in one inductive circuit in comparison with others.

22   A certain 220-volt generator shunt field has an inductance of 15 henrys and a resistance of 100 Ω.   How long, after the line voltage is applied, does it take for the current to reach 75 per cent of its maximum value?

23   A relay of 1.2 henrys inductance and 500 Ω resistance is to be used for keying a radio transmitter.   The relay is to be operated from a 110-volt line, and 0.175 amp is required to close the contacts.   How many words per minute will the relay carry if each word is considered as five letters of five impulses per letter?   The time of opening of the contacts is the same as the time required to close them.

HINT: $0.175 = \dfrac{110}{500} (1 - \epsilon^{-\frac{500t}{1.2}})$. t is the time required to close the relay.

24   Using the relay of Prob. 23, how many words per minute would it carry if 50 Ω resistance were connected in series with the relay?   The line voltage remains at 110 volts.

25   In a capacitive circuit the equation for the current is given by

$$i = \frac{E}{R} \epsilon^{-\frac{t}{RC}} \qquad \text{amp} \qquad\qquad [\,19\,]$$

where i = current, amp
        t = any elapsed time after switch is closed, sec
        E = impressed voltage, volts
        C = capacitance of the circuit, farads
        R = circuit resistance, Ω
        ϵ = base of natural system of logarithms

A capacitance of 20 μf in series with 500 Ω is connected across a 110-volt generator.

(*a*) What is the value of the current at the instant the switch is closed?
        HINT: $t = 0$.

(b) What is the value of the current 0.007 sec after the switch is closed? The circuit is shown in Fig. 36-4.

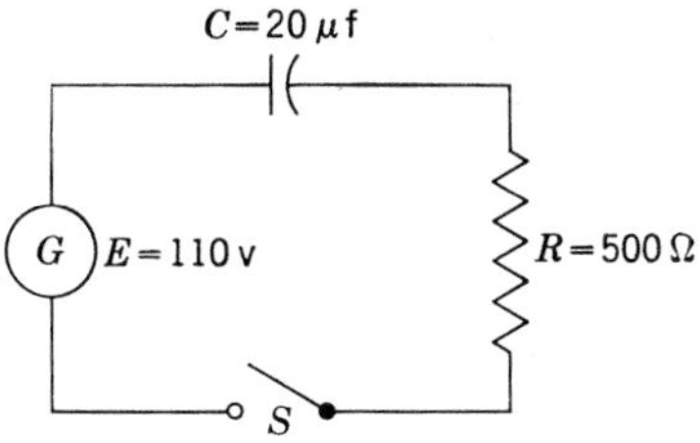

26 In the circuit of Fig. 36-4, how long after the switch is closed will the current have decayed to 30 per cent of its initial value? SOLUTION $E = 110$ volts, $R = 500$ Ω, $C = 20$ μf, and $i = 0.3E/R$. $t = ?$

$$i = \frac{0.3E}{R} = \frac{0.3 \times 110}{500} = 0.066 \text{ amp}$$

Substituting in Eq. [19],

Simplifying,

or

D:0.22,

By the law of exponents,

M:ϵ^{100t}

D:0.3,

Taking logarithms,

That is,

Then

or

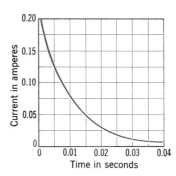

$C = 20\,\mu f$

G $E = 110$ v

$R = 500\,\Omega$

S

FIG. 36-4 Circuit of Probs. 25 and 26.

$$0.066 = \frac{110}{500}\,\epsilon^{-\frac{t}{500 \times 20 \times 10^{-6}}}$$

$$0.066 = 0.22\,\epsilon^{-\frac{t}{10^{-2}}}$$

$$0.066 = 0.22\,\epsilon^{-100t}$$

$$0.3 = \epsilon^{-100t}$$

$$0.3 = \frac{1}{\epsilon^{100t}}$$

$$0.3\epsilon^{100t} = 1$$

$$\epsilon^{100t} = 3.33$$

$$\log_{10} \epsilon^{100t} = \log_{10} 3.33$$

$$100t \log_{10} \epsilon = \log_{10} 3.33$$

$$100t \times 0.4343 = 0.5224$$

$$43.43t = 0.5224$$

$$\therefore t = 0.012 \text{ sec}$$

The decay of the current in the circuit of Fig. 36-4 is shown graphically in Fig. 36-5.

27 A 30-μf capacitor in series with a resistance of 1,000 Ω is connected across a 220-volt source.

(a) What is the initial value of the current?

(b) How long after the switch is closed will the current have decayed to 36.8 per cent of its initial value?

(c) Is the time obtained in (b) equal to CR sec? The product of CR, in seconds, is the time constant of a capacitive circuit.

28 The quantity of charge on a capacitor is given by

$$q = CE(1 - \epsilon^{-\frac{t}{CR}}) \qquad [20]$$

where q is the quantity of electricity in coulombs.

FIG. 36-5 Graph of current in RC circuit.

(a) Calculate the charge q in coulombs on a capacitor of 50 μf in series with a resistance of 2,000 Ω, 0.03 sec after being connected across a 100-volt source.

(b) What is the voltage across the capacitor at the end of 0.03 sec?

29 A key-click filter consisting of a 2-μf capacitor in series with a resistance is connected across the keying contacts of a transmitter. If the average time of impulse is 0.004 sec, calculate the value of the series resistance required in order that the capacitor can discharge 90 per cent in this time.

HINT: Under steady-state conditions, $q = CE$. Then

$$0.9CE = CE(1 - \epsilon^{-\frac{t}{RC}})$$

30 The emission current in amperes of a heated filament is given by

$$I = AT^2 \epsilon^{-\frac{B}{T}} \qquad [21]$$

For a tungsten filament, $A = 60$ and $B = 52,400$. Find the current of such a filament at a temperature $T = 2500°K$.

31 An important triode formula is

$$I_p + I_g = K\left(E_g + \frac{E_p}{\mu}\right)^{3/2}$$

where I_p = plate current
I_g = grid current
E_g = grid voltage
E_p = plate voltage
μ = amplification factor

Calculate $I_p + I_g$ if $K = 0.0005$, $E_g = 5$ volts, $E_p = 250$ volts, and $\mu = 8$.

32 The diameter of No. 0000 wire is 460 mils, and that of No. 36 is 5 mils. There are 38 wire sizes between No. 0000 and No. 36; therefore the ratio between cross-sectional areas of successive sizes is the thirty-ninth root of the ratio of the area of No. 0000 wire to that of No. 36 wire, or $\sqrt[39]{(460)^2/5^2}$. Compute the value of this ratio. Because this ratio is nearly equal to $\sqrt[3]{2}$, we can use the approximation that the cross-sectional area of a wire doubles for every decrease of three sizes, as explained in Sec. 14–5.

CHAPTER 37
APPLICATIONS OF LOGARITHMS

Proficiency in the use of logarithmic equations will be an asset as you study their application to decibels, transmission lines, and other aspects of electronic systems.

Derived from the original international transmission unit, which is called the *bel* in honor of the inventor of the telephone, Alexander Graham Bell, the decibel is probably the most widely used (and misused) unit in electronics engineering. A thorough understanding of the applications and uses of this unit is essential to the student of electronics.

37 – 1 Power ratios—the decibel

The Weber-Fechner law states that "the minimum change in stimulus necessary to produce a perceptible change in response is proportional to the stimulus already existing." With respect to our sense of hearing, this means that the ear considers as equal changes of sound intensity those changes which are in the same *ratio*.

The above is more easily understood from a consideration of sound intensities. Any volume of sound must be changed approximately 25 per cent before the ear notes a change in volume. If the volume is increased by this amount, in order for the ear to detect another increase in volume, the new value must be increased by an additional 25 per cent. For example, the output of an amplifier delivering 16 watts would have to be increased to a new output of 20 watts in order for the ear to discern the increase in volume. Then, in order for the ear to detect an additional increase in volume, the output would have to be increased 25 per cent of 20 watts to a new output of 25 watts.

From the foregoing it is apparent that a *change* of volume, for example, from 10 to 20 mw (a 10-mw change), would seem the same as the *change* from 100 to 200 mw (a 100-mw change) because $20/10 = 200/100$. Since these changes in hearing response are equally spaced on a logarithmic scale, it follows that the ear responds logarithmically to variations in sound intensity. Therefore, any unit used for expressing power gains or losses in communication circuits must, in order to be practical, vary logarithmically. This unit is the *decibel*, which is one-tenth (deci) of the bel previously mentioned. The abbreviation for decibel is db. A difference of 1 db between two sound intensities is just discernible to the ear. By definition,

$$\textbf{Decibels} = \textbf{db} = \textbf{10 log}_{10} \frac{P_2}{P_1} \qquad [1]$$

where P_2/P_1 is the ratio of the two powers being compared.

EXAMPLE 1   A power of 10 mw is required to drive an a-f amplifier. The output of the amplifier is 120 mw. What is the gain, expressed in decibels?
SOLUTION $P_1 = 10$ mw, and $P_2 = 120$ mw. db = ?
Substituting in Eq. [1],

$$db = 10 \log 120/10 = 10 \log 12 = 10.8 \text{ db gain}$$

EXAMPLE 2   A network has a loss of 16 db. What power ratio corresponds to this loss?

SOLUTION   Given $db = 10 \log \frac{P_2}{P_1}$ \qquad [1]

Substituting 16 for db, $16 = 10 \log \frac{P_2}{P_1}$

D:10, $1.6 = \log \frac{P_2}{P_1}$

Taking antilogs of both members,

$$39.8 = \frac{P_2}{P_1}$$

Thus, a loss of 16 db corresponds to a power ratio of 39.8:1.

Because db is 10 times the log of the power ratio, it is evident that power ratios of $10 = 10$ db, $100 = 20$ db, $1,000 = 30$ db, etc. Therefore, it could have been determined by inspection that the 16-db loss in the previous example represented a power ratio somewhere between 10 and 100. This is evident by the figure 1 of 16 db. The second digit 6 of 16 db is ten times the logarithm of 3.98; hence, 16 db represents a power ratio of 39.8.

A loss in decibels is customarily denoted by the minus sign. Thus, a loss of 16 db is written -16 db.

EXAMPLE 3   A certain radio receiver utilizes a type 6F6 vacuum tube as a final audio stage that delivers 4,500 mw to the loud-speaker. The owner is considering modifying the circuit in order to substitute a type 6L6 tube for the 6F6. The 6L6 tube will deliver 6,500 mw to the speaker. Is the gain in power sufficient to warrant the expense of making this change?

SOLUTION   By changing to the 6L6 tube the power output is increased by a ratio of 1.44, nearly 1.5 times. Those not familiar with the use of the decibel would probably think that an increase in power of almost 45 per cent would justify making the change. However, by expressing the power ratio in terms of decibels, it is evident that, as far as the ear is concerned, very little is gained.

Substituting in Eq. [1],

$$db = 10 \log {}^{6500}\!/_{4500} = 10 \times 0.1596 = 1.6$$

Such an increase in power would hardly be worth the owner's effort.

Expressing the gain or loss of various circuits or apparatus in terms of decibels obviates the necessity of computing gains or losses by multiplication and division. Because the decibel is a logarithmic unit, the total gain of a circuit is found by adding the individual decibel gains and losses of the various circuit components.

EXAMPLE 4   A dynamic microphone with an output of $-$ 85 db is connected to a preamplifier with a gain of 60 db. The output of the preamplifier is connected through an attenuation pad with a loss of 10 db to a final amplifier with a gain of 90 db. What is the total gain?

SOLUTION   In this example, all decibel values have been taken from a common reference level. Because the microphone is 85 db below reference level, the preamplifier brings the level up to $-85 + 60 = -25$ db. The attenuation pad then reduces the level to $-25 - 10 = -35$ db. Finally, the final amplifier causes a net gain of $-35 + 90 = 55$ db gain. Hence, it is apparent that the over-all gain in any system is simply the algebraic sum of the decibel gains or losses of the associated circuit components. Thus, $-85 + 60 - 10 + 90 = 55$ db gain.

37 – 2   Reference levels

You should remember that the decibel is not an absolute quantity but refers merely to a *change* which expresses a power ratio. It would be meaningless to say, for example, that a certain amplifier has an output of so many decibels unless that output is referred to some power level.

Several zero-reference or zero-decibel levels have been used in the past, and several are presently used. For example, telephone engineers use a transmission unit (TU) based on the attenuation of 1 mile of standard telephone cable which is equal to 1 db at a transmission frequency of approximately 796 cps (ω = 5,000). Several receiver and amplifier manufacturers use 0.006 watt (6 mw) as their reference, or zero, level.

A zero reference level of 1 mw is often expressed as zero dbm, where reference is given to the term db, and, as such, may be employed as a measure of absolute power values.

The volume unit, abbreviated VU, is used in broadcasting and is based on the amplitude of the program frequencies throughout the system. The standard volume indicator (VU meter) is calibrated in terms of decibels, with zero level corresponding to 1 mw of power in a 600-Ω line under steady-state conditions. Owing to the ballistic characteristics of the instrument, the scale markings are referred to as volume units and correspond to dbm only in the case of steady-state sine-wave voltages.

Other reference levels such as dba (db adjusted) and dbRN (db above reference noise) are in use. The importance of the foregoing is the realization of the necessity of knowing *what zero level* is being used in expressing gain or loss in decibels.

EXAMPLE 5   How much power is represented by a gain of 23 db if zero level is 6 mw?

SOLUTION   Substituting 23 for db and 6 for P_1 in Eq. [1],

$$23 = 10 \log \frac{P_2}{6}$$

D:10, $$2.3 = \log \frac{P_2}{6}$$

Taking antilogs of both members, $$199.5 = \frac{P_2}{6}$$

$$\therefore P^2 = 1,197 \text{ mw}$$

CHECK
$$23 = 10 \log \frac{1,197}{6}$$
$$23 = 10 \log 199.5$$
$$23 = 10 \times 2.3$$

ALTERNATE SOLUTION
$$2.3 = \log \frac{P_2}{6}$$

or $\qquad 2.3 = \log P_2 - \log 6$

Transposing, $\qquad \log P_2 = 2.3 + \log 6$

Substituting the value of log 6, $\qquad \log P_2 = 2.3 + 0.778$

$$\log P_2 = 3.078$$

Taking antilogs, $\qquad P_2 = 1,197 \text{ mw}$

EXAMPLE 6   How much power is represented by -64 db if zero level is 6 mw?

SOLUTION   Substituting -64 for db and 6 for P_1 in Eq. [1],

$$-64 = 10 \log \frac{P_2}{6}$$

D :10, $\qquad -6.4 = \log \frac{P_2}{6}$

The left member of the above equation is a logarithm with a negative mantissa because the entire number 6.4 is negative. Hence, to express this logarithm with a positive mantissa the equation is written

$$(3.6 - 10) = \log \frac{P_2}{6}$$

Taking antilogs of both members,
$$3.98 \times 10^{-7} = \frac{P_2}{6}$$

$$\therefore P_2 = 2.39 \times 10^{-6} \text{ mw}$$

CHECK $\qquad -64 = 10 \log \frac{2.39 \times 10^{-6}}{6} = 10 \log 3.98 \times 10^{-7}$

$$-64 = 10(3.6 - 10)$$
$$-64 = -64$$

ALTERNATE SOLUTION $\qquad -6.4 = \log \frac{P_2}{6}$

Then $\qquad -6.4 = \log P_2 - \log 6$

Transposing, $\qquad \log P_2 = \log 6 - 6.4$

Substituting the value of log 6, $\log P_2 = 0.778 - 6.4$

$$= (10.78 - 10) - 6.4$$

$$\therefore P_2 = 2.39 \times 10^{-6} \text{ mw}$$

If the larger power is always placed in the numerator of the power ratio, the quotient will always be greater than 1; therefore, the characteristic of the logarithm of the ratio will always be zero or a positive value. In this manner the use of a negative characteristic is avoided. As an illustration, from Example 6,

$$-6.4 = \log \frac{P_2}{6}$$

which is the same as $6.4 = \log 6 - \log P_2$

Hence, $6.4 = \log \frac{6}{P_2}$

It is always apparent whether there is a gain or a loss in decibels; therefore, the proper sign can be affixed after working the problem.

37 – 3   Current and voltage ratios

Fundamentally, the decibel is a measure of the ratio of two powers. However, voltage ratios and current ratios can be utilized for computing the decibel gain or loss provided that the input and output impedances are taken into account.

In the following derivations, P_1 and P_2 will represent the power input and power output, respectively, and R_1 and R_2 will represent the input and output impedances, respectively.

Then $P_1 = \dfrac{E_1{}^2}{R_1}$ and $P_2 = \dfrac{E_2{}^2}{R_2}$

Since $db = 10 \log \dfrac{P_2}{P_1}$

substituting for P_1 and P_2,

$$db = 10 \log \frac{E_2{}^2/R_2}{E_1{}^2/R_1}$$

$$\therefore db = 10 \log \frac{E_2{}^2 R_1}{E_1{}^2 R_2} = 10 \log \left(\frac{E_2}{E_1}\right)^2 \frac{R_1}{R_2}$$

$$= 10 \log \left(\frac{E_2}{E_1}\right)^2 + 10 \log \frac{R_1}{R_2}$$

$$= 20 \log \frac{E_2}{E_1} + 10 \log \frac{R_1}{R_2} \qquad [\,2\,]$$

$$= 20 \log \frac{E_2\sqrt{R_1}}{E_1\sqrt{R_2}} \qquad [\,3\,]$$

Similarly, $P_1 = I_1{}^2 R_1$ and $P_2 = I_2{}^2 R_2$

Then, since $db = 10 \log \dfrac{P_2}{P_1}$

by substituting for P_1 and P_2,

$$db = 10 \log \frac{I_2{}^2 R_2}{I_1{}^2 R_1}$$

$$= 20 \log \frac{I_2}{I_1} + 10 \log \frac{R_2}{R_1} \qquad [\,4\,]$$

$$= 20 \log \frac{I_2\sqrt{R_2}}{I_1\sqrt{R_1}} \qquad [\,5\,]$$

If, in both the above cases, the impedances R_1 and R_2 are *equal*, they will cancel and the following formulas will result:

$$\text{db} = 20 \log \frac{E_2}{E_1} \qquad\qquad [6]$$

and

$$\text{db} = 20 \log \frac{I_2}{I_1} \qquad\qquad [7]$$

It is evident that voltage or current ratios can be translated into decibels *only* when the impedances across which the voltages exist or into which the currents flow are taken into account.

EXAMPLE 7   An amplifier has an input resistance of 200 Ω and an output resistance of 6,400 Ω. When 0.5 volt is applied across the input, a voltage of 400 volts appears across the output. (*a*) What is the power output of the amplifier? (*b*) What is the gain in decibels?

SOLUTION   (*a*) Power output $= P_o = \dfrac{E_o^2}{R_o} = \dfrac{(400)^2}{6,400} = 25$ watts

(*b*) Power input $\;= P_i = \dfrac{E_i^2}{R_i} = \dfrac{(0.5)^2}{200} = 1.25 \times 10^{-3}$ watt

Power gain $\;= 10 \log \dfrac{P_o}{P_i} = 10 \log \dfrac{25}{1.25 \times 10^{-3}} = 43$ db

Check the solution by substituting the values of the voltages and resistances in Eq. [3].

$$\text{db} = 20 \log \frac{E_o}{E_i} \sqrt{\frac{R_i}{R_o}} = 20 \log \frac{400}{0.5} \sqrt{\frac{200}{6,400}} = 43$$

37 – 4   The merit, or gain, of an antenna

The merit of an antenna, especially one designed for directive transmission or reception, is usually expressed in terms of antenna *gain*. The gain is generally taken as the ratio of the power that must be supplied to some standard-comparison antenna to the power that must be supplied the antenna under test in order to produce the same field strengths in the desired direction at the receiving antenna. Similarly, the gain of one antenna over another could be taken as the ratio of their respective radiated fields.

The "effective radiated power" of an antenna is the product of the antenna power times the antenna power gain.

EXAMPLE 8   One kilowatt is supplied to a rhombic antenna which results in a field strength of 20 μv/meter at the receiving station. In order to produce the same field strength at the receiving station, a half-wave antenna, properly oriented and located near the rhombic, must be supplied with 16.6 kw. What is the gain of the rhombic?

SOLUTION   Because the same antenna is used for reception, both transmitting antennas deliver the same power to the receiver.

Hence, $$db = 10 \log \frac{P_2}{P_1} = 10 \log \frac{16.6}{1} = 12.2$$

PROBLEMS 37 – 1

1 How many decibels correspond to a power ratio of (a) 25, (b) 47.5, (c) $\frac{1}{195}$, (d) $\frac{1}{38}$?

2 Referred to equal impedances, how many decibels correspond to a voltage ratio of (a) 57, (b) 13.9, (c) $\frac{1}{115}$, (d) $\frac{1}{76}$?

3 If 0 db is taken as 6 mw, how much voltage across a 500-Ω load does this represent? How much current flows through the load?

4 If 0 db is taken as 6 mw, how much voltage across a 600-Ω load does this represent? How much current flows through the load?

5 If reference level is taken as 12.5 mw, how much voltage across a 500-Ω load does this represent? How much current flows through the load?

6 If reference level is taken as 12.5 mw, how much voltage across a 600-Ω load does this represent? How much current flows through the load?

7 If 0 db is 6 mw, compute the power in milliwatts and voltage across a 600-Ω load for the following output meter readings: (a) 5 db, (b) 12 db, (c) −6 db, (d) −10 db.

8 If 0 db is 12.5 mw, compute the power in milliwatts and voltage across a 600-Ω load for the following output meter readings: (a) 2 db, (b) 10 db, (c) −12 db, (d) −4 db.

9 An amplifier is rated as having a 90-db gain. What power ratio does this represent?

10 The amplifier of Prob. 9 has equal input and output impedances. What is the ratio of output current to input current?

11 An amplifier has a gain of 40 dbm. What is its power output?

12 The manufacturer of a high-fidelity 70-watt power amplifier claims that hum and noise in his amplifier is 90 db below full output. How much hum and noise power does this represent?

13 A network has a loss of 20 db. What power ratio corresponds to this loss?

14 If the network of Prob. 13 has equal input and output impedances, what is the ratio of the output voltage to the input voltage?

15 The noise level of a certain telephone line used for carrying broadcast programs is 55 db down from the program level of 12.5 mw. How much power is represented by the noise level?

16 A certain crystal microphone is rated at −80 db. There is on hand a

For radio frequencies, more accurate results are obtained by the approximate relation

$$L \cong 9.21 \times 10^{-9} \log_{10} \frac{d}{r} \qquad \textbf{henrys/cm} \qquad [\,9\,]$$

where L is the inductance in henrys per centimeter, with d and r having the same values as in Eq. [8].

37 – 7   **The capacitance of a line**

The capacitance of a two-wire open-air line is

$$C = \frac{0.0194l}{\log_{10}\dfrac{d}{r}} \qquad \mu\textbf{f} \qquad [\,10\,]$$

where C = capacitance of line, μf
     l = length of line, miles
     d = distance between wire centers
     r = radius of each wire (in same units as d)

EXAMPLE 10   What is the capacitance per mile of a line consisting of No. 00 copper wires spaced 4 ft apart?

SOLUTION   Diameter of No. 00 = 365 mils; thus radius = 0.1825 in.

$$\frac{d}{r} = \frac{48}{0.182} = 263$$

$$\log_{10} 263 = 2.42$$

Then $\quad C = \dfrac{0.0194}{2.42} = \dfrac{19.4 \times 10^{-3}}{2.42} = 8.02 \times 10^{-3}\ \mu\text{f/mile}$

For radio frequencies, more accurate results are obtained by the equation

$$C \cong \frac{1}{9.21 \times 10^{-9}\ c^2 \log_{10} \dfrac{d}{r}} \qquad \textbf{farads/cm} \qquad [\,11\,]$$

where C is the capacitance in farads per centimeter and c is the velocity of light (3×10^{10} cm/sec), with d and r having the same values as in Eq. [10].

The capacitance of submarine cables and of cables laid in metal sheaths is given by

$$C = \frac{0.0388Kl}{\log_{10} \dfrac{d_1}{d_2}} \qquad \mu\textbf{f} \qquad [\,12\,]$$

where C = capacitance of line, μf

$\quad\quad K$ = relative dielectric constant of insulation

$\quad\quad l$ = length of line, miles

$\quad\quad d_1$ = inside diameter of outer conductor

$\quad\quad d_2$ = outside diameter of inner conductor

EXAMPLE 11   A No. 14 copper wire is lead-sheathed. The wire is insulated with $\frac{1}{8}$-in. gutta percha. $(K = 4.1.)$ What is the capacitance for 1,000 ft of this cable?

SOLUTION $\quad\quad\quad\quad d_2$ = diameter of No. 14 = 0.0640 in.

$$d_1 = 0.0640 + 2(\tfrac{1}{8}) = 0.314 \text{ in.}$$

$$\log \frac{d_1}{d_2} = \log \frac{0.314}{0.0640} = \log 4.91 = 0.691$$

$$l = \frac{1,000}{5,280}$$

Then $\quad\quad C = \dfrac{0.0388Kl}{\log \dfrac{d_1}{d_2}} = \dfrac{0.0388 \times 4.1 \times 1,000}{0.691 \times 5,280} = 0.0436 \ \mu f$

PROBLEMS 37 – 2

1 What is the inductance of a 50-mile line consisting of two No. 0 copper wires spaced 3 ft between centers?

2 What is the inductance of a 14-mile line consisting of No. 10 copper wire spaced 2 ft between centers?

3 A transmission line 15,000 ft long consists of two No. 00 solid copper wires having a spacing of 20 in. between centers. Determine (a) the inductance of the line, (b) the capacitance of the line.

4 If the spacing of the above line was 4 ft between wire centers, what would be (a) the inductance of the line, (b) the capacitance of the line?

5 A two-wire line, 20 miles long, consisting of No. 0 solid copper is to be erected. In order that the capacitance of the line will not exceed 0.166 μf, what must be the minimum spacing between wire centers?

6 In order that a two-wire line, 13.5 miles long, consisting of No. 00 solid copper wire will not exceed a capacitance of 0.00750 μf/mile, what must be the minimum spacing between wire centers?

7 A lead-sheathed underground cable consists of No. 000 copper wire covered with 0.5 in. rubber insulation. $(K = 4.3.)$ What is the capacitance per mile?

8 A lead-sheathed cable consisting of No. 1 copper wire with 0.5 in. rubber insulation $(K = 4.3)$ is open-circuited. A capacitance bridge measures 0.19 μf between the conductor and sheath. How far out is the break?

9   What is the capacitance per mile of the cable of Prob. 8?

10 The cable of Prob. 7 becomes open-circuited. A capacitance bridge measures 0.622 μf. How far out is the break?

11 The value of the current in a line at a point l miles from the source of power is given by $i = I_o\epsilon^{-Kl}$, where I_o is the current at the source and K is the attenuation constant. In a certain line, the attenuation $K = 0.02$ db/mile. Find the length of line where i is 10 per cent of the original current I_o.

HINT: $0.1I_o = I_o\epsilon^{-0.02l}$. $l = ?$

12 If the attenuation of a line is 0.015 db/mile, how far from the power source will the current have decreased to 75 per cent of its original value?

13 A two-wire open-air transmission line is used to couple a receiving antenna to the receiver. The line is 500 ft long and consists of No. 12 wire spaced 6⅛ in. between centers. Using Eqs. [9] and [11], find (a) inductance per centimeter of the line, (b) capacitance per centimeter of the line, (c) inductance of the entire line, (d) capacitance of the entire line.

14 A two-wire open-air transmission line is used to couple a radio transmitter to the antenna. The line is 1,000 ft long and consists of No. 10 wire spaced 7.6 in. Using Eqs. [9] and [11], find (a) inductance of the line, (b) capacitance of the line?

37 – 8 Characteristic impedances of r-f transmission lines

The most important characteristic of a transmission line is the *characteristic impedance*, denoted by Z_0 and expressed in ohms. This impedance is often called *surge impedance, surge resistance,* or *iterative impedance.*

The value of the characteristic impedance is determined by the construction of the line, that is, by the size of the conductors and their spacing. At radio frequencies, the characteristic impedance can be considered to be a resistance, the value of which is given by

$$Z_0 = \sqrt{\frac{L}{C}} \quad \Omega \qquad [\,13\,]$$

where L and C are the inductance and capacitance, respectively, per unit length of line as given in Eqs. [9] and [11]. The unit of length selected for L and C is immaterial as long as the *same* unit is used for both.

Substituting the values of L and C for a two-wire open-air transmission line in Eq. [13] results in

$$Z_0 = 276 \log_{10} \frac{d}{r} \quad \Omega \qquad [\,14\,]$$

where d is the spacing between wire centers and r is the radius of the conductors *in the same units as d*. Note that the characteristic impedance is *not* a function of the length of the line.

EXAMPLE 12   A transmission line is made of No. 10 wire spaced 12 in. between centers. What is the characteristic impedance of the line?

SOLUTION $d = 12$ in. Diameter of No. 10 wire $= 0.102$ in.; therefore, $r = 0.051$ in.

$$Z_0 = 276 \log \frac{d}{r} = 276 \log \frac{12}{0.051}$$

$$= 276 \log 235 = 276 \times 2.37$$

$$Z_0 = 654 \; \Omega$$

The characteristic impedance of a concentric line is given by

$$Z_0 = 138 \log_{10} \frac{d_1}{d_2} \qquad \Omega \qquad\qquad [\,15\,]$$

where d_1 is the inside diameter of the outer conductor and d_2 is the outside diameter of the inner conductor.

EXAMPLE 13   The outer conductor of a concentric transmission line consists of copper tubing $\frac{1}{16}$ in. thick with an outside diameter of 1 in. The copper tubing comprising the inner conductor is $\frac{1}{32}$ in. thick with an outside diameter of $\frac{1}{4}$ in. What is the characteristic impedance of the line?

SOLUTION $d_1 = 1 - (2 \cdot \frac{1}{16}) = \frac{7}{8}$ in. $d_2 = \frac{1}{4}$ in.

$$Z_0 = 138 \log \frac{d_1}{d_2} = 138 \log \frac{\frac{7}{8}}{\frac{1}{4}} = 138 \log 3.5 = 138 \times 0.544 = 75.1 \; \Omega$$

PROBLEMS 37 – 3

1   What is the characteristic impedance of a two-wire open-air transmission line consisting of No. 12 wire spaced 6 in. between wire centers?

2   What is the characteristic impedance of a two-wire open-air transmission line consisting of No. 10 wire spaced 8 in. between wire centers?

3   What is the characteristic impedance of a transmission line consisting of No. 14 wire spaced 2 in. between wire centers?

4   It is desired to construct a 500-Ω transmission line. Number 10 wire is the only size available. What should be the spacing between wire centers?

5   It is necessary to construct a 700-Ω transmission line to couple a radio transmitter to a rhombic antenna. Number 14 wire is the only size available. What should be the spacing between wire centers?

6   The impedance at the center of a half-wave antenna is approximately
    74 Ω. For maximum power transfer between transmission line and
    antenna, the impedance of the transmission line must match that of the
    antenna. Is it physically possible to construct an open-wire line with a
    characteristic impedance as low as 74 Ω?

7   Plot a graph of the characteristic impedance in ohms against the ratio
    d/r, from $d/r = 1$ to $d/r = 150$, for two-wire open-air transmission
    lines.

8   It is desired to construct a 600-Ω two-wire line at a certain radio station.
    In the stockroom, there are on hand a large number of 10-in. spreader
    insulators. That is, these spreaders will space the *wires* 10 in. What
    sized wire should be used to obtain as near as possible the desired
    impedance if the 10-in. spreaders are used? HINT: $d = 10 + 2r$.

9   What size wire should be used to obtain as near as possible an impedance
    of 700 Ω by use of the spreaders described in Prob. 8?

10 What size copper tubing should be used to construct a quarter-wave
    matching stub having a characteristic impedance of 250 Ω if 1.5-in.
    spreaders are available?

11 What size tubing should be used to construct a quarter-wave matching
    stub having an impedance of 316 Ω if the spreaders of Prob. 10 are used?

12 The outer conductor of a concentric transmission line is a copper pipe $\frac{1}{8}$
    in. thick with an outside diameter of 3 in. The inner conductor is copper
    tubing with an outside diameter of $\frac{3}{4}$ in. What is the surge impedance
    of the line?

13 The inside diameter of the outer conductor of a concentric line is $\frac{1}{2}$
    in. The surge impedance of the line is 80 Ω. What is the diameter of the
    inner conductor?

14 Plot a graph of the characteristic impedance in ohms against the ratio
    d_1/d_2, from $d_1/d_2 = 2$ to $d_1/d_2 = 10$ for concentric transmission lines.

15 A certain grade of twisted-pair transmission line, which has a surge
    impedance of 72 Ω, has a loss of 0.064 db/ft. For a 100-ft length of
    line, what are (a) the total loss in decibels, (b) the efficiency of trans-
    mission?

    HINT: $\dfrac{\text{Power output}}{\text{Power input}} \times 100 = $ per cent efficiency

16 The twisted-pair line of Prob. 15 is replaced by a concentric cable that
    has a loss of 0.002 db/ft. What is the new efficiency of transmission?

17 For a two-wire transmission line, the attenuation in decibels per foot
    of *wire* is given by the equation

$$\alpha = \frac{0.0157 R_f}{\log_{10} \dfrac{d}{r}} \qquad \text{db/ft} \qquad\qquad [\,16\,]$$

where R_f is r-f resistance per foot of *wire*. One kilowatt of power, at a frequency of 16 Mc, is delivered to a 500-ft two-wire line consisting of No. 12 copper wire spaced 6 in. between wire centers. If the r-f resistance of No. 12 wire, at 16 Mc, is 30 times the d-c resistance, (*a*) what is the line loss in decibels, (*b*) what is the efficiency of transmission?

18 The transmission line of Prob. 17 is replaced by a two-wire line consisting of No. 8 wire spaced 12 in. between centers. If the r-f resistance of No. 8. wire, at 16 Mc, is 49 times the d-c resistance, (*a*) what is the line loss in decibels, (*b*) what is the efficiency of transmission?

19 The spacing of the transmission line of Prob. 18 is reduced to 6 in. between wire centers.
(*a*) What is the line loss in decibels?
(*b*) What is the efficiency of transmission?

20 For a concentric transmission line, the attenuation in decibels per foot of *line* is expressed by the relation

$$\alpha = \frac{4.6\sqrt{f}(d_1 + d_2)10^{-6}}{d_1 d_2 \log_{10} \dfrac{d_1}{d_2}} \quad \textbf{db/ft} \qquad [\,17\,]$$

where d_1 and d_2 are in inches and have the same meaning as in Eq. [15] and f is the frequency in megacycles. A concentric line 500 ft in length consists of an outer conductor with an inside diameter of ⅞ in. and an inner conductor that is ¼ in. in diameter. At a frequency of 16 Mc (*a*) what is the line loss in decibels, (*b*) what is the efficiency of transmission?

21 The capacitance of a vertical antenna, which is shorter than one-quarter wavelength at its operating frequency, can be computed by the equation

$$C_a = \frac{17l}{\left[\left(\log_\epsilon \dfrac{24l}{d}\right) - 1\right]\left[1 - \left(\dfrac{fl}{246}\right)^2\right]} \quad \mu\mu f \qquad [\,18\,]$$

where C_a = capacitance of antenna, $\mu\mu f$
l = height of antenna, ft
d = diameter of antenna conductor, in.
f = operating frequency, Mc
Determine the capacitance of a vertical antenna that is 125 ft high and consists of ⅜-in. wire. The antenna is being operated on 500 kc.

22 Find the capacitance of a vertical antenna that is 80 ft high and operates on 375 kc. The antenna is made of 7⁄16-in. wire.

23 The r-f resistance of a copper concentric transmission line can be computed by:

$$r = \sqrt{f}\left(\frac{1}{d_1} + \frac{1}{d_2}\right) \times 10^{-3} \qquad \Omega/\text{ft} \qquad\qquad [\,19\,]$$

where f = frequency, Mc

d_1 = inside diameter of outer conductor, in.

d_2 = outside diameter of inner conductor, in.

What is the resistance of a concentric line 100 ft long operating at 200 Mc if $d_1 = 1\frac{7}{8}$ in. and $d_2 = \frac{1}{4}$ in.?

24 What is the resistance of a concentric line 100 ft long operating at 200 Mc if $d_1 = \frac{3}{8}$ in. and $d_2 = \frac{1}{12}$ in.?

25 If an antenna is matched to a coaxial transmission line, the per cent efficiency is given by

$$\text{Efficiency} = \frac{100R_T}{Z_0 + R_T} \qquad\qquad [\,20\,]$$

where Z_0 = characteristic impedance of concentric line

R_T = effective resistance of line due to attenuation and is obtainable from line constants:

$$R_T = Z_0(\epsilon^{\frac{rl}{Z_0}} - 1) \qquad\qquad [\,21\,]$$

where r = r-f resistance per foot of line as found in Eq. [19]

l = length of line, ft.

Find the efficiency of transmission of a matched concentric transmission line with a characteristic impedance of 70 Ω. The line is 100 ft long and has an r-f resistance of 0.15 Ω/ft.

26 What is the efficiency of transmission of a matched concentric transmission line with a characteristic impedance of 80 Ω if the line is 500 ft long and has an r-f resistance of 0.08 Ω/ft?

APPENDIX

TABLE 1 MATHEMATICAL SYMBOLS

$\times$ or $\cdot$	multiplied by
$\div$ or $:$	divided by
$+$	positive, plus, add
$-$	negative, minus, subtract
$\pm$	positive or negative, plus or minus
$\mp$	negative or positive, minus or plus
$=$ or $::$	equals
$\equiv$	identity
$\cong$	is approximately equal to
$\neq$	does not equal
$>$	is greater than
$\gg$	is much greater than
$<$	is less than
$\ll$	is much less than
$\geqq$	greater than or equal to
$\leqq$	less than or equal to
$\therefore$	therefore
$\angle$	angle
$\perp$	perpendicular to
$\parallel$	parallel to
$|n|$	absolute value of n
Δ	increment of

TABLE 2 GREEK ALPHABET

name	capital	lower case	commonly used to designate
Alpha	A	α	angles, area, coefficients
Beta	B	β	angles, flux density, coefficients
Gamma	Γ	γ	conductivity, specific gravity
Delta	Δ	δ	variation, density
Epsilon	E	ϵ	base of natural logarithms
Zeta	Z	ζ	impedance, coefficients, coordinates
Eta	H	η	hysteresis coefficient, efficiency
Theta	Θ	θ	temperature, phase angle
Iota	I	ι	
Kappa	K	κ	dielectric constant, susceptibility
Lambda	Λ	λ	wavelength
Mu	M	μ	micro, amplification factor, permeability
Nu	N	ν	reluctivity
Xi	Ξ	ξ	
Omicron	O	o	
Pi	Π	π	ratio of circumference to diameter = 3.1416
Rho	P	ρ	resistivity
Sigma	Σ	σ	sign of summation
Tau	T	τ	time constant, time phase displacement
Upsilon	Υ	υ	
Phi	Φ	ϕ	magnetic flux, angles
Chi	X	χ	
Psi	Ψ	ψ	dielectric flux, phase difference
Omega	Ω	ω	capital: ohms; lower case: angular velocity

TABLE 3   ABBREVIATIONS AND LETTER SYMBOLS

This list, while far from complete, represents most of the abbreviations used in this book. They were formulated in an endeavor to have only one abbreviation for a given term, regardless of grammatical usage.*

alternating current	a-c	megacycle	Mc
ampere	amp	megohm	$M\Omega$
antenna	ant.	microampere	μa
antilogarithm	antilog	microfarad	μf
audio frequency	a-f	microvolt	μv
base of natural logarithms	ϵ	microvolts per meter	μv/meter
centimeter	cm	milliampere	ma
continuous waves	c-w	millihenry	mh
cycles per second	cps	millivolt	mv
decibel	db	millivolts per meter	mv/meter
direct current	d-c	milliwatt	mw
electromotive force	emf	ohm	Ω
feet	ft	power factor	pf
frequency	f	radio frequency	r-f
inch	in.	revolutions per minute	rpm
intermediate frequency	i-f	revolutions per second	rps
kilocycle	kc	ultra high frequency	uhf
kilohm	$k\Omega$	very high frequency	vhf
kilowatt	kw	very low frequency	vlf
logarithm	log	yard	yd

Abbreviations for metric prefixes

prefix	abbreviation	prefix	abbreviation
centi	c	kilo	k
deci	d	mega	M
deka	dk	micro	μ
hecto	h	milli	m

* N. M. Cooke and J. Markus, "Electronics Dictionary," McGraw-Hill Book Company, Inc., New York, 1945.

TABLE 4   CONVERSION FACTORS*

multiply	by	to obtain
abamperes	10	amperes
abamperes	3×10^{10}	statamperes
abamperes/square centimeter	64.52	amperes/square inch
abampere-turns	10	ampere-turns
abampere-turns	12.57	gilberts
abampere-turns/centimeter	25.40	ampere-turns/inch
abcoulombs	10	coulombs
abcoulombs	3×10^{10}	statcoulombs
abcoulombs/square centimeter	64.52	coulombs/square inch
abfarads	10^9	farads
abfarads	10^{15}	microfarads
abfarads	9×10^{20}	statfarads
abhenrys	10^{-9}	henrys
abhenrys	10^{-6}	millihenrys
abhenrys	$\frac{1}{9} \times 10^{-20}$	stathenrys
abmhos/centimeter cube	$10^5/\delta$	mhos/meter-gram
abmhos/centimeter cube	1.662×10^2	mhos/mil-foot
abmhos/centimeter cube	10^3	megmhos/centimeter cube
abohms	10^{-15}	megohms
abohms	10^{-3}	microhms
abohms	10^{-9}	ohms
abohms	$\frac{1}{9} \times 10^{-20}$	statohms
abohms/centimeter cube	10^{-3}	microhms/centimeter cube
abohms/centimeter cube	6.015×10^{-3}	ohms/mil-foot
abohms/centimeter cube	$10^{-5}\delta$†	ohms/meter-gram
abvolts	$\frac{1}{3} \times 10^{-10}$	statvolts
abvolts	10^{-8}	volts
amperes	$\frac{1}{10}$	abamperes
amperes	3×10^9	statamperes
amperes/square centimeter	6.452	amperes/square inch
amperes/square inch	0.01550	abamperes/square centimeter
amperes/square inch	0.1550	amperes/square centimeter
amperes/square inch	4.650×10^8	statamperes/square centimeter
ampere-turns	$\frac{1}{10}$	abampere-turns
ampere-turns	1.257	gilberts
ampere-turns/centimeter	2.540	ampere-turns/inch
ampere-turns/inch	0.03937	abampere-turns/centimeter
ampere-turns/inch	0.3937	ampere-turns/centimeter
ampere-turns/inch	0.4950	gilberts/centimeter
bars	10^6	dynes/square centimeter

* Reprinted by permission from Ralph G. Hudson, "The Engineers' Manual," 2d ed., John Wiley & Sons, Inc., New York, 1939.
† The symbol δ represents the density of a material expressed as a decimal fraction.

TABLE 4 CONVERSION FACTORS (continued)

multiply	by	to obtain
bars	14.50	pounds/square inch
btu	2.930×10^{-4}	kilowatt hours
centimeters	3.281×10^{-2}	feet
centimeters	0.3937	inches
centimeters	0.01	meters
centimeters	6.214×10^{-6}	miles
centimeters	10	millimeters
centimeters	393.7	mils
centimeters	1.094×10^{-2}	yards
centimeters/second	1.969	feet/minute
centimeters/second	0.03281	feet/second
centimeters/second	0.036	kilometers/hour
centimeters/second	0.6	meters/minute
centimeters/second	0.02237	miles/hour
centimeters/second	3.728×10^{-4}	miles/minute
circular mils	5.067×10^{-6}	square centimeters
circular mils	7.854×10^{-7}	square inches
circular mils	0.7854	square mils
coulombs/square inch	0.01550	abcoulombs/square centimeter
coulombs/square inch	0.1550	coulombs/square centimeter
coulombs/square inch	4.650×10^{8}	statcoulombs/square centimeter
dynes	1.020×10^{-3}	grams
dynes	7.233×10^{-5}	poundals
dynes	2.248×10^{-6}	pounds
dynes/square centimeter	10^{-6}	bars
farads	10^{-9}	abfarads
farads	10^{6}	microfarads
farads	9×10^{11}	statfarads
feet	30.48	centimeters
feet	12	inches
feet	0.3048	meters
feet	1.894×10^{-4}	miles
feet	⅓	yards
feet/minute	0.5080	centimeters/second
feet/minute	0.01667	feet/second
feet/minute	0.01829	kilometers/hour
feet/minute	0.3048	meters/minute
feet/minute	0.01136	miles/hour
feet/second	30.48	centimeters/second
feet/second	1.097	kilometers/hour
feet/second	0.5921	knots
feet/second	18.29	meters/minute
feet/second	0.6818	miles/hour

TABLE 4   CONVERSION FACTORS (continued)

multiply	by	to obtain
feet/second	0.01136	miles/minute
gauss	6.452	lines/square inch
gilberts	0.07958	abampere-turns
gilberts	0.7958	ampere-turns
gilberts/centimeter	2.021	ampere-turns/inch
grams	980.7	dynes
grams	15.43	grains
grams	10^{-3}	kilograms
grams	10^3	milligrams
grams	0.03527	ounces
grams	0.03215	ounces (troy)
grams	0.07093	poundals
grams	2.205×10^{-3}	pounds
henrys	10^9	abhenrys
henrys	10^3	millihenrys
henrys	$\frac{1}{9} \times 10^{-11}$	stathenrys
inches	2.540	centimeters
inches	8.333×10^{-2}	feet
inches	1.578×10^{-5}	miles
inches	10^3	mils
inches	2.778×10^{-2}	yards
joules (international)	9.480×10^{-4}	Btu
joules (international)	10^7	ergs
joules (international)	0.7378	foot-pounds
joules (international)	2.389×10^{-4}	kilogram-calories
joules (international)	0.1020	kilogram-meters
joules (international)	2.778×10^{-4}	watt-hours
kilograms	980,665	dynes
kilograms	10^3	grams
kilograms	70.93	poundals
kilograms	2.205	pounds
kilograms	1.102×10^{-3}	tons (short)
kilometers	0.6214	miles
kilometers/hour	54.68	feet/minute
kilometers/hour	0.9114	feet/second
kilowatts	56.88	Btu/minute
kilowatts	4.427×10^4	foot-pounds/minute
kilowatts	737.8	foot-pounds/second
kilowatts	1.341	horsepower
kilowatts	14.33	kilogram-calories/minute
kilowatts	10^3	watts
kilowatt-hours	3,413	Btu
kilowatt-hours	2.656×10^6	foot-pounds

TABLE 4   CONVERSION FACTORS (continued)

multiply	by	to obtain
kilowatt-hours	1.341	horsepower-hours
kilowatt-hours	3.6×10^6	joules
kilowatt-hours	860	kilogram-calories
kilowatt-hours	3.672×10^5	kilogram-meters
knots	101.33	feet/minute
knots	1.689	feet/second
lines/square centimeter	1	gauss
lines/square inch	0.1550	gauss
$\log_{10} N$	2.303	$\log_\epsilon N$ or $\ln N$
$\log_\epsilon N$ or $\ln N$	0.4343	$\log_{10} N$
lumens/square foot	1	foot-candles
maxwells	10^{-3}	kilolines
megalines	10^6	maxwells
megmhos/centimeter cube	10^{-3}	abmhos/centimeter cube
megmhos/centimeter cube	2.540	megmhos/inch cube
megmhos/centimeter cube	$10^2/\delta$*	mhos/meter-gram
megmhos/centimeter cube	0.1662	mhos/mil-foot
megmhos/inch cube	0.3937	megmhos/centimeter cube
megohms	10^6	ohms
meters	100	centimeters
meters	3.281	feet
meters	39.37	inches
meters	10^{-3}	kilometers
meters	6.214×10^{-4}	miles
meters	10^3	millimeters
meters	1.094	yards
mhos/mil-foot	6.015×10^{-3}	abmhos/centimeter cube
mhos/mil-foot	6.015	megmhos/centimeter cube
mhos/mil-foot	15.28	megmhos/inch cube
mhos/mil-foot	$601.5/\delta$	mhos/meter-gram
microfarads	10^{-15}	abfarads
microfarads	10^{-6}	farads
microfarads	9×10^5	statfarads
microhms	10^3	abohms
microhms	10^{-12}	megohms
microhms	10^{-6}	ohms
microhms	$\frac{1}{9} \times 10^{-17}$	statohms
miles	1.609×10^5	centimeters
miles	5,280	feet
miles	6.336×10^4	inches
miles	1.609	kilometers
miles	1,760	yards

* The symbol δ represents the density of a material expressed as a decimal fraction.

TABLE 4   CONVERSION FACTORS (continued)

multiply	by	to obtain
miles/hour	88	feet/minute
miles/hour	1.467	feet/second
mil-feet	9.425×10^{-6}	cubic inches
millihenrys	10^6	abhenrys
millihenrys	10^{-3}	henrys
millihenrys	$\frac{1}{9} \times 10^{-14}$	stathenrys
ohms	10^9	abohms
ohms	10^{-6}	megohms
ohms	10^6	microhms
ohms	$\frac{1}{9} \times 10^{-11}$	statohms
ohms/mil-foot	166.2	abohms/centimeter cube
ohms/mil-foot	0.1662	microhms/centimeter cube
ohms/mil-foot	0.06524	microhms/inch cube
ohms/mil-foot	$1.662 \times 10^{-3}\delta*$	ohms/meter-gram
poundals	13,826	dynes
poundals	14.10	grams
poundals	0.03108	pounds
pounds	444,823	dynes
pounds	7,000	grains
pounds	453.6	grams
pounds	16	ounces
pounds	32.17	poundals
pounds (troy)	0.8229	pounds (avoirdupois)
quadrants (angle)	90	degrees
quadrants (angle)	5,400	minutes
quadrants (angle)	1.571	radians
radians	57.30	degrees
radians	3,438	minutes
radians	0.6366	quadrants
radians/second	57.30	degrees/second
radians/second	9.549	revolutions/minute
radians/second	0.1592	revolutions/second
revolutions	360	degrees
revolutions	4	quadrants
revolutions	6.283	radians
revolutions/minute	6	degrees/second
revolutions/minute	0.1047	radians/second
revolutions/minute	0.01667	revolutions/second
revolutions/second	360	degrees/second
revolutions/second	6.283	radians/second
revolutions/second	60	revolutions/minute
seconds (angle)	4.848×10^{-6}	radians

* The symbol δ represents the density of a material expressed as a decimal fraction.

TABLE 4 CONVERSION FACTORS (continued)

multiply	by	to obtain
statamperes	$\frac{1}{3} \times 10^{-10}$	abamperes
statamperes	$\frac{1}{3} \times 10^{-9}$	amperes
statcoulombs	$\frac{1}{3} \times 10^{-10}$	abcoulombs
statcoulombs	$\frac{1}{3} \times 10^{-9}$	coulombs
statfarads	$\frac{1}{9} \times 10^{-20}$	abfarads
statfarads	$\frac{1}{9} \times 10^{-11}$	farads
statfarads	$\frac{1}{9} \times 10^{-5}$	microfarads
stathenrys	9×10^{20}	abhenrys
stathenrys	9×10^{11}	henrys
stathenrys	9×10^{14}	millihenrys
statohms	9×10^{20}	abohms
statohms	9×10^{5}	megohms
statohms	9×10^{17}	microhms
statohms	9×10^{11}	ohms
statvolts	3×10^{10}	abvolts
statvolts	300	volts
temperature (°C) + 273	1	absolute temperature (°C)
temperature (°C) + 17.8	1.8	temperature (°F)
temperature (°F) + 460	1	absolute temperature (°F)
temperature (°F) − 32	$\frac{5}{9}$	temperature (°C)
volts	10^{8}	abvolts
volts	$\frac{1}{300}$	statvolts
volts/inch	3.937×10^{7}	abvolts/centimeter
volts/inch	1.312×10^{-3}	statvolts/centimeter
watts	0.05688	Btu/minute
watts	10^{7}	ergs/second
watts	44.27	foot-pounds/minute
watts	0.7378	foot-pounds/second
watts	1.341×10^{-3}	horsepower
watts	0.01433	kilogram-calories/minute
watts	10^{-3}	kilowatts
watt-hours	3.413	Btu
watt-hours	2,656	foot-pounds
watt-hours	1.341×10^{-3}	horsepower-hours
watt-hours	0.860	kilogram-calories
watt-hours	367.2	kilogram-meters
watt-hours	10^{-3}	kilowatt-hours
webers	10^{8}	maxwells
yards	91.44	centimeters
yards	3	feet
yards	36	inches
yards	0.9144	meters
yards	5.682×10^{-4}	miles

TABLE 5 STANDARD ANNEALED COPPER WIRE, SOLID*

AMERICAN WIRE GAGE (BROWN AND SHARPE)

gage number	diameter, mils	area, cir mils	resistance, ohms per 1,000 ft, 25°C (77°F)	weight, pounds per 1,000 ft	allowable current capacity,† amp		
					rubber insulation	varnished cambric insulation	other insulations
0000	460.0	211,600.0	0.0500	641.0	225	270	325
000	410.0	167,800.0	0.0630	508.0	175	210	275
00	365.0	133,100.0	0.0795	403.0	150	180	225
0	325.0	105,500.0	0.100	319.0	125	150	200
1	289.0	83,690.0	0.126	253.0	100	120	150
2	258.0	66,370.0	0.159	201.0	90	110	125
3	229.0	52,640.0	0.201	159.0	80	95	100
4	204.0	41,740.0	0.253	126.0	70	85	90
5	182.0	33,100.0	0.319	100.0	55	65	80
6	162.0	26,250.0	0.403	79.5	50	60	70
7	144.0	20,820.0	0.508	63.0			
8	128.0	16,510.0	0.641	50.0	35	40	50
9	114.0	13,090.0	0.808	39.6			
10	102.0	10,380.0	1.02	31.4	25	30	30
11	91.0	8,234.0	1.28	24.9			
12	81.0	6,530.0	1.62	19.8	20	25	25
13	72.0	5,178.0	2.04	15.7			
14	64.0	4,107.0	2.58	12.4	15	18	20
15	57.0	3,257.0	3.25	9.86			
16	51.0	2,583.0	4.09	7.82	6		
17	45.0	2,048.0	5.16	6.20			
18	40.0	1,624.0	6.51	4.92	3		
19	36.0	1,288.0	8.21	3.90			
20	32.0	1,022.0	10.4	3.09			
21	28.5	810.0	13.1	2.45			
22	25.3	642.0	16.5	1.95			
23	22.6	509.0	20.8	1.54			
24	20.1	404.0	26.2	1.22			
25	17.9	320.0	33.0	0.970			
26	15.9	254.0	41.6	0.769			
27	14.2	202.0	52.5	0.610			
28	12.6	160.0	66.2	0.484			
29	11.3	127.0	83.4	0.384			
30	10.0	100.0	105.0	0.304			
31	8.9	79.7	133.0	0.241			
32	8.0	63.2	167.0	0.191			
33	7.1	50.1	211.0	0.152			
34	6.3	39.8	266.0	0.120			
35	5.6	31.5	335.0	0.0954			
36	5.0	25.0	423.0	0.0757			
37	4.5	19.8	533.0	0.0600			
38	4.0	15.7	673.0	0.0476			
39	3.5	12.5	848.0	0.0377			
40	3.1	9.9	1070.0	0.0299			

Bureau of Standards Circular 31.
† National Electrical Code.

TABLE 6 COMMON LOGARITHMS

no.	0	1	2	3	4	5	6	7	8	9
0	....	0000	3010	4771	6021	6990	7782	8451	9031	9542
1	0000	0414	0792	1139	1461	1761	2041	2304	2553	2788
2	3010	3222	3424	3617	3802	3979	4150	4314	4472	4624
3	4771	4914	5051	5185	5315	5441	5563	5682	5798	5911
4	6021	6128	6232	6335	6435	6532	6628	6721	6812	6902
5	6990	7076	7160	7243	7324	7404	7482	7559	7634	7709
6	7782	7853	7924	7993	8062	8129	8195	8261	8325	8388
7	8451	8513	8573	8633	8692	8751	8808	8865	8921	8976
8	9031	9085	9138	9191	9243	9294	9345	9395	9445	9494
9	9542	9590	9638	9685	9731	9777	9823	9868	9912	9956
10	0000	0043	0086	0128	0170	0212	0253	0294	0334	0374
11	0414	0453	0492	0531	0569	0607	0645	0682	0719	0755
12	0792	0828	0864	0899	0934	0969	1004	1038	1072	1106
13	1139	1173	1206	1239	1271	1303	1335	1367	1399	1430
14	1461	1492	1523	1553	1584	1614	1644	1673	1703	1732
15	1761	1790	1818	1847	1875	1903	1931	1959	1987	2014
16	2041	2068	2095	2122	2148	2175	2201	2227	2253	2279
17	2304	2330	2355	2380	2405	2430	2455	2480	2504	2529
18	2553	2577	2601	2625	2648	2672	2695	2718	2742	2765
19	2788	2810	2833	2856	2878	2900	2923	2945	2967	2989
20	3010	3032	3054	3075	3096	3118	3139	3160	3181	3201
21	3222	3243	3263	3284	3304	3324	3345	3365	3385	3404
22	3424	3444	3464	3483	3502	3522	3541	3560	3579	3598
23	3617	3636	3655	3674	3692	3711	3729	3747	3766	3784
24	3802	3820	3838	3856	3874	3892	3909	3927	3945	3962
25	3979	3997	4014	4031	4048	4065	4082	4099	4116	4133
26	4150	4166	4183	4200	4216	4232	4249	4265	4281	4298
27	4314	4330	4346	4362	4378	4393	4409	4425	4440	4456
28	4472	4487	4502	4518	4533	4548	4564	4579	4594	4609
29	4624	4639	4654	4669	4683	4698	4713	4728	4742	4757
30	4771	4786	4800	4814	4829	4843	4857	4871	4886	4900
31	4914	4928	4942	4955	4969	4983	4997	5011	5024	5038
32	5051	5065	5079	5092	5105	5119	5132	5145	5159	5172
33	5185	5198	5211	5224	5237	5250	5263	5276	5289	5302
34	5315	5328	5340	5353	5366	5378	5391	5403	5416	5428
35	5441	5453	5465	5478	5490	5502	5514	5527	5539	5551
36	5563	5575	5587	5599	5611	5623	5635	5647	5658	5670
37	5682	5694	5705	5717	5729	5740	5752	5763	5775	5786
38	5798	5809	5821	5832	5843	5855	5866	5877	5888	5899
39	5911	5922	5933	5944	5955	5966	5977	5988	5999	6010
40	6021	6031	6042	6053	6064	6075	6085	6096	6107	6117
41	6128	6138	6149	6160	6170	6180	6191	6201	6212	6222
42	6232	6243	6253	6263	6274	6284	6294	6304	6314	6325
43	6335	6345	6355	6365	6375	6385	6395	6405	6415	6425
44	6435	6444	6454	6464	6474	6484	6493	6503	6513	6522
45	6532	6542	6551	6561	6571	6580	6590	6599	6609	6618
46	6628	6637	6646	6656	6665	6675	6684	6693	6702	6712
47	6721	6730	6739	6749	6758	6767	6776	6785	6794	6803
48	6812	6821	6830	6839	6848	6857	6866	6875	6884	6893
49	6902	6911	6920	6928	6937	6946	6955	6964	6972	6981
50	6990	6998	7007	7016	7024	7033	7042	7050	7059	7067
no.	0	1	2	3	4	5	6	7	8	9

TABLE 6 COMMON LOGARITHMS (continued)

no.	0	1	2	3	4	5	6	7	8	9
50	6990	6998	7007	7016	7024	7033	7042	7050	7059	7067
51	7076	7084	7093	7101	7110	7118	7126	7135	7143	7152
52	7160	7168	7177	7185	7193	7202	7210	7218	7226	7235
53	7243	7251	7259	7267	7275	7284	7292	7300	7308	7316
54	7324	7332	7340	7348	7356	7364	7372	7380	7388	7396
55	7404	7412	7419	7427	7435	7443	7451	7459	7466	7474
56	7482	7490	7497	7505	7513	7520	7528	7536	7543	7551
57	7559	7566	7574	7582	7589	7597	7604	7612	7619	7627
58	7634	7642	7649	7657	7664	7672	7679	7686	7694	7701
59	7709	7716	7723	7731	7738	7745	7752	7760	7767	7774
60	7782	7789	7796	7803	7810	7818	7825	7832	7839	7846
61	7853	7860	7868	7875	7882	7889	7896	7903	7910	7917
62	7924	7931	7938	7945	7952	7959	7966	7973	7980	7987
63	7993	8000	8007	8014	8021	8028	8035	8041	8048	8055
64	8062	8069	8075	8082	8089	8096	8102	8109	8116	8122
65	8129	8136	8142	8149	8156	8162	8169	8176	8182	8189
66	8195	8202	8209	8215	8222	8228	8235	8241	8248	8254
67	8261	8267	8274	8280	8287	8293	8299	8306	8312	8319
68	8325	8331	8338	8344	8351	8357	8363	8370	8376	8382
69	8388	8395	8401	8407	8414	8420	8426	8432	8439	8445
70	8451	8457	8463	8470	8476	8482	8488	8494	8500	8506
71	8513	8519	8525	8531	8537	8543	8549	8555	8561	8567
72	8573	8579	8585	8591	8597	8603	8609	8615	8621	8627
73	8633	8639	8645	8651	8657	8663	8669	8675	8681	8686
74	8692	8698	8704	8710	8716	8722	8727	8733	8739	8745
75	8751	8756	8762	8768	8774	8779	8785	8791	8797	8802
76	8808	8814	8820	8825	8831	8837	8842	8848	8854	8859
77	8865	8871	8876	8882	8887	8893	8899	8904	8910	8915
78	8921	8927	8932	8938	8943	8949	8954	8960	8965	8971
79	8976	8982	8987	8993	8998	9004	9009	9015	9020	9025
80	9031	9036	9042	9047	9053	9058	9063	9069	9074	9079
81	9085	9090	9096	9101	9106	9112	9117	9122	9128	9133
82	9138	9143	9149	9154	9159	9165	9170	9175	9180	9186
83	9191	9196	9201	9206	9212	9217	9222	9227	9232	9238
84	9243	9248	9253	9258	9263	9269	9274	9279	9284	9289
85	9294	9299	9304	9309	9315	9320	9325	9330	9335	9340
86	9345	9350	9355	9360	9365	9370	9375	9380	9385	9390
87	9395	9400	9405	9410	9415	9420	9425	9430	9435	9440
88	9445	9450	9455	9460	9465	9469	9474	9479	9484	9489
89	9494	9499	9504	9509	9513	9518	9523	9528	9533	9538
90	9542	9547	9552	9557	9562	9566	9571	9576	9581	9586
91	9590	9595	9600	9605	9609	9614	9619	9624	9628	9633
92	9638	9643	9647	9652	9657	9661	9666	9671	9675	9680
93	9685	9689	9694	9699	9703	9708	9713	9717	9722	9727
94	9731	9736	9741	9745	9750	9754	9759	9763	9768	9773
95	9777	9782	9786	9791	9795	9800	9805	9809	9814	9818
96	9823	9827	9832	9836	9841	9845	9850	9854	9859	9863
97	9868	9872	9877	9881	9886	9890	9894	9899	9903	9908
98	9912	9917	9921	9926	9930	9934	9939	9943	9948	9952
99	9956	9961	9965	9969	9974	9978	9983	9987	9991	9996
100	0000	0004	0009	0013	0017	0022	0026	0030	0035	0039
no.	0	1	2	3	4	5	6	7	8	9

TABLE 7 NATURAL TRIGONOMETRIC FUNCTIONS

deg	function	0.0°	0.1°	0.2°	0.3°	0.4°	0.5°	0.6°	0.7°	0.8°	0.9°
0	sin	0.0000	0.0017	0.0035	0.0052	0.0070	0.0087	0.0105	0.0122	0.0140	0.0157
	cos	1.0000	1.0000	1.0000	1.0000	1.0000	1.0000	0.9999	0.9999	0.9999	0.9999
	tan	0.0000	0.0017	0.0035	0.0052	0.0070	0.0087	0.0105	0.0122	0.0140	0.0157
1	sin	0.0175	0.0192	0.0209	0.0227	0.0244	0.0262	0.0279	0.0297	0.0314	0.0332
	cos	0.9998	0.9998	0.9998	0.9997	0.9997	0.9997	0.9996	0.9996	0.9995	0.9995
	tan	0.0175	0.0192	0.0209	0.0227	0.0244	0.0262	0.0279	0.0297	0.0314	0.0332
2	sin	0.0349	0.0366	0.0384	0.0401	0.0419	0.0436	0.0454	0.0471	0.0488	0.0506
	cos	0.9994	0.9993	0.9993	0.9992	0.9991	0.9990	0.9990	0.9989	0.9988	0.9987
	tan	0.0349	0.0367	0.0384	0.0402	0.0419	0.0437	0.0454	0.0472	0.0489	0.0507
3	sin	0.0523	0.0541	0.0558	0.0576	0.0593	0.0610	0.0628	0.0645	0.0663	0.0680
	cos	0.9986	0.9985	0.9984	0.9983	0.9982	0.9981	0.9980	0.9979	0.9978	0.9977
	tan	0.0524	0.0542	0.0559	0.0577	0.0594	0.0612	0.0629	0.0647	0.0664	0.0682
4	sin	0.0698	0.0715	0.0732	0.0750	0.0767	0.0785	0.0802	0.0819	0.0837	0.0854
	cos	0.9976	0.9974	0.9973	0.9972	0.9971	0.9969	0.9968	0.9966	0.9965	0.9963
	tan	0.0699	0.0717	0.0734	0.0752	0.0769	0.0787	0.0805	0.0822	0.0840	0.0857
5	sin	0.0872	0.0889	0.0906	0.0924	0.0941	0.0958	0.0976	0.0993	0.1011	0.1028
	cos	0.9962	0.9960	0.9959	0.9957	0.9956	0.9954	0.9952	0.9951	0.9949	0.9947
	tan	0.0875	0.0892	0.0910	0.0928	0.0945	0.0963	0.0981	0.0998	0.1016	0.1033
6	sin	0.1045	0.1063	0.1080	0.1097	0.1115	0.1132	0.1149	0.1167	0.1184	0.1201
	cos	0.9945	0.9943	0.9942	0.9940	0.9938	0.9936	0.9934	0.9932	0.9930	0.9928
	tan	0.1051	0.1069	0.1086	0.1104	0.1122	0.1139	0.1157	0.1175	0.1192	0.1210
7	sin	0.1219	0.1236	0.1253	0.1271	0.1288	0.1305	0.1323	0.1340	0.1357	0.1374
	cos	0.9925	0.9923	0.9921	0.9919	0.9917	0.9914	0.9912	0.9910	0.9907	0.9905
	tan	0.1228	0.1246	0.1263	0.1281	0.1299	0.1317	0.1334	0.1352	0.1370	0.1388
8	sin	0.1392	0.1409	0.1426	0.1444	0.1461	0.1478	0.1495	0.1513	0.1530	0.1547
	cos	0.9903	0.9900	0.9898	0.9895	0.9893	0.9890	0.9888	0.9885	0.9882	0.9880
	tan	0.1405	0.1423	0.1441	0.1459	0.1477	0.1495	0.1512	0.1530	0.1548	0.1566
9	sin	0.1564	0.1582	0.1599	0.1616	0.1633	0.1650	0.1668	0.1685	0.1702	0.1719
	cos	0.9877	0.9874	0.9871	0.9869	0.9866	0.9863	0.9860	0.9857	0.9854	0.9851
	tan	0.1584	0.1602	0.1620	0.1638	0.1655	0.1673	0.1691	0.1709	0.1727	0.1745
10	sin	0.1736	0.1754	0.1771	0.1788	0.1805	0.1822	0.1840	0.1857	0.1874	0.1891
	cos	0.9848	0.9845	0.9842	0.9839	0.9836	0.9833	0.9829	0.9826	0.9823	0.9820
	tan	0.1763	0.1781	0.1799	0.1817	0.1835	0.1853	0.1871	0.1890	0.1908	0.1926
11	sin	0.1908	0.1925	0.1942	0.1959	0.1977	0.1994	0.2011	0.2028	0.2045	0.2062
	cos	0.9816	0.9813	0.9810	0.9806	0.9803	0.9799	0.9796	0.9792	0.9789	0.9785
	tan	0.1944	0.1962	0.1980	0.1998	0.2016	0.2035	0.2053	0.2071	0.2089	0.2107
12	sin	0.2079	0.2096	0.2113	0.2130	0.2147	0.2164	0.2181	0.2198	0.2215	0.2232
	cos	0.9781	0.9778	0.9774	0.9770	0.9767	0.9763	0.9759	0.9755	0.9751	0.9748
	tan	0.2126	0.2144	0.2162	0.2180	0.2199	0.2217	0.2235	0.2254	0.2272	0.2290
13	sin	0.2250	0.2267	0.2284	0.2300	0.2318	0.2334	0.2351	0.2368	0.2385	0.2402
	cos	0.9744	0.9740	0.9736	0.9732	0.9728	0.9724	0.9720	0.9715	0.9711	0.9707
	tan	0.2309	0.2327	0.2345	0.2364	0.2382	0.2401	0.2419	0.2438	0.2456	0.2475
14	sin	0.2419	0.2436	0.2453	0.2470	0.2487	0.2504	0.2521	0.2538	0.2554	0.2571
	cos	0.9703	0.9699	0.9694	0.9690	0.9686	0.9681	0.9677	0.9673	0.9668	0.9664
	tan	0.2493	0.2512	0.2530	0.2549	0.2568	0.2586	0.2605	0.2623	0.2642	0.2661
15	sin	0.2588	0.2605	0.2622	0.2639	0.2656	0.2672	0.2689	0.2706	0.2723	0.2740
	cos	0.9659	0.9655	0.9650	0.9646	0.9641	0.9636	0.9632	0.9627	0.9622	0.9617
	tan	0.2679	0.2698	0.2717	0.2736	0.2754	0.2773	0.2792	0.2811	0.2830	0.2849
16	sin	0.2756	0.2773	0.2790	0.2807	0.2823	0.2840	0.2857	0.2874	0.2890	0.2907
	cos	0.9613	0.9608	0.9603	0.9598	0.9593	0.9588	0.9583	0.9578	0.9573	0.9568
	tan	0.2867	0.2886	0.2905	0.2924	0.2943	0.2962	0.2981	0.3000	0.3019	0.3038
17	sin	0.2924	0.2940	0.2957	0.2974	0.2990	0.3007	0.3024	0.3040	0.3057	0.3074
	cos	0.9563	0.9558	0.9553	0.9548	0.9542	0.9537	0.9532	0.9527	0.9521	0.9516
	tan	0.3057	0.3076	0.3096	0.3115	0.3134	0.3153	0.3172	0.3191	0.3211	0.3230
18	sin	0.3090	0.3107	0.3123	0.3140	0.3156	0.3173	0.3190	0.3206	0.3223	0.3239
	cos	0.9511	0.9505	0.9500	0.9494	0.9489	0.9483	0.9478	0.9472	0.9466	0.9461
	tan	0.3249	0.3269	0.3288	0.3307	0.3327	0.3346	0.3365	0.3385	0.3404	0.3424
19	sin	0.3256	0.3272	0.3289	0.3305	0.3322	0.3338	0.3355	0.3371	0.3387	0.3404
	cos	0.9455	0.9449	0.9444	0.9438	0.9432	0.9426	0.9421	0.9415	0.9409	0.9403
	tan	0.3443	0.3463	0.3482	0.3502	0.3522	0.3541	0.3561	0.3581	0.3600	0.3620
20	sin	0.3420	0.3437	0.3453	0.3469	0.3486	0.3502	0.3518	0.3535	0.3551	0.3567
	cos	0.9397	0.9391	0.9385	0.9379	0.9373	0.9367	0.9361	0.9354	0.9348	0.9342
	tan	0.3640	0.3659	0.3679	0.3699	0.3719	0.3739	0.3759	0.3779	0.3799	0.3819

| deg | function | 0′ | 6′ | 12′ | 18′ | 24′ | 30′ | 36′ | 42′ | 48′ | 54′ |

TABLE 7   NATURAL TRIGONOMETRIC FUNCTIONS (continued)

deg	function	0.0°	0.1°	0.2°	0.3°	0.4°	0.5°	0.6°	0.7°	0.8°	0.9°
21	sin	0.3584	0.3600	0.3616	0.3633	0.3649	0.3665	0.3681	0.3697	0.3714	0.3730
	cos	0.9336	0.9330	0.9323	0.9317	0.9311	0.9304	0.9298	0.9291	0.9285	0.9278
	tan	0.3839	0.3859	0.3879	0.3899	0.3919	0.3939	0.3959	0.3979	0.4000	0.4020
22	sin	0.3746	0.3762	0.3778	0.3795	0.3811	0.3827	0.3843	0.3859	0.3875	0.3891
	cos	0.9272	0.9265	0.9259	0.9252	0.9245	0.9239	0.9232	0.9225	0.9219	0.9212
	tan	0.4040	0.4061	0.4081	0.4101	0.4122	0.4142	0.4163	0.4183	0.4204	0.4224
23	sin	0.3907	0.3923	0.3939	0.3955	0.3971	0.3987	0.4003	0.4019	0.4035	0.4051
	cos	0.9205	0.9198	0.9191	0.9184	0.9178	0.9171	0.9164	0.9157	0.9150	0.9143
	tan	0.4245	0.4265	0.4286	0.4307	0.4327	0.4348	0.4369	0.4390	0.4411	0.4431
24	sin	0.4067	0.4083	0.4099	0.4115	0.4131	0.4147	0.4163	0.4179	0.4195	0.4210
	cos	0.9135	0.9128	0.9121	0.9114	0.9107	0.9100	0.9092	0.9085	0.9078	0.9070
	tan	0.4452	0.4473	0.4494	0.4515	0.4536	0.4557	0.4578	0.4599	0.4621	0.4642
25	sin	0.4226	0.4242	0.4258	0.4274	0.4289	0.4305	0.4321	0.4337	0.4352	0.4368
	cos	0.9063	0.9056	0.9048	0.9041	0.9033	0.9026	0.9018	0.9011	0.9003	0.8996
	tan	0.4663	0.4684	0.4706	0.4727	0.4748	0.4770	0.4791	0.4813	0.4834	0.4856
26	sin	0.4384	0.4399	0.4415	0.4431	0.4446	0.4462	0.4478	0.4493	0.4509	0.4524
	cos	0.8988	0.8980	0.8973	0.8965	0.8957	0.8949	0.8942	0.8934	0.8926	0.8918
	tan	0.4877	0.4899	0.4921	0.4942	0.4964	0.4986	0.5008	0.5029	0.5051	0.5073
27	sin	0.4540	0.4555	0.4571	0.4586	0.4602	0.4617	0.4633	0.4648	0.4664	0.4679
	cos	0.8910	0.8902	0.8894	0.8886	0.8878	0.8870	0.8862	0.8854	0.8846	0.8838
	tan	0.5095	0.5117	0.5139	0.5161	0.5184	0.5206	0.5228	0.5250	0.5272	0.5295
28	sin	0.4695	0.4710	0.4726	0.4741	0.4756	0.4772	0.4787	0.4802	0.4818	0.4833
	cos	0.8829	0.8821	0.8813	0.8805	0.8796	0.8788	0.8780	0.8771	0.8763	0.8755
	tan	0.5317	0.5340	0.5362	0.5384	0.5407	0.5430	0.5452	0.5475	0.5498	0.5520
29	sin	0.4848	0.4863	0.4879	0.4894	0.4909	0.4924	0.4939	0.4955	0.4970	0.4985
	cos	0.8746	0.8738	0.8729	0.8721	0.8712	0.8704	0.8695	0.8686	0.8678	0.8669
	tan	0.5543	0.5566	0.5589	0.5612	0.5635	0.5658	0.5681	0.5704	0.5727	0.5750
30	sin	0.5000	0.5015	0.5030	0.5045	0.5060	0.5075	0.5090	0.5105	0.5120	0.5135
	cos	0.8660	0.8652	0.8643	0.8634	0.8625	0.8616	0.8607	0.8599	0.8590	0.8581
	tan	0.5774	0.5797	0.5820	0.5844	0.5867	0.5890	0.5914	0.5938	0.5961	0.5985
31	sin	0.5150	0.5165	0.5180	0.5195	0.5210	0.5225	0.5240	0.5255	0.5270	0.5284
	cos	0.8572	0.8563	0.8554	0.8545	0.8536	0.8526	0.8517	0.8508	0.8499	0.8490
	tan	0.6009	0.6032	0.6056	0.6080	0.6104	0.6128	0.6152	0.6176	0.6200	0.6224
32	sin	0.5299	0.5314	0.5329	0.5344	0.5358	0.5373	0.5388	0.5402	0.5417	0.5432
	cos	0.8480	0.8471	0.8462	0.8453	0.8443	0.8434	0.8425	0.8415	0.8406	0.8396
	tan	0.6249	0.6273	0.6297	0.6322	0.6346	0.6371	0.6395	0.6420	0.6445	0.6469
33	sin	0.5446	0.5461	0.5476	0.5490	0.5505	0.5519	0.5534	0.5548	0.5563	0.5577
	cos	0.8387	0.8377	0.8368	0.8358	0.8348	0.8339	0.8329	0.8320	0.8310	0.8300
	tan	0.6494	0.6519	0.6544	0.6569	0.6594	0.6619	0.6644	0.6669	0.6694	0.6720
34	sin	0.5592	0.5606	0.5621	0.5635	0.5650	0.5664	0.5678	0.5693	0.5707	0.5721
	cos	0.8290	0.8281	0.8271	0.8261	0.8251	0.8241	0.8231	0.8221	0.8211	0.8202
	tan	0.6745	0.6771	0.6796	0.6822	0.6847	0.6873	0.6899	0.6924	0.6950	0.6976
35	sin	0.5736	0.5750	0.5764	0.5779	0.5793	0.5807	0.5821	0.5835	0.5850	0.5864
	cos	0.8192	0.8181	0.8171	0.8161	0.8151	0.8141	0.8131	0.8121	0.8111	0.8100
	tan	0.7002	0.7028	0.7054	0.7080	0.7107	0.7133	0.7159	0.7186	0.7212	0.7239
36	sin	0.5878	0.5892	0.5906	0.5920	0.5934	0.5948	0.5962	0.5976	0.5990	0.6004
	cos	0.8090	0.8080	0.8070	0.8059	0.8049	0.8039	0.8028	0.8018	0.8007	0.7997
	tan	0.7265	0.7292	0.7319	0.7346	0.7373	0.7400	0.7427	0.7454	0.7481	0.7508
37	sin	0.6018	0.6032	0.6046	0.6060	0.6074	0.6088	0.6101	0.6115	0.6129	0.6143
	cos	0.7986	0.7976	0.7965	0.7955	0.7944	0.7934	0.7923	0.7912	0.7902	0.7891
	tan	0.7536	0.7563	0.7590	0.7618	0.7646	0.7673	0.7701	0.7729	0.7757	0.7785
38	sin	0.6157	0.6170	0.6184	0.6198	0.6211	0.6225	0.6239	0.6252	0.6266	0.6280
	cos	0.7880	0.7869	0.7859	0.7848	0.7837	0.7826	0.7815	0.7804	0.7793	0.7782
	tan	0.7813	0.7841	0.7869	0.7898	0.7926	0.7954	0.7983	0.8012	0.8040	0.8069
39	sin	0.6293	0.6307	0.6320	0.6334	0.6347	0.6361	0.6374	0.6388	0.6401	0.6414
	cos	0.7771	0.7760	0.7749	0.7738	0.7727	0.7716	0.7705	0.7694	0.7683	0.7672
	tan	0.8098	0.8127	0.8156	0.8185	0.8214	0.8243	0.8273	0.8302	0.8332	0.8361
40	sin	0.6428	0.6441	0.6455	0.6468	0.6481	0.6494	0.6508	0.6521	0.6534	0.6547
	cos	0.7660	0.7649	0.7638	0.7627	0.7615	0.7604	0.7593	0.7581	0.7570	0.7559
	tan	0.8391	0.8421	0.8451	0.8481	0.8511	0.8541	0.8571	0.8601	0.8632	0.8662
41	sin	0.6561	0.6574	0.6587	0.6600	0.6613	0.6626	0.6639	0.6652	0.6665	0.6678
	cos	0.7547	0.7536	0.7524	0.7513	0.7501	0.7490	0.7478	0.7466	0.7455	0.7443
	tan	0.8693	0.8724	0.8754	0.8785	0.8816	0.8847	0.8878	0.8910	0.8941	0.8972
deg	function	0′	6′	12′	18′	24′	30′	36′	42′	48′	54′

TABLE 7 NATURAL TRIGONOMETRIC FUNCTIONS (continued)

deg	function	0.0°	0.1°	0.2°	0.3°	0.4°	0.5°	0.6°	0.7°	0.8°	0.9°
42	sin	0.6691	0.6704	0.6717	0.6730	0.6743	0.6756	0.6769	0.6782	0.6794	0.6807
	cos	0.7431	0.7420	0.7408	0.7396	0.7385	0.7373	0.7361	0.7349	0.7337	0.7325
	tan	0.9004	0.9036	0.9067	0.9099	0.9131	0.9163	0.9195	0.9228	0.9260	0.9293
43	sin	0.6820	0.6833	0.6845	0.6858	0.6871	0.6884	0.6896	0.6909	0.6921	0.6934
	cos	0.7314	0.7302	0.7290	0.7278	0.7266	0.7254	0.7242	0.7230	0.7218	0.7206
	tan	0.9325	0.9358	0.9391	0.9424	0.9457	0.9490	0.9523	0.9556	0.9590	0.9623
44	sin	0.6947	0.6959	0.6972	0.6984	0.6997	0.7009	0.7022	0.7034	0.7046	0.7059
	cos	0.7193	0.7181	0.7169	0.7157	0.7145	0.7133	0.7120	0.7108	0.7096	0.7083
	tan	0.9657	0.9691	0.9725	0.9759	0.9793	0.9827	0.9861	0.9896	0.9930	0.9965
45	sin	0.7071	0.7083	0.7096	0.7108	0.7120	0.7133	0.7145	0.7157	0.7169	0.7181
	cos	0.7071	0.7059	0.7046	0.7034	0.7022	0.7009	0.6997	0.6984	0.6972	0.6959
	tan	1.0000	1.0035	1.0070	1.0105	1.0141	1.0176	1.0212	1.0247	1.0283	1.0319
46	sin	0.7193	0.7206	0.7218	0.7230	0.7242	0.7254	0.7266	0.7278	0.7290	0.7302
	cos	0.6947	0.6934	0.6921	0.6909	0.6896	0.6884	0.6871	0.6858	0.6845	0.6833
	tan	1.0355	1.0392	1.0428	1.0464	1.0501	1.0538	1.0575	1.0612	1.0649	1.0686
47	sin	0.7314	0.7325	0.7337	0.7349	0.7361	0.7373	0.7385	0.7396	0.7408	0.7420
	cos	0.6820	0.6807	0.6794	0.6782	0.6769	0.6756	0.6743	0.6730	0.6717	0.6704
	tan	1.0724	1.0761	1.0799	1.0837	1.0875	1.0913	1.0951	1.0990	1.1028	1.1067
48	sin	0.7431	0.7443	0.7455	0.7466	0.7478	0.7490	0.7501	0.7513	0.7524	0.7536
	cos	0.6691	0.6678	0.6665	0.6652	0.6639	0.6626	0.6613	0.6600	0.6587	0.6574
	tan	1.1106	1.1145	1.1184	1.1224	1.1263	1.1303	1.1343	1.1383	1.1423	1.1463
49	sin	0.7547	0.7559	0.7570	0.7581	0.7593	0.7604	0.7615	0.7627	0.7638	0.7649
	cos	0.6561	0.6547	0.6534	0.6521	0.6508	0.6494	0.6481	0.6468	0.6455	0.6441
	tan	1.1504	1.1544	1.1585	1.1626	1.1667	1.1708	1.1750	1.1792	1.1833	1.1875
50	sin	0.7660	0.7672	0.7683	0.7694	0.7705	0.7716	0.7727	0.7738	0.7749	0.7760
	cos	0.6428	0.6414	0.6401	0.6388	0.6374	0.6361	0.6347	0.6334	0.6320	0.6307
	tan	1.1918	1.1960	1.2002	1.2045	1.2088	1.2131	1.2174	1.2218	1.2261	1.2305
51	sin	0.7771	0.7782	0.7793	0.7804	0.7815	0.7826	0.7837	0.7848	0.7859	0.7869
	cos	0.6293	0.6280	0.6266	0.6252	0.6239	0.6225	0.6211	0.6198	0.6184	0.6170
	tan	1.2349	1.2393	1.2437	1.2482	1.2527	1.2572	1.2617	1.2662	1.2708	1.2753
52	sin	0.7880	0.7891	0.7902	0.7912	0.7923	0.7934	0.7944	0.7955	0.7965	0.7976
	cos	0.6157	0.6143	0.6129	0.6115	0.6101	0.6088	0.6074	0.6060	0.6046	0.6032
	tan	1.2799	1.2846	1.2892	1.2938	1.2985	1.3032	1.3079	1.3127	1.3175	1.3222
53	sin	0.7986	0.7997	0.8007	0.8018	0.8028	0.8039	0.8049	0.8059	0.8070	0.8080
	cos	0.6018	0.6004	0.5990	0.5976	0.5962	0.5948	0.5934	0.5920	0.5906	0.5892
	tan	1.3270	1.3319	1.3367	1.3416	1.3465	1.3514	1.3564	1.3613	1.3663	1.3713
54	sin	0.8090	0.8100	0.8111	0.8121	0.8131	0.8141	0.8151	0.8161	0.8171	0.8181
	cos	0.5878	0.5864	0.5850	0.5835	0.5821	0.5807	0.5793	0.5779	0.5764	0.5750
	tan	1.3764	1.3814	1.3865	1.3916	1.3968	1.4019	1.4071	1.4124	1.4176	1.4229
55	sin	0.8192	0.8202	0.8211	0.8221	0.8231	0.8241	0.8251	0.8261	0.8271	0.8281
	cos	0.5736	0.5721	0.5707	0.5693	0.5678	0.5664	0.5650	0.5635	0.5621	0.5606
	tan	1.4281	1.4335	1.4388	1.4442	1.4496	1.4550	1.4605	1.4659	1.4715	1.4770
56	sin	0.8290	0.8300	0.8310	0.8320	0.8329	0.8339	0.8348	0.8358	0.8368	0.8377
	cos	0.5592	0.5577	0.5563	0.5548	0.5534	0.5519	0.5505	0.5490	0.5476	0.5461
	tan	1.4826	1.4882	1.4938	1.4994	1.5051	1.5108	1.5166	1.5224	1.5282	1.5340
57	sin	0.8387	0.8396	0.8406	0.8415	0.8425	0.8434	0.8443	0.8453	0.8462	0.8471
	cos	0.5446	0.5432	0.5417	0.5402	0.5388	0.5373	0.5358	0.5344	0.5329	0.5314
	tan	1.5399	1.5458	1.5517	1.5577	1.5637	1.5697	1.5757	1.5818	1.5880	1.5941
58	sin	0.8480	0.8490	0.8499	0.8508	0.8517	0.8526	0.8536	0.8545	0.8554	0.8563
	cos	0.5299	0.5284	0.5270	0.5255	0.5240	0.5225	0.5210	0.5195	0.5180	0.5165
	tan	1.6003	1.6066	1.6128	1.6191	1.6255	1.6319	1.6383	1.6447	1.6512	1.6577
59	sin	0.8572	0.8581	0.8590	0.8599	0.8607	0.8616	0.8625	0.8634	0.8643	0.8652
	cos	0.5150	0.5135	0.5120	0.5105	0.5090	0.5075	0.5060	0.5045	0.5030	0.5015
	tan	1.6643	1.6709	1.6775	1.6842	1.6909	1.6977	1.7045	1.7113	1.7182	1.7251
60	sin	0.8660	0.8669	0.8678	0.8686	0.8695	0.8704	0.8712	0.8721	0.8729	0.8738
	cos	0.5000	0.4985	0.4970	0.4955	0.4939	0.4924	0.4909	0.4894	0.4879	0.4863
	tan	1.7321	1.7391	1.7461	1.7532	1.7603	1.7675	1.7747	1.7820	1.7893	1.7966
61	sin	0.8746	0.8755	0.8763	0.8771	0.8780	0.8788	0.8796	0.8805	0.8813	0.8821
	cos	0.4848	0.4833	0.4818	0.4802	0.4787	0.4772	0.4756	0.4741	0.4726	0.4710
	tan	1.8040	1.8115	1.8190	1.8265	1.8341	1.8418	1.8495	1.8572	1.8650	1.8728
62	sin	0.8829	0.8838	0.8846	0.8854	0.8862	0.8870	0.8878	0.8886	0.8894	0.8902
	cos	0.4695	0.4679	0.4664	0.4648	0.4633	0.4617	0.4602	0.4586	0.4571	0.4555
	tan	1.8807	1.8887	1.8967	1.9047	1.9128	1.9210	1.9292	1.9375	1.9458	1.9542
deg	function	0′	6′	12′	18′	24′	30′	36′	42′	48′	54′

TABLE 7   NATURAL TRIGONOMETRIC FUNCTIONS (continued)

deg	function	0.0°	0.1°	0.2°	0.3°	0.4°	0.5°	0.6°	0.7°	0.8°	0.9°
63	sin	0.8910	0.8918	0.8926	0.8934	0.8942	0.8949	0.8957	0.8965	0.8973	0.8980
	cos	0.4540	0.4524	0.4509	0.4493	0.4478	0.4462	0.4446	0.4431	0.4415	0.4399
	tan	1.9626	1.9711	1.9797	1.9883	1.9970	2.0057	2.0145	2.0233	2.0323	2.0413
64	sin	0.8988	0.8996	0.9003	0.9011	0.9018	0.9026	0.9033	0.9041	0.9048	0.9056
	cos	0.4384	0.4368	0.4352	0.4337	0.4321	0.4305	0.4289	0.4274	0.4258	0.4242
	tan	2.0503	2.0594	2.0686	2.0778	2.0872	2.0965	2.1060	2.1155	2.1251	2.1348
65	sin	0.9063	0.9070	0.9078	0.9085	0.9092	0.9100	0.9107	0.9114	0.9121	0.9128
	cos	0.4226	0.4210	0.4195	0.4179	0.4163	0.4147	0.4131	0.4115	0.4099	0.4083
	tan	2.1445	2.1543	2.1642	2.1742	2.1842	2.1943	2.2045	2.2148	2.2251	2.2355
66	sin	0.9135	0.9143	0.9150	0.9157	0.9164	0.9171	0.9178	0.9184	0.9191	0.9198
	cos	0.4067	0.4051	0.4035	0.4019	0.4003	0.3987	0.3971	0.3955	0.3939	0.3923
	tan	2.2460	2.2566	2.2673	2.2781	2.2889	2.2998	2.3109	2.3220	2.3332	2.3445
67	sin	0.9205	0.9212	0.9219	0.9225	0.9232	0.9239	0.9245	0.9252	0.9259	0.9265
	cos	0.3907	0.3891	0.3875	0.3859	0.3843	0.3827	0.3811	0.3795	0.3778	0.3762
	tan	2.3559	2.3673	2.3789	2.3906	2.4023	2.4142	2.4262	2.4383	2.4504	2.4627
68	sin	0.9272	0.9278	0.9285	0.9291	0.9298	0.9304	0.9311	0.9317	0.9323	0.9330
	cos	0.3746	0.3730	0.3714	0.3697	0.3681	0.3665	0.3649	0.3633	0.3616	0.3600
	tan	2.4751	2.4876	2.5002	2.5129	2.5257	2.5386	2.5517	2.5649	2.5782	2.5916
69	sin	0.9336	0.9342	0.9348	0.9354	0.9361	0.9367	0.9373	0.9379	0.9385	0.9391
	cos	0.3584	0.3567	0.3551	0.3535	0.3518	0.3502	0.3486	0.3469	0.3453	0.3437
	tan	2.6051	2.6187	2.6325	2.6464	2.6605	2.6746	2.6889	2.7034	2.7179	2.7326
70	sin	0.9397	0.9403	0.9409	0.9415	0.9421	0.9426	0.9432	0.9438	0.9444	0.9449
	cos	0.3420	0.3404	0.3387	0.3371	0.3355	0.3338	0.3322	0.3305	0.3289	0.3272
	tan	2.7475	2.7625	2.7776	2.7929	2.8083	2.8239	2.8397	2.8556	2.8716	2.8878
71	sin	0.9455	0.9461	0.9466	0.9472	0.9478	0.9483	0.9489	0.9494	0.9500	0.9505
	cos	0.3256	0.3239	0.3223	0.3206	0.3190	0.3173	0.3156	0.3140	0.3123	0.3107
	tan	2.9042	2.9208	2.9375	2.9544	2.9714	2.9887	3.0061	3.0237	3.0415	3.0595
72	sin	0.9511	0.9516	0.9521	0.9527	0.9532	0.9537	0.9542	0.9548	0.9553	0.9558
	cos	0.3090	0.3074	0.3057	0.3040	0.3024	0.3007	0.2990	0.2974	0.2957	0.2940
	tan	3.0777	3.0961	3.1146	3.1334	3.1524	3.1716	3.1910	3.2106	3.2305	3.2506
73	sin	0.9563	0.9568	0.9573	0.9578	0.9583	0.9588	0.9593	0.9598	0.9603	0.9608
	cos	0.2924	0.2907	0.2890	0.2874	0.2857	0.2840	0.2823	0.2807	0.2790	0.2773
	tan	3.2709	3.2914	3.3122	3.3332	3.3544	3.3759	3.3977	3.4197	3.4420	3.4646
74	sin	0.9613	0.9617	0.9622	0.9627	0.9632	0.9636	0.9641	0.9646	0.9650	0.9655
	cos	0.2756	0.2740	0.2723	0.2706	0.2689	0.2672	0.2656	0.2639	0.2622	0.2605
	tan	3.4874	3.5105	3.5339	3.5576	3.5816	3.6059	3.6305	3.6554	3.6806	3.7062
75	sin	0.9659	0.9664	0.9668	0.9673	0.9677	0.9681	0.9686	0.9690	0.9694	0.9699
	cos	0.2588	0.2571	0.2554	0.2538	0.2521	0.2504	0.2487	0.2470	0.2453	0.2436
	tan	3.7321	3.7583	3.7848	3.8118	3.8391	3.8667	3.8947	3.9232	3.9520	3.9812
76	sin	0.9703	0.9707	0.9711	0.9715	0.9720	0.9724	0.9728	0.9732	0.9736	0.9740
	cos	0.2419	0.2402	0.2385	0.2368	0.2351	0.2334	0.2317	0.2300	0.2284	0.2267
	tan	4.0108	4.0408	4.0713	4.1022	4.1335	4.1653	4.1976	4.2303	4.2635	4.2972
77	sin	0.9744	0.9748	0.9751	0.9755	0.9759	0.9763	0.9767	0.9770	0.9774	0.9778
	cos	0.2250	0.2232	0.2215	0.2198	0.2181	0.2164	0.2147	0.2130	0.2113	0.2096
	tan	4.3315	4.3662	4.4015	4.4374	4.4737	4.5107	4.5483	4.5864	4.6252	4.6646
78	sin	0.9781	0.9785	0.9789	0.9792	0.9796	0.9799	0.9803	0.9806	0.9810	0.9813
	cos	0.2079	0.2062	0.2045	0.2028	0.2011	0.1994	0.1977	0.1959	0.1942	0.1925
	tan	4.7046	4.7453	4.7867	4.8288	4.8716	4.9152	4.9594	5.0045	5.0504	5.0970
79	sin	0.9816	0.9820	0.9823	0.9826	0.9829	0.9833	0.9836	0.9839	0.9842	0.9845
	cos	0.1908	0.1891	0.1874	0.1857	0.1840	0.1822	0.1805	0.1788	0.1771	0.1754
	tan	5.1446	5.1929	5.2422	5.2924	5.3435	5.3955	5.4486	5.5026	5.5578	5.6140
80	sin	0.9848	0.9851	0.9854	0.9857	0.9860	0.9863	0.9866	0.9869	0.9871	0.9874
	cos	0.1736	0.1719	0.1702	0.1685	0.1668	0.1650	0.1633	0.1616	0.1599	0.1582
	tan	5.6713	5.7297	5.7894	5.8502	5.9124	5.9758	6.0405	6.1066	6.1742	6.2432
81	sin	0.9877	0.9880	0.9882	0.9885	0.9888	0.9890	0.9893	0.9895	0.9898	0.9900
	cos	0.1564	0.1547	0.1530	0.1513	0.1495	0.1478	0.1461	0.1444	0.1426	0.1409
	tan	6.3138	6.3859	6.4596	6.5350	6.6122	6.6912	6.7720	6.8548	6.9395	7.0264
82	sin	0.9903	0.9905	0.9907	0.9910	0.9912	0.9914	0.9917	0.9919	0.9921	0.9923
	cos	0.1392	0.1374	0.1357	0.1340	0.1323	0.1305	0.1288	0.1271	0.1253	0.1236
	tan	7.1154	7.2066	7.3002	7.3962	7.4947	7.5958	7.6996	7.8062	7.9158	8.0285
83	sin	0.9925	0.9928	0.9930	0.9932	0.9934	0.9936	0.9938	0.9940	0.9942	0.9943
	cos	0.1219	0.1201	0.1184	0.1167	0.1149	0.1132	0.1115	0.1097	0.1080	0.1063
	tan	8.1443	8.2636	8.3863	8.5126	8.6427	8.7769	8.9152	9.0579	9.2052	9.3572

deg	function	0′	6′	12′	18′	24′	30′	36′	42′	48′	54′

TABLE 7   NATURAL TRIGONOMETRIC FUNCTIONS (continued)

deg	function	0.0°	0.1°	0.2°	0.3°	0.4°	0.5°	0.6°	0.7°	0.8°	0.9°
84	sin	0.9945	0.9947	0.9949	0.9951	0.9952	0.9954	0.9956	0.9957	0.9959	0.9960
	cos	0.1045	0.1028	0.1011	0.0993	0.0976	0.0958	0.0941	0.0924	0.0906	0.0889
	tan	9.5144	9.6768	9.8448	10.02	10.20	10.39	10.58	10.78	10.99	11.20
85	sin	0.9962	0.9963	0.9965	0.9966	0.9968	0.9969	0.9971	0.9972	0.9973	0.9974
	cos	0.0872	0.0854	0.0837	0.0819	0.0802	0.0785	0.0767	0.0750	0.0732	0.0715
	tan	11.43	11.66	11.91	12.16	12.43	12.71	13.00	13.30	13.62	13.95
86	sin	0.9976	0.9977	0.9978	0.9979	0.9980	0.9981	0.9982	0.9983	0.9984	0.9985
	cos	0.0698	0.0680	0.0663	0.0645	0.0628	0.0610	0.0593	0.0576	0.0558	0.0541
	tan	14.30	14.67	15.06	15.46	15.89	16.35	16.83	17.34	17.89	18.46
87	sin	0.9986	0.9987	0.9988	0.9989	0.9990	0.9990	0.9991	0.9992	0.9993	0.9993
	cos	0.0523	0.0506	0.0488	0.0471	0.0454	0.0436	0.0419	0.0401	0.0384	0.0366
	tan	19.08	19.74	20.45	21.20	22.02	22.90	23.86	24.90	26.03	27.27
88	sin	0.9994	0.9995	0.9995	0.9996	0.9996	0.9997	0.9997	0.9997	0.9998	0.9998
	cos	0.0349	0.0332	0.0314	0.0297	0.0279	0.0262	0.0244	0.0227	0.0209	0.0192
	tan	28.64	30.14	31.82	33.69	35.80	38.19	40.92	44.07	47.74	52.08
89	sin	0.9998	0.9999	0.9999	0.9999	0.9999	1.000	1.000	1.000	1.000	1.000
	cos	0.0175	0.0157	0.0140	0.0122	0.0105	0.0087	0.0070	0.0052	0.0035	0.0017
	tan	57.29	63.66	71.62	81.85	95.49	114.6	143.2	191.0	286.5	573.0

deg	function	0′	6′	12′	18′	24′	30′	36′	42′	48′	54′

TABLE 8 SQUARES, SQUARE ROOTS, AND RECIPROCALS

no.	square	sq. root	reciprocal	no.	square	sq. root	reciprocal
1	1	1.0000	1.000000000	51	2,601	7.1414	.019607843
2	4	1.4142	.500000000	52	2,704	7.2111	.019230769
3	9	1.7321	.333333333	53	2,809	7.2801	.018867925
4	16	2.0000	.250000000	54	2,916	7.3485	.018518519
5	25	2.2361	.200000000	55	3,025	7.4162	.018181818
6	36	2.4495	.166666667	56	3,136	7.4833	.017857143
7	49	2.6458	.142857143	57	3,249	7.5498	.017543860
8	64	2.8284	.125000000	58	3,364	7.6158	.017241379
9	81	3.0000	.111111111	59	3,481	7.6811	.016949153
10	100	3.1623	.100000000	60	3,600	7.7460	.016666667
11	121	3.3166	.090909091	61	3,721	7.8102	.016393443
12	144	3.4641	.083333333	62	3,844	7.8740	.016129032
13	169	3.6056	.076923077	63	3,969	7.9373	.015873016
14	196	3.7417	.071428571	64	4,096	8.0000	.015625000
15	225	3.8730	.066666667	65	4,225	8.0623	.015384615
16	256	4.0000	.062500000	66	4,356	8.1240	.015151515
17	289	4.1231	.058823529	67	4,489	8.1854	.014925373
18	324	4.2426	.055555556	68	4,624	8.2462	.014705882
19	361	4.3589	.052631579	69	4,761	8.3066	.014492754
20	400	4.4721	.050000000	70	4,900	8.3666	.014285714
21	441	4.5826	.047619048	71	5,041	8.4261	.014084507
22	484	4.6904	.045454545	72	5,184	8.4853	.013888889
23	529	4.7958	.043478261	73	5,329	8.5440	.013698630
24	576	4.8990	.041666667	74	5,476	8.6023	.013513514
25	625	5.0000	.040000000	75	5,625	8.6603	.013333333
26	676	5.0990	.038461538	76	5,776	8.7178	.013157895
27	729	5.1962	.037037037	77	5,929	8.7750	.012987013
28	784	5.2915	.035714286	78	6,084	8.8318	.012820513
29	841	5.3852	.034482759	79	6,241	8.8882	.012658228
30	900	5.4772	.033333333	80	6,400	8.9443	.012500000
31	961	5.5678	.032258065	81	6,561	9.0000	.012345679
32	1,024	5.6569	.031250000	82	6,724	9.0554	.012195122
33	1,089	5.7446	.030303030	83	6,889	9.1104	.012048193
34	1,156	5.8310	.029411765	84	7,056	9.1652	.011904762
35	1,225	5.9161	.028571429	85	7,225	9.2195	.011764706
36	1,296	6.0000	.027777778	86	7,396	9.2736	.011627907
37	1,369	6.0828	.027027027	87	7,569	9.3274	.011494253
38	1,444	6.1644	.026315789	88	7,744	9.3808	.011363636
39	1,521	6.2450	.025641026	89	7,921	9.4340	.011235955
40	1,600	6.3246	.025000000	90	8,100	9.4868	.011111111
41	1,681	6.4031	.024390244	91	8,281	9.5394	.010989011
42	1,764	6.4807	.023809524	92	8,464	9.5917	.010869565
43	1,849	6.5574	.023255814	93	8,649	9.6437	.010752688
44	1,936	6.6332	.022727273	94	8,836	9.6954	.010638298
45	2,025	6.7082	.022222222	95	9,025	9.7468	.010526316
46	2,116	6.7823	.021739130	96	9,216	9.7980	.010416667
47	2,209	6.8557	.021276596	97	9,409	9.8489	.010309278
48	2,304	6.9282	.020833333	98	9,604	9.8995	.010204082
49	2,401	7.0000	.020408163	99	9,801	9.9499	.010101010
50	2,500	7.0711	.020000000	100	10,000	10.0000	.010000000

TABLE 8 SQUARES, SQUARE ROOTS, AND RECIPROCALS (continued)

no.	square	sq. root	reciprocal	no.	square	sq. root	reciprocal
101	10,201	10.0499	.009900990	151	22,801	12.2882	.006622517
102	10,404	10.0995	.009803922	152	23,104	12.3288	.006578947
103	10,609	10.1489	.009708738	153	23,409	12.3693	.006535948
104	10,816	10.1980	.009615385	154	23,716	12.4097	.006493506
105	11,025	10.2470	.009523810	155	24,025	12.4499	.006451613
106	11,236	10.2956	.009433962	156	24,336	12.4900	.006410256
107	11,449	10.3441	.009345794	157	24,649	12.5300	.006369427
108	11,664	10.3923	.009259259	158	24,964	12.5698	.006329114
109	11,881	10.4403	.009174312	159	25,281	12.6095	.006289308
110	12,100	10.4881	.009090909	160	25,600	12.6491	.006250000
111	12,321	10.5357	.009009009	161	25,921	12.6886	.006211180
112	12,544	10.5830	.008928571	162	26,244	12.7279	.006172840
113	12,769	10.6301	.008849558	163	26,569	12.7671	.006134969
114	12,996	10.6771	.008771930	164	26,896	12.8062	.006097561
115	13,225	10.7238	.008695652	165	27,225	12.8452	.006060606
116	13,456	10.7703	.008620690	166	27,556	12.8841	.006024096
117	13,689	10.8167	.008547009	167	27,889	12.9228	.005988024
118	13,924	10.8628	.008474576	168	28,224	12.9615	.005952381
119	14,161	10.9087	.008403361	169	28,561	13.0000	.005917160
120	14,400	10.9545	.008333333	170	28,900	13.0384	.005882353
121	14,641	11.0000	.008264463	171	29,241	13.0767	.005847953
122	14,884	11.0454	.008196721	172	29,584	13.1149	.005813953
123	15,129	11.0905	.008130081	173	29,929	13.1529	.005780347
124	15,376	11.1355	.008064516	174	30,276	13.1909	.005747126
125	15,625	11.1803	.008000000	175	30,625	13.2288	.005714286
126	15,876	11.2250	.007936508	176	30,976	13.2665	.005681818
127	16,129	11.2694	.007874016	177	31,329	13.3041	.005649718
128	16,384	11.3137	.007812500	178	31,684	13.3417	.005617978
129	16,641	11.3578	.007751938	179	32,041	13.3791	.005586592
130	16,900	11.4018	.007692308	180	32,400	13.4164	.005555556
131	17,161	11.4455	.007633588	181	32,761	13.4536	.005524862
132	17,424	11.4891	.007575758	182	33,124	13.4907	.005494505
133	17,689	11.5326	.007518797	183	33,489	13.5277	.005464481
134	17,956	11.5758	.007462687	184	33,856	13.5647	.005434783
135	18,225	11.6190	.007407407	185	34,225	13.6015	.005405405
136	18,496	11.6619	.007352941	186	34,596	13.6382	.005376344
137	18,769	11.7047	.007299270	187	34,969	13.6748	.005347594
138	19,044	11.7473	.007246377	188	35,344	13.7113	.005319149
139	19,321	11.7898	.007194245	189	35,721	13.7477	.005291005
140	19,600	11.8322	.007142857	190	36,100	13.7840	.005263158
141	19,881	11.8743	.007092199	191	36,481	13.8203	.005235602
142	20,164	11.9164	.007042254	192	36,864	13.8564	.005208333
143	20,449	11.9583	.006993007	193	37,249	13.8924	.005181347
144	20,736	12.0000	.006944444	194	37,636	13.9284	.005154639
145	21,025	12.0416	.006896552	195	38,025	13.9642	.005128205
146	21,316	12.0830	.006849315	196	38,416	14.0000	.005102041
147	21,609	12.1244	.006802721	197	38,809	14.0357	.005076142
148	21,904	12.1655	.006756757	198	39,204	14.0712	.005050505
149	22,201	12.2066	.006711409	199	39,601	14.1067	.005025126
150	22,500	12.2474	.006666667	200	40,000	14.1421	.005000000

TABLE 8   SQUARES, SQUARE ROOTS, AND RECIPROCALS (continued)

no.	square	sq. root	reciprocal	no.	square	sq. root	reciprocal
201	40,401	14.1774	.004975124	251	63,001	15.8430	.003984064
202	40,804	14.2127	.004950495	252	63,504	15.8745	.003968254
203	41,209	14.2478	.004926108	253	64,009	15.9060	.003952569
204	41,616	14.2829	.004901961	254	64,516	15.9374	.003937008
205	42,025	14.3178	.004878049	255	65,025	15.9687	.003921569
206	42,436	14.3527	.004854369	256	65,536	16.0000	.003906250
207	42,849	14.3875	.004830918	257	66,049	16.0312	.003891051
208	43,264	14.4222	.004807692	258	66,564	16.0624	.003875969
209	43,681	14.4568	.004784689	259	67,081	16.0935	.003861004
210	44,100	14.4914	.004761905	260	67,600	16.1245	.003846154
211	44,521	14.5258	.004739336	261	68,121	16.1555	.003831418
212	44,944	14.5602	.004716981	262	68,644	16.1864	.003816794
213	45,369	14.5945	.004694836	263	69,169	16.2173	.003802281
214	45,796	14.6287	.004672897	264	69,696	16.2481	.003787879
215	46,225	14.6629	.004651163	265	70,225	16.2788	.003773585
216	46,656	14.6969	.004629630	266	70,756	16.3095	.003759398
217	47,089	14.7309	.004608295	267	71,289	16.3401	.003745318
218	47,524	14.7648	.004587156	268	71,824	16.3707	.003731343
219	47,961	14.7986	.004566210	269	72,361	16.4012	.003717472
220	48,400	14.8324	.004545455	270	72,900	16.4317	.003703704
221	48,841	14.8661	.004524887	271	73,441	16.4621	.003690037
222	49,284	14.8997	.004504505	272	73,984	16.4924	.003676471
223	49,729	14.9332	.004484305	273	74,529	16.5227	.003663004
224	50,176	14.9666	.004464286	274	75,076	16.5529	.003649635
225	50,625	15.0000	.004444444	275	75,625	16.5831	.003636364
226	51,076	15.0333	.004424779	276	76,176	16.6132	.003623188
227	51,529	15.0665	.004405286	277	76,729	16.6433	.003610108
228	51,984	15.0997	.004385965	278	77,284	16.6733	.003597122
229	52,441	15.1327	.004366812	279	77,841	16.7033	.003584229
230	52,900	15.1658	.004347826	280	78,400	16.7332	.003571429
231	53,361	15.1987	.004329004	281	78,961	16.7631	.003558719
232	53,824	15.2315	.004310345	282	79,524	16.7929	.003546099
233	54,289	15.2643	.004291845	283	80,089	16.8226	.003533569
234	54,756	15.2971	.004273504	284	80,656	16.8523	.003521127
235	55,225	15.3297	.004255319	285	81,225	16.8819	.003508772
236	55,696	15.3623	.004237288	286	81,796	16.9115	.003496503
237	56,169	15.3948	.004219409	287	82,369	16.9411	.003484321
238	56,644	15.4272	.004201681	288	82,944	16.9706	.003472222
239	57,121	15.4596	.004184100	289	83,521	17.0000	.003460208
240	57,600	15.4919	.004166667	290	84,100	17.0294	.003448276
241	58,081	15.5242	.004149378	291	84,681	17.0587	.003436426
242	58,564	15.5563	.004132231	292	85,264	17.0880	.003424658
243	59,049	15.5885	.004115226	293	85,849	17.1172	.003412969
244	59,536	15.6205	.004098361	294	86,436	17.1464	.003401361
245	60,025	15.6525	.004081633	295	87,025	17.1756	.003389831
246	60,516	15.6844	.004065041	296	87,616	17.2047	.003378378
247	61,009	15.7162	.004048583	297	88,209	17.2337	.003367003
248	61,504	15.7480	.004032258	298	88,804	17.2627	.003355705
249	62,001	15.7797	.004016064	299	89,401	17.2916	.003344482
250	62,500	15.8114	.004000000	300	90,000	17.3205	.003333333

TABLE 8   SQUARES, SQUARE ROOTS, AND RECIPROCALS (continued)

no.	square	sq. root	reciprocal	no.	square	sq. root	reciprocal
301	90,601	17.3494	.003322259	351	123,201	18.7350	.002849003
302	91,204	17.3781	.003311258	352	123,904	18.7617	.002840909
303	91,809	17.4069	.003300330	353	124,609	18.7883	.002832861
304	92,416	17.4356	.003289474	354	125,316	18.8149	.002824859
305	93,025	17.4642	.003278689	355	126,025	18.8414	.002816901
306	93,636	17.4929	.003267974	356	126,736	18.8680	.002808989
307	94,249	17.5214	.003257329	357	127,449	18.8944	.002801120
308	94,864	17.5499	.003246753	358	128,164	18.9209	.002793296
309	95,481	17.5784	.003236246	359	128,881	18.9473	.002785515
310	96,100	17.6068	.003225806	360	129,600	18.9737	.002777778
311	96,721	17.6352	.003215434	361	130,321	19.0000	.002770083
312	97,344	17.6635	.003205128	362	131,044	19.0263	.002762431
313	97,969	17.6918	.003194888	363	131,769	19.0526	.002754821
314	98,596	17.7200	.003184713	364	132,496	19.0788	.002747253
315	99,225	17.7482	.003174603	365	133,225	19.1050	.002739726
316	99,856	17.7764	.003164557	366	133,956	19.1311	.002732240
317	100,489	17.8045	.003154574	367	134,689	19.1572	.002724796
318	101,124	17.8326	.003144654	368	135,424	19.1833	.002717391
319	101,761	17.8606	.003134796	369	136,161	19.2094	.002710027
320	102,400	17.8885	.003125000	370	136,900	19.2354	.002702703
321	103,041	17.9165	.003115265	371	137,641	19.2614	.002695418
322	103,684	17.9444	.003105590	372	138,384	19.2873	.002688172
323	104,329	17.9722	.003095975	373	139,129	19.3132	.002680965
324	104,976	18.0000	.003086420	374	139,876	19.3391	.002673797
325	105,625	18.0278	.003076923	375	140,625	19.3649	.002666667
326	106,276	18.0555	.003067485	376	141,376	19.3907	.002659574
327	106,929	18.0831	.003058104	377	142,129	19.4165	.002652520
328	107,584	18.1108	.003048780	378	142,884	19.4422	.002645503
329	108,241	18.1384	.003039514	379	143,641	19.4679	.002638522
330	108,900	18.1659	.003030303	380	144,400	19.4936	.002631579
331	109,561	18.1934	.003021148	381	145,161	19.5192	.002624672
332	110,224	18.2209	.003012048	382	145,924	19.5448	.002617801
333	110,889	18.2483	.003003003	383	146,689	19.5704	.002610966
334	111,556	18.2757	.002994012	384	147,456	19.5959	.002604167
335	112,225	18.3030	.002985075	385	148,225	19.6214	.002597403
336	112,896	18.3303	.002976190	386	148,996	19.6469	.002590674
337	113,569	18.3576	.002967359	387	149,769	19.6723	.002583979
338	114,244	18.3848	.002958580	388	150,544	19.6977	.002577320
339	114,921	18.4120	.002949853	389	151,321	19.7231	.002570694
340	115,600	18.4391	.002941176	390	152,100	19.7484	.002564103
341	116,281	18.4662	.002932551	391	152,881	19.7737	.002557545
342	116,964	18.4932	.002923977	392	153,664	19.7990	.002551020
343	117,649	18.5203	.002915452	393	154,449	19.8242	.002544529
344	118,336	18.5472	.002906977	394	155,236	19.8494	.002538071
345	119,025	18.5742	.002898551	395	156,025	19.8746	.002531646
346	119,716	18.6011	.002890173	396	156,816	19.8997	.002525253
347	120,409	18.6279	.002881844	397	157,609	19.9249	.002518892
348	121,104	18.6548	.002873563	398	158,404	19.9499	.002512563
349	121,801	18.6815	.002865330	399	159,201	19.9750	.002506266
350	122,500	18.7083	.002857143	400	160,000	20.0000	.002500000

TABLE 8 SQUARES, SQUARE ROOTS, AND RECIPROCALS (continued)

no.	square	sq. root	reciprocal	no.	square	sq. root	reciprocal
401	160,801	20.0250	.002493766	451	203,401	21.2368	.002217295
402	161,604	20.0499	.002487562	452	204,304	21.2603	.002212389
403	162,409	20.0749	.002481390	453	205,209	21.2838	.002207506
404	163,216	20.0998	.002475248	454	206,116	21.3073	.002202643
405	164,025	20.1246	.002469136	455	207,025	21.3307	.002197802
406	164,836	20.1494	.002463054	456	207,936	21.3542	.002192982
407	165,649	20.1742	.002457002	457	208,849	21.3776	.002188184
408	166,464	20.1990	.002450980	458	209,764	21.4009	.002183406
409	167,281	20.2237	.002444988	459	210,681	21.4243	.002178649
410	168,100	20.2485	.002439024	460	211,600	21.4476	.002173913
411	168,921	20.2731	.002433090	461	212,521	21.4709	.002169197
412	169,744	20.2978	.002427184	462	213,444	21.4942	.002164502
413	170,569	20.3224	.002421308	463	214,369	21.5174	.002159827
414	171,396	20.3470	.002415459	464	215,296	21.5407	.002155172
415	172,225	20.3715	.002409639	465	216,225	21.5639	.002150538
416	173,056	20.3961	.002403846	466	217,156	21.5870	.002145923
417	173,889	20.4206	.002398082	467	218,089	21.6102	.002141328
418	174,724	20.4450	.002392344	468	219,024	21.6333	.002136752
419	175,561	20.4695	.002386635	469	219,961	21.6564	.002132196
420	176,400	20.4939	.002380952	470	220,900	21.6795	002127660
421	177,241	20.5183	.002375297	471	221,841	21.7025	.002123142
422	178,084	20.5426	.002369668	472	222,784	21.7256	.002118644
423	178,929	20.5670	.002364066	473	223,729	21.7486	.002114165
424	179,776	20.5913	.002358491	474	224,676	21.7715	.002109705
425	180,625	20.6155	.002352941	475	225,625	21.7945	.002105263
426	181,476	20.6398	.002347418	476	226,576	21.8174	.002100840
427	182,329	20.6640	.002341920	477	227,529	21.8403	.002096436
428	183,184	20.6882	.002336449	478	228,484	21.8632	.002092050
429	184,041	20.7123	.002331002	479	229,441	21.8861	.002087683
430	184,900	20.7364	.002325581	480	230,400	21.9089	.002083333
431	185,761	20.7605	.002320186	481	231,361	21.9317	.002079002
432	186,624	20.7846	.002314815	482	232,324	21.9545	.002074689
433	187,489	20.8087	.002309469	483	233,289	21.9773	.002070393
434	188,356	20.8327	.002304147	484	234,256	22.0000	.002066116
435	189,225	20.8567	.002298851	485	235,225	22.0227	.002061856
436	190,096	20.8806	.002293578	486	236,196	22.0454	.002057613
437	190,969	20.9045	.002288330	487	237,169	22.0681	.002053388
438	191,844	20.9284	.002283105	488	238,144	22.0907	.002049180
439	192,721	20.9523	.002277904	489	239,121	22.1133	.002044990
440	193,600	20.9762	.002272727	490	240,100	22.1359	.002040816
441	194,481	21.0000	.002267574	491	241,081	22.1585	.002036660
442	195,364	21.0238	.002262443	492	242,064	22.1811	.002032520
443	196,249	21.0476	.002257336	493	243,049	22.2036	.002028398
444	197,136	21.0713	.002252252	494	244,036	22.2261	.002024291
445	198,025	21.0950	.002247191	495	245,025	22.2486	.002020202
446	198,916	21.1187	.002242152	496	246,016	22.2711	.002016129
447	199,809	21.1424	.002237136	497	247,009	22.2935	.002012072
448	200,704	21.1660	.002232143	498	248,004	22.3159	.002008032
449	201,601	21.1896	.002227171	499	249,001	22.3383	.002004008
450	202,500	21.2132	.002222222	500	250,000	22.3607	.002000000

TABLE 8 SQUARES, SQUARE ROOTS, AND RECIPROCALS (continued)

no.	square	sq. root	reciprocal	no.	square	sq. root	reciprocal
501	251,001	22.3830	.001996008	551	303,601	23.4734	.001814882
502	252,004	22.4054	.001992032	552	304,704	23.4947	.001811594
503	253,009	22.4277	.001988072	553	305,809	23.5160	.001808318
504	254,016	22.4499	.001984127	554	306,916	23.5372	.001805054
505	255,025	22.4722	.001980198	555	308,025	23.5584	.001801802
506	256,036	22.4944	.001976285	556	309,136	23.5797	.001798561
507	257,049	22.5167	.001972387	557	310,249	23.6008	.001795332
508	258,064	22.5389	.001968504	558	311,364	23.6220	.001792115
509	259,081	22.5610	.001964637	559	312,481	23.6432	.001788909
510	260,100	22.5832	.001960784	560	313,600	23.6643	.001785714
511	261,121	22.6053	.001956947	561	314,721	23.6854	.001782531
512	262,144	22.6274	.001953125	562	315,844	23.7065	.001779359
513	263,169	22.6495	.001949318	563	316,969	23.7276	.001776199
514	264,196	22.6716	.001945525	564	318,096	23.7487	.001773050
515	265,225	22.6936	.001941748	565	319,225	23.7697	.001769912
516	266,256	22.7156	.001937984	566	320,356	23.7908	.001766784
517	267,289	22.7376	.001934236	567	321,489	23.8118	.001763668
518	268,324	22.7596	.001930502	568	322,624	23.8328	.001760563
519	269,361	22.7816	.001926782	569	323,761	23.8537	.001757469
520	270,400	22.8035	.001923077	570	324,900	23.8747	.001754386
521	271,441	22.8254	.001919386	571	326,041	23.8956	.001751313
522	272,484	22.8473	.001915709	572	327,184	23.9165	.001748252
523	273,529	22.8692	.001912046	573	328,329	23.9374	.001745201
524	274,576	22.8910	.001908397	574	329,476	23.9583	.001742160
525	275,625	22.9129	.001904762	575	330,625	23.9792	.001739130
526	276,676	22.9347	.001901141	576	331,776	24.0000	.001736111
527	277,729	22.9565	.001897533	577	332,929	24.0208	.001733102
528	278,784	22.9783	.001893939	578	334,084	24.0416	.001730104
529	279,841	23.0000	.001890359	579	335,241	24.0624	.001727116
530	280,900	23.0217	.001886792	580	336,400	24.0832	.001724138
531	281,961	23.0434	.001883239	581	337,561	24.1039	.001721170
532	283,024	23.0651	.001879699	582	338,724	24.1247	.001718213
533	284,089	23.0868	.001876173	583	339,889	24.1454	.001715266
534	285,156	23.1084	.001872659	584	341,056	24.1661	.001712329
535	286,225	23.1301	.001869159	585	342,225	24.1868	.001709402
536	287,296	23.1517	.001865672	586	343,396	24.2074	.001706485
537	288,369	23.1733	.001862197	587	344,569	24.2281	.001703578
538	289,444	23.1948	.001858736	588	345,744	24.2487	.001700680
539	290,521	23.2164	.001855288	589	346,921	24.2693	.001697793
540	291,600	23.2379	.001851852	590	348,100	24.2899	.001694915
541	292,681	23.2594	.001848429	591	349,281	24.3105	.001692047
542	293,764	23.2809	.001845018	592	350,464	24.3311	.001689189
543	294,849	23.3024	.001841621	593	351,649	24.3516	.001686341
544	295,936	23.3238	.001838235	594	352,836	24.3721	.001683502
545	297,025	23.3452	.001834862	595	354,025	24.3926	.001680672
546	298,116	23.3666	.001831502	596	355,216	24.4131	.001677852
547	299,209	23.3880	.001828154	597	356,409	24.4336	.001675042
548	300,304	23.4094	.001824818	598	357,604	24.4540	.001672241
549	301,401	23.4307	.001821494	599	358,801	24.4745	.001669449
550	302,500	23.4521	.001818182	600	360,000	24.4949	.001666667

TABLE 8   SQUARES, SQUARE ROOTS, AND RECIPROCALS (continued)

no.	square	sq. root	reciprocal	no.	square	sq. root	reciprocal
601	361,201	24.5153	.001663894	651	423,801	25.5147	.001536098
602	362,404	24.5357	.001661130	652	425,104	25.5343	.001533742
603	363,609	24.5561	.001658375	653	426,409	25.5539	.001531394
604	364,816	24.5764	.001655629	654	427,716	25.5734	.001529052
605	366,025	24.5967	.001652893	655	429,025	25.5930	.001526718
606	367,236	24.6171	.001650165	656	430,336	25.6125	.001524390
607	368,449	24.6374	.001647446	657	431,649	25.6320	.001522070
608	369,664	24.6577	.001644737	658	432,964	25.6515	.001519757
609	370,881	24.6779	.001642036	659	434,281	25.6710	.001517451
610	372,100	24.6982	.001639344	660	435,600	25.6905	.001515152
611	373,321	24.7184	.001636661	661	436,921	25.7099	.001512859
612	374,544	24.7386	.001633987	662	438,244	25.7294	.001510574
613	375,769	24.7588	.001631321	663	439,569	25.7488	.001508296
614	376,996	24.7790	.001628664	664	440,896	25.7682	.001506024
615	378,225	24.7992	.001626016	665	442,225	25.7876	.001503759
616	379,456	24.8193	.001623377	666	443,556	25.8070	.001501502
617	380,689	24.8395	.001620746	667	444,889	25.8263	.001499250
618	381,924	24.8596	.001618123	668	446,224	25.8457	.001497006
619	383,161	24.8797	.001615509	669	447,561	25.8650	.001494768
620	384,400	24.8998	.001612903	670	448,900	25.8844	.001492537
621	385,641	24.9199	.001610306	671	450,241	25.9037	.001490313
622	386,884	24.9399	.001607717	672	451,584	25.9230	.001488095
623	388,129	24.9600	.001605136	673	452,929	25.9422	.001485884
624	389,376	24.9800	.001602564	674	454,276	25.9615	.001483680
625	390,625	25.0000	.001600000	675	455,625	25.9808	.001481481
626	391,876	25.0200	.001597444	676	456,976	26.0000	.001479290
627	393,129	25.0400	.001594896	677	458,329	26.0192	.001477105
628	394,384	25.0599	.001592357	678	459,684	26.0384	.001474926
629	395,641	25.0799	.001589825	679	461,041	26.0576	.001472754
630	396,900	25.0998	.001587302	680	462,400	26.0768	.001470588
631	398,161	25.1197	.001584786	681	463,761	26.0960	.001468429
632	399,424	25.1396	.001582278	682	465,124	26.1151	.001466276
633	400,689	25.1595	.001579779	683	466,489	26.1343	.001464129
634	401,956	25.1794	.001577287	684	467,856	26.1534	.001461988
635	403,225	25.1992	.001574803	685	469,225	26.1725	.001459854
636	404,496	25.2190	.001572327	686	470,596	26.1916	.001457726
637	405,769	25.2389	.001569859	687	471,969	26.2107	.001455604
638	407,044	25.2587	.001567398	688	473,344	26.2298	.001453488
639	408,321	25.2784	.001564945	689	474,721	26.2488	.001451379
640	409,600	25.2982	.001562500	690	476,100	26.2679	.001449275
641	410,881	25.3180	.001560062	691	477,481	26.2869	.001447178
642	412,164	25.3377	.001557632	692	478,864	26.3059	.001445087
643	413,449	25.3574	.001555210	693	480,249	26.3249	.001443001
644	414,736	25.3772	.001552795	694	481,636	26.3439	.001440922
645	416,025	25.3969	.001550388	695	483,025	26.3629	.001438849
646	417,316	25.4165	.001547988	696	484,416	26.3818	.001436782
647	418,609	25.4362	.001545595	697	485,809	26.4008	.001434720
648	419,904	25.4558	.001543210	698	487,204	26.4197	.001432665
649	421,201	25.4755	.001540832	699	488,601	26.4386	.001430615
650	422,500	25.4951	.001538462	700	490,000	26.4575	.001428571

TABLE 8   SQUARES, SQUARE ROOTS, AND RECIPROCALS (continued)

no.	square	sq. root	reciprocal	no.	square	sq. root	reciprocal
701	491,401	26.4764	.001426534	751	564,001	27.4044	.001331558
702	492,804	26.4953	.001424501	752	565,504	27.4226	.001329787
703	494,209	26.5141	.001422475	753	567,009	27.4408	.001328021
704	495,616	26.5330	.001420455	754	568,516	27.4591	.001326260
705	497,025	26.5518	.001418440	755	570,025	27.4773	.001324503
706	498,436	26.5707	.001416431	756	571,536	27.4955	.001322751
707	499,849	26.5895	.001414427	757	573,049	27.5136	.001321004
708	501,264	26.6083	.001412429	758	574,564	27.5318	.001319261
709	502,681	26.6271	.001410437	759	576,081	27.5500	.001317523
710	504,100	26.6458	.001408451	760	577,600	27.5681	.001315789
711	505,521	26.6646	.001406470	761	579,121	27.5862	.001314060
712	506,944	26.6833	.001404494	762	580,644	27.6043	.001312336
713	508,369	26.7021	.001402525	763	582,169	27.6225	.001310616
714	509,796	26.7208	.001400560	764	583,696	27.6405	.001308901
715	511,225	26.7395	.001398601	765	585,225	27.6586	.001307190
716	512,656	26.7582	.001396648	766	586,756	27.6767	.001305483
717	514,089	26.7769	.001394700	767	588,289	27.6948	.001303781
718	515,524	26.7955	.001392758	768	589,824	27.7128	.001302083
719	516,961	26.8142	.001390821	769	591,361	27.7308	.001300390
720	518,400	26.8328	.001388889	770	592,900	27.7489	.001298701
721	519,841	26.8514	.001386963	771	594,441	27.7669	.001297017
722	521,284	26.8701	.001385042	772	595,984	27.7849	.001295337
723	522,729	26.8887	.001383126	773	597,529	27.8029	.001293661
724	524,176	26.9072	.001381215	774	599,076	27.8209	.001291990
725	525,625	26.9258	.001379310	775	600,625	27.8388	.001290323
726	527,076	26.9444	.001377410	776	602,176	27.8568	.001288660
727	528,529	26.9629	.001375516	777	603,729	27.8747	.001287001
728	529,984	26.9815	.001373626	778	605,284	27.8927	.001285347
729	531,441	27.0000	.001371742	779	606,841	27.9106	.001283697
730	532,900	27.0185	.001369863	780	608,400	27.9285	.001282051
731	534,361	27.0370	.001367989	781	609,961	27.9464	.001280410
732	535,824	27.0555	.001366120	782	611,524	27.9643	.001278772
733	537,289	27.0740	.001364256	783	613,089	27.9821	.001277139
734	538,756	27.0924	.001362398	784	614,656	28.0000	.001275510
735	540,225	27.1109	.001360544	785	616,225	28.0179	.001273885
736	541,696	27.1293	.001358696	786	617,796	28.0357	.001272265
737	543,169	27.1477	.001356852	787	619,369	28.0535	.001270648
738	544,644	27.1662	.001355014	788	620,944	28.0713	.001269036
739	546,121	27.1846	.001353180	789	622,521	28.0891	.001267427
740	547,600	27.2029	.001351351	790	624,100	28.1069	.001265823
741	549,081	27.2213	.001349528	791	625,681	28.1247	.001264223
742	550,564	27.2397	.001347709	792	627,264	28.1425	.001262626
743	552,049	27.2580	.001345895	793	628,849	28.1603	.001261034
744	553,536	27.2764	.001344086	794	630,436	28.1780	.001259446
745	555,025	27.2947	.001342282	795	632,025	28.1957	.001257862
746	556,516	27.3130	.001340483	796	633,616	28.2135	.001256281
747	558,009	27.3313	.001338688	797	635,209	28.2312	.001254705
748	559,504	27.3496	.001336898	798	636,804	28.2489	.001253133
749	561,001	27.3679	.001335113	799	638,401	28.2666	.001251564
750	562,500	27.3861	.001333333	800	640,000	28.2843	.001250000

TABLE 8   SQUARES, SQUARE ROOTS, AND RECIPROCALS (continued)

no.	square	sq. root	reciprocal	no.	square	sq. root	reciprocal
801	641,601	28.3019	.001248439	851	724,201	29.1719	.001175088
802	643,204	28.3196	.001246883	852	725,904	29.1890	.001173709
803	644,809	28.3373	.001245330	853	727,609	29.2062	.001172333
804	646,416	28.3549	.001243781	854	729,316	29.2233	.001170960
805	648,025	28.3725	.001242236	855	731,025	29.2404	.001169591
806	649,636	28.3901	.001240695	856	732,736	29.2575	.001168224
807	651,249	28.4077	.001239157	857	734,449	29.2746	.001166861
808	652,864	28.4253	.001237624	858	736,164	29.2916	.001165501
809	654,481	28.4429	.001236094	859	737,881	29.3087	.001164144
810	656,100	28.4605	.001234568	860	739,600	29.3258	.001162791
811	657,721	28.4781	.001233046	861	741,321	29.3428	.001161440
812	659,344	28.4956	.001231527	862	743,044	29.3598	.001160093
813	660,969	28.5132	.001230012	863	744,769	29.3769	.001158749
814	662,596	28.5307	.001228501	864	746,496	29.3939	.001157407
815	664,225	28.5482	.001226994	865	748,225	29.4109	.001156069
816	665,856	28.5657	.001225490	866	749,956	29.4279	.001154734
817	667,489	28.5832	.001223990	867	751,689	29.4449	.001153403
818	669,124	28.6007	.001222494	868	753,424	29.4618	.001152074
819	670,761	28.6182	.001221001	869	755,161	29.4788	.001150748
820	672,400	28.6356	.001219512	870	756,900	29.4958	.001149425
821	674,041	28.6531	.001218027	871	758,641	29.5127	.001148106
822	675,684	28.6705	.001216545	872	760,384	29.5296	.001146789
823	677,329	28.6880	.001215067	873	762,129	29.5466	.001145475
824	678,976	28.7054	.001213592	874	763,876	29.5635	.001144165
825	680,625	28.7228	.001212121	875	765,625	29.5804	.001142857
826	682,276	28.7402	.001210654	876	767,376	29.5973	.001141553
827	683,929	28.7576	.001209190	877	769,129	29.6142	.001140251
828	685,584	28.7750	.001207729	878	770,884	29.6311	.001138952
829	687,241	28.7924	.001206273	879	772,641	29.6479	.001137656
830	688,900	28.8097	.001204819	880	774,400	29.6648	.001136364
831	690,561	28.8271	.001203369	881	776,161	29.6816	.001135074
832	692,224	28.8444	.001201923	882	777,924	29.6985	.001133787
833	693,889	28.8617	.001200480	883	779,689	29.7153	.001132503
834	695,556	28.8791	.001199041	884	781,456	29.7321	.001131222
835	697,225	28.8964	.001197605	885	783,225	29.7489	.001129944
836	698,896	28.9137	.001196172	886	784,996	29.7658	.001128668
837	700,569	28.9310	.001194743	887	786,769	29.7825	.001127396
838	702,244	28.9482	.001193317	888	788,544	29.7993	.001126126
839	703,921	28.9655	.001191895	889	790,321	29.8161	.001124859
840	705,600	28.9828	.001190476	890	792,100	29.8329	.001123596
841	707,281	29.0000	.001189061	891	793,881	29.8496	.001122334
842	708,964	29.0172	.001187648	892	795,664	29.8664	.001121076
843	710,649	29.0345	.001186240	893	797,449	29.8831	.001119821
844	712,336	29.0517	.001184834	894	799,236	29.8998	.001118568
845	714,025	29.0689	.001183432	895	801,025	29.9166	.001117318
846	715,716	29.0861	.001182033	896	802,816	29.9333	.001116071
847	717,409	29.1033	.001180638	897	804,609	29.9500	.001114827
848	719,104	29.1204	.001179245	898	806,404	29.9666	.001113586
849	720,801	29.1376	.001177856	899	808,201	29.9833	.001112347
850	722,500	29.1548	.001176471	900	810,000	30.0000	.001111111

TABLE 8   SQUARES, SQUARE ROOTS, AND RECIPROCALS (continued)

no.	square	sq. root	reciprocal	no.	square	sq. root	reciprocal
901	811,801	30.0167	.001109878	951	904,401	30.8383	.001051525
902	813,604	30.0333	.001108647	952	906,304	30.8545	.001050420
903	815,409	30.0500	.001107420	953	908,209	30.8707	.001049318
904	817,216	30.0666	.001106195	954	910,116	30.8869	.001048218
905	819,025	30.0832	.001104972	955	912,025	30.9031	.001047120
906	820,836	30.0998	.001103753	956	913,936	30.9192	.001046025
907	822,649	30.1164	.001102536	957	915,849	30.9354	.001044932
908	824,464	30.1330	.001101322	958	917,764	30.9516	.001043841
909	826,281	30.1496	.001100110	959	919,681	30.9677	.001042753
910	828,100	30.1662	.001098901	960	921,600	30.9839	.001041667
911	829,921	30.1828	.001097695	961	923,521	31.0000	.001040583
912	831,744	30.1993	.001096491	962	925,444	31.0161	.001039501
913	833,569	30.2159	.001095290	963	927,369	31.0322	.001038422
914	835,396	30.2324	.001094092	964	929,296	31.0483	.001037344
915	837,225	30.2490	.001092896	965	931,225	31.0644	.001036269
916	839,056	30.2655	.001091703	966	933,156	31.0805	.001035197
917	840,889	30.2820	.001090513	967	935,089	31.0966	.001034126
918	842,724	30.2985	.001089325	968	937,024	31.1127	.001033058
919	844,561	30.3150	.001088139	969	938,961	31.1288	.001031992
920	846,400	30.3315	.001086957	970	940,900	31.1448	.001030928
921	848,241	30.3480	.001085776	971	942,841	31.1609	.001029866
922	850,084	30.3645	.001084599	972	944,784	31.1769	.001028807
923	851,929	30.3809	.001083424	973	946,729	31.1929	.001027749
924	853,776	30.3974	.001082251	974	948,676	31.2090	.001026694
925	855,625	30.4138	.001081081	975	950,625	31.2250	.001025641
926	857,476	30.4302	.001079914	976	952,576	31.2410	.001024590
927	859,329	30.4467	.001078749	977	954,529	31.2570	.001023541
928	861,184	30.4631	.001077586	978	956,484	31.2730	.001022495
929	863,041	30.4795	.001076426	979	958,441	31.2890	.001021450
930	864,900	30.4959	.001075269	980	960,400	31.3050	.001020408
931	866,761	30.5123	.001074114	981	962,361	31.3209	.001019368
932	868,624	30.5287	.001072961	982	964,324	31.3369	.001018330
933	870,489	30.5450	.001071811	983	966,289	31.3528	.001017294
934	872,356	30.5614	.001070664	984	968,256	31.3688	.001016260
935	874,225	30.5778	.001069519	985	970,225	31.3847	.001015228
936	876,096	30.5941	.001068376	986	972,196	31.4006	.001014199
937	877,969	30.6105	.001067236	987	974,169	31.4166	.001013171
938	879,844	30.6268	.001066098	988	976,144	31.4325	.001012146
939	881,721	30.6431	.001064963	989	978,121	31.4484	.001011122
940	883,600	30.6594	.001063830	990	980,100	31.4643	.001010101
941	885,481	30.6757	.001062699	991	982,081	31.4802	.001009082
942	887,364	30.6920	.001061571	992	984,064	31.4960	.001008065
943	889,249	30.7083	.001060445	993	986,049	31.5119	.001007049
944	891,136	30.7246	.001059322	994	988,036	31.5278	.001006036
945	893,025	30.7409	.001058201	995	990,025	31.5436	.001005025
946	894,916	30.7571	.001057082	996	992,016	31.5595	.001004016
947	896,809	30.7734	.001055966	997	994,009	31.5753	.001003009
948	898,704	30.7896	.001054852	998	996,004	31.5911	.001002004
949	900,601	30.8058	.001053741	999	998,001	31.6070	.001001001
950	902,500	30.8221	.001052632	1000	1,000,000	31.6228	.001000000

INDEX

ANSWERS
EVEN-NUMBERED PROBLEMS

PROBLEMS 2–1

2 1,906   4 55,730   6 28,936   8 20,755
10 160,009   12 126,387   14 10,989,944   16 4,166 miles
18 96,381,000 sq miles   20 (a) $76.76
                               (b) $22.70

PROBLEMS 2–2

2 10,300 Ω   4 43 μf

PROBLEMS 2–3

2 62   4 211   6 37
8 2,860   10 4,867   12 8,679
14 35,703   16 1,010   18 10,029
20 61,094   22 19,185 gal   24 Add the sum of 87 and 64.

PROBLEMS 3–1

2 3,451   4 73,890   6 12,628   8 53,739
10 67,452   12 1,526,477   14 2,506,196   16 18,883,056
18 43,326,012   20 877,205,742   22 2,250 $\mu\mu$f   24 30 miles

PROBLEMS 3–2

2 97   4 973   6 $42\frac{3}{17}$ 8 105
10 $7,006\frac{67}{93}$ 12 $89\frac{200}{637}$ 14 49   16 19 hr
18 $16 per ton   20 $256 per acre   22 13,623   24 3,094

PROBLEMS 3–3

2 2,052   4 4,735 Ω   6 263 $\mu\mu$f   8 50 $\mu\mu$f
10 12,500 Ω

PROBLEMS 4–1

2 (a) $8\frac{1}{9}$ 4 (a) $102\frac{2}{11}$
   (b) $6\frac{3}{9}$ (b) $99\frac{9}{13}$
   (c) $15\frac{3}{9}$ (c) $107\frac{2}{23}$
   (d) $38\frac{7}{9}$ (d) $113\frac{3}{19}$
   (e) $61\frac{2}{9}$ (e) $335\frac{5}{43}$

PROBLEMS 4–2

2 (a) $28\frac{1}{3}$ (d) $114\frac{48}{87}$
   (b) $19\frac{5}{9}$ (e) $250\frac{9}{473}$
   (c) $222\frac{2}{23}$

PROBLEMS 4–3
2 $\frac{1}{2}$ 4 $\frac{3}{4}$ 6 $\frac{3}{8}$ 8 $\frac{5}{6}$
10 $\frac{2}{9}$ 12 $\frac{5}{9}$ 14 $\frac{2}{3}$ 16 $1\frac{1}{12}$
18 $\frac{47}{48}$ 20 $\frac{23}{32}$

PROBLEMS 4–4
2 2, 2, 3, 5   4 3, 5, 5, 7   6 7, 11, 13   8 3, 13, 29
10 2, 2, 2, 3, 3, 3, 5, 11, 17

PROBLEMS 4–5
2 180   4 165   6 2,025   8 540   10 1,080

PROBLEMS 4–6
2 $\frac{3}{48}, \frac{20}{48}, \frac{14}{48}$ 4 $\frac{14}{20}, \frac{5}{20}, \frac{8}{20}$ 6 $\frac{15}{100}, \frac{80}{100}, \frac{28}{100}$
8 $\frac{715}{990}, \frac{231}{990}, \frac{234}{990}, \frac{825}{990}$ 10 $\frac{16}{50}$

PROBLEMS 4–7
2 $\frac{3}{7}$ 4 1   6 1   8 $\frac{3}{22}$ 10 $1\frac{1}{12}$
12 $1\frac{29}{40}$ 14 $9\frac{37}{42}$ 16 $9\frac{19}{90}$ 18 $14\frac{14}{15}$ 20 $\frac{9}{10}$

PROBLEMS 4–8
2 $\frac{1}{16}$ 4 $\frac{7}{12}$ 6 $4\frac{1}{2}$ 8 10   10 $63\frac{5}{24}$
12 12   14 $2\frac{1}{2}$ 16 $1\frac{7}{8}$ 18 $\frac{135}{182}$ 20 $1\frac{1}{768}$

PROBLEMS 5–1
2 168.623   4 48.405   6 796.935   8 1,287.756   10 796.8287
12 86.83   14 0.00036   16 0.8995   18 0.99676   20 1.7203

PROBLEMS 5–2
2 44   4 36.4554   6 573.5988   8 188.496
10 0.00451268   12 2.478   14 4.7   16 435,000
18 0.794   20 0.272   22 91.44 cm   24 $10.98

PROBLEMS 5–3
2 2   4 21.32   6 2.5 per cent   8 125 per cent
10 No

PROBLEMS 6–1
2 16   4 63   6 129   8 109   10 76.3
12 0.142   14 30.07   16 6.436   18 0.728   20 0.000414
22 0.571   24 0.469

PROBLEMS 6–2
2 1.296   4 137.84   6 24.362   8 166.19   10 0.2902

PROBLEMS 6–3
2 53.98   4 8,988.92   6 7.3512   8 90,954.6   10 11,776.01

PROBLEMS 6–4
2 1,054   4 0.0159   6 5.0732   8 0.9309   10 0.9909

PROBLEMS 6–5
2 24,892   4 366.966   6 0.0040432   8 43,746,146   10 66,430.118

PROBLEMS 6–6
2 384   4 1.5076   6 200.9

PROBLEMS 6–7

2 $\frac{5}{9}$ 4 $8\frac{2}{9}$ 6 $156\frac{8}{15}$ 8 $8^{11}\frac{1}{15}$ 10 25.176

PROBLEMS 6–8

2 35   4 0.175   6 2   8 $1,285\frac{5}{7}$

PROBLEMS 6–9

2 3.76   4 $\frac{1}{3}$

PROBLEMS 7–1

2 (a) 35 amp   4 (a) 35 cents   6 Second resistance $= 3R\ \Omega$
   (b) 240 watts   (b) $35x$ cents   Third resistance $= 18R\ \Omega$
   (c) 9.6 Ω

8 6   10 3   12 1

14 $100 - R\ \Omega$ 16 (a) 2.4 μf   18 0.001075 sec
                              (b) 146 $\mu\mu$f

20 (a) 12.4 miles
    (b) 0.32 ft
    (c) 0.0733 ft

PROBLEMS 7–2

2 60,000   4 40   6 10,080
8 4,315   10 1,500   12 Binomial
14 Monomial   16 Binomial   18 Binomial
20 Monomial   22 $E = IR$ 24 $P = I^2R$

26 $Z^2 = R^2 + X^2$ 28 $M = k\sqrt{L_1 L_2}$ 30 $\eta = \dfrac{P}{E_p I_p}$

32 652 μh. Note that, all other factors remaining equal, if the number of turns are
    doubled, the inductance is quadrupled.

34 (a) 529 watts   36 (a) Decreased by a factor of $\frac{1}{4}$
    (b) 288 watts   (b) Increased by a factor of 4
                              (c) Increased by a factor of 9
                              (d) Increased by a factor of 16

PROBLEMS 8–1

2 14   4 -71 6 $-1,245$ 8 -0.00016 10 61.46
12 $-11^{29}\frac{}{36}$ 14 $-1\frac{1}{28}$

PROBLEMS 8–2

2 138   4 -104 6 63.1   8 -0.0765 10 -1.812
12 $-7^{11}\frac{1}{40}$ 14 $-\frac{7}{30}$ 16 18°   18 17°   20 23°
22 345 volts

PROBLEMS 8–3

2 $-42i^2r$ 4 $-42ei$
6 $-3i - 9I$ 8 $45\theta - 118\phi$
10 $56IZ + 6EI + 12\omega L_1$ 12 $4IZ - IX - 4IR$
14 $0.658eI + 0.06I^2R + 32W$ 16 $35IR - 33iZ$
18 $9.82\omega L - 6.03X + 25Z - 21$ 20 $\frac{5}{6}i^2r - 1\frac{1}{12}ei - \frac{7}{120}I^2x$
22 $\mu E_g - 51E_s$ 24 $26.3Z - 1.3\omega L$

PROBLEMS 8–4

2 $4\theta - 6\phi + 2$　　　　　4 $6i^2r - 12ei + 8$　　　　　6 $-2R - 3\omega L$

8 $3 + ei + 2w$　　　　　10 $30R - 19X + 19Z - 18$

PROBLEMS 8–5

2 $\theta + (2\phi - 6\omega - \lambda)$　　　　　4 $\dfrac{E}{Z} + \left(-\dfrac{3E}{R} - \dfrac{e}{z} + \dfrac{6e}{r}\right)$

6 $6i^2r - (-2ei + iz - 9I^2R)$　　　　　8 $3\phi - (13\theta - 2\omega + 16°)$

10 $\dfrac{e}{r} + \dfrac{E}{X} - \left(-\dfrac{E}{Z} + 9i + 0.5I\right)$　　　　　12 $80 - I$ amp

14 $Z - \sqrt{r^2 + x^2}$

PROBLEMS 9–1

2 -15　　　　　4 68.8　　　　　6 $\frac{1}{24}$　　　　　8 75.6

10 $-mnop$　　　　　12 $\dfrac{\lambda}{\theta\phi\beta}$　　　　　14 $\dfrac{I^2R}{ir}$

PROBLEMS 9–2

2 $-n^3$　　　　　4 $\theta^4\phi^2$　　　　　6 $-48\alpha\beta^2$　　　　　8 $-0.1218I^2R$

10 $-15a^{2n}$　　　　　12 $125i^6R^3$　　　　　14 $\frac{2}{5}i^3rz^2$　　　　　16 $-0.025E^2e^3I^5R$

18 10^6　　　　　20 $-0.1512ei^2I^3rR^3Z^4$

PROBLEMS 9–3

2 $6iR - 27ir$　　　　　4 $31.5x - 5jxX$

6 $15\alpha^2 + 24\alpha^3 - 3\alpha^4$　　　　　8 $42\omega^2L^2fM + 21\omega^3L^2M^2 - 12\omega^3L^4M$

10 $6\theta^4\phi^3 + 12\theta^3\phi^4 - 27\theta^2\phi^5 - 12\theta\phi^2$　　　　　12 $0.01\alpha^4\beta - 0.0005\alpha^3\beta^2 + 0.00015\alpha^2\beta^3$

14 $\dfrac{e^4i^4r}{3} - \dfrac{e^3i^3r}{12} + \dfrac{2e^2i^2r}{15} - \dfrac{ei^2r}{6}$　　　　　16 $24C + 16c$

18 $IR - 11IR_1$　　　　　20 $12\omega L - 3\omega M$

22 $6\phi\theta - 9.4\phi\beta - 11\phi\alpha^2$　　　　　24 $3E - 2e + E_1$

26 $5IR - 3ir + \dfrac{5e}{2}$　　　　　28 $10IR - 6IR_1 + 11Ir$

30 $\dfrac{\lambda^2\theta^2\phi}{10} - \dfrac{\lambda^2\beta^2\theta}{10} - \dfrac{13\lambda^2\alpha^2}{6}$

PROBLEMS 9–4

2 $i^2 - 2i + 1$　　　　　4 $R^2 + 6R + 9$

6 $R^2 - 9$　　　　　8 $Z^2 - 13Z + 30$

10 $\omega^2L^2 + 2\omega L - 143$　　　　　12 $3P^2 - 17PW - 6W^2$

14 $24\theta^2 + 45\theta\phi - 6\phi^2$　　　　　16 $5E^2 - 26EIR - 24I^2R^2$

18 $72R_1^2 - 6R_1R^2 - 3R_2^2$　　　　　20 $0.008Z^2 - 0.036Zz - 0.18z^2$

22 $3.9E^4 - 1.265E^2i^2z^2 + 0.02i^4z^4$　　　　　24 $E^3 + 3E^2e + 3Ee^2 + e^3$

26 $6I^3 + 21I^2 - 5I + 28$　　　　　28 $R^3 - 3R^2r + 3Rr^2 - r^3$

30 $4Z^4 - 12Z^3 + 25Z^2 - 24Z + 16$　　　　　32 $R_1^2 - \dfrac{949R_1R_2}{450} + R_2^2$

34 $6e^4 - 110e^3 + 53e^2 + 12e - 3$　　　　　36 $-15I^3 + 143I^2 - 96I - 380$

38 $-5R^4 + 5R^3X + 9R^2X^2 - RX^3 - 2X^4$

40 $74\alpha^2\omega^2 - 44\alpha\beta\omega^2 + 34\alpha\omega^3 - 46\beta^2\omega^2 + 22\beta\omega^3 - \omega^4$

PROBLEMS 9–5

2 -3

4 $8,000$

6 -1.8

8 $-\dfrac{E^2}{R}$

10 $-\dfrac{7e}{r}$

12 -6

14 -12

PROBLEMS 9–6

2 $-3x^4z$

4 $-4\omega^3L^4$

6 $-3IR$

8 $-0.004\alpha^4\beta\theta$

10 $1.5q^5s$

12 $-\dfrac{5x^3}{yz}$

14 $\dfrac{0.005\theta^2}{\alpha\lambda}$

16 $-\dfrac{0.375\phi^3}{\theta^5\omega^6}$

18 $-\dfrac{0.0000007n^4}{m^4p^9}$

20 $-\dfrac{20xy^7z}{21}$

PROBLEMS 9–7

2 $2x + 5y$

4 $4R_1 + R_2 - 5R_3$

6 $IZ^2 - \dfrac{Z^2}{R} + Z^2$

8 $2r^3R^3 + 3rR^2 + 5$

10 $R^3 - 28R^2Z + 20RZ^2$

12 $1,605,000r^3 - 5ir^2 + 75,000i^2r - 0.625i^3$

14 $4 + b$

16 $i - I - 3$

18 2

20 $\alpha + \beta$

PROBLEMS 9–8

2 $x + 5$

4 $R - 6$

6 $3\omega^2 - 6\omega + 4$

8 $8r + 3Z$

10 $I^2 + 7I + 14 + \dfrac{6}{I - 1}$

12 $R^2 + RZ + Z^2$

14 $R^2 - RZ + Z^2$

16 $R^4 - R^3Z + R^2Z^2 - RZ^3 + Z^4$

18 $R^3 - R^2Z + RZ^2 - Z^3$

20 $\theta - 3$

22 $1 - 3\lambda - \lambda^2$

24 $6r - \dfrac{i}{3} - \dfrac{1}{2}$

PROBLEMS 10–1

2 7.86×10^3

4 6.84×10^3

6 9.44×10^{-9}

8 2.76×10^{-2}

10 5.73×10

12 2.68×10^{-9}

14 2.04×10

16 3.00×10^{-12}

18 1.42×10^{-6}

20 1.04×10^{-10}

PROBLEMS 10–2

2 1.00×10^3

4 5.70×10^{-5}

6 2.03×10^7

8 3.11×10^7

10 2.13×10^{-7}

12 $1.26 \times 10^3 \, \Omega$

14 $9.42 \times 10^2 \, \Omega$

PROBLEMS 10–3

2 3.00×10^9

4 1.00×10^{-19}

6 9.49×10^{-3}

8 1.06×10^2

10 7.96×10^{-6}

12 $1.33 \times 10^2 \, \Omega$

14 $2.27 \times 10^2 \, \Omega$

PROBLEMS 10–4

2 10^{21}

4 36×10^{-8}

6 512×10^{-9}

8 27×10^3

10 3.2×10^{-3}

12 120

14 1.01×10^4

16 $91.9 \, \text{cps}$

18 $3.56 \times 10^5 \, \text{cps}$

20 $1.44 \times 10^8 \, \text{cps}$

PROBLEMS 11-1

2 (a) 5.25×10^3 ma   4 (a) 7.5×10^4 μa   6 (a) 5×10^6 μμf

     (b) 5.25×10^6 μa   (b) 7.5×10^{-2} amp   (b) 5×10^{-6} farad

8 (a) 2.5×10^4 mh   10 (a) 3.5×10^3 msec   12 (a) 5×10^4 Ω

     (b) 2.5×10^7 μh   (b) 3.5×10^6 μsec   (b) 2×10^{-5} mho

                                                (c) 5×10^{-2} MΩ

14 (a) 1.5×10^{-1} mh   16 (a) 5×10^{-6} sec   18 (a) 6.6×10^3 volts

     (b) 1.5×10^{-4} henry   (b) 5×10^{-3} msec   (b) 6.6×10^{-3} Mv

                                                (c) 6.6×10^6 mv

20 (a) 2.5×10^2 watts   22 (a) 4.4×10^5 kc   24 (a) 5×10^5 μsec

     (b) 2.5×10^5 mw   (b) 4.4×10^8 cps   (b) 5×10^{-1} sec

     (c) 2.5×10^8 μw

26 (a) 2.5×10^{-3} mho   28 (a) 10 volts   30 (a) 2.81×10^7 cps

     (b) 4×10^2 Ω   (b) 10^4 mv   (b) 2.81×10 Mc

PROBLEMS 11-2

2 (a) 11.5 ft   4 (a) 4.83 km

     (b) 3.83 yd   (b) 15,840 ft

     (c) 3.5×10^{-3} km   (c) 4.83×10^5 cm

6 88 fps   8 0.130 cm

10 4.98×10^{-3} μf/km   12 0.210 db/meter

16 $X_L = 2\pi f L$ Ω   18 $f = \dfrac{159}{\sqrt{LC}}$ Mc

20 $\delta = \dfrac{2.61 \times 10^{-3}}{\sqrt{f}}$ in.   22 $R_{ac} = 9.98 \times 10^{-4} \dfrac{\sqrt{f}}{d}$ Ω/ft

26 139 in.   28 80.4 in.

30 (a) 28.5 in.   32 (a) 26.0 in.   (d) 11.1 in.

     (b) 29.9 in.   (b) 27.4 in.   (e) 5.54 in.

     (c) 12.1 in.   (c) 24.8 in.

PROBLEMS 12-1

2 $E = 5$ 4 $i = 7$ 6 $Z = \frac{2}{3}$ 8 $\phi = -6$ 10 $\theta = 4.5$

12 $r = 1$ 14 $Z = 1$ 16 $\alpha = 1$ 18 $i = 1$ 20 $I = 4$

PROBLEMS 12-2

2 $I + i$ amp   4 $R = 55$ Ω   6 37, 38

8 95   10 $h = \dfrac{v}{wl}$ ft   12 $E - e = r - R$

14 First side = 70 ft

     Second side = 80 ft

     Third side = 20 ft

PROBLEMS 12-3

2 $E = IZ$ 4 $P = I^2 R$ 6 $R_t = R_1 + R_2 + R_3$

     $Z = \dfrac{E}{I}$

8 $r = \dfrac{C}{2\pi}$ 10 $X_L = 2\pi f L$ 12 $\phi = AH$

14 $N_p = \dfrac{E_p N_s}{E_s}$

16 $N = \dfrac{120f}{P}$

$f = \dfrac{NP}{120}$

18 $F = HiL$

20 $G_m = \dfrac{\mu}{R_p}$

22 $g = \dfrac{V^2}{2h}$

24 $\omega = 2\pi n$

26 $l = \dfrac{8\omega\mu}{AB^2}$

$\omega = \dfrac{AB^2 l}{8\mu}$

28 $m = \dfrac{F}{4\pi^2 n^2 r}$

$F = 4\pi^2 r n^2 m$

30 $C = 2K + D$

32 $R = Xpf$

34 $k = \dfrac{M}{\sqrt{L_1 L_2}}$

36 $10\,\Omega$

38 Four poles

40 69 Mc

PROBLEMS 13–1

2 $88.5\,\Omega$ 4 30 volts   6 75 volts   8 28.1 volts   10 $14\,\Omega$

PROBLEMS 13–2

2 (a) 37,300 watts   4 1,440 watts   6 48.4 watts
  (b) 50 hp

8 2.27 amp   10 0.212 watt   12 (a) 64 mw
                                                         (b) 8 volts

14 7½ cents   16 (a) 9.95 kw   18 23.9 kw
                            (b) 22.6 amp
                            (c) $33.42

20 (a) 4.91 kw   (d) 1.38 amp
  (b) 21.3 amp   (e) 56.2 per cent
  (c) 2.76 kw

PROBLEMS 13–3

2 (a) 58.6 volts   4 (a) $121\,\Omega$ 6 (a) $18.4\,\Omega$
  (b) 129 watts   (b) 100 watts   (b) $47.9\,\Omega$
                                                           (c) 1.30 amp
                                                             (d) 31.3 watts

8 $281\,\Omega$ $(300\,\Omega$ will do)   10 (a) 440 volts
                                               (b) 704 watts
                                             (c) 75.2 volts

PROBLEMS 13–4

2 (a) $2570\,\Omega$ 4 (a) $148\,\Omega$
  (b) 126 mw   (b) $38,500\,\Omega$
  (c) 198 volts

PROBLEMS 14–1

2 $2.56\,\Omega$ 4 $0.126\,\Omega$ 6 $0.0256\,\Omega$ 8 $0.323\,\Omega$
10 250 ft   12 3.05 ft

PROBLEMS 14–2

  2 83,500 cir mils   4 15.9 mils   6 0.0285 in.   8 239,000 cir mils

10 637,000 cir mils

PROBLEMS 14–3

  2 $2.31 \, \Omega$ 4 $1.0 \, \Omega$ 6 $627 \, \Omega/\text{mil-ft}$ 8 1,000 ft   10 2.39 miles

PROBLEMS 14–4

  2 $35.3 \, \Omega$ 4 69.9°C

PROBLEMS 14–5

  2 (a) $4.26 \, \Omega$ 4 (a) 62.0 lb   6 $10.7 \, \Omega$ 8 (a) 226 volts

      (b) 840 lb   (b) 5,000 ft   (b) 98.3 per cent

10 (a) No. 1 wire

      (b) 231.4 volts

PROBLEMS 15–1

  2 a^3b^3 4 $36\pi^4\theta^2$ 6 $8\phi^9\theta^6$ 8 $81e^4i^2$

10 $-\omega^4\theta^6\phi^2$ 12 $64\pi^6r^3t^9$ 14 $169\lambda^4f^2C^2$ 16 $\dfrac{9\alpha^4\beta^2\pi^2}{16\theta^4}$

18 $-\dfrac{i^4r^2}{9P^2}$ 20 $\dfrac{27\theta^6\phi^3\pi^9}{\omega^6\lambda^3}$

PROBLEMS 15–2

  2 8   4 $\pm 3r^2$ 6 $\pm 4ei^2$ 8 -3

10 $\pm 12\alpha\beta^2R^4$ 12 $\pm 10\pi fL^2$ 14 $2\omega^2C$ 16 $\pm \tfrac{4}{5}ir^2z$

18 $-\dfrac{3ZR^3X^4}{7\omega^2\lambda^3}$ 20 $\pm \dfrac{7\alpha^3\beta\gamma^4}{12\theta\phi^2\pi^5}$ 22 $\dfrac{3\pi^2\omega^3\lambda}{2rz^2}$ 24 $\pm \dfrac{13r^3st^2u^4}{15m^2np^5}$

PROBLEMS 15–3

  2 $\tfrac{1}{8}(2\theta + \phi)$ 4 $\dfrac{\omega f}{18}(6\omega - 3f + 2)$

  6 $\dfrac{2E^2}{R}\left(1 + \dfrac{8E}{R} - 4r^2\right)$ 8 $2\pi fL(2\pi fL + 15\pi^2 - 1)$

10 $\dfrac{\alpha^2\beta}{18}(3\alpha^2 - 6\alpha + 2\beta)$ 12 $\dfrac{R^2r}{162}(2 + 6r^2 + 9R^2r)$

14 $\dfrac{\omega\lambda}{60}(4\lambda + 3\omega\lambda^2 - 12)$

PROBLEMS 15–4

  2 $R^2 - 12R + 36$ 4 $4\omega^2 + 4\omega f + f^2$

  6 $\lambda^2 - 6\lambda F + 9F^2$ 8 $I^2 + 8IR + 16R^2$

10 $r^2 + 12rR + 36R^2$ 12 $\theta^4 + 2\theta^2\phi^3 + \phi^6$

14 $25L^4 - 80L^2C^2 + 64C^4$ 16 $\omega^4 + 6\omega^2f^3 + 9f^6$

18 $49R^2 + 14Rr^2 + r^4$ 20 $4\alpha^4 + 16\alpha^2\beta^3 + 16\beta^6$

22 $9i^4 + 30i^2I + 25I^2$ 24 $9L^6 + 24L^3f^2 + 16f^4$

26 $e^2 + \tfrac{2}{3}e + \tfrac{1}{9}$ 28 $\beta^2 + \tfrac{1}{2}\beta + \tfrac{1}{16}$

30 $R^2 + \dfrac{4R}{5} + \tfrac{4}{25}$ 32 $Z^2 + \dfrac{4Z}{7} + \tfrac{4}{49}$

34 $L^4 + \tfrac{8}{5}L^2 + \tfrac{16}{25}$

PROBLEMS 15-5

2	$2EI$	4	$20C$	6	$80xy$	8	16

10	$121f^4$	12	$\frac{1}{49}$	14	$\dfrac{x^2}{9}$	16	$\pm(i + 6r)$

18   $\pm(3a + 9b)$ 20 $\pm(6r + 7Z)$ 22 $\pm\left(\dfrac{\theta}{3} - \pi\right)$ 24 $\pm\left(\dfrac{3r}{5} + \dfrac{2R}{7}\right)$

PROBLEMS 15-6

2   $3i^2(5r - 3z)^2$ 4 $4E(3e + 1)^2$ 6 $\dfrac{5e^2}{r}(I - 3i)^2$ 8 $\dfrac{\beta}{\alpha}(\theta - \tfrac{1}{4})^2$

10   $\dfrac{21L}{C}(F^2 + 6f)^2$

PROBLEMS 15-7

2   $Z^2 - z^2$ 4 $9E^2 - e^2$ 6 $\frac{1}{4} - \theta^2$ 8 $\dfrac{9I^4R^2}{16} - \dfrac{4E^4}{R^2}$

10   $\dfrac{\theta^4}{100\phi^2} - \dfrac{\omega^2}{64}$

PROBLEMS 15-8

2   $(R + 4r)(R - 4r)$ 4 $(1 + E)(1 - E)$ 6 $(2\theta + 9\phi)(2\theta - 9\phi)$

8   $\left(\dfrac{e}{6} + 7\right)\left(\dfrac{e}{6} - 7\right)$ 10 $\left(\dfrac{1}{\lambda} + \dfrac{5\mu}{8}\right)\left(\dfrac{1}{\lambda} - \dfrac{5\mu}{8}\right)$ 12 $\left(\dfrac{Z}{7} + \dfrac{10}{z}\right)\left(\dfrac{Z}{7} - \dfrac{10}{z}\right)$

14   $\left(\dfrac{E}{R} + \dfrac{Z}{r}\right)\left(\dfrac{E}{R} - \dfrac{Z}{r}\right)$

PROBLEMS 15-9

2	$R^2 + 5R + 4$	4	$\theta^2 + 10\theta + 24$	6	$I^2 - 7I + 12$
8	$r^2 - 16r + 39$	10	$I^2 - 2I - 35$	12	$f^2 - 17f - 60$

14   $\lambda^2 + \dfrac{9\lambda}{2} + 2$ 16 $I^2R^2 - \dfrac{IR}{2} + \frac{1}{16}$ 18 $\dfrac{4e^2}{r^2} - \dfrac{3ei}{2r} - \dfrac{i^2}{4}$

20   $\alpha^2\theta^4 - \dfrac{\alpha\theta^2}{4} - \frac{1}{8}$

PROBLEMS 15-10

2	$(\theta + 1)(\theta + 1)$	4	$(e - 6)(e - 5)$	6	$(i - 2)(i + 1)$
8	$(\omega + 8)(\omega - 7)$	10	$(\phi - 5)(\phi + 4)$	12	$(\omega + 23f)(\omega - 5f)$
14	$(R + 8)(R + 12)$	16	$(\pi + 16)(\pi - 2)$	18	$(E - 25)(E - 2)$
20	$(ei - 7)(ei + 5)$				

PROBLEMS 15-11

2	$12R^2 + 26R + 12$		4	$3E^2 + 3E - 18$
6	$\omega^2 + 3\omega - 28$		8	$45e^2 + 30e - 40$
10	$I^2 - 3I - 54$		12	$5 + 32\phi - 21\phi^2$
14	$8Z^2 + 15Z - 27$		16	$v^2t^2 - 11vts - 26s^2$
18	$3\mu^2 + 19\mu\gamma - 14\gamma^2$		20	$18W^2 - 33WP + 5P^2$
22	$2x^2 - x - 1$		24	$32e^2i^2 + 4eiI^2R - 45I^4R^2$

26   $30\theta^2 - \dfrac{2\theta}{3\phi} - \dfrac{4}{9\phi^2}$ 28 $0.18\omega^2 + 5.4\omega + 16$

30   $12Z^2 - 0.5ZR - 0.25R^2$

PROBLEMS 15–12

2　$(2L + 1)(L + 2)$　　　　4　$(3r + 2)(r + 3)$　　　　6　$(2\beta + 1)(\beta - 1)$

8　$(4f - 5)(3f + 7)$　　　10　$(5 + 5R)(2 - 3R)$　　　12　$(2 + z)(1 - 2z)$

14　$(5 + 4x)(4 - 5x)$　　　16　$(8I + Z)(3I - 4Z)$　　　18　$(L - 16C)(L + 15C)$

20　$\left(\omega - \dfrac{\pi}{2}\right)\left(\omega - \dfrac{\pi}{2}\right)$　　22　$\left(\dfrac{\alpha}{3} - \beta\right)\left(\dfrac{\alpha}{3} - \beta\right)$　　24　$\left(3\theta + \dfrac{\phi}{6}\right)\left(\theta - \dfrac{\phi}{3}\right)$

PROBLEMS 15–13

2　$-125\alpha^6\beta^9\omega^3 f^9$　　　　　　　　　4　$-6\theta\phi^2\omega\pi^3$

6　$-4ei^2EI^3$　　　　　　　　　　　8　$-\dfrac{15IP^2W}{11ERZ^3}$

10　$\omega(F + f_o)(F - f_o)$　　　　　　12　$0.0125i^2(10r_1 + 20r_2 - z)$

14　$\dfrac{\alpha}{5}\left(3\beta - \theta - 2\phi\right)$　　　　　　16　$E^2 + 22E + 121$

18　$100E^2 + 8E + \frac{4}{25}$　　　　　20　$0.0625E^2 - 1.5Ee + 9e^2$

22　$12IR$　　　　　　　　　　　24　$9f^2$

26　$\frac{1}{9}L^2$　　　　　　　　　　　28　$\pm(e - 9)$

30　$\pm\left(\dfrac{\alpha}{2} + 1\right)$　　　　　　　32　$\pm\left(\dfrac{2\mu}{7} + \dfrac{5\lambda}{6}\right)$

34　$a^2 - 9b^2$　　　　　　　　　　36　$\dfrac{9R^2}{64} - \dfrac{Z^2}{25}$

38　$(Z + 3)(Z - 3)$　　　　　　40　$(\alpha\beta\gamma + \mu)(\alpha\beta\gamma - \mu)$

42　$(0.05\omega t + 0.7\theta\phi)(0.05\omega t - 0.7\theta\phi)$　　44　$2 - \pi$

46　$\frac{1}{2}\alpha - \frac{1}{3}\beta$　　　　　　　　48　$I + R + 9$

50　$\theta^2 - 3\theta - 18$　　　　　　　52　$0.1R^2 + 2.975R - 0.75$

54　$W^2 - \frac{1}{4}W - \frac{1}{8}$　　　　　　56　$24P^2 - 45PW - 6W^2$

58　$1.8i^2 - 0.6ir + 0.05r^2$　　　　60　$84\pi^2 - 2\pi t - \dfrac{2t^2}{21}$

62　$(\phi - 5)(\phi + 3)$　　　　　　64　$(E + 0.2)(E + 0.1)$

66　$(\lambda - \frac{1}{3})(\lambda + \frac{1}{4})$　　　　　68　$(3L + 4C)(L - 5C)$

70　$(3e - 0.5z)(e + 0.3z)$　　　　72　$\left(\dfrac{i}{9} + r\right)\left(\dfrac{i}{9} + r\right)$

74　$(4\omega + f)(12\omega + 3f)$　　　　76　$I(X_L + X_C)(X_L - X_C)$

78　$4(\alpha + 5)(\alpha - 5)$　　　　　80　$\alpha(15\beta + \frac{4}{17})(15\beta - \frac{4}{17})$

PROBLEMS 16–1

2　15　　　　　　4　$3xy^2$　　　　　6　$17\alpha\beta\gamma$　　　8　$5F^3L^3C^2$

10　$\lambda + \pi$　　　　12　$e - 3$　　　　14　$2\mu + 3f$

PROBLEMS 16–2

2　2,310　　　　　　　4　e^2i^2r　　　　　　　6　$30\theta^2\phi^2\omega^2$

8　$84a^2bc^3$　　　　　　　　　　　10　$Z(Z + 1)(Z - 1)$

12　$\pi(\pi + 1)(\pi - 10)(\pi - 1)$　　　　14　$(4\mu - 5\lambda)(2\mu - 7\lambda)(\mu + \lambda)$

PROBLEMS 16–3

2　20　　　　　　　4　$9ac$　　　　　　6　$\theta^2 + 4\theta - 21$

8　-9　　　　　　10　$4\phi - \phi^2$　　　　12　$2\frac{4}{40}$

14　$\dfrac{R_1 - R_2}{R_1^2 - R_2^2}$

PROBLEMS 16–4

2 $\frac{4}{9}$ 4 $\frac{6}{13}$ 6 $\dfrac{a}{2b}$ 8 $\dfrac{5I}{8E}$

10 $\dfrac{Z + R}{Z - R}$ 12 $\dfrac{\theta}{\theta + 1}$ 14 $\dfrac{\omega(\pi - 4)}{\pi + 5}$

PROBLEMS 16–5

2 $\dfrac{\omega f}{f - f_o}$ 4 $\dfrac{P + W}{ei - I^2 R}$ 6 $\dfrac{Ir + iR}{E + e}$

8 $\dfrac{1}{E + e}$ 10 $-\dfrac{1}{a + b}$ 12 $\dfrac{\phi}{6\alpha + \beta}$

14 1

PROBLEMS 16–6

2 $37\frac{1}{7}$ 4 $\dfrac{IZ + E}{Z}$ 6 $\dfrac{v - st}{t}$

8 $\dfrac{35\alpha^2}{36}$ 10 $-\dfrac{6\pi^2\mu^2}{49}$ 12 $\dfrac{x^2 + xy + y}{x + y}$

14 $\dfrac{2\beta^2 - 7\beta - 1}{\beta - 3}$ 16 $\dfrac{r^3 + 3r^2 + 3r + 5}{r + 2}$ 18 $\dfrac{3W^3 + 2W^2 + 4W + 2}{W^2 + 1}$

20 $-\dfrac{E^2}{E - 1}$ 22 $13\frac{1}{3}$ 24 $4a - 1 + \dfrac{3}{4a}$

26 $1 + \dfrac{5}{I + 2}$ 28 $1 - \dfrac{5}{i + 3}$ 30 $1 + \dfrac{4}{5\omega - 3L}$

PROBLEMS 16–7

2 $\frac{6}{54}, \frac{27}{54}, \frac{2}{54}$ 4 $\dfrac{\beta}{\alpha\beta}, \dfrac{\alpha}{\alpha\beta}$

6 $\dfrac{e}{Ee}, \dfrac{E}{Ee}, \dfrac{e^2}{Ee}$ 8 $\dfrac{E^2 R_1 r}{RR_1 r}, \dfrac{ERr}{RR_1 r}, \dfrac{e^2 RR_1}{RR_1 r}, \dfrac{3e R_1 r}{RR_1 r}$

10 $\dfrac{3v + 3t}{v^2 - t^2}, \dfrac{sv - st}{v^2 - t^2}, \dfrac{vt^2 + t^3}{v^2 - t^2}$

12 $\dfrac{2r - 6}{(r + 1)(r + 2)(r - 3)}, \dfrac{3r + 6}{(r + 1)(r + 2)(r - 3)}$

14 $\dfrac{4\omega^2 - 8\omega f + 4f^2}{2(2\omega - 3f)(\omega^2 - f^2)}, \dfrac{\omega^2 + 2\omega f + f^2}{2(2\omega - 3f)(\omega^2 - f^2)}$

PROBLEMS 16–8

2 $23\frac{3}{24}$ 4 $-\dfrac{75\lambda}{88}$ 6 $\dfrac{17z}{16}$

8 $\dfrac{65E}{48R}$ 10 $\dfrac{39R + 9I^2 - 2}{3I^2 R}$ 12 $\dfrac{\alpha r_2 r_3 + \beta r_1 r_3 - \theta r_1 r_2}{r_1 r_2 r_3}$

14 $\dfrac{5Z - 111}{24}$ 16 $\dfrac{4a - 61}{a^2 - 3a - 28}$ 18 $\dfrac{7\phi}{1 - \phi^2}$

20 $\dfrac{s^2 - 3st - t^2}{t(s - t)}$ 22 0 24 $\dfrac{2\mu^2 - 11}{\mu - 4}$

26 $\dfrac{2}{F^2 - 10F + 24}$ 28 $\dfrac{3}{P^2 + P - 2}$ 30 $\dfrac{32}{4 - 3\omega}$

32 $\dfrac{13 - 5I}{6(I^2 - 1)}$ 34 $\dfrac{9\alpha^2 + 17\alpha - 8}{\alpha(\alpha + 3)(\alpha + 5)}$ 36 $\dfrac{3\pi + 2}{(\pi - 2)(\pi + 1)(\pi - 1)}$

38 $\dfrac{1}{2\alpha + 1}$ 40 $\dfrac{48\theta^3}{(\phi^2 - \theta^2)(\phi^2 - 9\theta^2)}$

PROBLEMS 16–9

2 $11\frac{1}{36}$ 4 $19\frac{3}{7}$ 6 5   8 $\dfrac{5\lambda^2}{12\pi\omega^2}$ 10 $\dfrac{2E - 3}{12E}$

12 $\dfrac{4\phi + 3\theta}{\phi + 2}$ 14 $\dfrac{\mu - 1}{\mu + 2}$ 16 $\dfrac{C}{L^3}$ 18 $\dfrac{2R - 3}{2R - 1}$ 20 $\dfrac{r - 4}{r + 1}$

22 $\dfrac{\beta + 1}{\beta - 1}$ 24 1   26 $\dfrac{1}{R + E}$ 28 $\dfrac{2E^2 - 3E + 1}{4E^2 - E}$ 30 $5F^2$

PROBLEMS 16–10

2 $33\frac{4}{7}$ 4 $\dfrac{3}{4I}$ 6 $\dfrac{\lambda^2 - \omega^2}{\lambda^2 + \omega^2}$ 8 $\dfrac{R}{z}$ 10 $\dfrac{\omega(\omega + 3)}{\omega + 4}$

12 $\dfrac{e^2 - e + 1}{2e - 1}$ 14 $\dfrac{\phi - \theta}{\phi + \theta}$

PROBLEMS 17–1

2 $\beta = 21$ 4 $\omega = -\frac{2}{3}$ 6 $E = 3$ 8 $Z = 9$ 10 $\theta = 5$

12 $r = 3$ 14 $I = \frac{3}{10}$

PROBLEMS 17–2

2 $i = \frac{1}{2}$ 4 $r = 2$ 6 $\theta = -5$ 8 $\pi = -2$ 10 $I = -11$

12 $E = \frac{3}{2}$ 14 $e = 3$

PROBLEMS 17–3

2 $r = 3$ 4 $\pi = 2$ 6 $R = 3$

8 $\pi = 40$ 10 $e = -6$ 12 $\theta = 2$

14 $R = -\frac{4}{5}$ 16 $\phi = -2$ 18 $z = 3$

20 $\alpha = -2$ 22 $13\frac{1}{13}$ hr   26 2.73 hr

28 $n = \dfrac{xyz}{xz + yz - xy}$ hr   30 1.64 gal   32 90 lb

34 288, 12   36 420, 13   38 42, 35

40 $\frac{6}{18}$ 42 10   44 18, 15, and 8 in.

PROBLEMS 17–4

2 $h = \dfrac{2A}{a + b}$ 4 $W = \dfrac{aW_2 - W_1}{a - 1}$ 6 $R_{eq} = R(F - 1)$

$b = \dfrac{2A - ah}{h}$ $W_2 = \dfrac{W(a - 1) + W_1}{a}$ $R = \dfrac{R_{eq}}{F - 1}$

8 $G_2 = G_L + \dfrac{g_p}{\mu + 2}$ 10 $a = p(1 + rt)$ 12 $a = \dfrac{b}{x}$

$r = \dfrac{a - p}{pt}$

14 $\alpha = -(4\theta + 3\phi)$ 16 $E_t = E_g - IR$ 18 $a = \dfrac{2s - NL}{N}$

$E_g = E_t + IR$ $N = \dfrac{2s}{a + L}$

20 $a = \dfrac{Pt - d}{d^2}$

22 $C = \dfrac{kab}{b - a}$

$b = \dfrac{aC}{C - ka}$

24 $a = Lr - sr + s$

$s = \dfrac{Lr - a}{r - 1}$

26 $D = \dfrac{c - AL}{12}$

28 $\Delta = \dfrac{\phi}{\theta}$

30 $A = \dfrac{h(b_1 + b_2)}{2}$

$h = \dfrac{2A}{b_1 + b_2}$

32 $p = \dfrac{I^2{}_{\max} R_b}{2}$

34 $C = \tfrac{5}{9}(F - 32)$

36 $R_t = \dfrac{R_1 R_2}{R_1 + R_2}$

$R_1 = \dfrac{R_2 R_t}{R_2 - R_t}$

$R_2 = \dfrac{R_1 R_t}{R_1 - R_t}$

38 $g_m = \dfrac{G(R_{pg} + r_p)}{R_{pg} r_p}$

$r_p = \dfrac{G R_{pg}}{g_m R_{pg} - G}$

40 $m = \dfrac{p(d^2 - L^2)}{2L}$

42 $E_b = k\left(\dfrac{E_p}{\mu} + E_g\right)$

$E_g = \dfrac{\mu E_b - k E_p}{k\mu}$

44 $\mu = \dfrac{E_p - E_p'}{E_g' - E_g}$

46 $r_1 = \dfrac{r_2 r_3}{r_4}$

$r_4 = \dfrac{r_2 r_3}{r_1}$

48 $I_2 = \dfrac{ER_o}{R_1 R_o + R_1 R_2 + R_2 R_o}$

50 $e_2 = \dfrac{\mu e}{\omega C(r_p + Z_e + r_p Z_e / Z_c)}$

52 $E_2 = E\left(\dfrac{3k}{2k_1 + k_2}\right)$

54 $i_p = \dfrac{\mu e_g}{\omega L_b + r_p + R_b}$

56 $I_s = \dfrac{E}{Z_2/a + aZ_1}$

58 $e_1 = \mu e_g\left(\dfrac{R_p}{R_p + Z_1}\right)$

60 $R_1 = \dfrac{R_p[(E_b - E_c) - \mu(E_c + E_s)]}{\mu E_c - E_b + E_c}$

62 $\alpha = \dfrac{4\pi r^2 - MHT^2}{8r^2}$

64 $d = \dfrac{0.08r^2 N^2 - 6Lr - 10Lt}{9L}$

66 $Z_1 = \dfrac{e_2 r_p R_2}{\mu e_g Z_2 - e_2(r_p + R_2)}$

$e_2 = \dfrac{\mu e_g Z_1 Z_2}{Z_1(r_p + R_2) + r_p R_2}$

68 $\pi = \dfrac{\alpha^2(\beta - \alpha)}{\alpha + 2\beta}$

70 $S_2 = 90$ units

72 $K = 6.67 \times 10^{-8}$

74 $Z_1 = 6\ \Omega$

76 $V_2 = 34$ volts

78 $F = C$ at $-40°$

80 $t = 59.5°C$

82 $C_2 = 6\mu f$

84 $q = 80$

88 $E = 2.1$ volts

92 $\mu = \dfrac{i_p(r_p + r_b)}{e_g}$

$r_p = \dfrac{\mu e_g - i_p r_b}{i_p} \, \Omega$

94 $M = 75$

100 $b_1 = 50$

104 $b = -47.4$

108 $C = 15 \, \mu\text{f}$

86 (a) Increased by a factor of 4.
    (b) Halved.

90 $R = \dfrac{n(E - Ir)}{I} \, \Omega$

$n = \dfrac{IR}{E - Ir}$ cells

98 $r = 4$

102 $V_1 = 10$

106 $\mu = 50$

110 $R_3 = 2.14 \, \Omega$

PROBLEMS 18-1

2 $30 \, \Omega$ 4 $4.97 \, \Omega$ 6 $R_t = \dfrac{R}{2} \, \Omega$ 8 505 watts

10 9 watts   12 20 watts   14 $333,000 \, \Omega$

PROBLEMS 18-2

2 $9.30 \, \Omega$ 4 $4.96 \, \Omega$ 6 $684 \, \Omega$ 8 (a) $33.3 \, \Omega$
                                                     (b) $25 \, \Omega$
                                                     (c) $20 \, \Omega$

10 $30 \, \Omega$ 12 (a) 14 amp   14 $10,000 \, \Omega$
                            (b) 2 amp
                            (c) 8 amp
                            (d) $8 \, \Omega$
                            (e) 448 watts

PROBLEMS 18-3

2 3.90 watts   4 280 ma   6 74.5 ma   8 (a) 133 watts
                                                     (b) 500 ma

10 8 ma   12 2.09 ma   14 (a) 3.65 amp
                                   (b) 729 watts

PROBLEMS 19-1

2 $8.89 \, \Omega$ 4 10   6 $R_1 = 990 \, \Omega$
                                     $R_2 = 99 \, \Omega$
                                     $R_3 = 9.9 \, \Omega$
                                     $R_4 = 0.99 \, \Omega$
                                     $R_5 = 0.11 \, \Omega$

PROBLEMS 19-2

2 (a) 36.6 volts
   (b) 75 volts
   (c) 375 μa

PROBLEMS 20-1

2 140 to 294 volts   4 14 watts

6 75.9 watts   8 420 volts

PROBLEMS 20–2

2 112.6 volts   4 (a) 115.4 volts   6 (a) 109.9 volts   8 113.5 volts
                      (b) 103.8 volts   (b) 110.3 volts
                      (c) 190.4 watts

10 (a) $A = 99.8$ volts
         $B = 97.3$ volts
         $C = 96.1$ volts
         $D = 97.3$ volts
    (b) $E_{gen} = 114.6$ volts

PROBLEMS 20–3

2 $0.00943\ \Omega$ 4 19.32 miles

PROBLEMS 21–1

2 With velocity constant, distance varies directly as time. (Graph of distance
   is a straight line.)
4 (a) 4 hr
   (b) 300 miles
   (c) 50 miles
6 Third, sixth, ninth, fifteenth
8 (a) 5 weeks
   (b) Third and seventh weeks
   (c) Twenty-fifth week

PROBLEMS 21–5

2 $x = 1, y = -2$ 4 $x = 4, y = -2$ 6 $i = 3, I = -2$
8 $e = 1, E = 2$ 10 $\alpha = 4, \beta = 1$

PROBLEMS 21–6

2 $\alpha = 6, \beta = 2$ 4 $\theta = 5, \phi = 3$ 6 $s = 10, t = 8$
8 $\alpha = 40, \beta = 5$ 10 $I = 12, i = 10$ 12 $R_1 = \frac{1}{2}, R_2 = 4$
14 $\pi = -2, \lambda = -3$ 16 $\theta = -2, \phi = 3$ 18 $Z_1 = 12, Z_2 = 9$
20 $\alpha = -3,500, \beta = 7,500$

PROBLEMS 21–7

2 $E = 2, e = 3$ 4 $R = 2, r = 1$ 6 $s = 8, t = 9$
8 $Z_1 = 15\frac{4}{7}, Z_2 = 25\frac{5}{7}$ 10 $\alpha = 11, \beta = -5$ 12 $e = \frac{1}{3}, e_1 = \frac{1}{2}$
14 $R_1 = 1, R_2 = 2$ 16 $f = 4, F = 5$ 18 $\omega = 10, \pi = 10$
20 $\theta = 5, \phi = 4$

PROBLEMS 21–8

2 $I = 2, i = 3$ 4 $\omega = 5, \pi = 12$ 6 $\theta = 5, \phi = 8$
8 $x = 4, y = -1$ 10 $Z_1 = 10, Z_2 = 3$

PROBLEMS 21–9

2 $\theta = 6, \phi = 8$ 4 $R = 51, r = 17$ 6 $Z = 7, Z_1 = 3$
8 $\omega = 7, F = 10$ 10 $\theta = 3, \phi = -4$

PROBLEMS 21–10

2 $\theta = \frac{1}{3}, \phi = \frac{1}{5}$ 4 $i = -15\frac{4}{7}, I = 15\frac{5}{11}$ 6 $Z = 9, Z_1 = -5$
8 $\pi = 1, \omega = -2$ 10 $r = 5, r_1 = 2$

PROBLEMS 21–11

2 $\alpha = \dfrac{\pi + 5\omega}{2}, \beta = \dfrac{\pi - 5\omega}{2}$

4 $\alpha = \dfrac{3(R + Z)}{RZ}, \beta = \dfrac{5(R + Z)}{RZ}$

6 $R = \omega, r = \pi$

8 $R = \dfrac{iZ_1 + Z_z}{I + i}, r = \dfrac{IZ_1 - Z_z}{I + i}$

PROBLEMS 21–12

2 $x = 9, y = 2, z = -4$

4 $r = 7, R = 6, Z = 5$

6 $I = 1, I_1 = 3, i = 2$

8 $\alpha = -\frac{3}{2}, \beta = \frac{3}{13}, \gamma = -\frac{3}{10}$

10 $R_1 = -\dfrac{2}{\beta + \gamma}, R_2 = -\dfrac{2}{\alpha + \gamma}, R_3 = -\dfrac{2}{\alpha + \beta}$

PROBLEMS 21–13

2 6 and 19

4 Resistors 9 cents, capacitors 12 cents

6 $\dfrac{90 + \theta°}{2}, \dfrac{90 - \theta°}{2}$

8 $v = \dfrac{2s}{t}$

10 $W = \dfrac{Q^2}{2C}$

12 $t = \dfrac{mv}{2f}$

14 $D_L = \dfrac{\pi}{Q}$

16 $R = \dfrac{I_1 R_1}{I - I_1}$

18 $H = 0.24\ Pt$ cal

20 $R_1 = \dfrac{\beta\omega - \gamma\phi}{\beta\theta - \alpha\phi}$

$R_2 = \dfrac{\gamma\theta - \alpha\omega}{\beta\theta - \alpha\phi}$

PROBLEMS 22–1

2 (a) 240 volts   4 (a) 222 volts   6 124 volts   8 2.56 per cent
   (b) 5.53 kw   (b) 220 volts
   (c) 238 volts   (c) 11.6 kw

PROBLEMS 22–2

2 1,560 amp   4 218 volts   6 2.89 Ω   8 (a) 2.75 amp
                                                              (b) 438 volts
                                                              (c) 0.06 Ω
                                                              (d) 440 volts

10 (a) 1.28 amp   (c) 226 volts   (e) 85.3 per cent
    (b) 0.2 Ω   (d) 230 volts   (f) 6.92 Ω

PROBLEMS 22–3

2 (a) 733 ma   4 (a) 0.18 Ω   6 (a) 1.0 amp   8 3.84 watts
   (b) 450 mw   (b) 0.22 Ω   (b) 600 mw
                     (c) 10 watts   (c) 15 amp
                     (d) 11.1 amp

10 (a) 4.8 amp   12 (a) 0.0733 Ω
    (b) 288 mw   (b) 200 amp
14 $E = 1.2$ volts, $r = 0.3$ Ω   16 $I = 8$ amp, $r = 0.05$ Ω
18 $E = 1.6$ volts, $r = 0.04$ Ω

PROBLEMS 23–1

2 e^6 　　　　4 a^9 　　　　6 β^{5e} 　　　　8 θ^{2r}

10 b^7 　　　　12 π^{x+1} 　　　14 E^8 　　　　16 z^4Z^6

18 $f^{2\alpha}$ 　　　20 $\omega^4f^4F^{4\theta}$ 　　22 $e^{12}I^8Z^8$ 　　24 $\dfrac{L^{4\alpha}}{C^{2\alpha}}$

26 $\dfrac{\theta^{2en}}{\phi^{2\pi n}}$ 　　28 $-\dfrac{I^6}{i^{12}}$ 　　30 $\dfrac{x^{6rt}}{y^{6st}}$ 　　32 $\dfrac{1}{zZ^2}$

34 $\dfrac{6}{b^3}$ 　　36 $\dfrac{1}{(4\omega F)^{2e}}$ 　　38 $\dfrac{r^2R^2Z^2}{3}$ 　　40 $\dfrac{8\gamma^2z^3}{3}$

PROBLEMS 23–2

2 -2 　　　　4 2 　　　　6 fF^2 　　　　8 $\dfrac{4\alpha^2}{\beta}$

10 $a^2x^6y^4$ 　　12 $\sqrt[3]{4}$ 　　14 $3\sqrt{\phi}$ 　　16 $\sqrt[4]{\omega^3F^6}$

18 $R^{5/2}$ 　　20 $2L^{3/4}C$ 　　22 $9\gamma^{5/4}$ 　　24 $3s(vt)^{2/3}$

PROBLEMS 23–3

2 $3\sqrt{3}$ 　　4 $3\sqrt{11}$ 　　6 $5\sqrt{2}$ 　　8 $7\sqrt{2}$ 　　10 $2x\sqrt{5}$ 　　12 $4I\sqrt{2R}$ 　　14 $27\theta^2\sqrt{\phi}$

16 $9rz\sqrt{7r}$ 　　　　18 $18\alpha\beta^2\sqrt{3}$ 　　　　20 $6\gamma^2svt\sqrt{2s}$

PROBLEMS 23–4

2 $\dfrac{\sqrt{3}}{3}$ 　　4 $\dfrac{\sqrt{30}}{6}$ 　　6 $\dfrac{\sqrt{10}}{4}$ 　　8 $2\sqrt{7}$

10 $\dfrac{2\sqrt{\alpha}}{3\alpha}$ 　　12 $\dfrac{\sqrt{\theta\phi}}{\phi}$ 　　14 $\sqrt{E}$ 　　16 $\dfrac{\mu\sqrt{3}}{3}$

18 $\dfrac{\sqrt{r^2-R^2}}{r-R}$ 　　20 $\dfrac{5C\sqrt{2}}{7}$

PROBLEMS 23–5

2 $3\sqrt{2}$ 　　4 $-\sqrt{7}$ 　　6 $(3-\mu)\sqrt{\mu}$ 　　8 $-12\sqrt{11}$

10 $\dfrac{10\sqrt{7}}{7}$ 　　12 $\dfrac{x}{2}(2-\sqrt{3})$ 　　14 $(a+1)\sqrt{abc}$

PROBLEMS 23–6

2 12 　　4 $28\sqrt{6}$ 　　6 $240\sqrt{3}$ 　　8 $\omega\pi^3\sqrt{\omega\pi}$ 　　10 33

12 $e-ir$ 　　14 $2L-3-2\sqrt{L^2-3L}$ 　　16 $2(\lambda-\sqrt{\lambda^2-1})$

18 $\dfrac{\theta\sqrt{2(1+2\sqrt{3})}}{3}$ 　　20 $\dfrac{1}{6}\sqrt[10]{\dfrac{t}{z}}$

PROBLEMS 23–7

2 $\dfrac{15-3\sqrt{2}}{23}$ 　　4 $\dfrac{4-\sqrt{6}}{2}$ 　　6 $\dfrac{36-9\sqrt{5}}{22}$

8 $\dfrac{i-2I\sqrt{i}+I^2}{i-I^2}$ 　　10 $\dfrac{t-2\sqrt{s}}{t}$

PROBLEMS 23–8

2 $j2$ 　　　4 $-j6$ 　　　6 $-j\sqrt{5}$ 　　8 $-j\dfrac{1}{\omega C}$ 　　10 $j\frac{3}{4}$

12 $j\dfrac{4\sqrt{2}}{5}$ 　　14 $-j\alpha\sqrt{\beta}$

PROBLEMS 23–9

2 $18 - j2$ 4 $-59 + j54$ 6 $14 - j16$ 8 $12 + j22$
10 $-91 + j26$ 12 $-14 - j62$

PROBLEMS 23–10

2 $39 + j2$ 4 2 6 $R^2 + \omega^2 Z^2$

8 $-j$ 10 $1 - j1$ 12 $\dfrac{19 - j2}{10}$

14 $\dfrac{\alpha^2 - j2\alpha\beta - \beta^2}{\alpha^2 + \beta^2}$

PROBLEMS 23–11

2 $r = 25$ 4 $\mu = 36$ 6 $Z = 38$ 8 $\pi = 60$ 10 $f = 6$

12 $F = \dfrac{mm'}{r^2}$ 14 $h = 5{,}590$

16 $\dfrac{d_o}{d_1} = \left(\dfrac{r}{R_t} + 1\right)^2$ 18 $A = 12.56$ in.^{2}

20 $L = 5.17 \times 10^{-5}$ henry   24 $C_b = 3.75 \times 10^{-8}$

28 $g_m{}^2 = \dfrac{G_L(G_1 - G_a{}^2)}{R_{eq}(G_a{}^2 - G_1) - G_1}$

PROBLEMS 24–1

2 $t = \pm 4$ 4 $\lambda = \pm 0.4$ 6 $\theta = \pm 0.15$ 8 $\gamma = \pm 1.5$
10 $C = \pm \tfrac{2}{3}$ 12 $L = \pm 1$ 14 $\beta = \pm \tfrac{5}{3}$

PROBLEMS 24–2

2 $\lambda = 2$ or 6 4 $\mu = 9$ or 6 6 $\alpha = 25$ or 2
8 $I = 16$ or 10 10 $\theta = 3$ or -2 12 $I = 13$ or 2
14 $L = \tfrac{3}{2}$ or -7

PROBLEMS 24–3

2 $v = -7$ or -5 4 $\theta = -3$ or -8 6 $z = -5 \pm \sqrt{10}$

8 $R = 11$ or $11\frac{1}{2}$ 10 $\phi = 2$ or $\tfrac{1}{3}$ 12 $\mu = \dfrac{3 \pm \sqrt{129}}{12}$

14 $\alpha = 2$ or $-\tfrac{2}{15}$

PROBLEMS 24–4

2 $x = 3$ or -2 4 $L = 24$ or -2 6 $\lambda = 6$ or 0.3

8 $\phi = \dfrac{-1 \pm \sqrt{5}}{2}$ 10 $\mu = \pm \sqrt{2}$ 12 $R = 7.5$ or -10.5

14 $F = \tfrac{2}{3}$ or $-\tfrac{6}{5}$

PROBLEMS 24–6

2 22 and 24 4 $6, 8, 10$ 6 13 or -14 8 $D = \pm \sqrt{\dfrac{2.53H}{N}}$

10 $\dfrac{d_o}{d_i} = \pm \sqrt{\dfrac{r + R_t}{R_t}}$ 12 $c_1 = \pm \dfrac{1}{\omega R_1} \sqrt{\dfrac{R_b - R_2}{R_2 R_a}}$

$$c_2 = \pm \dfrac{1}{\omega} \sqrt{\dfrac{R_a}{R_2(R_b - R_2)}}$$

14 $d = -6 \pm \sqrt{36 + 2d}$ ft   16 (a) 5 sec   18 80.0 Ω   20 3 Ω
                                       (b) 88¾ sec
                                       (c) $h \cong 32{,}500$ ft

22 234 volts   24 (a) 2 amp   26 20 volts and 15 amp or
                               (b) 120 volts   60 volts and 5 amp
                               (c) $R_1 = 10$ Ω
                                   $R_2 = 20$ Ω
                                   $R_3 = 30$ Ω

PROBLEMS 25–1

2 80.9 ma   4 1 Ω   6 98.1 volts   8 (a) 2.55 amp
                                                                (b) 28.4 volts

10 Zero

PROBLEMS 25–2

2 28 volts   4 220 volts   6 16.3 watts
8 (a) 2.0 amp, which is furnished by batteries
   (b) From b to a

PROBLEMS 25–3

2 (a) 110 volts   4 (a) 119 volts   6 (a) $E_1 = 110$ volts
   (b) 128 volts   (b) 3.48 kw $E_2 = 106$ volts
   (c) 3.30 kw   (c) 116 volts $E_3 = 117$ volts
                                                  $E_4 = 114$ volts
                                               (b) 6.36 kw

8 (a) 2.23 kw   10 (a) 209 volts
   (b) $E_1 = 112$ volts   (b) 11.7 kw
       $E_2 = 108$ volts
       $E_3 = 110$ volts
       $E_4 = 108$ volts

PROBLEMS 25–4

2 (a) 5.31 amp   4 (a) 31.9 watts   6 (a) 588 watts
   (b) 291 watts   (b) 5.65 volts   (b) 12.7 volts
8 (a) 20.5 volts   10 (a) 87.9 watts
   (b) 303 watts   (b) 19.4 watts
12 (a) 3.12 volts   14 None
    (b) 6.25 amp through battery from d to c

PROBLEMS 25–5

2 $R_a = 3.00$ Ω   4 $R_1 = 35$ Ω   6 $R_1 = R_2 = R_3 = 300$ Ω
   $R_b = 4.00$ Ω $R_2 = 43.8$ Ω
   $R_c = 5.02$ Ω $R_3 = 23.3$ Ω
8 1.42 amp   10 4.67 amp   12 12 Ω   14 3.46 amp
16 66.0 ma

PROBLEMS 26–1

2 (a) 153°
   (b) 75°
   (c) −35°
   (d) −90°
   (e) −150°
   (f) 258°

6 (a) 150°
   (b) 300°

8 (a) 360°/min
   (b) 6°/min
   (c) 0.5°/min

10 50π fps

PROBLEMS 26–2

2 (a) 171.9°
   (b) 22.9°
   (c) 135.0°
   (d) 18.2°
   (e) 4.6°
   (f) 120.0°

4 140π radians

6 (a) $\dfrac{\pi}{30}$ radian/sec

   (b) $\dfrac{\pi}{1,800}$ radian/sec

   (c) $\dfrac{\pi}{21,600}$ radian/sec

8 $\dfrac{\pi}{5}$ radians/sec

10 $\dfrac{\pi}{720}$ radian/min

PROBLEMS 26–3

2 180 and 255 mm
6 $a = 8$, $b = 5$, $C = 34°$
10 $a = 35$, $A = 60°$, $C = 60°$

4 $A = 36.9°$, $B = 53.1°$, $C = 90°$
8 $c = 7$, $A = 45°$, $B = 45°$

PROBLEMS 26–4

2 $a = 56$, $A = 75°$
8 132 ft

4 2,654 nautical miles
10 585 ft

6 9 ft

PROBLEMS 27–1

2 (a) $\sin \alpha = \dfrac{OR}{PR}$

   (b) $\sin \beta = \dfrac{OP}{PR}$

   (c) $\cot \beta = \dfrac{OR}{OP}$

   (d) $\sec \alpha = \dfrac{PR}{OP}$

   (e) $\tan \alpha = \dfrac{OR}{OP}$

4 $\sin \alpha = 0.8$ $\sin \beta = 0.6$
   $\cos \alpha = 0.6$ $\cos \beta = 0.8$
   $\tan \alpha = 1.33$ $\tan \beta = 0.75$
   $\cot \alpha = 0.75$ $\cot \beta = 1.33$
   $\sec \alpha = 1.67$ $\sec \beta = 1.25$
   $\csc \alpha = 1.25$ $\csc \beta = 1.67$

6 $\sin \theta = 0.866$
   $\cos \theta = 0.500$
   $\tan \theta = 1.73$

8 (a) $\csc \theta = 2$
   (b) $\cos \alpha = \frac{1}{3}$
   (c) $\tan \beta = \frac{5}{4}$
   (d) $\sec \phi = \frac{3}{2}$
   (e) $\cot \phi = \frac{1}{10}$
   (f) $\sin \alpha = \frac{1}{5}$

10 $\sin = \frac{3}{5}$
    $\cos = \frac{4}{5}$
    $\cot = \frac{4}{3}$
    $\sec = \frac{5}{4}$
    $\csc = \frac{5}{3}$

12 (a) $\tan \theta$ (c) $\sec \theta$
    (b) $\cot \theta$ (d) $\csc \theta$

PROBLEMS 27-2

2 I or IV   4 II or IV   6 II   8 II

10 I   12 II or III   14 -12.8 16 sin $= -$
                                                 cos $= -$
                                                 tan $= +$

18 sin $= -$ 20 sin $= +$ 24 sin $\theta = \frac{3}{5}$ cot $\theta = \frac{4}{3}$
    cos $= +$ cos $= +$ cos $\theta = \frac{4}{5}$ sec $\theta = \frac{5}{4}$
    tan $= -$ tan $= +$ tan $\theta = \frac{3}{4}$ csc $\theta = \frac{5}{3}$

26 sin $\theta = \frac{3}{5}$ 28 sin $\theta = -\dfrac{5\sqrt{61}}{61}$ 30 sin $\theta = -\frac{4}{5}$
    cos $\theta = -\frac{4}{5}$ cos $\theta = -\frac{3}{5}$
    tan $\theta = -\frac{3}{4}$ cos $\theta = \dfrac{6\sqrt{61}}{61}$ tan $\theta = \frac{4}{3}$
    cot $\theta = -\frac{4}{3}$ cot $\theta = \frac{3}{4}$
    sec $\theta = -\frac{5}{4}$ tan $\theta = -\frac{5}{6}$ sec $\theta = -\frac{5}{3}$
    csc $\theta = \frac{5}{3}$ cot $\theta = -\frac{6}{5}$ csc $\theta = -\frac{5}{4}$

                                          sec $\theta = \dfrac{\sqrt{61}}{6}$

                                          csc $\theta = -\dfrac{\sqrt{61}}{5}$

PROBLEMS 27-3

2 -1 4 ∞

PROBLEMS 28-1

2 (a) sin 15° $= 0.2588$ 4 (a) sin 7.49° $= 0.1303$
       cos 15° $= 0.9659$ cos 7.49° $= 0.9914$
       tan 15° $= 0.2679$ tan 7.49° $= 0.1315$
   (b) sin 85.4° $= 0.9968$ (b) sin 10.27° $= 0.1783$
       cos 85.4° $= 0.0802$ cos 10.27° $= 0.9840$
       tan 85.4° $= 12.43$ tan 10.27° $= 0.1812$
   (c) sin 71.1° $= 0.9461$ (c) sin 25.75° $= 0.4344$
       cos 71.1° $= 0.3239$ cos 25.75° $= 0.9007$
       tan 71.1° $= 2.9208$ tan 25.75° $= 0.4823$
   (d) sin 0.5° $= 0.0087$ (d) sin 37.55° $= 0.6094$
       cos 0.5° $= 1.0000$ cos 37.55° $= 0.7928$
       tan 0.5° $= 0.0087$ tan 37.55° $= 0.7687$
   (e) sin 23.3° $= 0.3955$ (e) sin 2.14° $= 0.0373$
       cos 23.3° $= 0.9184$ cos 2.14° $= 0.9993$
       tan 23.3° $= 0.4307$ tan 2.14° $= 0.0374$

PROBLEMS 28-2

2 (a) 3.7°   4 (a) 84.7°
   (b) 89.1°   (b) 37.4°
   (c) 55.1°   (c) 72.8°
   (d) 71.5°   (d) 2.3°
   (e) 11.6°   (e) 63.9°

PROBLEMS 28-3

2 (a) 185°: sin $= -0.0872$, cos $= -0.9962$, tan $= 0.0875$
   (b) 267°: sin $= -0.9986$, cos $= -0.0523$, tan $= 19.08$
   (c) 220.7°: sin $= -0.6521$, cos $= -0.7581$, tan $= 0.8601$
   (d) 180.2°: sin $= -0.0035$, cos $= -1.0000$, tan $= 0.0035$
   (e) 229.6°: sin $= -0.7615$, cos $= -0.6481$, tan $= 1.1750$

4 (a) 500°: sin $= 0.6428$, cos $= -0.7660$, tan $= -0.8391$
   (b) 683°: sin $= -0.6018$, cos $= 0.7986$, tan $= -0.7536$
   (c) $-147.3°$: sin $= -0.5402$, cos $= -0.8415$, tan $= 0.6420$
   (d) 936.4°: sin $= -0.5934$, cos $= -0.8049$, tan $= 0.7373$
   (e) $-333.7°$: sin $= 0.4431$, cos $= 0.8965$, tan $= 0.4942$

6 (a) 8.6°   (d) $-87.8°$
   (b) 27.3°   (e) $-41.1°$
   (c) 80.5°

8 $d = \sqrt{\dfrac{I \cos \theta}{E}}$, $I = \dfrac{Ed^2}{\cos \theta}$, $\theta = \arccos \dfrac{Ed^2}{I}$ 10   0.369 ft-c

12 $h = \sqrt{\dfrac{I \cos^3 \theta}{E_h}}$, $I = \dfrac{h^2 E_h}{\cos^3 \theta}$, $\theta = \arccos \sqrt[3]{\dfrac{h^2 E_h}{I}}$ 14   62,500 ft-c

16   514 cp

PROBLEMS 29-1

2   $Z = 464$, $X = 186$, $\phi = 66.4°$ 4 $Z = 39.7$, $R = 11.4$, $\phi = 16.7°$
6   $Z = 7.14$, $R = 4.79$, $\phi = 42.1°$ 8 $Z = 3,100$, $X = 512$, $\theta = 9.5°$
10 $Z = 229$, $R = 111$, $\theta = 60.9°$ 12 $Z = 2,160$, $R = 1,200$, $\theta = 56.3°$
14 $Z = 0.378$, $R = 0.0500$, $\theta = 82.4°$

PROBLEMS 29-2

2   $R = 71.9$, $X = 4.39$, $\phi = 86.5°$ 4 $R = 35.5$, $X = 6.19$, $\theta = 9.9°$

6   $R = 11.5$, $X = 6.94$, $\theta = 31.2°$ 10 $R = \dfrac{\sqrt{2}}{2}$, $X = \dfrac{\sqrt{6}}{2}$, $\theta = 60°$

8   $R = 8.85 \times 10^5$, $X = 4.65 \times 10^5$, $\theta = 27.7°$

PROBLEMS 29-3

2   $\theta = 78.5°$, $\phi = 11.5°$, $X = 50.6$ 4 $\theta = 83.6°$, $\phi = 6.4°$, $R = 5.43$
6   $\theta = 57.3°$, $\phi = 32.7°$, $R = 556$ 8 $\theta = 38.4°$, $\phi = 51.6°$, $R = 7.84 \times 10^3$

10 $\theta = 30°$, $\phi = 60°$, $R = \dfrac{\sqrt{3}}{2}$

PROBLEMS 29-4

2   $\theta = 8.1°$, $\phi = 81.9°$, $Z = 407$ 4 $\theta = 73.5°$, $\phi = 16.5°$, $Z = 1,600$
6   $\theta = 58.6°$, $\phi = 31.4°$, $Z = 478$ 8 $\theta = 10.4°$, $\phi = 79.6°$, $Z = 0.948$
10 $\theta = \phi = 45°$, $Z = 1$

PROBLEMS 29-5

2   33.7°   4   300 ft   6   235 ft   8   33.5 ft, 73.4°
10   1,296 ft   12   1,250 ft

PROBLEMS 30–2

2 (a) 12π radians/sec   4 (a) 50π radians/sec   6 (a) 0.588
  (b) 2,160°/sec   (b) 9,000°/sec   (b) 0.951
                                                           (c) −0.809
                                                           (d) −0.951

PROBLEMS 30–3

2 (a) 32   4 (a) E_m 12 (b) $y = 12 \sin (88t + 23°)$
  (b) 37.7   (b) 157   (c) 4.69 in.
  (c) 6   (c) 25   (d) 10.9 in.
  (d) ⅙   (d) 0.04   (e) 84π radians
  (e) 10° lag   (e) 17° lead

PROBLEMS 31–1

2 132 at 327.8°   4 76.8 at 348.6

PROBLEMS 31–2

2 $x = 106, y = 20.4$ 4 $x = -454, y = 1,530$ 6 $x = 94.8, y = -351$
8 $x = -45.9, y = -40.5$ 10 $x = -18.2, y = 36.6$ 12 1.45 mile/min
14 498 lb, 44.3 lb

PROBLEMS 31–3

2 217 at 63.8°   4 10.7 at 32.8°   6 46.1 at 0°   8 233 at 120.2°
10 65.4 at 319.9°   12 110 at 40.3°   14 214 at 328.5°

PROBLEMS 32–1

2 115 volts   4 (a) 12.4 amp   6 151 volts   8 60 and 120°
              (b) −23.3 amp
              (c) 63.8 amp
              (d) −54.5 amp
              (e) 3.40 amp

10 −12.3 amp

PROBLEMS 32–2

2 (a) 60 cps   4 (a) 24 poles   6 60 cps
  (b) $e = 70.5 \sin 377t$ (b) $e = 170 \sin 5,030t$
                       (c) −129 volts
8 (a) 150 μa   10 $e = (1.55 \times 10^{-4}) \sin (4.46 \times 10^6)t$
  (b) 32.2 Mc

PROBLEMS 32–3

2 314 volts   4 41.4 μv   6 325 volts   8 38.5 volts   10 11.3 amp

PROBLEMS 32–4

2 (a) $i = 990 \sin (157t - 22°)$ 4 306 amp
  (b) 465 amp
6 −3,140 volts   8 −39.3 amp
10 (a) $i = 42.4 \sin (377t \pm 50°)$
  (b) 209 volts

PROBLEMS 33-1

2   (a) $e = 778 \sin 377t$ (d) 231 watts   4   100 volts
    (b) $i = 9.34 \sin 377t$ (e) 1.41 amp
    (c) 55 volts   (f) 438 ma

PROBLEMS 33-2

2   754 Ω   4   3,740 Ω   6   5.25 μh   8   −344 μa

10 (a) X_L is proportional to frequency.
    (b) X_L is proportional to inductance.

PROBLEMS 33-3

2   39.8 Ω   4   65.0 Ω   6   2.41 amp   8   440 volts   10   −598 volts

12 (a) 362 ma
    (b) The 4-μf capacitor (greater reactance)

14 (a) X_C is inversely proportional to frequency.
    (b) X_C is inversely proportional to capacitance.

PROBLEMS 33-4

2   (a) 2,400 Ω, 70.5°   4   (a) 67.6 Ω, 68.3°   6   104 Ω, −76.1°
    (b) 834 ma   (b) 414 ma
    (c) 667 volts
    (d) 1,885 volts

8   126 Ω, −53.4°   10   760 μμf

PROBLEMS 33-5

2   (a) 1,278 /62° Ω   4   (a) 52.5 /17.9° Ω
    (b) 0.516 amp   (b) 2.1 amp
    (c) $i = 0.730 \sin (157t − 62°)$ (c) $i = 2.97 \sin [(5.02 \times 10^3)t − 17.9°]$
    (d) 47 per cent   (d) 95.2 per cent
    (e) 160 watts   (e) 220 watts

6   (a) 74.7 /−74.5° Ω
    (b) 13.4 ma
    (c) $i = 0.019 \sin [(6.28 \times 10^6)t + 74.5°]$
    (d) 26.8 per cent
    (e) 3.59 mw

8   (a) 17.1 /−74.7 Ω
    (b) 2.92 amp
    (c) $i = 4.13 \sin [(1.76 \times 10^8)t + 74.7°]$
    (d) 26.3 per cent
    (e) 38.4 watts

10 (a) 203 /9.9° Ω   12   23.3 mw
    (b) 1.08 amp
    (c) $i = 1.53 \sin (377t − 9.9°)$
    (d) 98.5 per cent
    (e) 235 watts

14 23 + j37.5 Ω   16 $e = v_r + v_x$

PROBLEMS 33-6

2   $Q = 58.3$ 4   (a) 75.4   (c) 2.5 volts
                                           (b) 56.3 μμf   (d) 188 volts

PROBLEMS 34–1

2 (a) 0.174 amp
  (b) 71.9 per cent lagging
  (c) 4,140 + j4,000 Ω

4 (a) 777 kc
  (b) 8,000 Ω

PROBLEMS 34–2

2 (a) 99 per cent
  (b) 552 watts

4 (a) 663 /50° Ω
  (b) 426 + j508 Ω
  (c) 64.3 per cent lagging

6 (a) 740 /−68° Ω
  (b) 277 − j686 Ω
  (c) 37.5 per cent leading

8 (a) 42,300 /0° Ω
  (b) 42,300 + j0 Ω
  (c) 100 per cent

10 (a) 13.1 amp
  (b) 14 μf
  (c) 10 amp

12 (a) 57.4 Ω
  (b) 87.5 mh

14 (a) 24.2 amp
  (b) 5.65 kw

16 (a) 80.5 per cent lagging
  (b) 13.1 kw
  (c) 132 μf

18 (a) 890 /77.5° Ω
  (b) 1,006 volts

20 (a) 2.75 /2.7° amp
  (b) 99.9 per cent
  (c) 207 volts
  (d) 436 ma

22 8.2 μf

24 7.77 amp

PROBLEMS 34–3

2 (a) 3.733 Mc (c) 3.751 Mc   4 15.2 watts   6 0.177 watt   8 248 μh
  (b) 3.750 Mc (d) Q = 10

10 Q = 99.7

PROBLEMS 35–1

2 131 /−40.5°   4 40.4 /−82°   6 538 /−126°   8 20.2 /−42.4°

10 106 /−125.9°

PROBLEMS 35–2

2 546 /78.2°   4 598 /0°   6 78.2 /−147.5°   8 1.14 /51.9°

10 0.05 /36.9°

PROBLEMS 35–3

2 131 /−40.5°   4 40.4 /−82°   6 538 /−126°   8 20.2 /−42.4

10 106 /125.9°

PROBLEMS 35–4

2 316 /37°   4 77.2 /−157.3°   6 6.62 /0°   8 18.2 /10°

10 1.84 /−60°   12 0.474 /3°   14 24 /−11.5°   16 2.89 /−140°

18 7/−6.2°   20 81 /−72°

PROBLEMS 35–5

2 53.5 /−42.4° Ω   4 170 /2.34° Ω   6 96.4 /−81° Ω   8 78.4 /−73.8° Ω

10 30.7 /2.88° Ω   12 10 /0° Ω   14 59.4 /−162° ma

PROBLEMS 35–6

2   $Z_a = 50.9\ \underline{/86.8°}\ \Omega$ 4 $Z_a = 2.58\ \underline{/0°}\ \Omega$ 6   0.505 amp   8   0.64 amp

     $Z_b = 62.7\ \underline{/-20.2°}\ \Omega$ $Z_b = 2.58\ \underline{/-40°}\ \Omega$

     $Z_c = 44.5\ \underline{/8.8°}\ \Omega$ $Z_c = 2.58\ \underline{/40°}\ \Omega$

10   0.52 amp   12   0.74 amp   14   1.7 amp   16   12.5 ma

18   290 mw

PROBLEMS 36–1

2   $5 = \log_{10} 100{,}000$ 4 $3 = \log_4 64$ 6 $0 = \log_a 1$ 8 $0.5 = \log_9 3$

10   $2x = \log_3 M$ 12 $10^3 = 1{,}000$ 14 $4^3 = 64$ 16 $\epsilon^1 = \epsilon$

18   $10^1 = 10$ 20 $10^0 = 1$ 22 $x = 4$ 24 $x = 3$

26   $x = 125$ 28 $b^1 = b$ 30   1, 2, 3, 4, 5, 6

PROBLEMS 36–2

2   2   4   1   6   3   8   0

10   $\bar{2}$, or $8 - 10$ 12   1   14 $\bar{1}$, or $9 - 10$ 16   5

18   $\bar{3}$, or $7 - 10$ 20 $\bar{1}$, or $9 - 10$ 22   1   24 -0.5

28   $\log 9.30 + \log 479 - (\log 3.42 + \log 4{,}869)$

30   $\frac{1}{4}(\log 7{,}182 + \log 17.53 + \log 69.3)$

32   $3 \log x + 4 \log y - (\log a + \frac{1}{3} \log b)$

34   3.6861   36 $\bar{4}.6861$, or $6.6861 - 10$

38   $\bar{1}.6861$, or $9.6861 - 10$ 40 $\bar{6}.6861$, or $4.6861 - 10$

42   8.162×10^3 44 8.162×10^6

46   8.162×10^{-9} 48 8.162×10^{-3} 50 8.162×10^{-8}

PROBLEMS 36–3

2   2.4771   4   2.5514   6   2.8733   8   2.6990

10   $5.6981 - 10$ 12   6.6695   14   5.1514   16   5.3915

18   9.8471   20   0.4972   22   2.5762   24   5.8727

26   6.7517   28 $5.7782 - 10$ 30 $6.5395 - 10$

PROBLEMS 36–4

2   7.559×10^3 4 9.881×10^2 6 1.359×10^4 8 7.389×10^5

10   8.79×10^{-7} 12   2   14   6.28   16   7.856

18   6.753×10^4 20 3.207×10^2 22 5.898×10^3 24   2.902

26   3.477×10^2 28 9.121×10^{-12} 30 7.178×10^{-11}

PROBLEMS 36–5

2   9.8552   4 $4.2510 - 10$ 6 $6.7296 - 10$

8   3.5789   10   1.5305   12 $9.6734 - 20$

PROBLEMS 36–6

2   2.52×10^2 4 10^3 6 -1.596×10^3

8   -1.125×10^{-1} 10 -2.174×10^{-3} 12 -2.152×10^3

14   1.680×10^3 16 3.197×10 18 -3.516×10

20   1.839×10^{11}

PROBLEMS 36–7

2   5   4 -7×10^2 6 -8.335×10^{-1}

8   -1.049×10^{-4} 10 9.232×10^3

PROBLEMS 36–8

2	1.336	4	3.183	6	4.533×10^{-1}
8	6.113×10	10	9.998×10^{-6}		

PROBLEMS 36–9

2	6.808×10^{10}	4	3.354×10^{-1}	6	± 5.343
8	9.351×10^{-1}	10	± 5.519	12	1.847×10
14	3.096×10^{-8}	16	1.177×10	18	5.33
20	$\pm 6.963 \times 10^{13}$				

PROBLEMS 36–10

2	$x = 2.231 \times 10^{-1}$	4	$x = 10^{50}$	6	$P = 4.00 \times 10^{16}$
8	$E = 4.766$	10	$x = 6$	12	$x = \overline{4}$
14	$x = 4.096$	16	$x = 3.151$	18	0.325 amp
20	0.0347 sec	22	0.208 sec	24	265 words/min
28	(a) 1.30×10^{-3} coulomb	30	0.296 amp		
	(b) 25.9 volts				

PROBLEMS 37–1

2	(a) 35.1 db	4	1.90 volts, 3.16 ma	6	2.74 volts, 4.56 ma
	(b) 22.9 db				
	(c) -41.2 db				
	(d) -37.6 db				
8	(a) 19.8 mw, 3.45 volts	10	3.16×10^4	12	0.070 μw
	(b) 125 mw, 8.66 volts				
	(c) 0.788 mw, 0.688 volt				
	(d) 4.97 mw, 1.73 volts				
14	10^{-1}	16	95 db	18	2.58×10^6
20	51.8 db	22	14.1 db	24	225 μw
26	(a) 27.2 watts	28	77.7 db	30	1.59 db
	(b) 61.3 db				
	(c) 3,500				
32	15.8	34	1 db = 0.115 neper	36	102 kw
			1 neper = 8.69 db		
38	26 db	40	3 db		

PROBLEMS 37–2

2	0.0576 henry	4	(a) 10.6 mh	6	70.4 in.
			(b) 0.0228 μf		
8	3,900 ft	10	2 miles	12	19.2 miles
14	(a) 610 μh				
	(b) 1,690 $\mu\mu$f				

PROBLEMS 37–3

2	606 Ω	4	3.33 in.	6	No
8	No. 8	10	$\frac{1}{2}$-in. tubing	12	77.8 Ω
16	95.5 per cent	18	(a) 0.217 db	20	(a) 0.0869 db
			(b) 95.1 per cent		(b) 98.0 per cent
22	187 $\mu\mu$f	24	20.7 Ω	26	39.4 per cent